P9-BUI-794

BNi. Building News

A DESIGN COST DATA COMPANY
DATA YOU CAN TRUST

SQUARE FOOT
2021 COSTBOOK
CSI. MasterFormat®

DATA YOU CAN TRUST

EDITOR-IN-CHIEF

William D. Mahoney, P.E.

TECHNICAL SERVICES

Joan Hamilton
Eric Mahoney, AIA
Ana Varela

GRAPHIC DESIGN

Robert O. Wright Jr.

BNi Publications, Inc.

VISTA
990 PARK CENTER DRIVE, SUITE E
VISTA, CA 92081

1-888-BNI-BOOK (1-888-264-2665)
www.bnibooks.com

ISBN 978-1-58855-201-3

Copyright © 2020 by BNi Publications, Inc. All rights reserved. Printed in Canada. Except as permitted under the United States Copyright Act of 1976, no part of this publication may be reproduced or distributed in any form or by any means, or stored in a data base or retrieval system, without the prior written permission of the publisher.

While diligent effort is made to provide reliable, accurate and up-to-date information, neither BNi Publications Inc., nor its authors or editors, can place a guarantee on the correctness of the data or information contained in this book. BNi Publications Inc., and its authors and editors, do hereby disclaim any responsibility or liability in connection with the use of this book or of any data or other information contained therein.

Table of Contents

Construction Trends

The next page shows how the overall cost of construction has changed since 1970.

The following graph, "Construction Inflation Rates," is drawn from Design & Construction Resources Inflation Rates. The Inflation Rates Table is made up of 30 components: for example, portland cement, lumber, structural steel, and common (unskilled) labor.

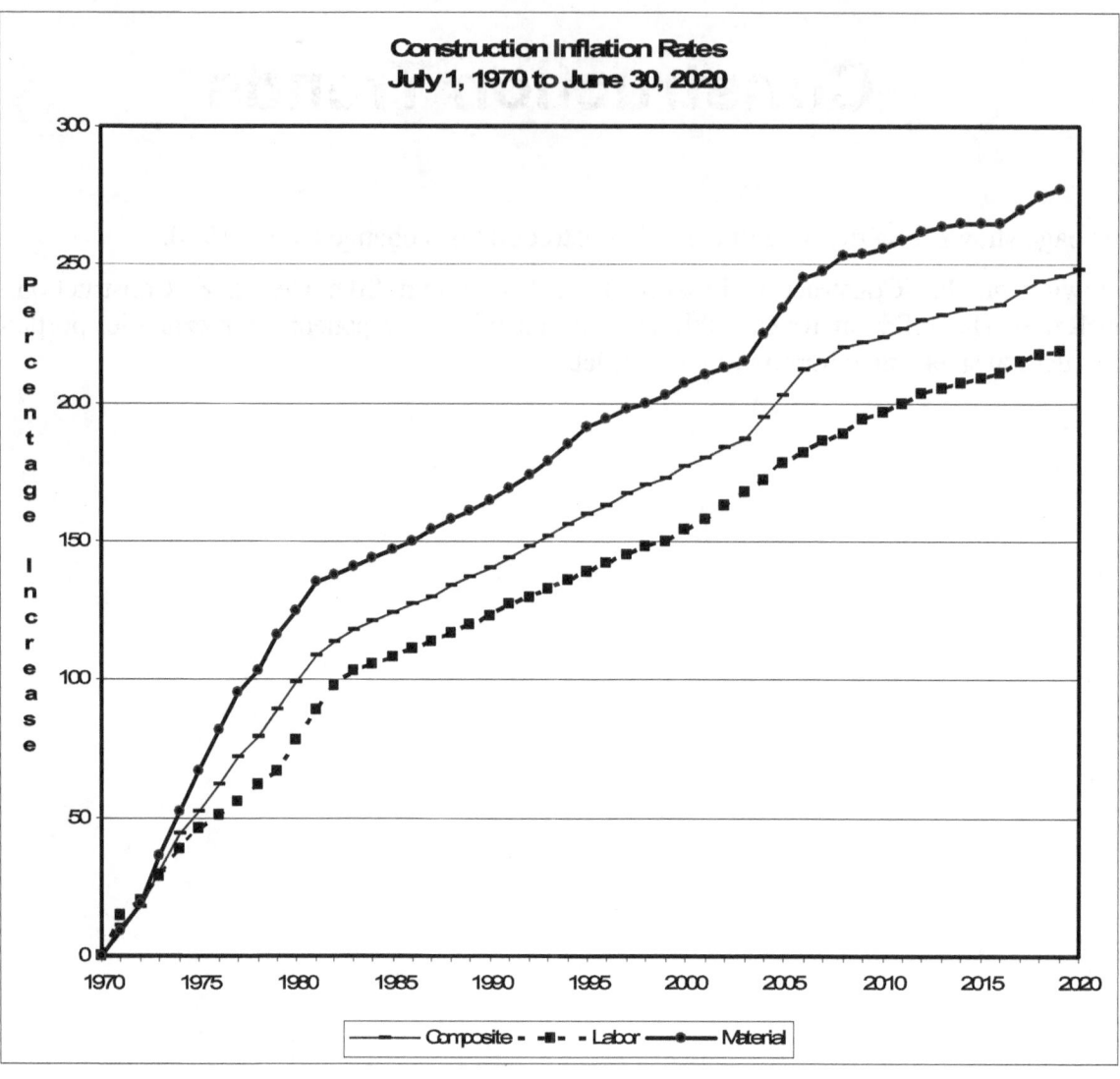

Construction Inflation Rates
July 1, 1970 to June 30, 2020

NOTE: Over the past 50 years, the composite for construction inflation has risen 248%, while labor and material have risen 221% and 280% respectively. Some materials have increased this year with noticeable increases in cement and several decreases in others. For the year, this now represents increases of 2% in the cost of labor and 3% in the cost of material.

> **EXAMPLE:** A $1,000,000 project built in 1970 would increase 248% to $3,480,000 in today's dollars.

Base price 1970 = $1,000,000
Increase to 2020 = 248%

1,000,000 X 2.48 (248%) = **$2,480,000** (this is the increase)
1,000,000 (original price) + 2,480,000 (increase) = **$3,480,000**

How to Use This Book

There are four main sections to this manual – **Square Foot Cost Studies, Unit-In-Place Costs, Assemblies**, and **Supporting Reference Tables** (Metro Multipliers & Square Foot Tables).

Square Foot Cost Studies

Each square-foot cost study is based on an actual job – not a hypothetical model. This study may match the type of project you are estimating. It can provide you with a "feel" or breakout of the costs by division for the type of project you are estimating. Each study provides details of the updated costs per square foot of each major division, as well as the division percentage of the overall costs – based on an actual project. Subcontractors will find the percentage of the total cost by division very useful.

For example, if you are estimating the cost of a fire station, you could find actual square-foot costs. Not all buildings are exactly the same, but you would have a square-foot cost to turn to as a baseline for your estimate.

Along with the cost summary, you'll find an image of the project and a short narrative listing the special circumstances and requirements behind the design and construction. This data can help you match and adjust your own project's cost with those in the study. Applying the additional facts pertaining to the study (listed in the narrative) should help you sharpen your ballpark estimate on a specific project.

To fine tune your square-foot cost estimate, the second part of this book includes thousands of unit-in-place costs, assemblies and additional square foot costs to help you get an even more accurate estimate.

Unit-in-Place Costs

Unit costs located in the back of this book help you further detail your estimate by providing you with unit costs to help you compile an item-by-item estimate. To find the material, job or unit you need to estimate, find the item in either the index in the back of the book, or using the CSI division numbers. Go to that page. You'll find the item, followed by a unit of measurement, the man-hours for that unit of measurement, the labor cost, the material cost and a total cost.

Material Costs: The material costs used in the unit-in-place costs represent national averages for prices that a contractor would expect to pay, plus an allowance for freight (if applicable), handling, and storage. These costs reflect the typical average costs for that material. Material costs can fluctuate and, when the highest degree of accuracy is required, it is always best to check current prices from local suppliers.

Labor: Labor columns are based on prevailing Davis-Bacon labor wage rates and need to be adjusted to your location by using the modification factors for your area (included in this book). Labor and material prices can range widely depending on where your job site is located. Wage rates in this book include Worker's Comp, along with allowances for overhead and profit for the contractor. Each company has their own markup percentage (see below). Each job has its own general conditions.

Overhead and Profit: An allowance for these is included in the labor costs in the unit-in-place costs section. No cost allowances or fees are included for management of subcontractors by the general contractor or general manager. These costs, where appropriate, must be added to the costs listed in this book.

The allowance for overhead is included for office overhead and the contractor's typical cost of doing business. These costs normally include in-house staff salaries and benefits, office rent and operating expenses, professional fees, vehicle costs and other operating costs which are not directly applicable to specific jobs. It should be noted that for this book, office overhead needs to be distinguished from project overhead, the General

Requirements (Division 1) which is specific to particular projects. Project overhead should be included on an item-by-item basis for each job.

Equipment costs: Costs for various types and pieces of equipment are include in Division 1 (General Requirements), and can be included in an estimate, when required, either as a total "equipment" category, or with specific appropriate trades. In this book, costs for equipment are added, when appropriate, to the installation costs.

Estimating using the unit-in-place costs: Each item includes the name of the item (ridge boards), followed by the unit of measure. This is usually followed by the labor cost to furnish (install, dig, pour, etc.) the unit of measure to fulfill that job. This is followed by a total cost. Units of measure used in this book are:

SF – Square Foot
EA – Each
CY – Cubic Yard
LF – Linear Foot
SQ – Square

Suppose you were going to estimate the price of a wood 24-foot fence. First, you would go to the section on wood fence, under Division 2, Site Construction. There you'll find fences of different type materials, listed as either picket or privacy. For a privacy fence that is made of 1 x 6 planks, you will find the labor, material, and a total price.

For a 24-foot-long fence at 6-foot high, you would have to multiply 6 times 24 for a total of 144 square feet. In this instance, the price of the posts and fasteners are included in total square foot composite price.

Where do these unit in-place prices come from? These prices are from a proprietary database based on input from an extensive network of contractors, subcontractors, engineers, architects and material suppliers throughout the U.S.

Assemblies

To help speed up the estimating process, we now include an assemblies section. Assemblies group together a project by items such as walls, floors, roofs, and foundations. The unit prices to make up these "systems" are detailed so you, the estimator, can add or delete items to create your own assembly that more closely represents what's in your actual project.

Remember that estimating is an art and not a science. Material prices can change throughout the year depending on availability. Nothing in this book is meant to be a substitute for your own good judgment. Use it as a guide and combine it with your experience and common sense.

Stumped? Give us a call at 1-888-264-2665 from 7 a.m. to 4 p.m. PST. We'll do our best to help.

Part One
Square Foot Costs

Every case study is described in a short summary. These summaries are given to provide insight into the circumstances and requirements behind the design. A building's function or location often influences the choice of building materials and thus the cost. Site limitations and local building and zoning codes are factors that have to be taken into consideration. Budget constraints, material availability and personal expertise of an individual builder all affect a project's outcome. Wherever appropriate, these types of issues are explained in the descriptions that accompany each case study. Further, when costs within one or more of the CSI divisions for the project are abnormally high or low, an explanation is usually provided.

© Copyright 2020. For a more in-depth report on additional case studies contact DC&D
@ 800-533-5680, or www.DCD.com

Civic/Government

FILE 1:

The Palmetto Library was part of the Atlanta-Fulton Public Library System Capital Improvement Program managed by Heery/Russell, a program manager Joint Venture. This program was initiated to improve current library facilities, as well as provide solutions to reach areas without easy access to a low-cost media/publication source. New South Construction was the selected construction manager for the new Palmetto Library, located a short drive southwest of Atlanta.

Houser-Walker managed the design of the project and incorporated cutting-edge building products and systems that, while not native to this area of Georgia, worked in harmony with the surroundings. Some notable features included the utilization of metal, cypress, and composite siding that acted as a rain screen feature that encompassed the majority of the exterior skin and the four pods making up the layout of the building. They played a crucial role in providing exterior and interior highlights. The pods physically divided the library into sections based on subject and/or age level of materials. Another focus point of the construction was the use of a raised access floor that housed the air distribution for the spaces. This attribute eliminated the above-ceiling ductwork, allowing higher ceilings and increasing the overall energy efficiency, which led to more building flexibility.

The project was scheduled as a ten-and-a-half-month-long project beginning in December 2013. The virgin site was conducive to this structure, although a detention pond and municipal utility tie-in work was forecasted. The 11,000-square-foot structure provided many opportunities for coordination amongst historically residential-type products in conjunction with typical commercial construction, most notably the exterior skin. The construction materials and systems achieved the LEED® credits that pushed this project to the Silver certification that was initially anticipated.

New South Construction worked hand-in-hand with Fulton County as well as the town of Palmetto to provide opportunities for local trade contractor opportunities. Additionally, Houser-Walker and its consultants led to a successful project that exceeded the expectations originally set out by the program.

Code	Division Name	%	S F Cost	Projected
00	Procurement and Contracting Require	6.79	30.77	344,615
01	General Requirements	12.53	56.75	635,615
03	Concrete	6.36	28.82	322,743
05	Metals	12.58	57.00	638,446
06	Wood, Plastics, and Composites	4.05	18.36	205,634
07	Thermal and Moisture Protection	11.95	54.16	606,534
08	Openings	4.45	20.14	225,613
09	Finishes	12.68	57.47	643,614
10	Specialties	1.27	5.76	64,535
11	Equipment	0.16	0.72	8,055
12	Furnishings	5.07	22.96	257,166
21	Fire Suppression	0.84	3.81	42,643
22	Plumbing	1.93	8.73	97,819
23	HVAC	9.16	41.48	464,531
26	Electrical	10.18	46.13	516,595
	Total Building Costs	100.00	453.05	5,074,158

COST PER SQUARE FOOT = $453.05

© Copyright 2020. For a more in-depth report on this building or additional case studies contact DC&D @ 800-533-5680, or www.DCD.com

File 2:

From conception, the design team sought to create a focal point for community engagement, to expand economic opportunities by preserving the existing downtown character, and to create a modern library.

The space was constructed to house over 75,000 books. In addition to having specific reading spaces for separate age groups and having advanced technology center availability, the entire lower level of the library serves as a storefront for new business.

Both the construction and design process for the 23,000-square-foot facility received LEED® points for:

Sustainable Site (site selection, development density and community connectivity, low-emitting and fuel efficient vehicle involvement, quality control of storm water management and heat island effect for the roof)

Water Efficiency (water efficient landscaping and water use reduction)

Energy and Atmosphere (optimize energy performance and enhanced refrigerant management)

Materials and Resources (construction waste management, recycled content, regional materials, and certified wood)

Indoor Environmental Quality (IAQ performance, outdoor air delivery monitoring, IAQ management plan, low-emitting materials: paints and coatings, low emitting materials: carpet systems, thermal comfort design, thermal comfort verification, daylight and views: daylight for 75% of spaces, and daylight and views: views for 90% of spaces)

Innovation and Design Process (construction application, design application, and LEED accredited professional)

While the project envisioned new economic and community horizons from its inception, it did not overlook significant traditions long held dear by its community. In the final days before the grand opening, many volunteers gathered to help transfer books by hand to the new location. This much anticipated Book Brigade was held just a few days prior to doors being opened to the public for the very first time. Excited locals showed up to participate, including Mary Plumb, retired Crozet Librarian, and the third and fourth grade classes from Crozet Elementary School.

Code	Division Name	%	S F Cost	Projected
00	Procurement and Contracting Require	0.86	2.89	66,914
01	General Requirements	6.98	23.53	545,959
03	Concrete	8.43	28.42	659,295
04	Masonry	13.85	46.70	1,083,368
05	Metals	13.97	47.09	1,092,480
06	Wood, Plastics, and Composites	1.00	3.37	78,246
07	Thermal and Moisture Protection	7.51	25.32	587,425
08	Openings	4.87	16.43	381,129
09	Finishes	9.31	31.39	728,365
10	Specialties	1.20	4.04	93,809
12	Furnishings	1.23	4.15	96,254
14	Conveying Systems	1.10	3.72	86,370
21	Fire Suppression	0.83	2.79	64,784
22	Plumbing	1.94	6.55	151,958
23	HVAC	14.65	49.39	1,145,889
26	Electrical	11.90	40.13	930,897
28	Electronic Safety and Security	0.35	1.17	27,172
	Total Building Costs	100.00	337.10	7,820,316

COST PER SQUARE FOOT = $337.10

© Copyright 2020. For a more in-depth report on this building or additional case studies contact DC&D @ 800-533-5680, or www.DCD.com

File 3:

The City of Grand Forks, North Dakota, has recently experienced rapid growth and development on the city's south side. This was beginning to affect the fire department's response time to emergency situations from their current facilities.

Fortunately, the city had anticipated this growth, and had set aside a parcel of land for a new fire station that was ideally located to minimize response time. Unfortunately, the residential growth around this empty parcel resulted in this green space being used for a neighborhood park.

Instead of displacing this green space, the city elected to evaluate the parcels available a few blocks west of the original site, in a more commercial portion of the city. Three acres of land were selected on a site that bordered a residential neighborhood and a large public hockey arena.

The primary focus of the new fire station was to improve response time and help bridge the design gap between these two vastly different building types. City council members and the fire department were especially concerned about adversely affecting the adjacent residential properties.

The overall site design utilized many measures to reduce the impact on the existing areas. Operational functions, such as the apparatus bays, were placed closer to the public hockey arena rather than the residential areas. The entrance to the station living quarters were given more of a residential "front porch" design style. Also, a line of evergreen trees were provided along the shared property line with residential neighbors.

The building design and plan configuration further emphasizes the focus of the design by working to balance the civic and residential aspects of this area. The plan is laid out to separate public and private functions along a main circulation path. The exterior is clad in brick which is used in both commercial and residential applications.

This station also takes steps towards integrating multiple city departments into a more collaborative facility, through the addition of a "police mobile office" and fuel depot for city vehicles.

The final design was a successful blend of commercial and residential influences, and creates an ideal bridging facility for the City of Grand Forks.

Code	Division Name	%	S F Cost	Projected
00	Procurement and Contracting Require	0.73	2.42	22,057
01	General Requirements	4.09	13.65	124,156
03	Concrete	7.76	25.91	235,573
04	Masonry	14.62	48.83	443,900
05	Metals	9.45	31.57	286,966
06	Wood, Plastics, and Composites	6.93	23.13	210,326
07	Thermal and Moisture Protection	9.08	30.33	275,793
08	Openings	5.76	19.25	175,001
09	Finishes	5.73	19.14	174,024
10	Specialties	0.83	2.77	25,183
11	Equipment	0.42	1.41	12,748
21	Fire Suppression	1.04	3.46	31,413
22	Plumbing	7.23	24.15	219,575
23	HVAC	9.69	32.35	294,179
26	Electrical	14.66	48.97	445,151
27	Communications	1.40	4.66	42,333
28	Electronic Safety and Security	0.58	1.95	17,652
	Total Building Costs	100.00	333.96	3,036,027

COST PER SQUARE FOOT = $333.96

© Copyright 2020. For a more in-depth report on this building or additional case studies contact DC&D
@ 800-533-5680, or www.DCD.com

File 4:

Situated in the heart of historic downtown Katy, TX, the new Katy City Hall pays tribute to the City's thriving old town heritage and looks forward to its continued growth and prosperity.

This imposing three-story, 36,000-square-foot municipal center houses the city council, public service, and administrative functions of local governance, all on a multi-story atrium that provides an interior space that encourages public discourse.

A significant portion of the new structure's ground level is devoted to public interface and services. Utility invoice payments and other civic transactions are conducted here, as well as building permits, tax payments, building inspections, and planning/zoning applications.

Following the community-wide request that the structure carry through the historic feel of the city, the Federalist neo-classical design is a statement of the history and traditions of the city. The project is also the first stage in a master plan for the revitalization of old town Katy.

As the first stage of a multi-phase effort, the project involved moving public services and administrative functions across the street from the existing city hall. During the transition, it was crucial for the current building to maintain operations prior to its partial demolition. The remaining part of the existing structure will be converted to public meeting space, and new hardscape and landscape will be built on the adjoining streets.

The Architect's "family" of cost control spreadsheets was utilized to maintain the project budget from start to finish. The spreadsheets tracked expenditures in a comprehensive way, and included costs for building construction, site development, fixed equipment, furnishings, soft costs, and contingencies.

© Copyright 2020. For a more in-depth report on this building or additional case studies contact DC&D
@ 800-533-5680, or www.DCD.com

Code	Division Name	%	S F Cost	Projected
00	Procurement and Contracting Require	1.51	4.55	158,816
01	General Requirements	13.95	42.08	1,467,451
03	Concrete	8.88	26.80	934,177
04	Masonry	6.71	20.25	705,977
05	Metals	11.21	33.81	1,178,949
06	Wood, Plastics, and Composites	7.30	22.02	767,772
07	Thermal and Moisture Protection	4.22	12.72	443,753
08	Openings	6.51	19.65	685,111
09	Finishes	13.26	40.01	1,394,989
10	Specialties	1.54	4.66	162,356
12	Furnishings	0.16	0.50	17,239
14	Conveying Systems	1.30	3.93	137,012
21	Fire Suppression	1.60	4.82	168,052
22	Plumbing	2.93	8.83	307,888
23	HVAC	7.86	23.72	827,036
26	Electrical	10.73	32.37	1,128,535
28	Electronic Safety and Security	0.33	0.99	34,584
	Total Building Costs	100.00	301.72	10,519,700

COST PER SQUARE FOOT = $301.72

© Copyright 2020. For a more in-depth report on this building or additional case studies contact DC&D @ 800-533-5680, or www.DCD.com

FILE 5:

The City of Folsom, California is known for its beautiful location in the foothills of the Sierra Nevada mountain range, with views and vistas of Folsom Lake and Folsom Dam.

But the spectacular views and comfortable living come with some risks: the sloping terrain and the combination of rainy winters and long hot summers promote the growth of grasses, brush, and oak timber that can propagate a wildland fire. In Folsom, the encroachment of development into wildland areas has increased the fire hazard.

Folsom Fire Station 39 is Folsom's fifth fire station, located at the foot of the Folsom Bluffs and strategically placed for a fast response. The construction of the station was long overdue; planned 12 years ago, the financial hardship of the Great Recession delayed the project until now.

The +/-10,000-square-foot station features three apparatus bays - each large enough to house a fire engine, brush engine and ambulance. It also has five single dorms for the personnel that operate the machines.

Station 39 is designed in a Craftsman Style: gable roofs with broad overhangs and exposed bracing as part of the building composition. The site is adjacent to a future city park, and in the middle of a growing residential neighborhood.

High operational functionality and low maintenance dictate the interior layout. The apparatus room, sized to accommodate five apparatuses, is located for quick response in the heart of the station, with office and day quarters on one side and sleeping quarters on the other.

Polished concrete floors are throughout the apparatus room, offices, and day quarters, and aluminum diamond plate serves as a wainscot in the apparatus room. Hydronic heating of the insulated concrete slab provides a comfortable environment for work and living.

Station 39 was warmly received by the community in a public open house, and is now serving and protecting its immediate area of response. Station 39 continues the Folsom Fire Department tradition of service, with its roots in California's Gold Rush era.

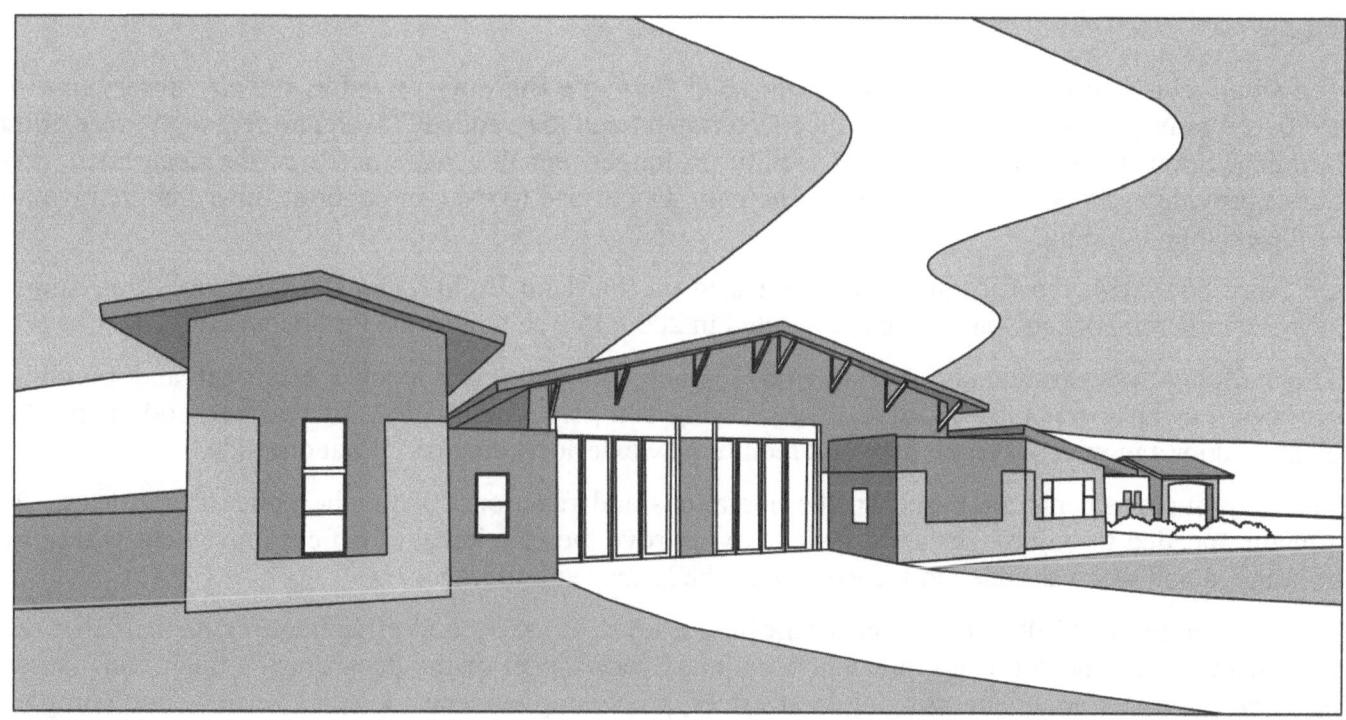

Code	Division Name	%	S F Cost	Projected
01	General Requirements	18.84	67.98	777,374
03	Concrete	5.71	20.59	235,420
04	Masonry	2.85	10.29	117,673
05	Metals	1.68	6.05	69,230
06	Wood, Plastics	12.77	46.06	526,659
07	Thermal and Moisture	8.02	28.93	330,845
08	Openings	6.64	23.96	274,022
09	Finishes	7.19	25.95	296,770
10	Specialties	1.99	7.19	82,188
11	Equipment	0.98	3.53	40,328
12	Furnishings	1.51	5.45	62,318
13	Special Construction	1.29	4.65	53,159
21	Fire Suppression	1.37	4.96	56,745
22	Plumbing	6.76	24.39	278,906
23	HVAC	6.29	22.7	259,531
26	Electrical	14.36	51.8	592,310
28	Electronic Security	0.47	1.71	19,527
	Total Building Costs	100.00	360.77	4,125,431

COST PER SQUARE FOOT = $360.77

© Copyright 2020. For a more in-depth report on this building or additional case studies contact DC&D @ 800-533-5680, or www.DCD.com

File 6:

The small, classical revival, one-story, multi-level Carnegie Building served as the city library until in 1970, it was re-purposed into Yreka Police Department and they added 700 square feet to the rear of the building. Soon the existing multi-level facility no longer met the space needs of the department, and didn't provide appropriate ADA access. The City was forced to examine options other than renovation of the existing building.

On April 17, 2014, the City of Yreka purchased the Fairlane Building, a 10,000-square-foot, single-story, commercial office-warehouse constructed in 2000, for the replacement police facility.

The building was structurally sound, with 13-foot ceilings and adequate electrical and plumbing services, but no mechanical systems. The existing composition shingle roof was in good shape, but existing door and window removal would require new exterior siding on all but one side.

The new improvements are based on the operations and functionality for the police department. The structure needed to be brought up to code. To improve the efficiency of officer movement within the building, a hallway was added to the exterior of the L-shaped building.

The new station is 11,000 square feet and offers a level of safety and efficiency for its staff that was unthinkable at the department's previous location. Every aspect of the department's operations is now new and improved, including bringing in arrestees, processing evidence, keeping records, and going out on calls.

Covered parking protects the patrol cars, and officers have a dedicated space for each separate aspect of their work, helping to improve organization and efficiency. In addition to police functions – including records, evidence, administration, patrol, and investigations – the new station provides a dispatch center, emergency operations center, interview rooms, and a sexual assault exam room.

The existing 13-foot ceiling heights add to the spaciousness of the facility. Exterior siding was replaced with low maintenance metal siding and energy-efficient storefront windows. The site is secured with a security wall and fencing and even provides dog kennels for stray dogs.

© Copyright 2020. For a more in-depth report on this building or additional case studies contact DC&D @ 800-533-5680, or www.DCD.com

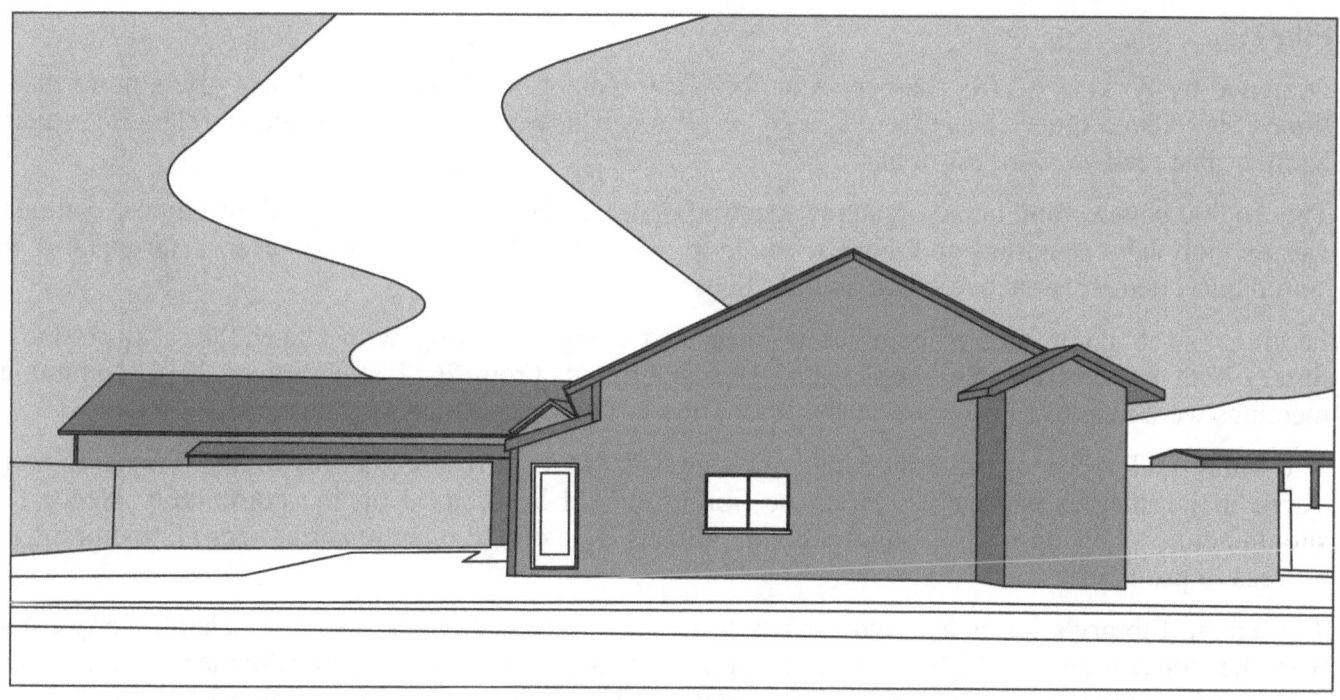

Code	Division Name	%	S F Cost	Projected
01	General Requirements	3.82	8.77	87,174
03	Concrete	6.75	15.47	153,804
04	Metals	0.07	0.17	1,668
05	Wood, Plastics	7.21	16.53	164,280
06	Thermal and Moisture	8.83	20.25	201,282
07	Openings	8.75	20.06	199,372
08	Finishes	14.78	33.9	336,986
10	Specialties	7.44	17.05	169,540
12	Furnishings	4.18	9.58	95,282
13	Special Construction	2.59	5.94	59,074
22	Plumbing	4.86	11.14	110,758
23	HVAC	9.26	21.24	211,123
26	Electrical	19.66	45.08	448,140
27	Communications	1.80	4.12	40,909
	Total Building Costs	100.00	229.29	2,279,393

COST PER SQUARE FOOT = $229.29

© Copyright 2020. For a more in-depth report on this building or additional case studies contact DC&D @ 800-533-5680, or www.DCD.com

File 7:

Designed by Perkins + Will, the new Alice McKean Young Neighborhood Library offers more than a library: it's also a quiet escape from a noisy chaotic world, where patrons can focus, relax, investigate, learn, or just read – regardless of age.

The 16,000-square-foot library features meeting spaces, abundant technological resources, computer classes, job labs, gaming, and homework help sessions. It provides easy access throughout the community, being near active metro and bus lines.

Perkins + Will committed to community-integrated design, working with stakeholders to produce a library both by, and for, the people of the neighborhood. From 2012 to February 2014, community meetings were held to engage in a deeper discussion of the needs of the neighborhood.

The intent and focus of these meetings are some of the keys to the success of the Young Library. Three major themes came out. First, the library should be focused on the community. Second, it should act as a beacon for the neighborhood. And third, it should offer resources for all visitors, from retirees to pre-readers.

The Young Library's location is another key to its success. Situated next to KIPP schools, catty-corner from the Houston Texans' YMCA, across from a new mixed-income housing development, and just down the street from the Palm Center Transit Center station on Metro's Purple Line, the library is at the center of the development of the neighborhood. As such, the design had to consider community access. With input from stakeholders, Perkins + Will strategically designed two main entrances that increase safety and ease of use and accommodate the range of transportation options that community members use.

The Young Library does provide books, but also DVDs, computer resources, even a makerspace for rapid prototyping. Non-physical resources like language classes, employment help and veteran services are also held there, fulfilling the multipurpose goals set forth by the community. The Young Library provides a true public space for Southeast Houston, and a worthwhile alternative for young people.

Code	Division Name	%	S F Cost	Projected
00	Procurement	12.35	103.93	1,746,092
01	General Requirements	5.93	49.85	837,470
03	Concrete	8.24	69.29	1,164,008
04	Masonry	2.74	23.03	386,931
05	Metals	7.41	62.33	1,047,106
06	Wood, Plastics	1.16	9.72	163,233
07	Thermal and Moisture	9.59	80.70	1,355,816
08	Openings	5.02	42.26	709,887
09	Finishes	13.08	110.03	1,848,550
10	Specialties	1.44	12.15	204,057
11	Equipment	4.95	41.61	699,131
12	Furnishings	0.46	3.89	65,369
21	Fire Suppression	1.04	8.71	146,367
23	HVAC	13.23	111.29	1,869,743
26	Electrical	10.92	91.83	1,542,787
27	Communications	1.18	9.96	167,375
28	Electronic Security	1.27	10.67	179,295
	Total Building Costs	100.00	841.26	14,133,218

COST PER SQUARE FOOT = $841.26

© Copyright 2020. For a more in-depth report on this building or additional case studies contact DC&D @ 800-533-5680, or www.DCD.com

File 8:

This project created an enlarged version of the prototype station for Hillsborough County Fire Rescue, to better serve the growing East Lake area of Northeast Hillsborough County.

The 12,000-square-foot facility includes an apparatus area consisting of four double bays for Fire Rescue vehicles and other auxiliary equipment. Additionally, the work and living space provides 13 individual bunk spaces, dining and day room, a commercial grade kitchen, employee restrooms, shower facilities, laundry, an exercise room, a safe room, a command center, a telecom room, a mechanical room, and storage facilities.

These fire rescue stations are designed and detailed to blend with the character of the individual residential neighborhoods they serve. Exterior materials are highly durable and low maintenance to provide lower total cost over a longer service life for the facility. The building envelope and MEP systems are high-efficiency, high performance and supported by a full-load backup generator.

Exterior amenities include barbeque patio, a truck and equipment fueling station, and native landscaping. Interior amenities include an exercise room, a Command Center, private Captain's Bunk, private Shift Commander's Office, bunker gear storage off the apparatus bays, crew work room, and a large open-plan kitchen and multi-purpose gathering space.

Full civil site design services included preparation of construction documents depicting demolition of an existing building, geometry, pavement section design and striping, grading, drainage, stormwater management system design, erosion control, potable/fire water design, sanitary sewer design, and related details of the work to be performed.

The engineering and design of the stormwater management system included the preparation of the calculations and drawings required to meet the regulatory requirements of Hillsborough County Development Services, the Florida Department of Transportation (FDOT), and the Southwest Florida Water Management District (SWFWMD).

Code	Division Name	%	S F Cost	Projected
00	Procurement	1.87	6.05	70,709
01	General Requirements	27.23	88.18	1,030,366
03	Concrete	8.00	25.90	302,648
04	Masonry	3.74	12.10	141,418
05	Metals	1.22	3.95	46,206
06	Wood, Plastics	6.34	20.53	239,864
07	Thermal and Moisture	6.71	21.74	254,052
08	Openings	4.96	16.05	187,583
09	Finishes	7.04	22.78	266,225
10	Specialties	1.67	5.41	63,271
11	Equipment	0.69	2.22	25,903
12	Furnishings	0.05	0.15	1,806
21	Fire Suppression	1.04	3.37	39,345
22	Plumbing	3.62	11.71	136,852
23	HVAC	8.94	28.93	337,990
26	Electrical	15.74	50.96	595,446
27	Communications	0.49	1.59	18,629
28	Electronic Security	0.66	2.14	25,014
	Total Building Costs	100.00	323.78	3,783,329

COST PER SQUARE FOOT = $323.78

© Copyright 2020. For a more in-depth report on this building or additional case studies contact DC&D @ 800-533-5680, or www.DCD.com

© Copyright 2020. For a more in-depth report on this building or additional case studies contact DC&D @ 800-533-5680, or www.DCD.com

Commercial

© Copyright 2020. For a more in-depth report on this building or additional case studies contact DC&D
@ 800-533-5680, or www.DCD.com

FILE 9:

In 2015, Korte & Luitjohan Contractors, Inc., completed a six-month-long removal and expansion of the Sales Office and Showroom for Tri Ford, Inc., a Ford dealership in Highland, Illinois. The dealership undertook reconstruction to update its facility and match the new branding look of Fordland dealerships.

K&L worked with EWR & Associates to design the dealership renovation in accordance with Fordland's requirements and specifications. The design-build renovation required significant demolition and reconstruction, while ensuring that current operation of sales, management and automobile repair services remained open. Therefore, planning and coordination with Tri Ford, Inc. was essential to ensure completion of the project in the six-month schedule, which began June 15, 2015, and was completed by November 16, 2015.

Safety concerns required fencing and securing a significant portion of the main building. A trailer for the sales staff was positioned up front in a highly visible, user-friendly area. Accounting and management areas were relocated to a separate building with an available conference room which provided office space, and the automobile service and parts area was relocated to the rear of the main shop area.

All relocations required installation of temporary phone, internet, computer, HVAC and restroom accommodations, in order to provide seamless transition to the temporary quarters. Directional signs were strategically placed outside to control and direct customer traffic patterns to their appropriate destinations. For the convenience of its customers, Tri Ford, Inc. escorted customers in golf carts around the location during the renovation.

All sales and management offices were demolished and re-built, as well as the parts department and service counter. The main showroom floor now boasts a larger floor plan with a 14-foot ceiling, complete with floor-to-ceiling glass panes. The new service entry expansion and service counter accommodate indoor customer deliveries, and the parts mezzanine was also renovated. The service floor was resurfaced with an epoxy coating system. Finally, K&L re-graded and resurfaced the north entrance and driveway, and installed a new storm water drainage system.

With the project complete, Tri Ford, Inc. now enjoys a newly renovated space consistent with the new branding vision Fordland has for its dealerships.

© Copyright 2020. For a more in-depth report on this building or additional case studies contact DC&D @ 800-533-5680, or www.DCD.com

Code	Division Name	%	S F Cost	Projected
01	General Requirements	15.79	18.27	235,260
03	Concrete	5.30	6.13	78,907
05	Metals	23.28	26.94	347,023
06	Wood, Plastics, and Composites	5.74	6.64	85,513
07	Thermal and Moisture Protection	2.09	2.42	31,219
08	Openings	9.18	10.63	136,927
09	Finishes	17.95	20.77	267,444
22	Plumbing	6.43	7.44	95,747
23	HVAC	2.67	3.09	39,813
26	Electrical	9.66	11.18	143,945
28	Electronic Safety and Security	1.92	2.22	28,549
	Total Building Costs	100.00	115.70	1,490,348

COST PER SQUARE FOOT = $115.70

© Copyright 2020. For a more in-depth report on this building or additional case studies contact DC&D @ 800-533-5680, or www.DCD.com

FILE 10:

Located in the heart of the vibrant Tower District in Fresno, California, the FAB Dayclub/Nightclub is located in a redbrick, single-story commercial building. It appears to date back to the late 1930s or early 1940s, and uses steel bowstring trusses and 2x14 rafters. The Tower District includes many historic buildings, including the fully restored 1939 Tower Theater, which lends its name to the district.

The firm of Alan T. Hendry, Architect was hired to assist the owners in designing the FAB space to be not only code-compliant, but also budget conscious. Because of the change of use, a Conditional Use Permit was required through the City of Fresno. The project also had to meet requirements of Fresno's "Tower District Specific Plan."

The dayclub/nightclub project required gutting the existing non-load-bearing walls and the non-compliant toilet rooms, and removing the original existing single-glazed storefront system. The interior of the building was reconfigured to provide a new bar area, a small platform for performers, a DJ booth, and VIP seating. The plans also called for a pocketing mall-front door system leading to a new patio that is open to the sidewalk and streetscape.

A new code-compliant path of travel was created from the rear exit of the building to the adjacent parking area. This also required a compliant-accessible ramp, due to height differences between the original finished floor and the adjacent grade.

Due to the structure's age, it was necessary to X-ray and core the existing concrete header beams and columns ringing the original structure, to determine whether there was reinforcing steel present. If so, it had to be determined whether it would be sufficient to meet current codes without additional reinforcement. Brad Young & Associates (structural engineer for the project) determined that no major work was required.

R.J. Miller Construction, the general contractor for the project, worked closely with the architect and brought onboard a design-build team of subcontractors for the mechanical, electrical, and plumbing.

The project is characterized by the distinctive bright pink and black motif used throughout, the low patio wall with wavy top that is punctured by holes of varying sizes, and the sliding mall-front doors that allow views both into and out of the club.

With the exposed original bowstring trusses and exposed brick, the space feels open and inviting. A lit, liquid oil and water bar top dazzles the patrons while they imbibe.

FAB Dayclub/Nightclub was conceived by Cisco Mendez and his husband Terry Story as a "… safe place for everyone," particularly those in the LGBT community.

© Copyright 2020. For a more in-depth report on this building or additional case studies contact DC&D @ 800-533-5680, or www.DCD.com

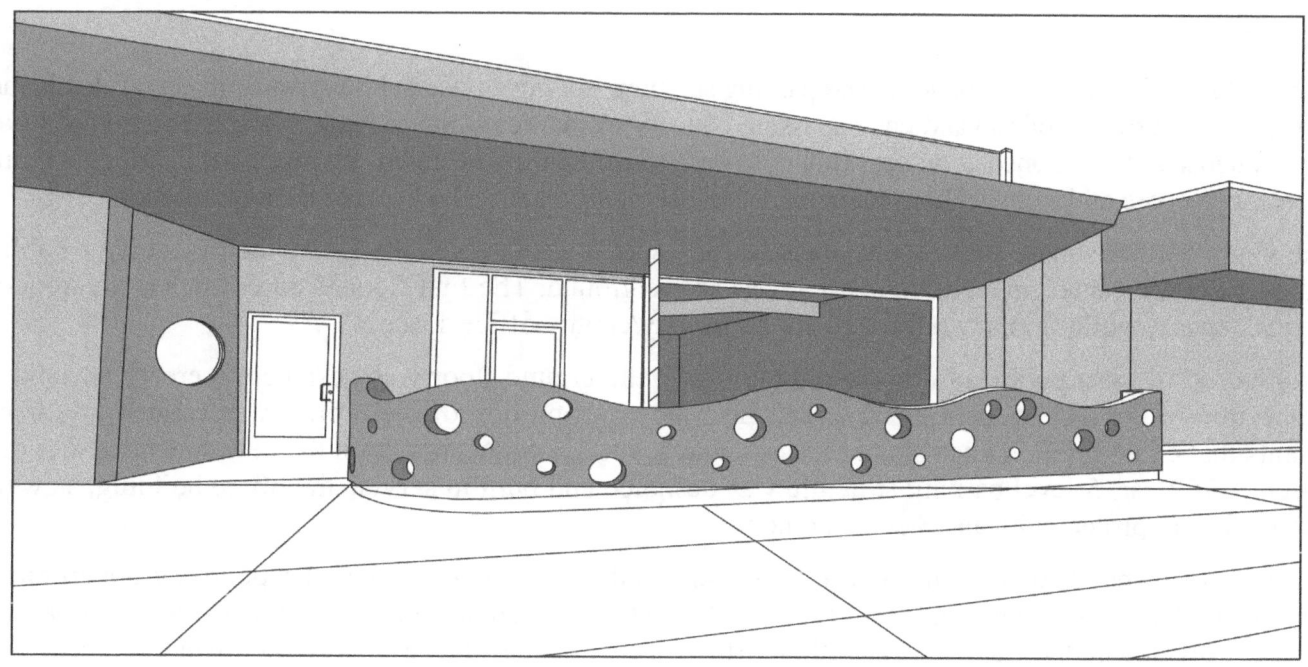

Code	Division Name	%	S F Cost	Projected
01	General Requirements	25.15	16.06	54,488
03	Concrete	0.27	0.17	593.469
04	Masonry	1.37	0.88	2,966
05	Metals	1.35	0.86	2,937
06	Wood, Plastics, and Composites	5.36	3.43	11,627
07	Thermal and Moisture Protection	1.18	0.76	2,551
08	Openings	10.10	6.45	21,897
09	Finishes	16.20	10.35	35,094
10	Specialties	2.96	1.89	6,431
12	Furnishings	13.15	8.40	28,476
22	Plumbing	12.83	8.19	27,800
23	HVAC	1.84	1.18	3,999
26	Electrical	8.19	5.23	17,738
	Total Building Costs	100.00	63.88	216,593

COST PER SQUARE FOOT = $63.88

© Copyright 2020. For a more in-depth report on this building or additional case studies contact DC&D @ 800-533-5680, or www.DCD.com

File 11:

The Tenth Street Place office building and parking structure is a mixed-use public/private project located in the center of downtown Modesto and encompassing one city block. Tenth Street Place is a collaboration of local governments and envisioned as an opportunity to enliven the aging downtown. It also assists in bringing more people to the core of the city by housing more than 620 employees from both city and county entities.

The new 250,000-square-foot facility includes one subterranean level shared by the city/county Public Administration Center, in addition to six levels above ground. The first floor features 28,000 square feet of retail space, while floors two through six house city/county office space.

As opposed to most public administration buildings, the ground floor was designed to create a friendly connection to the rest of the town. For instance, the retail portion of the project was created to attract tenants that could provide after-hours services which work in connection with the new cinema across the street. A 700-car, 5-level parking structure was designed and built to service the office building, as well as an adjacent project with an 18-screen cinema.

The project owner's main focus was to consolidate city and county offices, keeping key government services in the "downtown area" and providing "one-stop" customer service for citizens. As a major part of the downtown Modesto revitalization effort, Tenth Street Place meets the owner's needs by combining city/county service counters, meeting chambers, conference areas, and support services in one location. The overall downtown effort includes expansion and modernization of the Modesto Police Department, expansion of the Stanislaus County courtrooms and county school administration facilities, and renovation of the former city hall buildings for county uses.

The building was designed to blend with the turn-of-the-century context and rich urban fabric of small brick commercial buildings reflective of the agricultural seat of Modesto. The facility consists of 10 individual facades utilizing precast, brick veneer and high-end EIFS to simulate stone. The urban design for the Public Administration building appears as a series of interconnected smaller buildings, thus capturing and complementing the historic downtown Modesto environment. In keeping with the building's theme, a public plaza area features brick paving stones and decorative grates around the tree bases. This area will be used for outdoor dining and gatherings. The building's interior boasts a tile mosaic lobby floor as well as other interior design elements that complement the exterior design intent.

While the superstructure's appearance may be turn-of-the-century, the materials used to construct the building and the interior are far more modern. The building utilizes a structural system with a concrete basement foundation and steel framed superstructure with lightweight concrete on metal decking suspended slabs. Interlaced throughout the building's seven stories is nearly $1 million in the latest telecommunications wiring, along with assorted high-tech devices for security and employee comfort, developing the "smart" building components.

The parking structure is comprised of four above-grade levels and one subterranean level. The structural system in the garage is composed of a concrete basement foundation and post-tensioned beams and decks. The exterior finish includes cast-in-place concrete walls, thin set brick over plaster, exterior glazing, and curtainwall, as well as colored concrete walls at the street level.

The Tenth Street Place project not only fulfills current and future facility needs for both the city and county, but it also will rejuvenate the downtown Modesto area, drawing private restaurants, retailers, and entertainment to the city's historic core.

Code	Division Name	%	S F Cost	Projected
01	General Requirements	3.75	4.50	2,121,199
03	Concrete	23.75	28.45	13,445,913
04	Masonry	2.96	3.55	1,676,615
05	Metals	17.40	20.84	9,850,983
06	Wood & Plastics	1.17	1.41	665,140
07	Thermal & Moisture Protection	1.27	1.51	717,795
08	Doors & Windows	5.76	6.90	3,262,503
09	Finishes	15.70	18.80	8,889,104
10	Specialties	1.02	1.22	576,654
11	Equipment	0.29	0.35	165,544
14	Conveying Systems	2.64	3.16	1,494,855
15	Mechanical	12.71	15.22	7,195,520
16	Electrical	11.58	13.88	6,555,726
	Total Building Costs	100.00	119.77	56,617,549

COST PER SQUARE FOOT = $119.77

© Copyright 2020. For a more in-depth report on this building or additional case studies contact DC&D @ 800-533-5680, or www.DCD.com

File 12:

Starting this retail store project wasn't going to be easy (not many projects that have this much exposure are). A convenience store for the same owner was finished the year before in another small town south of Troy. That project seemed to be fairly easy – due to the fact it was out by itself on a major highway with no surrounding buildings or any competition.

This project was different; there was competition with other convenience stores all around. The owner of this project wanted to accomplish two things. First it was understood that the client is a very detailed person who wanted "first class" finish and a lot of "flash". The second was that he had other business ventures, so he didn't want any high maintenance or problem areas that would take up much of his time.

The interior layout of the building was adopted from the previous store, so with a little tweaking, and a lot more flair, the design was laid out. It was intended that the exterior of the building be eye catching from the highway.

The entire building was designed around the NASCAR theme. This same theme was carried from the interior to the exterior with black and white colors checkered with red accents.

The interior of the car wash bays were finished in quarry tile, the pattern was again black and white checkered with a band of red. This proved to be cost effective due to the fact that the entire amount of field tile was given on discount from the manufacturer. The exterior fascia was wrapped in a brushed aluminum along with a red neon strip which helped illuminate the building brilliantly during early mornings and throughout the night.

The biggest challenge was the fact that the lot was narrow and deep and did not lay well for visibility to the car wash. So it was decided to stair step the building, allowing for visibility and car stacking at the car wash bays. Under the canopy the owner wanted to have no shadows, as people would feel more comfortable coming in at night, so we opted to use approximately sixty-four 350-watt Scottsdale fixtures to illuminate this area. The same was done to the parking lot and car wash bays where lighting and the feeling of openness was of great concern.

Glass was added between the bays in order to keep blind spots to a minimum.

The roof style was picked out in many patterns to help complement the remainder of the structure and be very eye-catching. The salt and pepper brick was a new product that became available during the project.

© Copyright 2020. For a more in-depth report on this building or additional case studies contact DC&D @ 800-533-5680, or www.DCD.com

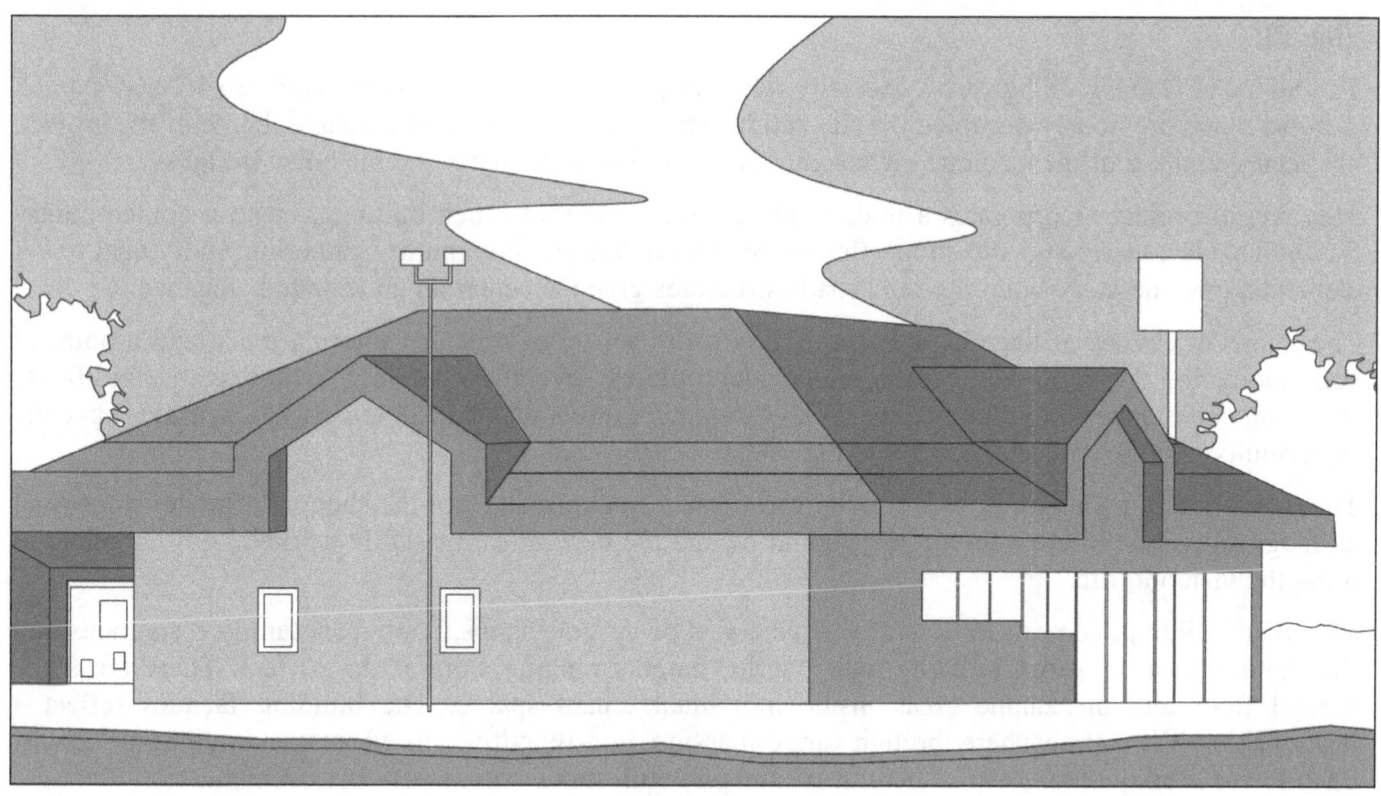

Code	Division Name	%	S F Cost	Projected
01	General Requirements	0.86	3.33	26,949
03	Concrete	12.57	48.89	396,164
04	Masonry	4.73	18.39	149,040
05	Metals	4.38	17.05	138,130
06	Wood & Plastics	6.83	26.57	215,385
07	Thermal & Moisture Protection	2.23	8.66	70,160
08	Doors & Windows	3.32	12.93	104,790
09	Finishes	6.32	24.58	199,142
10	Specialties	8.78	34.16	276,764
11	Equipment	21.40	83.23	674,481
12	Furnishings	0.27	1.04	8,434
13	Special Construction	12.73	49.50	401,146
15	Mechanical	5.94	23.09	187,085
16	Electrical	9.65	37.51	303,979
	Total Building Costs	100.00	388.90	3,151,649

COST PER SQUARE FOOT = $388.90

© Copyright 2020. For a more in-depth report on this building or additional case studies contact DC&D @ 800-533-5680, or www.DCD.com

File 13:

The Shops at Gainey Village are a specialty retail property in Scottsdale, Arizona on a 14.3-acre parcel. A horse ranch previously occupied the site and it strongly influences the design and theme of the project, - reflected in the rooflines, unique towers, and even the fountains that resemble horse troughs.

The overall project incorporates a traditional, historical view of ranch buildings, with a contemporary flavor. This is a warm and stylish meeting place that encourages community gathering. Individual tower elements, low one-story buildings, and shade structures give the center an understated elegance.

The Shops at Gainey Village have become, in a short period of time, a gathering place and a point of community for the area. The center, which incorporates several restaurants, is unlike the traditional shopping experiences found in the area. With shopping, dining, and skillful tenant mix, families have the opportunity to walk and ride bicycles to the shops.

The overall design encourages this activity and creates an experience for the shopper. The developer had a thoughtful vision of what the project should be and the design team at DFD worked with the client to bring the vision to life.

The main building, comprised of 91,000 square feet of upscale shops, boutiques, family restaurants and fine dining, is a one-story building with interior heights ranging from 16 to 20 feet. There are some second floor and mezzanine areas inside individual tenant spaces. The building façades reflect a fashionable village atmosphere through varied massing, non-repetitive storefronts, and quality materials. Each tower is unique, with varied heights creating a comfortable community environment.

Four freestanding pad buildings comprise an additional 47,000 square feet of space. These buildings conform to the overall design character set by the main building through massing, detailing, and specified material usage. The pad buildings are similar in character, but complement the overall design.

On-site parking is placed between the main building and pads, and is designed for ease of orientation and access. Project landscaping includes the use of date palms and other vegetation common to the area.

The site layout encourages pedestrian activity within a series of linked outdoor plazas. There are connections to adjacent properties, such as the Hyatt Resort, Gainey Suites, and nearby office developments. The plazas feature unique paving patterns with abundant landscaping that create environments for outdoor dining, kiosk retailing, and visitor enjoyment.

Both the developer and the city encouraged the heavy use of stone and articulated façades. The arcades, colors, and textures made the project unique, especially in light of the other area design projects that tend to be flamboyant and pretentious.

The Shops at Gainey Village integrate a rich use of color, material, and texture to create a look of casual elegance.

© Copyright 2020. For a more in-depth report on this building or additional case studies contact DC&D @ 800-533-5680, or www.DCD.com

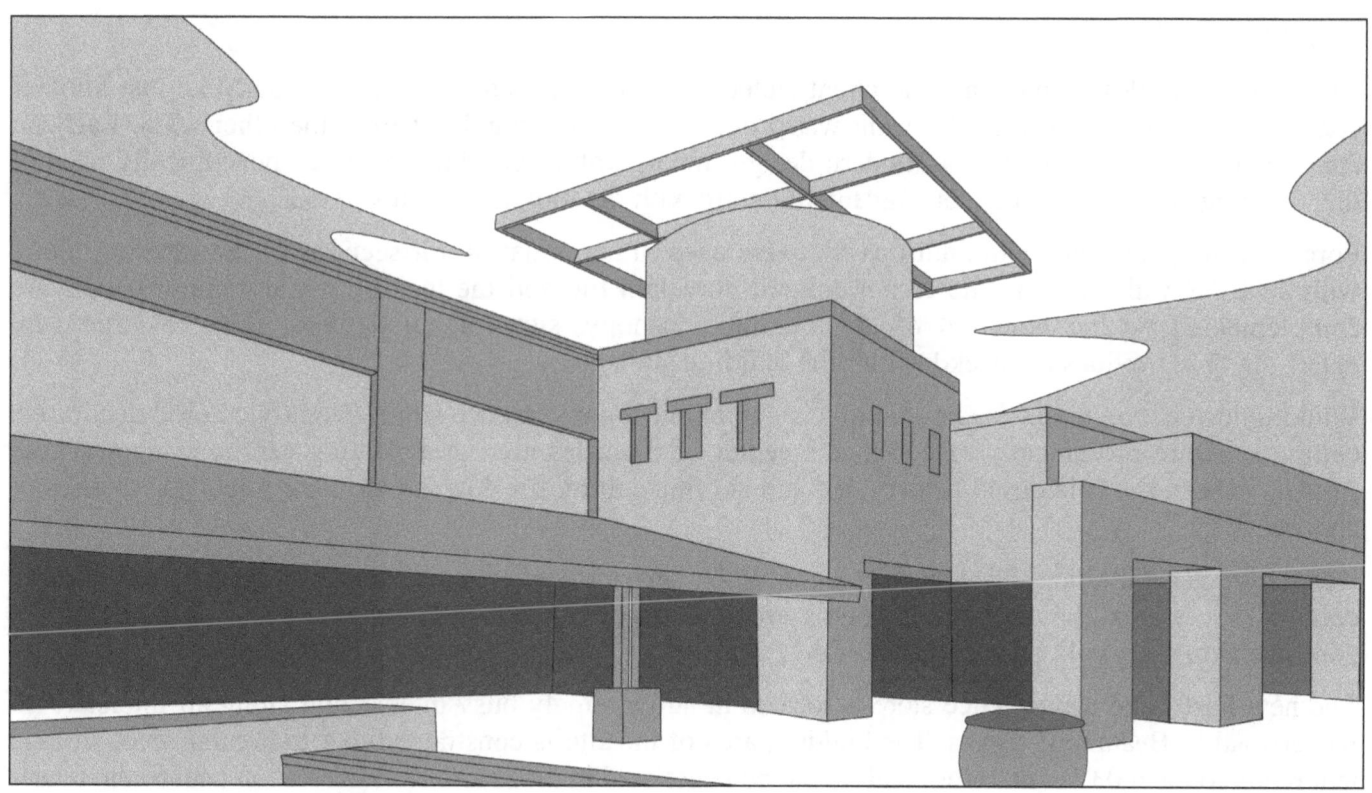

Code	Division Name	%	S F Cost	Projected
00	Bidding Requirements	6.14	10.81	1,497,105
01	General Requirements	0.57	0.99	138,220
03	Concrete	10.51	18.51	2,563,015
04	Masonry	9.88	17.41	2,410,070
05	Metals	25.76	45.39	6,281,774
06	Wood & Plastics	0.53	0.93	128,387
07	Thermal & Moisture Protection	6.71	11.82	1,635,635
08	Doors & Windows	5.55	9.78	1,353,226
09	Finishes	14.39	25.35	3,508,394
10	Specialties	0.16	0.28	39,347
15	Mechanical	6.42	11.32	1,566,250
16	Electrical	13.38	23.59	3,263,830
	Total Building Costs	100.00	176.18	24,385,256

COST PER SQUARE FOOT = $176.18

© Copyright 2020. For a more in-depth report on this building or additional case studies contact DC&D
@ 800-533-5680, or www.DCD.com

File 14:

During the first design meeting, the client stated they did not want this store to look like just another convenience store. What they did want was a design to help it stand out from the others. The LaBiche Architectural Group developed a modern design, incorporating building materials not typically used in this building type, to provide this convenience store with the look the client wanted.

Porcelain tile panels and aluminum panels were used in combination for sections of the exterior, along with an EIFS wall system. The cream colored porcelain tile and the teak-brown aluminum panels are complemented by the bold red of the aluminum canopy, sun-shading devices, and the large wall extension that provides the backdrop for the building signage.

Walking inside, you realize again that this is not a typical convenience store. Brightly colored decorative ceiling sails are prominently placed in the center of the sales area in a floating ceiling system. These sails tie in with the kaleidoscopically hued and curving ceiling fur-downs over the coolers and check-out counter.

Decorative glass tiles and LED back-lit signage also provide the interior a modern look not seen in other convenience stores. The public restrooms are not forgotten in the design either – the bright colors continue along the wall tile at the lavatories.

The new Fast Lane convenience store is located at an extremely busy intersection along an Interstate 10 feeder road in Beaumont, Texas. The building area of the site is constrained to a triangular piece of land that required the 4,035-square-foot building to be negotiated in place to maximize curb appeal to the feeder road and Laurel Avenue – a major artery from a densely populated area connecting to the interstate. The building actually has two facades, one to service Laurel Avenue and one for the feeder road.

The final touch that sets this convenience store apart from others is the arranged landscaping that borders the perimeter and then continues to interact with the building along the façade, providing harmony and symmetry with nature.

Code	Division Name	%	S F Cost	Projected
00	Procurement	4.28	21.34	86,099
01	General Requirements	17.13	85.45	344,788
03	Concrete	4.60	22.96	92,645
04	Masonry	1.02	5.10	20,568
05	Metals	15.19	75.76	305,709
06	Wood, Plastics	2.30	11.47	46,267
07	Thermal and Moisture	14.56	72.61	292,999
08	Openings	2.42	12.07	48,686
09	Finishes	8.17	40.75	164,428
10	Specialties	3.28	16.34	65,924
11	Equipment	0.31	1.55	6,261
22	Plumbing	3.96	19.75	79,687
23	HVAC	3.38	16.84	67,940
26	Electrical	18.15	90.55	365,352
27	Communications	0.87	4.34	17,506
28	Electronic Security	0.38	1.91	7,700
	Total Building Costs	100.00	498.78	2,012,558

COST PER SQUARE FOOT = $498.78

© Copyright 2020. For a more in-depth report on this building or additional case studies contact DC&D
@ 800-533-5680, or www.DCD.com

File 15:

Lowland Credit Union began operations in 1953 with only $6,600 in assets. It was originally built on the site of American Enka, an old textile factory. Currently, Lowland Credit Union is the only locally-owned financial institution in Morristown, Tennessee, and serves over 12,000 members with assets in excess of $100 million. Lowland Credit Union is the longest continuously-operating financial institution in Morristown.

In 2016, plans began to formulate for a modern headquarters that would reflect the direction toward which the credit union wanted to move. With the help of the Studio Four Design team, the credit union achieved the concept they were looking for. The exterior of the building reflects a contemporary style, compared to the nearby buildings in downtown Morristown. The interior reflects the technology-driven concept toward which the credit union wants to move.

The design to completion was almost three years in the making, and well worth the effort. Lowland held its ribbon cutting on October 22, 2019 to a packed house, and a special guest appearance by NASCAR legend Rusty Wallace.

As President/CEO Mark Creech stated, "The collaboration between Studio Four Design, Burke-Ailey Construction (the general contractor), and the credit union was a great partnership that yielded a state-of-the-art facility that will take Lowland Credit Union well into the future."

The contemporary style of the new building achieves that look into the future that a cutting-edge headquarters would be proud to reflect.

Code	Division Name	%	S F Cost	Projected
01	General Requirements	4.79	18.51	167,311
03	Concrete	10.07	38.93	351,926
04	Masonry	8.21	31.73	286,877
05	Metals	13.97	54.01	488,319
06	Wood, Plastics	5.16	19.96	180,447
07	Thermal and Moisture	8.62	33.32	301,221
08	Openings	11.95	46.20	417,717
09	Finishes	9.29	35.89	324,500
10	Specialties	0.71	2.75	24,859
12	Furnishings	1.80	6.96	62,937
14	Conveying Systems	1.93	7.45	67,390
21	Fire Suppression	1.58	6.11	55,226
22	Plumbing	3.01	11.62	105,075
23	HVAC	5.64	21.80	197,133
26	Electrical	7.79	30.10	272,114
27	Communications	1.46	5.63	50,868
28	Electronic Security	0.91	3.53	31,949
41	Material Handling Equip.	0.42	1.62	14,638
44	Pollution Control Equipment	0.42	1.64	14,865
48	Electrical Power Generation	1.33	5.15	46,577
	Total Building Costs	100.00	386.48	3,494,206

COST PER SQUARE FOOT = $386.48

© Copyright 2020. For a more in-depth report on this building or additional case studies contact DC&D @ 800-533-5680, or www.DCD.com

File 16:

Charles Perry Partners, Inc. (CPPI) completed the 48,280-square-foot UF Innovate | The Hub Phase II project in January of 2018. UF Innovate | The Hub serves as a business incubator for North Central Florida startup companies. The program offers state-of-the-art laboratory, manufacturing, and office space, as well as advising and mentoring to help startups succeed and to grow Florida's entrepreneurial ecosystem.

The second phase expansion doubled the Hub's building size to over 100,000 square feet, allowing the incubator program that the building houses to serve about 50 startup companies in Gainesville, Florida.

Features of The Hub's Phase II space include laboratory access, advanced audio visual capabilities, and flexible office space, all of which work to provide customized support for each startup company's mission. CPPI also completed Phase I of the UF Innovate | The Hub building, which provided the program with its initial 48,707 square feet of office, laboratory, and conference room space.

UF Innovate | The Hub Phase II received its LEED Gold certification in December of 2018, and was awarded an Associated Builders and Contractors (ABC) Eagle Award for excellence in construction in Florida's Gulf Coast region in May of 2019.

Founded in 1968, CPPI specializes in educational, commercial, healthcare, governmental and institutional construction. CPPI has been named a 2019 ENR Top 400 Contractor and a Florida Trend Best Company to Work For.

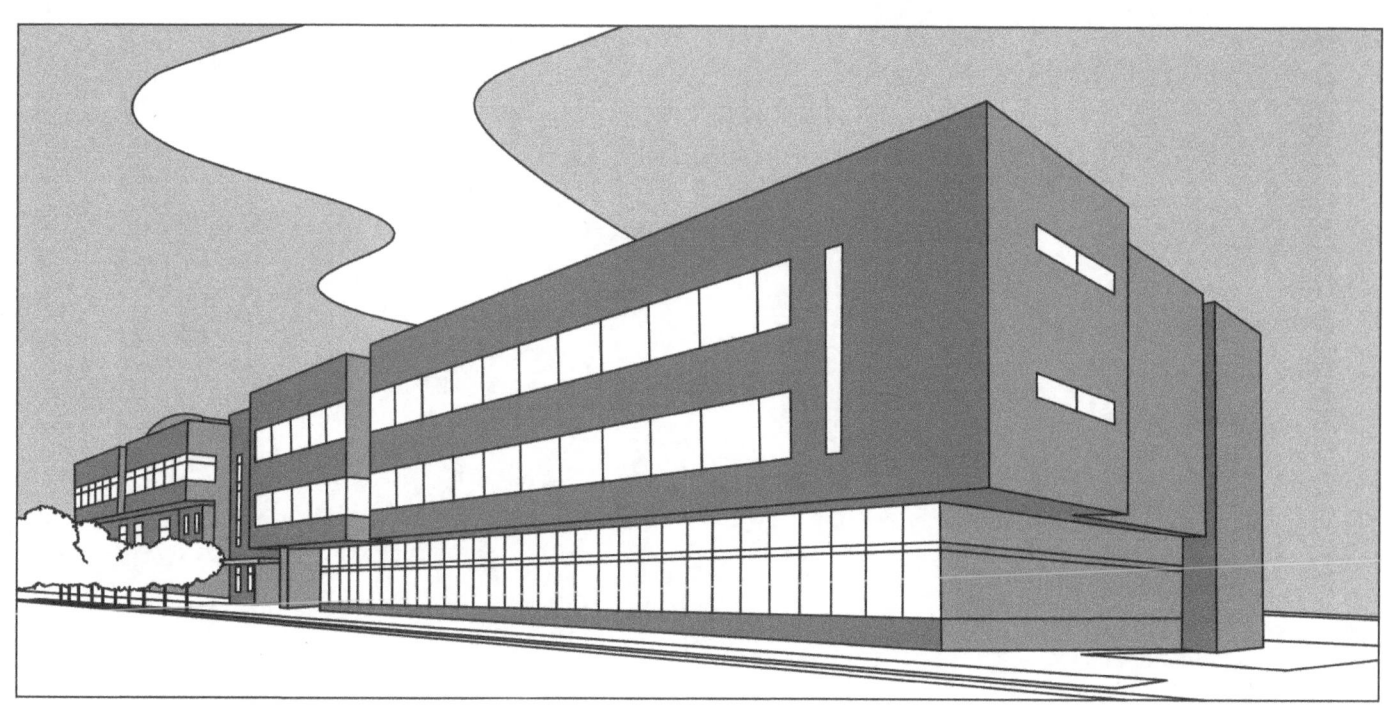

Code	Division Name	%	S F Cost	Projected
01	General Requirements	11.09	48.24	2,328,890
03	Concrete	7.72	33.59	1,621,563
04	Masonry	0.32	1.39	67,340
05	Metals	9.51	41.37	1,997,140
06	Wood, Plastics	0.38	1.64	79,297
07	Thermal and Moisture	9.59	41.74	2,015,419
08	Openings	7.86	34.19	1,650,529
09	Finishes	12.60	54.83	2,647,317
10	Specialties	0.51	2.23	107,847
12	Furnishings	2.40	10.46	504,809
21	Fire Suppression	1.26	5.47	264,225
22	Plumbing	3.72	16.20	782,177
23	HVAC	14.14	61.52	2,970,244
25	Integrated Automation	2.59	11.29	545,284
26	Electrical	16.31	70.95	3,425,259
	Total Building Costs	100.00	435.11	21,007,340

COST PER SQUARE FOOT = $435.11

© Copyright 2020. For a more in-depth report on this building or additional case studies contact DC&D @ 800-533-5680, or www.DCD.com

© Copyright 2020. For a more in-depth report on this building or additional case studies contact DC&D
@ 800-533-5680, or www.DCD.com

Educational

© Copyright 2020. For a more in-depth report on this building or additional case studies contact DC&D
@ 800-533-5680, or www.DCD.com

File 17:

This high school culinary arts classroom provides a modern, commercial kitchen aesthetic with a design and finishes worthy of a Food Network stage set.

Students are grouped around four workstations, each featuring its own gas range, double sink and dishwasher. The student workstations are configured as a large, contiguous U-shaped kitchen island located along the perimeter of the classroom.

The center of the classroom is designed as an open, flexible area to accommodate movable, stainless steel bar-height tables and stools. The dedicated workstation for the teacher is located near the front of the classroom, for performing instructional demonstrations and lectures. To stir up an appetite, vision panels are installed in the wall between the classroom and the corridor student lounge that allow outside viewing of all cooking activities. Monitors are used to display demonstrations to the students and visitors.

The culinary arts classroom embraces a "commercial kitchen" aesthetic, but maintains a residential standard. The room finishes are functional and durable, while incorporating bright colors, quartz counters, dark maple cabinetry, and epoxy flooring, along with stainless steel appliances and work tables.

Epoxy floor and wall finishes are brightly colored, and provide a lively, hardwearing surface. Blue accent wall and ceiling trim colors reflect the blue color of the appliances, and provide an expressive and cohesive interior design.

Each gas-fired range is equipped with a Type 1 stainless steel range hood ducted to the exterior of the building. Each hood is also equipped with an automatic fire suppression system. A new roof-top exhaust fan was installed to handle the new range hoods.

The range hoods also required the installation of a makeup air unit on the roof, ducted back down into the culinary arts classroom. Commercial standalone refrigerators and a freezer were provided as part of this project. A new dry pantry room was repurposed from the adjoining photography lab office area.

The new culinary arts classroom and its built-in audio visual features provide an exciting, modern culinary focus to Summit High School. The project was completed in December 2018 on budget, and was ready for occupancy in January 2019.

Code	Division Name	%	S F Cost	Projected
01	General Requirements	24.02	89.66	188,286
03	Concrete	1.33	4.96	10,411
04	Masonry	0.64	2.40	5,032
05	Metals	3.14	11.71	24,595
07	Thermal and Moisture	1.00	3.72	7,808
08	Openings	1.88	7.02	14,748
09	Finishes	9.57	35.73	75,042
10	Specialties	0.11	0.42	890
12	Furnishings	13.46	50.23	105,484
21	Fire Suppression	0.94	3.51	7,374
22	Plumbing	9.13	34.08	71,572
23	HVAC	26.01	97.08	203,872
26	Electrical	8.78	32.76	68,796
	Total Building Costs	100.00	373.29	783,911

COST PER SQUARE FOOT = $373.29

© Copyright 2020. For a more in-depth report on this building or additional case studies contact DC&D
@ 800-533-5680, or www.DCD.com

File 18:

The new administration center for the Newton Community School District, of Newton, Iowa, is representative of the city's perseverance. After being known as the "washing machine capitol of the world" Newton was devastated when the Maytag manufacturing plant shut down in 2007. Today, the city's economy has reemerged with strength, diversity and focus on Green Manufacturing and sustainability.

Looking to help revitalize the main thoroughfare to downtown, the Newton Community School District chose to renovate and relocate their administrative services to an abandoned grocery store, which had served the community for many decades. After a total renovation and transformation, the store's shell now serves as the school district's administration and educational hub.

The newly reimagined building is separated into two functions, with the front half of the building serving as the administration center and the back half dedicated to an education center. The new administration center houses the administrative staff offices, a large conference room, and support spaces for the district. The main public entrance parallels with the street and uses the existing canopy structure, which is a distinct feature of the original design.

The entry leads into the main lobby space that has direct access to the large conference room and administration reception. The reception then continues on to the offices and support spaces. The large conference room serves as the district's boardroom and professional development space, and can be subdivided into three separate conference spaces, creating the ultimate flexibility.

At the north end of the building, a large cardinal red wing wall uniquely defines the main entry to the educational center. The education center provides a reception space, classrooms, commons, offices, and support spaces. The educational center also includes a kiln room, science classroom, computer labs, and a fitness room.

The building site improvements incorporate new parking and a variety of landscaped areas, including a new seating area for the educational center that helps soften the impact of what once was a sea of uninterrupted asphalt.

The school district's new administration and educational hub expresses the city's resilience over difficulty and a desire to change and grow into the future.

Code	Division Name	%	S F Cost	Projected
00	Bidding Requirements	1.21	1.59	34,173
01	General Requirements	9.81	12.88	276,500
03	Concrete	2.37	3.12	66,898
04	Masonry	1.70	2.24	48,004
05	Metals	4.01	5.27	113,077
06	Wood & Plastics	2.96	3.89	83,454
07	Thermal & Moisture Protection	14.14	18.57	398,656
08	Doors & Windows	5.81	7.63	163,756
09	Finishes	18.40	24.16	518,660
10	Specialties	1.69	2.22	47,746
15	Mechanical	27.65	36.3	779,521
16	Electrical	10.23	13.43	288,318
	Total Building Costs	100.00	131.28	2,818,761

COST PER SQUARE FOOT = $131.28

© Copyright 2020. For a more in-depth report on this building or additional case studies contact DC&D @ 800-533-5680, or www.DCD.com

File 19:

The Maricopa Institute of Technology of Phoenix, AZ teaches a unique and advanced STEM curriculum to junior high students. Architects set out to reinforce and enhance their curriculum through the built environment of the new school.

Housing 600 students, a central atrium, doubling as a cafeteria or assembly space, opens up to an exterior amphitheater through large overhead doors for outdoor events. Stemming from the atrium, architects designed hallways to serve as learning environments, with breakout spaces for collaborative and individual study. Students working within the hallways can have a unique environment in which to study, while having the resources available there to help them.

Classrooms were designed to accommodate Riverside's unique curriculum, with rooms tailored to offer classes for engineering, advanced science, and technology. Research lab spaces are on either side of the school, extending to covered outdoor yards through large doors, so students can work on larger projects. Furniture and equipment are incorporated in rooms to accommodate for a wide range of research and experiments involving chemistry, biology, physics, drone manufacturing, robotics and 3D printing.

With every classroom, teachers have their own work rooms, with full visibility to the hallway and classrooms. These rooms can be used to prepare lesson plans, collaborate with each other, or as a place to meet with parents and students.

The building envelope is designed for maximum energy savings. Glazed wall areas shaded with large roof overhangs protect it from the direct heat of the summer while letting the winter sun come in. The exterior walls are constructed with Insulated Concrete Forms, adding more R-value to the envelope. Skylights with sun tracking devices are also incorporated along hallways and research labs, allowing plenty of natural light into the spaces and reducing the use of artificial lighting. The building is also equipped with an Energy Management System which offers the owner computer-aided tools to control, monitor, and optimize the building performance.

Code	Division Name	%	S F Cost	Projected
00	Procurement	4.03	13.60	815,837
01	General Requirements	22.15	74.73	4,483,935
03	Concrete	7.27	24.53	1,471,772
05	Metals	8.84	29.82	1,789,141
06	Wood & Plastics	0.89	3.00	179,868
07	Thermal and Moisture	6.22	20.98	1,258,963
08	Openings	8.20	27.66	1,659,667
09	Finishes	8.61	29.05	1,743,251
10	Specialties	0.95	3.21	192,695
12	Furnishings	0.40	1.34	80,496
14	Conveying Systems	0.40	1.36	81,717
21	Fire Suppression	0.76	2.55	152,939
22	Plumbing	4.17	14.08	844,854
23	HVAC	12.92	43.61	2,616,530
26	Electrical	13.33	44.99	2,699,594
27	Communications	0.15	0.49	29,364
28	Electronic Security	0.71	2.41	144,470
	Total Building Costs	100.00	337.42	20,245,094

COST PER SQUARE FOOT = $337.42

© Copyright 2020. For a more in-depth report on this building or additional case studies contact DC&D
@ 800-533-5680, or www.DCD.com

File 20:

Located prominently on the main road through town, the new gymnasium, with its textured block and brick and new lighted signage, provides a WOW factor as soon as you enter the Decatur city limits. The unique design and renovations made this project a standout of which the community can be proud.

The electrical service entry was updated and brought up to current NEC code. New roof areas have a minimum ¼" per foot slope drop for positive drainage, and the metal walls and roof panels serve as an efficient material to enclose the upper portion of the building. Existing floor elevations were raised and adjusted to accommodate ADA requirements. The oldest classrooms in the original building were demolished due to asbestos hazards, which opened up room for a new gymnasium.

Roof insulation was added to the addition, allowing the use of a more economical wet fire sprinkler system. Old batt insulation was removed to provide access to computer cables. The decision to move the Middle School to this location allowed for additional classroom space to accommodate growth. In addition, both dressing rooms in the gym and one storage room (which were in the middle of the building with no exterior windows), received a concrete roof, which made a safe place for students to go to during a storm.

A floating wood floor with cushioned pad and moisture barrier were installed in the gym. The school colors were used on bleachers, which include ADA spaces. New lighted scoreboards were provided, one on each end of the gymnasium, which is flooded with natural light from the windows. Also included were basketball goals and a removable net and poles for volleyball competitions.

The new gym will serve as a home for a variety of activities and events, including physical education classes, assemblies, graduation ceremonies and more.

The school colors help to unify otherwise disparate sections of the school such as the girl's toilet room, the reception area, and the nurses' station area.

Also included in the new design was a private school board entry area for school board sessions, which doubles as a computer classroom, and an area for efficient and safe pick up and drop off of students.

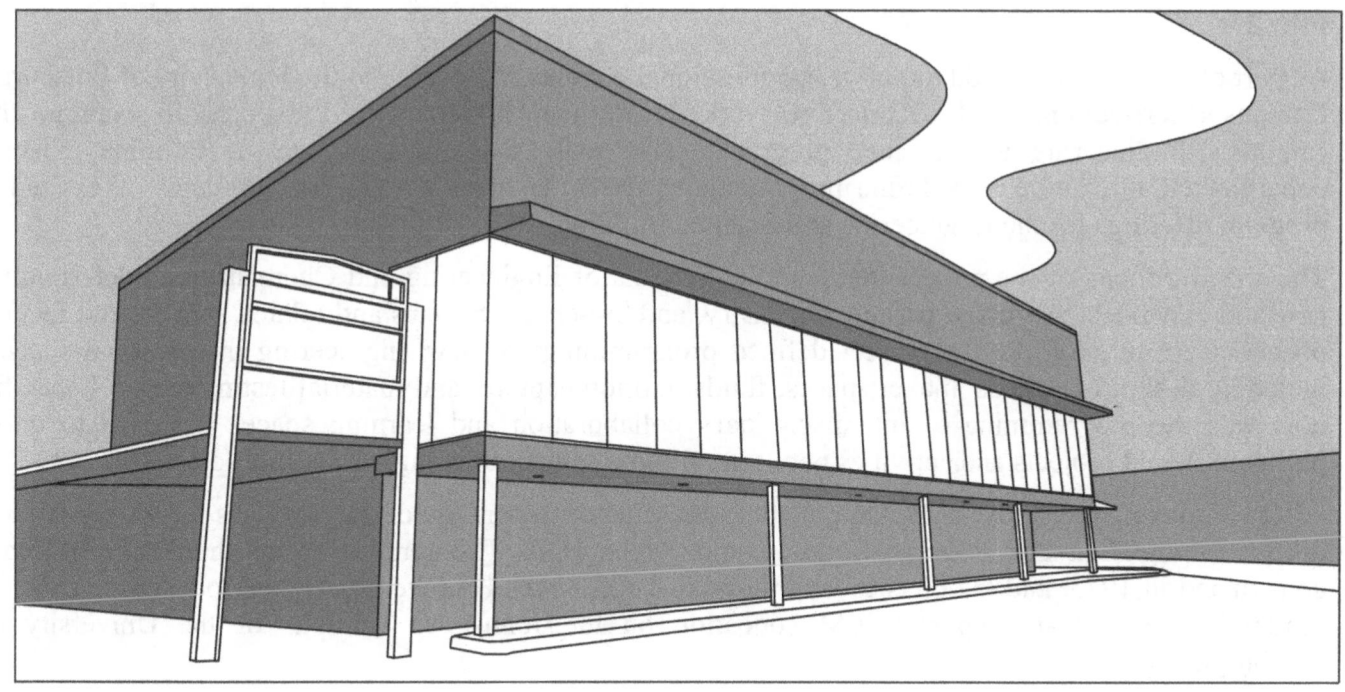

Code	Division Name	%	S F Cost	Projected
00	Procurement	3.77	3.16	98,890
01	General Requirements	13.61	11.40	356,841
03	Concrete	8.06	6.75	211,304
04	Masonry	8.73	7.31	228,836
05	Metals	2.30	1.93	60,358
06	Wood & Plastics	0.90	0.75	23,427
07	Thermal and Moisture	5.90	4.94	154,441
08	Openings	6.26	5.24	163,874
09	Finishes	11.28	9.45	295,741
10	Specialties	1.19	1.00	31,323
12	Furnishings	2.54	2.13	66,774
13	Special Construction	10.66	8.93	279,489
21	Fire Suppression	5.49	4.60	143,944
23	HVAC	10.15	8.50	266,125
26	Electrical	7.83	6.56	205,319
28	Electronic Security	1.31	1.10	34,281
	Total Building Costs	100.00	83.75	2,620,968

COST PER SQUARE FOOT = $83.75

© Copyright 2020. For a more in-depth report on this building or additional case studies contact DC&D @ 800-533-5680, or www.DCD.com

File 21:

As part of an initiative to add a four year professional engineering degree to the University of Pittsburgh Campus's curriculum, IKM Architecture worked with the University of Pittsburgh to examine the campus's Engineering and Science programs. The goal of the project was to examine existing departmental utilization and define programmatic needs to meet the forecast demand of expanded program offerings for the Engineering and Science Building.

The specific focus of the project involved the Schools of Engineering and Chemistry and determining new and expanded chemistry, organic chemistry, and bio-chemistry labs and related support and faculty office space. In addition, the project defined programming for new engineering instructional spaces, including design build labs, maker spaces, fluids, motion capture, and material testing labs. Of specific note was the programming of interdisciplinary collaboration and learning spaces designed to cross pollinate shared projects and activities between multiple science and engineering sub-disciplines.

After completing the study, IKM Architecture was selected to perform design services for the renovation of the Engineering and Science Building and Krebs Hall. The renovation of the E&S Building, constructed in 1973, and the physics laboratory space in Krebs Hall were designed to improve existing academic spaces that support STEM education on the Johnstown Campus of the University of Pittsburgh.

The project consisted of a 65,400-square-foot renovation to encompass the laboratories, classrooms, offices, storage, student lounges and club, and designated spaces for the engineering technology and chemistry departments.

The program identifies engineering instructional labs, chemistry instructional and research space, classrooms, lecture halls, and 38 faculty offices and related workspaces.

The design sought to incorporate more opportunities for cross-disciplinary collaboration and informal meeting space within the existing building footprint. In addition, exhibit space, popular in today's scientific communities as an extension of learning and sharing knowledge, is included for the Chemistry and Engineering Departments.

Code	Division Name	%	S F Cost	Projected
00	Bidding Requirements	2.58	7.24	472,350
01	General Requirements	16.27	45.74	2,984,388
03	Concrete	2.24	6.29	410,482
04	Masonry	2.07	5.82	379,944
05	Metals	5.39	15.16	988,966
06	Wood & Plastics	0.48	1.34	87,446
07	Thermal & Moisture Protection	6.67	18.75	1,223,257
08	Doors & Windows	3.85	10.83	706,315
09	Finishes	12.08	33.95	2,215,300
10	Specialties	1.23	3.47	226,094
11	Equipment	2.42	6.81	444,022
12	Furnishings	1.32	3.72	242,843
14	Conveying Systems	0.49	1.38	90,057
15	Mechanical	26.41	74.26	4,844,834
16	Electrical	16.50	46.40	3,027,350
	Total Building Costs	100.00	281.15	18,343,647

COST PER SQUARE FOOT = $281.15

© Copyright 2020. For a more in-depth report on this building or additional case studies contact DC&D @ 800-533-5680, or www.DCD.com

File 22:

The new two-story, two-wing building, tucked into its neighborhood on an eight-acre site, houses pre-K-5 classrooms, a cafeteria, and a gymnasium, as well as administrative offices. VHGA worked in a collaborative process to plan and design the new school.

"The opportunity to unify two separate elementary schools on one campus is of great benefit to the community," said Ronald Triplehorn, Director of Facilities for the school district. "Beyond the savings in operating costs for one, modern, energy efficient building, specifically designed to meet the students' educational and social needs, we believe the expanded interactions of the larger student population and their teachers will have a deeply positive impact."

The new school, constructed on an eight-acre site, is situated to flood the school interiors with natural light and to mitigate the harsh winter elements by placing entry points on the south. Building mass provides protected outdoor multi-functional gathering areas. Age-appropriate hard surface and turf play areas and equipment are easily accessed.

Energy efficiency and technology infrastructure are key to the design. A simple layout provides designated parking and circulation pathways, with a focus on student safety by channeling and separating buses, deliveries, staff, and visitor traffic.

In this efficient plan, classrooms radiate from the centralized core, the gym and cafeteria occupy a separate wing, and wide hallways and gathering spaces support group activities. The clean, contemporary architecture of the masonry and stucco building, accented by metal panels and details, responds to its context and climate.

Brightly colored walls throughout the spaces provide a lively backdrop for displays, and create youth-friendly settings for learning and socializing – from the classrooms to the library and gym.

Code	Division Name	%	S F Cost	Projected
01	General Requirements	15.91	48.20	2,980,471
03	Concrete	8.09	24.49	1,514,426
04	Masonry	2.26	6.83	422,335
05	Metals	10.24	31.03	1,919,031
06	Wood & Plastics	0.85	2.56	158,227
07	Thermal and Moisture	6.33	19.18	1,185,957
08	Openings	5.50	16.66	1,030,419
09	Finishes	12.93	39.16	2,421,659
10	Specialties	0.81	2.46	152,255
11	Equipment	2.13	6.46	399,566
12	Furnishings	3.27	9.89	611,829
14	Conveying Systems	0.47	1.43	88,160
21	Fire Suppression	4.15	12.56	776,739
22	Plumbing	3.84	11.64	719,481
23	HVAC	9.90	30.00	1,855,111
26	Electrical	13.31	40.32	2,493,307
	Total Building Costs	100.00	302.88	18,728,972

COST PER SQUARE FOOT = $302.88

© Copyright 2020. For a more in-depth report on this building or additional case studies contact DC&D @ 800-533-5680, or www.DCD.com

File 23:

Flansburgh Architects studied nine options for Holbrook Public Schools. After long and careful consideration, the Town of Holbrook selected an "all-district" Pre K-12 solution to consolidate all three deteriorating existing schools into one new facility. This single phase construction project reduced disruption to students during construction, resolved the issue of three antiquated schools, and satisfied 21st century learning goals.

The new 217,353-s.f., two-story building serves the 1,095 students in the district. The school houses two cafeterias and a 320-seat auditorium, as well as two larger gymnasiums with divisible basketball courts and 500-seat bleachers, new baseball and softball fields, a new synthetic turf multi-purpose field, and a running track for both school and community use.

Grades Pre K-5 are completely separated from grades 6-12; each section of the school has its own entrance, administration, and facilities. Spaces include larger classrooms, new media centers, and science labs that conform to 21st century education standards. Also included are dedicated art, music, band, computer labs, special education spaces, and a STEAM commons to enhance the learning process by thinking creatively.

The design features numerous "green" elements that will improve operational efficiency of the school such as occupancy sensors for lighting, an energy efficient displacement air system, and a building-wide energy management system, in addition to improved student safety with new building security, access control, fire alarm, and fire suppression systems.

The project utilized the CM-at-Risk project delivery method focusing on logistics with traffic, an occupied existing school on site, and schedule. Flansburgh managed three earlier bid packages (site, steel, & masonry) and the final bid package to release the project six months before schedule. This is the first Pre K-12 school project funded by the Massachusetts School Building Authority (MSBA) in the Commonwealth.

Code	Division Name	%	S F Cost	Projected
00	Procurement	3.87	12.14	2,638,419
01	General Requirements	13.04	40.95	8,900,352
03	Concrete	4.84	15.19	3,301,036
04	Masonry	5.25	16.47	3,580,808
05	Metals	7.73	24.27	5,274,108
06	Wood & Plastics	3.20	10.06	2,187,641
07	Thermal and Moisture	9.89	31.05	6,749,669
08	Openings	4.87	15.30	3,325,487
09	Finishes	14.43	45.29	9,843,560
10	Specialties	1.44	4.51	980,707
11	Equipment	1.62	5.08	1,104,410
12	Furnishings	2.41	7.56	1,642,743
14	Conveying Systems	0.41	1.30	281,635
21	Fire Suppression	1.25	3.92	852,464
22	Plumbing	4.13	12.96	2,817,735
23	HVAC	10.39	32.62	7,091,123
26	Electrical	11.14	34.97	7,601,190
27	Communications	0.05	0.15	32,564
28	Electronic Security	0.04	0.12	26,504
	Total Building Costs	100.00	313.92	68,232,154

COST PER SQUARE FOOT = $313.92

© Copyright 2020. For a more in-depth report on this building or additional case studies contact DC&D @ 800-533-5680, or www.DCD.com

File 24:

A classically-inspired façade and enhanced safety and security were the primary design criteria for Florence Middle School. The exterior drew inspiration from Tuscan detailing, using cast stone complementing face brick, acknowledging the original 1917 school that was replaced in 1951.

Security was integrally designed using clear lines-of-sight, electronically controlled public access, and secure exterior/interior student spaces. For safety, the gymnasium doubles as a FEMA-rated storm shelter accommodating three times the school population. Michael Dorn, of Safe Havens International, commented that the school ranks in his Top 5 safest school designs of the more than 7,800 schools he has reviewed.

The design was organized around a central commons, connecting academics, fine arts and athletics, while also serving as a pre-function space for public events. The academic wing's prominent two-story façade was placed west of the commons, taking advantage of traffic visibility along the campus' west edge, while wrapping itself around an outdoor courtyard with controlled access.

The auditorium anchors the fine art wing surrounding it, and is located north of the commons. It hosts public events year round, providing optimum professionally-designed acoustics. The gymnasium, east of the commons, aligns with the existing high school competition gymnasium, allowing their simultaneous use for tournaments/events.

The north/south corridor between the auditorium and cafeteria directly aligns with entry gates to the Braly football stadium to the north, home to Florence High School and the University of North Alabama. On game day, the commons/cafeteria/restrooms are open to the public for pregame use while providing direct stadium access through the space.

Code	Division Name	%	S F Cost	Projected
00	Procurement	1.41	3.56	642,494
01	General Requirements	5.03	12.68	2,288,343
03	Concrete	9.68	24.37	4,396,603
04	Masonry	14.82	37.33	6,736,047
05	Metals	9.53	23.99	4,329,331
06	Wood & Plastics	1.85	4.65	839,436
07	Thermal and Moisture	6.46	16.28	2,938,296
08	Openings	5.36	13.50	2,436,204
09	Finishes	7.52	18.95	3,418,612
10	Specialties	0.92	2.32	418,365
11	Equipment	2.13	5.37	969,693
12	Furnishings	4.01	10.09	1,819,950
14	Conveying Systems	0.25	0.62	112,132
21	Fire Suppression	1.95	4.92	888,401
22	Plumbing	5.30	13.34	2,406,717
23	HVAC	13.77	34.68	6,257,625
26	Electrical	10.00	25.19	4,544,803
	Total Building Costs	100.00	251.84	45,443,052

COST PER SQUARE FOOT = $251.84

© Copyright 2020. For a more in-depth report on this building or additional case studies contact DC&D @ 800-533-5680, or www.DCD.com

© Copyright 2020. For a more in-depth report on this building or additional case studies contact DC&D @ 800-533-5680, or www.DCD.com

Hotel

© Copyright 2020. For a more in-depth report on this building or additional case studies contact DC&D
@ 800-533-5680, or www.DCD.com

CASE STUDY

File 25:

This extended-stay hotel is in close proximity to both commercial and residential developments. The owner's goals were to minimize square footage in order to minimize construction costs and maximize return on investments, as well as to minimize support space in order to maximize room for guests. The city included additional requirements for building finishes, landscaping, parking and chimneys.

The project scope called for design development through non-site-specific construction and purchasing documents, in order to create a design that could be adapted to any site. The company's prototype design called for a three-story building with either a "U," straight or "L" shape.

Prototypes also included a mid-rise variation of six to ten floors. The exterior of the structure is rendered in a palette of weathered stone, horizontal siding and simulated stucco with bronzed anodized, multi-paned windows. The architect specified stacked stone, EIFS and vinyl siding. The exterior is heavily landscaped to comply with city requirements.

The interior design contains a combination of studio, one-bedroom and two-bedroom plans. Floor-to-ceiling windows in the main lobby provide extensive natural daylighting. The lobby also contains a central stone fireplace. The facility features a fitness center, on-site convenience store, outdoor pool, barbecue grills and an adjacent 6-mile running/biking trail.

Market research, industry tours, design charettes and in-progress mock-ups were used to ensure appropriate design and compliance with city requirements. An outside consultant was used to provide an independent cost estimate and cost controls.

A franchisee construction information package was provided and includes single line drawings, non-site-specific construction drawings and specifications for standard design elements. These non-site-specific specifications allow for site adaptability and flexibility in the number of units in the hotel, increasing the design's appeal to potential franchisees.

Code	Division Name	%	S F Cost	Projected
01	General Requirements	1.18	2.15	160,247
03	Concrete	3.86	7.00	522,912
04	Masonry	2.66	4.82	359,853
05	Metals	1.87	3.39	253,022
06	Wood & Plastics	11.94	21.66	1,616,530
07	Thermal & Moisture Protection	6.45	11.71	872,926
08	Doors & Windows	5.29	9.61	716,896
09	Finishes	32.57	59.12	4,411,019
10	Specialties	0.93	1.70	126,511
11	Equipment	0.31	0.56	42,170
12	Furnishings	4.36	7.91	590,385
14	Conveying Systems	0.86	1.57	116,671
15	Mechanical	17.44	31.66	2,361,541
16	Electrical	10.28	18.65	1,391,621
	Total Building Costs	100.00	181.52	13,542,307

COST PER SQUARE FOOT = $181.52

© Copyright 2020. For a more in-depth report on this building or additional case studies contact DC&D @ 800-533-5680, or www.DCD.com

File 26:

Located in a historic district of Chicago, this site required the facility's design to match that of the surrounding architecture.

The exterior of this high-rise hotel features metal windows and storefronts, an EPDM rubber roofing membrane and steel canopy, and revolving doors.

The hotel offers 128 standard, king and double guest rooms, 60 two-room suites, 40 studios and two VIP suites. The interior features resilient vinyl composite tile flooring and wood doors. Elevators service all floors. The main lobby features high ceilings, formal living-room-style furniture and patterned carpeting. An open wood staircase connects the lobby to the second floor and an open wood railing encloses the overhang. High windows and wall sconces provide natural and artificial lighting.

The facility also houses six meeting rooms, an enclosed swimming pool, a whirlpool spa and an exercise facility. A 4,500-square-foot restaurant is located on the first floor and a second floor skywalk connects the hotel with the neighboring Ruth's Chris Steak House. The lobby showcases a collection of artifacts from famous Chicago buildings.

© Copyright 2020. For a more in-depth report on this building or additional case studies contact DC&D @ 800-533-5680, or www.DCD.com

Code	Division Name	%	S F Cost	Projected
00	Bidding Requirements	9.25	15.52	2,515,428
03	Concrete	25.06	42.08	6,818,565
04	Masonry	4.06	6.82	1,104,811
05	Metals	1.39	2.32	377,566
06	Wood & Plastics	5.54	9.30	1,506,041
07	Thermal & Moisture Protection	1.17	1.96	317,553
08	Doors & Windows	6.72	11.30	1,829,167
09	Finishes	11.81	19.84	3,211,405
10	Specialties	0.19	0.32	52,224
11	Equipment	0.06	0.10	16,759
12	Furnishings	0.06	0.10	15,931
13	Special Construction	0.56	0.94	151,818
14	Conveying Systems	3.24	5.45	881,858
15	Mechanical	21.92	36.82	5,964,307
16	Electrical	8.97	15.07	2,440,266
	Total Building Costs	100.00	167.95	27,203,698

COST PER SQUARE FOOT = $167.95

© Copyright 2020. For a more in-depth report on this building or additional case studies contact DC&D @ 800-533-5680, or www.DCD.com

File 27:

The Hampton Inn of Carol Stream is located in the northwest suburb of Carol Stream, Illinois. The new hotel is situated on a well-planned 3.3-acre development at 205 West North Avenue (Route 64).

This six-story, 71,000-square-foot hotel offers 116 standard, double suite, king and king suite guestrooms. Hotel amenities include seven meeting/seminar rooms, an indoor swimming pool and whirlpool spa, exercise facility and many amenities that cater to the business traveler or family on vacation.

The building, which is primarily a pre-cast insulated frame and floor deck structure, was erected and closed in four months from start to finish. The choice of pre-cast material was important to the role of bringing in the project on time and within budget.

This project combined the effort of BABCO Construction, Inc., along with the ownership and development team of Arrowhead Management and the architecture group of Karson & Associates, Inc.

© Copyright 2020. For a more in-depth report on this building or additional case studies contact DC&D @ 800-533-5680, or www.DCD.com

Code	Division Name	%	S F Cost	Projected
00	Bidding Requirements	10.22	19.03	1,350,612
03	Concrete	23.58	43.90	3,116,799
04	Masonry	0.31	0.58	41,558
05	Metals	1.57	2.92	207,787
06	Wood & Plastics	5.82	10.83	768,810
07	Thermal & Moisture Protection	3.38	6.29	446,742
08	Doors & Windows	5.45	10.16	721,019
09	Finishes	19.41	36.15	2,566,164
10	Specialties	0.58	1.08	76,881
13	Special Construction	0.90	1.66	118,439
14	Conveying Systems	2.23	4.15	295,057
15	Mechanical	15.47	28.79	2,044,621
16	Electrical	11.08	20.63	1,464,894
	Total Building Costs	100.00	186.17	13,219,383

COST PER SQUARE FOOT = $186.17

© Copyright 2020. For a more in-depth report on this building or additional case studies contact DC&D @ 800-533-5680, or www.DCD.com

File 28:

This hotel is located on a fully-landscaped, two-acre site along the north end of a major expressway.

The ten-story hotel is a steel frame and glazed curtain wall structure with composite steel deck floors and pre-cast concrete, metal panel and EIFS columns running the height of the structure's two towers. Roofing is of EPDM rubber membrane. Glass curtain wall is used along the exterior façade to provide natural lighting. The site includes aboveground and underground parking for over 130 vehicles.

The hotel contains 245 suites with living areas and kitchenettes, as well as an indoor swimming pool, two-story lobby, exercise facilities, over 8,000 square feet of conference space, first floor restaurant space and the Marilyn Miglin Boutique.

The mechanical system includes two-pipe horizontal fan coil units with chilled water cooling and electric heating, as well as 600 tons of cooling supplied by rooftop chillers to supplement the fan coils in the hotel's public areas.

Construction included plumbing, electrical, fire protection and life safety systems. A hydraulic service elevator and an electric geared shuttle car, in addition to three passenger elevators, service the hotel. Interior finishes include tile flooring in the lobby and elevators and carpet in guest rooms and hallways where acoustics are a concern.

© Copyright 2020. For a more in-depth report on this building or additional case studies contact DC&D @ 800-533-5680, or www.DCD.com

Code	Division Name	%	S F Cost	Projected
0	Procurement and Contracting Require	9.67	15.38	2,946,831
3	Concrete	1.99	3.17	607,785
4	Masonry	0.54	0.86	165,759
5	Metals	7.76	12.36	2,366,673
6	Wood, Plastics, and Composites	1.60	2.55	488,068
7	Thermal and Moisture Protection	3.33	5.30	1,014,816
8	Openings	10.63	16.92	3,241,515
9	Finishes	15.24	24.24	4,644,942
10	Specialties	0.48	0.77	147,341
11	Equipment	0.33	0.53	101,297
12	Furnishings	1.48	2.35	451,234
14	Conveying Systems	3.03	4.82	924,568
21	Fire Suppression	2.51	3.99	764,335
22	Plumbing	12.99	20.67	3,959,805
23	HVAC	13.90	22.12	4,236,070
26	Electrical	14.50	23.07	4,420,248
	Total Building Costs	100.00	159.09	30,481,288

COST PER SQUARE FOOT = $159.09

© Copyright 2020. For a more in-depth report on this building or additional case studies contact DC&D @ 800-533-5680, or www.DCD.com

File 29:

Wanting to increase their presence, the owner of a casino/restaurant in Billings, Montana decided to build a motel adjacent to his property. CBG Architects developed a plan that allowed for the maximum adequate sized number of rooms while keeping with parking and landscaping requirements.

A basic pattern for the parking in an "L" shaped pattern provided the most spaces laid out along with the "H" basic pattern for the rooms allowed to provide the most number of rooms. The number of parking spaces matched the number of motel rooms that would be provided. The motel also includes a drive-thru covered entry for guest convenience.

The motel layout includes sixteen guest rooms on the main floor along with a lobby area, registration, office, laundry, toilets, a meeting room and a manager's apartment. Two of the main floor guest rooms are handicap accessible as are the toilets. The second floor has 23 rooms, three of which have corner whirlpool tubs and separate showers. Four of the other rooms include standard whirlpool tubs and separate showers.

The design includes a standard concrete foundation wall construction with slab on grade. The exterior and interior walls are one-hour wood construction. The floor/ceiling between the first and second floor is 22-inch-deep floor trusses of one-hour construction. The roof is cantilevered with pre-manufactured roof trusses with wood sheathing and asphalt shingles. A fire protection system is installed throughout the building.

The motel exterior is brick veneer wainscot and steel siding above the brick. Each guest room includes a six- by four-foot vinyl sliding window. Each room is carpeted with ceramic tile in the bathrooms. Internet access is available, with connections at the nightstand and desk. The overall rustic design intent of the motel includes 12-inch-round half logs installed every 28 feet from foundation to the eave. The gable ends are also trimmed with 6-inch-round half logs.

© Copyright 2020. For a more in-depth report on this building or additional case studies contact DC&D @ 800-533-5680, or www.DCD.com

Code	Division Name	%	S F Cost	Projected
1	General Requirements	3.80	4.14	90,832
3	Concrete	5.48	5.97	131,187
4	Masonry	2.18	2.37	52,083
5	Metals	1.01	1.10	24,217
6	Wood, Plastics, and Composites	19.59	21.32	468,721
7	Thermal and Moisture Protection	8.63	9.38	206,375
8	Openings	7.56	8.23	180,797
9	Finishes	17.88	19.45	427,694
10	Specialties	0.50	0.54	11,955
11	Equipment	1.88	2.04	45,042
22	Plumbing	12.84	13.98	307,314
23	HVAC	8.02	8.72	191,778
26	Electrical	8.68	9.46	207,768
28	Electronic Safety and Security	1.95	2.13	46,772
	Total Building Costs	100.00	108.82	2,392,534

COST PER SQUARE FOOT = $108.82

© Copyright 2020. For a more in-depth report on this building or additional case studies contact DC&D @ 800-533-5680, or www.DCD.com

File 30:

This motel is located on a 1.37-acre site that can be accessed from two sides, and is fronted by streets on three. The owner required an existing oak tree on the north side of the building to be preserved, in order to enhance the building's aesthetic appeal.

The design called for wood-frame construction and slab-on-grade foundations. The exterior of the building utilizes vinyl siding and a masonry wainscot featured on an entrance canopy, to visually break up the massing of the elevation.

The entrance canopy is detailed with dentil moldings and over-the-post railings to achieve a country-style façade. A shingle roof adds aesthetic interest. Forty-two parking stalls were provided, including two handicapped stalls located near the front canopy. Parking extends to three sides of the facility.

The motel contains 40 units with integral pool, spa, and breakfast area. It is arranged in a traditional double-loaded corridor design, ensuring that square footage is utilized with maximum efficiency.

Units were not built above the pool area for acoustical reasons; this design also allows for a higher ceiling and an overlook from the second floor to the pool and spa below. The building is fully equipped with a fire alarm system and sprinkler system. Interior finishes include carpeting, vinyl composite and ceramic tile and vinyl wall covering.

The motel features king-sized suites with whirlpool baths, handicapped units and a hospitality room serving continental breakfast.

Code	Division Name	%	S F Cost	Projected
1	General Requirements	17.84	22.84	480,272
3	Concrete	4.74	6.08	127,679
4	Masonry	2.18	2.80	58,757
6	Wood & Plastics	25.01	32.02	673,254
7	Thermal & Moisture Protection	2.96	3.78	79,697
8	Doors & Windows	0.82	1.05	21,942
9	Finishes	12.35	15.80	332,423
10	Specialties	2.31	2.96	62,123
13	Special Construction	2.64	3.38	71,064
15	Mechanical	18.57	23.78	500,018
16	Electrical	10.58	13.54	284,955
	Total Building Costs	100.00	128.03	2,692,182

COST PER SQUARE FOOT = $128.03

© Copyright 2020. For a more in-depth report on this building or additional case studies contact DC&D
@ 800-533-5680, or www.DCD.com

File 31:

This facility is an 80-unit motel built on a very small site with a substantial grade change parallel to the building. The location was selected as it is near the state capitol and also on an intersection of two major highways.

Since the intended use is to provide guest rooms for tourists, as well as government officials, the building has nine different guest room styles. Some provide spacious work areas; others have whirlpool spas for complete relaxation. In addition, the facility has a breakfast area, indoor pool, spa, exercise room, lounge with a fireplace, and an outdoor patio.

Face brick and a standing seam metal roof were used for curb appeal, accent, and durability. EIFS, a cementitious lap siding, and asphalt shingles complement the brick and metal and serve to keep the project within the predetermined budget.

Guest rooms are heated and cooled by individual Amana PTAC units. The pool and lobby are on separate HVAC units. Guest room baths are exhausted in groups of ten to twelve rooms, with one exhaust fan in continual operation to maintain fresh air in the rooms. All windows are operable.

The owners desired to achieve a blend with the mountain landscape of Montana. This was done with heavy landscaping.

The motel has been in operation for approximately one year and has met all of the owner's expectations.

Code	Division Name	%	S F Cost	Projected
1	General Requirements	17.39	25.33	785,276
3	Concrete	7.59	11.05	342,528
4	Masonry	0.37	0.55	16,917
5	Metals	1.76	2.56	79,401
6	Wood & Plastics	16.33	23.77	737,032
7	Thermal & Moisture Protection	9.69	14.11	437,602
8	Doors & Windows	5.68	8.27	256,589
9	Finishes	13.39	19.50	604,725
10	Specialties	0.93	1.36	42,118
11	Equipment	0.42	0.61	18,914
12	Furnishings	0.62	0.90	27,924
13	Special Construction	2.56	3.72	115,376
14	Conveying Systems	2.02	2.94	91,406
15	Mechanical	13.70	19.96	618,679
16	Electrical	7.54	10.97	340,250
	Total Building Costs	100.00	145.59	4,514,740

COST PER SQUARE FOOT = $145.59

© Copyright 2020. For a more in-depth report on this building or additional case studies contact DC&D @ 800-533-5680, or www.DCD.com

File 32:

This Arizona casino complex is located on a site originally planned for an industrial park and features a casino, hotel with 131 units, RV park with room for 50 vehicles, spa, 18-hole golf course, conference center and convenience store.

The casino is a large rectangular building, while the connecting hotel is an "L" shaped structure. Low maintenance exterior walls of CMU, EIFS and aluminum windows were emphasized. The roof features standard and long span steel joints and rolled steel shapes. Interior walls are of gypsum board construction. Flooring throughout the interior is a combination of ceramic tile, quarry tile and carpeting.

The casino compact with the state of Arizona allows for a maximum of 500 slot machines with no future expansion. The interior design scheme of the casino places slots in the center of the building and wraps additional support and gaming functions − such as poker, keno, off-track betting, food service, meeting rooms, show lounge and back-of-the-house operations − around the central lowered slot floor.

Design schemes utilize the intense colors featured in Apache beadwork and clothing, as well as free interpretations of Apache motifs. These designs were agreed upon by the San Carlos Apache tribe, who did not want direct interpretations of their sacred motifs reflected in the casino.

© Copyright 2020. For a more in-depth report on this building or additional case studies contact DC&D @ 800-533-5680, or www.DCD.com

Code	Division Name	%	S F Cost	Projected
00	Bidding Requirements	4.21	13.42	1,391,166
01	General Requirements	7.78	24.81	2,573,707
03	Concrete	6.99	22.29	2,312,026
04	Masonry	1.55	4.95	512,858
05	Metals	9.46	30.16	3,127,665
06	Wood & Plastics	4.36	13.89	1,441,237
07	Thermal & Moisture Protection	8.69	27.73	2,875,405
08	Doors & Windows	3.92	12.50	1,295,834
09	Finishes	13.15	41.93	4,348,651
10	Specialties	0.54	1.73	179,526
11	Equipment	0.62	1.97	204,779
14	Conveying Systems	0.30	0.94	97,798
15	Mechanical	19.22	61.29	6,356,558
16	Electrical	19.21	61.28	6,354,693
	Total Building Costs	100.00	318.91	33,071,900

COST PER SQUARE FOOT = $318.91

© Copyright 2020. For a more in-depth report on this building or additional case studies contact DC&D @ 800-533-5680, or www.DCD.com

© Copyright 2020. For a more in-depth report on this building or additional case studies contact DC&D
@ 800-533-5680, or www.DCD.com

Industrial

© Copyright 2020. For a more in-depth report on this building or additional case studies contact DC&D
@ 800-533-5680, or www.DCD.com

File 33:

This headquarters creates a statement of possibility for light manufacturing facilities that are environmentally responsible, worker-friendly, cost competitive, and architecturally significant.

The project includes a 8,000-square-foot office space, a 34,000-square-foot light manufacturing shop, and storage area. In the nexus that links the shop and the office is a wall-to-wall window that provides a visual reminder of the dual nature of the business. In the conference room, straw bale walls were selected for their unparalleled ability to insulate (R 42), minimal embodied energy, appropriateness for an organic design, and contribution to the local economy.

In the shop, low-tech earth tubes naturally cool air by passing it underneath the building, while large fans draw hot air up and let it escape through operable clerestories. In the office, a ground source heat pump uses six 300-foot-deep wells to exchange their temperature with the ground to provide efficient air conditioning as well as heating.

Key to the building's environmental response is its relationship to the path of the sun. With a 189 KW solar system soon to be installed, the company's building will soon be producing 90% of the energy it uses.

These facilities were completed to LEED Gold Standards and are modeled to use 50% less energy than a comparable building. The natural surroundings are not ignored, but instead celebrated through nature trails, as well as native meadows, vegetated swales that account for 100% of infiltrated storm-water mitigation on site. Special attention not only to the work environment, but also to the workers, was given through the creation of day-lit spaces to improve worker conditions, and through the inclusion of the entire company in a 5-day integrated design charrette to involve them in the design process.

Code	Division Name	%	S F Cost	Projected
01	General Requirements	7.49	13.00	520,338
03	Concrete	9.93	17.24	689,585
04	Masonry	0.53	0.93	37,065
05	Metals	9.00	15.62	624,607
06	Wood & Plastics	8.01	13.90	555,979
07	Thermal & Moisture Protection	14.33	24.88	995,230
08	Doors & Windows	5.56	9.65	386,077
09	Finishes	4.97	8.64	345,270
10	Specialties	0.62	1.08	43,144
11	Equipment	0.59	1.03	41,216
12	Furnishings	0.56	0.97	38,548
13	Special Construction	8.96	15.56	622,411
15	Mechanical	14.60	25.35	1,014,042
16	Electrical	14.84	25.76	1,030,414
	Total Building Costs	100.00	173.60	6,943,927

COST PER SQUARE FOOT = $173.60

© Copyright 2020. For a more in-depth report on this building or additional case studies contact DC&D
@ 800-533-5680, or www.DCD.com

File 34:

This 17,000-square-foot, 28-foot-high light industrial facility is situated on more than five acres, encountering existing and seasonal demands prior to breaking ground on the new structure.

Its basic construction is type 2B Non-combustible/New. The foundation is cast-in-place, pier & grade beam, reinforced concrete and slab-on-grade. The exterior walls are CMU, brick and insulated metal panels. The interior walls are CMU, metal stud drywall and metal panels.

The building was comprised of approximately 4,800 square feet of administrative office space while allowing 12,000 square feet of shop space. The environmentally sensitive ITT encouraged fundamental green design best management practices, which included a low-slope "cool roof," per the Solar Reflectance Index rating, and 1½ acres of concrete pavement; both positive contributors to the lessening of the "heat island effect." Additionally, concrete foundations from the three razed structures were crushed onsite into aggregate and used as base material underneath site pavement. A 5-foot band of translucent panels running the perimeter of the 19-foot eave in the shop and a low-emissive coating on storefront glass, situated on the north side of the structure, provided passive natural lighting. Energy efficient, high-bay T5 fluorescent fixtures were the chosen shop luminaires.

The shop was also outfitted with a 12.5-ton twin-hoist top-running crane that eased handling concerns with the cumbersome pumps manufacturers and services. The crane runway beams were integrated into the structural design of the pre-engineered metal building. Four one-ton jib cranes added auxiliary lifting capacity for smaller workstations. A 27- by 100-foot wash bay with a heated pressure washer provided equipment cleaning facilities for the service team.

© Copyright 2020. For a more in-depth report on this building or additional case studies contact DC&D @ 800-533-5680, or www.DCD.com

Code	Division Name	%	S F Cost	Projected
00	Procurement and Contracting Require	1.79	1.85	31,444
01	General Requirements	20.98	21.73	369,236
03	Concrete	10.76	11.16	189,482
04	Masonry	5.10	5.28	89,779
05	Metals	1.08	1.11	19,026
06	Wood, Plastics, and Composites	0.09	0.09	1,516
07	Thermal and Moisture Protection	0.20	0.21	3,537
08	Openings	4.08	4.23	71,763
09	Finishes	4.16	4.31	73,292
10	Specialties	0.64	0.65	11,186
11	Equipment	7.34	7.60	129,238
12	Furnishings	0.26	0.27	4,570
13	Special Construction	22.60	23.41	397,789
21	Fire Suppression	1.62	1.68	28,449
22	Plumbing	6.30	6.53	110,904
23	HVAC	4.81	4.97	84,636
26	Electrical	7.85	8.14	138,171
28	Electronic Safety and Security	0.36	0.38	6,316
	Total Building Costs	100.00	103.60	1,760,334

COST PER SQUARE FOOT = $103.60

© Copyright 2020. For a more in-depth report on this building or additional case studies contact DC&D @ 800-533-5680, or www.DCD.com

File 35:

This university research center is located at the crossroads of an airport access road and a state highway. Site considerations included the need for adequate space for deliveries.

The facility has a brick exterior with an EIFS frieze. A rear entrance under a covered porch can be easily accessed by delivery trucks.

The facility provides office space and controlled laboratories for entomology, aquatics, agronomy and peanut research, as well as a conference room equipped with teleconferencing capabilities. The main entrance opens into a spacious lobby. The front portion of the building is divided between the Agricultural Experiment Station and the Research Center. A shared break room, copy area and conference room are centrally located, with restrooms across from the conference rooms.

Large, operable windows provide natural light to all of the administrative spaces. The rear hall leads to controlled laboratories. The peanut laboratory has a set of doors opening onto a rear porch; these doors, in addition to dust control systems, help reduce dust infiltration. The Entomology, Agronomy and Aquatics laboratories have fume hoods with an experiment counter and a low counter for computer and data collection.

Each space is designed to contain the necessary specialized equipment for each lab. There is also a Distance Diagnostics Center located in the lab area that is used to transfer information back to the main university campus.

© **Copyright 2020. For a more in-depth report on this building or additional case studies contact DC&D @ 800-533-5680, or www.DCD.com**

Code	Division Name	%	S F Cost	Projected
01	General Requirements	10.50	26.32	256,411
03	Concrete	5.67	14.20	138,338
04	Masonry	13.81	34.61	337,166
05	Metals	0.86	2.15	20,978
06	Wood, Plastics, and Composites	12.31	30.86	300,575
07	Thermal and Moisture Protection	3.63	9.09	88,620
08	Openings	6.64	16.66	162,207
09	Finishes	13.85	34.72	338,205
10	Specialties	1.18	2.96	28,926
11	Equipment	0.65	1.63	15,947
12	Furnishings	0.19	0.48	4,625
21	Fire Suppression	3.45	8.65	84,149
22	Plumbing	8.26	20.70	201,666
23	HVAC	8.72	21.87	212,923
26	Electrical	10.27	25.75	250,801
	Total Building Costs	100.00	250.66	2,441,537

COST PER SQUARE FOOT = $250.66

© Copyright 2020. For a more in-depth report on this building or additional case studies contact DC&D
@ 800-533-5680, or www.DCD.com

File 36:

This 22,000-square-foot public works facility is located on a narrow tract of land bordered by railroad tracks to the south and residential areas to the north. It is accessed by a narrow approach parallel to the building's 254-foot length.

A fuel dispensing station and a landscaped parking area flank the facility to the right and left, respectively. An existing maintenance repair garage, salt shed and open yard storage lie beyond the new facility. Storm water is handled through an infiltration system, while a tight tank collects interior floor drain run-off.

The facility consists entirely of a pre-engineered metal building, except for a 1,500-square-foot storage mezzanine above the administrative area, which is framed conventionally. A "screen wall" visually divides the public and administrative areas from the vehicle storage areas beyond. An entry canopy is supported by painted steel I-beams. A horizontally corrugated accent wall leads into a 1½-story lobby illuminated by an aluminum storefront wall. Also facing the front elevation is a wash bay with fully glazed overhead door enclosure and the director's and town engineer's offices.

A deep curving fascia and tile floor pattern lead to a glazed conference wall. A galley kitchen connects the conference room with an employee break room, copy room and secure plan room. On the opposite side, the corrugated exterior wall continues into the lobby to accent the north wall, which opens to the men's and women's locker rooms.

A central corridor extends from the administrative area into the fleet maintenance and vehicle storage areas. The maintenance bays include hydraulic lifts, an overhead crane and fully glazed overhead doors to maximize daylight. Internal spaces include a highway sign room, tool storage and mechanical room. A metal stairway parallel to the corridor leads to the mezzanine storage above.

© Copyright 2020. For a more in-depth report on this building or additional case studies contact DC&D @ 800-533-5680, or www.DCD.com

Code	Division Name	%	S F Cost	Projected
00	Bidding Requirements	18.19	25.51	559,016
03	Concrete	10.69	14.99	328,462
04	Masonry	3.78	5.31	116,287
05	Metals	2.74	3.85	84,356
06	Wood & Plastics	0.79	1.11	24,399
07	Thermal & Moisture Protection	2.08	2.91	63,789
08	Doors & Windows	8.05	11.30	247,479
09	Finishes	6.79	9.52	208,716
10	Specialties	0.48	0.68	14,825
11	Equipment	2.46	3.45	75,689
13	Special Construction	16.55	23.21	508,653
15	Mechanical	17.51	24.56	538,351
16	Electrical	9.88	13.86	303,665
	Total Building Costs	100.00	140.26	3,073,688

COST PER SQUARE FOOT = $140.26

© Copyright 2020. For a more in-depth report on this building or additional case studies contact DC&D @ 800-533-5680, or www.DCD.com

File 37:

The design of this manufacturing plant called for a 205,000-square-foot manufacturing and two-story office facility constructed utilizing the tilt-up concrete method.

The exterior of the building features horizontal rustications in the tilt walls. A tri-color paint combination accentuates the rustications. Horizontal and vertical aluminum strip windows with colored reflective glass wrap around the building, with a two-story glass entrance curtain wall. The rear of the building contains five dock doors and one drive-in door. Insulated tilt panels were used to reduce energy costs.

The 26-foot ceiling provides the necessary interior flexibility for specialty process rooms, toilet/locker rooms and employee cafeteria. Reinforced in-floor machinery pits were poured to accommodate the height of the machines and to provide access to the equipment.

To alleviate heat build-up, a series of eight-foot by seven-foot motorized wall louvers were installed on the east and west walls and interlocked with multiple roof fans, each circulating 44,000 cubic feet of air per minute. Room for storage racking and process machinery is provided by 50 foot × 50 foot column grid spacing throughout the warehouse and manufacturing area.

Roof smoke/skylights were installed to bring natural light to the interior. The building was equipped with twelve roof smoke hatches that can be opened to release smoke and fumes. The office space includes a glass entry vestibule within a two-story atrium, open office space, private offices, meeting rooms and restrooms.

Code	Division Name	%	S F Cost	Projected
01	General Requirements	5.96	3.95	808,096
03	Concrete	25.04	16.56	3,393,864
04	Masonry	1.61	1.08	218,179
05	Metals	17.90	11.83	2,425,382
06	Wood, Plastics, and Composites	0.23	0.14	30,796
07	Thermal and Moisture Protection	7.79	5.16	1,056,051
08	Openings	4.54	3.01	614,604
09	Finishes	8.26	5.47	1,119,355
10	Specialties	0.42	0.28	57,137
11	Equipment	0.40	0.28	54,330
14	Conveying Systems	0.64	0.42	86,092
21	Fire Suppression	4.74	3.12	641,671
22	Plumbing	4.92	3.25	666,453
23	HVAC	6.10	4.03	826,799
26	Electrical	10.81	7.16	1,465,565
28	Electronic Safety and Security	0.64	0.42	87,132
	Total Building Costs	100.00	66.10	13,551,500

COST PER SQUARE FOOT = $66.10

© Copyright 2020. For a more in-depth report on this building or additional case studies contact DC&D @ 800-533-5680, or www.DCD.com

File 38:

For over 30 years, family-owned Kitchen Magic has designed, manufactured, and installed beautiful, top-quality kitchens. Previously headquartered in Phillipsburg, NJ, they were located on several overcrowded floors and needed to expand. A vacant building totaling 63,000 square feet near Nazareth, PA gave them the ideal space for all their offices and manufacturing areas – along with space for future growth – all on one floor.

Their timeframe was quite aggressive, with only a four-month window of opportunity. Boyle Construction of Allentown met the challenge and finished the conversion on time and within budget. This included a brand new parking lot for approximately 80 employees.

A small, inefficient second floor over the entrance was removed in favor of a high, open ceiling area for the entrance showroom. Karndean International supplied the "hand hewn look" of the vinyl wood plank flooring reminiscent of an old manufacturing facility, along with exposed spiral ductwork. A new EIFS entrance with lots of glass was added to immerse the showroom in plenty of natural daylight.

In the manufacturing area, the existing concrete floor was ground and polished, making post-shift clean-up an easy process. New energy efficient fluorescent light fixtures were installed throughout. Three new insulated overhead doors with dock seals were installed to streamline the shipping/receiving areas.

The office area, taking up about 25% of the total space, contains corporate offices as well as a telemarketing area and a large sales meeting room. Soft, warm reds and yellows, and neutral tones of beige, provide a very soothing working environment.

Code	Division Name	%	S F Cost	Projected
01	General Requirements	11.15	3.68	231,376
03	Concrete	2.16	0.71	44,767
04	Masonry	2.20	0.72	45,710
05	Metals	1.01	0.32	20,850
06	Wood & Plastics	0.53	0.17	11,038
07	Thermal & Moisture Protection	23.35	7.70	484,398
08	Doors & Windows	5.85	1.92	121,421
09	Finishes	21.11	6.95	437,853
10	Specialties	0.77	0.26	15,945
15	Mechanical	16.50	5.43	342,188
16	Electrical	15.37	5.07	318,884
	Total Building Costs	100.00	32.94	2,074,431

COST PER SQUARE FOOT = $32.94

© Copyright 2020. For a more in-depth report on this building or additional case studies contact DC&D
@ 800-533-5680, or www.DCD.com

File 39:

Maltese Construction worked with Lee Steel Corporation on planning and building a new 180,000-square-foot steel processing plant with a railroad connection in the suburbs of Detroit. D.J. Maltese and Lee Steel Corporation have enjoyed a long business relationship through the years with other building projects for Lee Steel Corporation.

Working together, D. J. Maltese and Zack Taylor, owner of Lee Steel, began looking for a suitable parcel of land for Lee Steel's needs. A 32-acre site was located in Romulus, Michigan on the I-275 highway corridor that had access to a railway with 50% woodland coverage. An Environment Consultant was brought on to help with the Environmental Protection Agency and the Department of Environmental Quality concerning the site plan.

Numerous issues with the EPA and DEQ required attention: 1) The dead trees on the building area had to be removed in a 2-week time frame because of bat migration, 2) 10 acres of land needed to be cleared, but the land had to be cleared within a month time frame due to bird migration, 3) As a result of the removal of the woodland/wetlands, 1½ x of new woodland/wetlands had to be developed to offset what was removed. Added to these issues, the DEQ required the Owner to maintain the new woodland/wetlands for 20 years, with a yearly major upkeep. Taylor, after much negotiating with the DEQ, purchased an additional 30-acre parcel nearby and donated it to the City, along with $25,000 to maintain it.

In addition to the issues with the EPA and DEQ, the project hit another snag with the CSX rail company. A rail spur was possible; however it would take at least 9 months to get approval. During this time, the design and the site plan were refined. Preliminary approval from CSX was finally given for the rail spur and working drawings were completed and building permits were secured.

Construction started in September with the ordering of the pre-engineered building, site clearing and installation of the building pad (a stone and sand base), followed by the foundations and site improvements. Building erection began in October. By the end of January, the roof was on and plumbing, concrete, HVAC, and electrical work was underway.

Due to Owner changes the project grew about 25%. Changes included the addition of over 100 windows in the plant, changing the concrete floor to include stainless steel fibers, adding a third rail on the new spur, increasing the steel sizes to accommodate five 35-ton cranes, increasing electrical service to include an electrical sub-station on site and larger service panels to service the new green steel pickling line, complete interior painting of the steel to white, etc. There was a large cost savings by changing from an epoxy floor to a polished floor.

Lee Steel has been able to double production output due to the larger, well-designed facility. Taylor and his staff are pleased with the new facility and have received numerous accolades from their clients.

© Copyright 2020. For a more in-depth report on this building or additional case studies contact DC&D @ 800-533-5680, or www.DCD.com

Code	Division Name	%	S F Cost	Projected
00	Procurement and Contracting Require	0.12	0.09	17,101
01	General Requirements	4.34	3.15	630,934
03	Concrete	13.49	9.77	1,961,146
04	Masonry	0.46	0.34	67,438
05	Metals	15.13	10.96	2,199,742
06	Wood, Plastics, and Composites	2.08	1.50	302,609
07	Thermal and Moisture Protection	17.83	12.93	2,592,408
08	Openings	2.73	1.98	396,506
09	Finishes	4.38	3.18	636,239
11	Equipment	0.10	0.06	14,256
22	Plumbing	2.11	1.52	306,684
23	HVAC	2.35	1.71	341,966
26	Electrical	2.77	2.01	402,197
27	Communications	0.86	0.63	125,413
28	Electronic Safety and Security	0.59	0.42	85,113
48	Electrical Power Generation	30.68	22.23	4,460,737
	Total Building Costs	100.00	72.48	14,540,490

COST PER SQUARE FOOT = $72.48

© Copyright 2020. For a more in-depth report on this building or additional case studies contact DC&D @ 800-533-5680, or www.DCD.com

File 40:

Frederick Ward Associates, Inc. (FWA) provided architectural, survey, and civil engineering services for a new 6,055-square-foot barn built on 15 acres of sweeping farmland in Harford County, Maryland.

The property is owned by a local business person, and includes the original farmhouse, which is currently used as a private residence. The owner reached out to FWA with the desire to construct a barn for heavy farm equipment storage at the site of the property's original barn.

At first glance, the building looks more like a sophisticated event venue than a storage barn, with its red cedar board-and-batten wood frame, stone veneer base with complementary pressure-treated cedar-mitered columns, forest green metal seam roof, and copper cupolas. The design carries over to the covered front porch that oversees the sprawling farmland. Nestled into the foothills behind the building is a handsome, 12-foot-tall retaining wall.

The main interior level of the barn is outfitted with stained T1-11 interior siding that clears 14 feet to the airy loft, which was designed for additional storage and an office. Dormers in the roof provide natural light that floods the interior space through the double-hung, white vinyl framed windows. In addition to being aesthetically pleasing, the 14 x 14 foot barn doors facilitate the transportation of large machinery in and out of the barn.

The design of this building focuses on the quintessential nature of Harford County's strong agricultural roots, while providing functionality and ease of use for the owner.

© Copyright 2020. For a more in-depth report on this building or additional case studies contact DC&D @ 800-533-5680, or www.DCD.com

Code	Division Name	%	S F Cost	Projected
01	General Requirements	1.35	1.71	10,379
03	Concrete	7.91	10.05	60,881
04	Masonry	5.27	6.70	40,550
06	Wood & Plastics	40.75	51.77	313,440
07	Thermal and Moisture	26.79	34.04	206,137
08	Openings	5.17	6.57	39,787
09	Finishes	7.77	9.87	59,739
22	Plumbing	0.13	0.17	1,021
26	Electrical	4.86	6.17	37,340
	Total Building Costs	100.00	127.05	769,275

COST PER SQUARE FOOT = $127.05

© Copyright 2020. For a more in-depth report on this building or additional case studies contact DC&D @ 800-533-5680, or www.DCD.com

© Copyright 2020. For a more in-depth report on this building or additional case studies contact DC&D @ 800-533-5680, or www.DCD.com

Medical

File 41:

When the world-renowned Texas Spine and Joint Hospital in Tyler, Texas, needed to expand capacity to better serve its patients, it called on UEB Builders. Texas Spine and Joint is best known for its outstanding treatment and surgery capabilities in hip and knee replacement, spinal surgery, and pain management. The expansion work was delivered in four phases over a 20-month period, which included 55,000 square feet of new patient clinic facilities, 18,000 square feet of patient beds, the renovation of 33,000 square feet of existing operating rooms, and extensive modifications to site infrastructure.

The new additions were designed by the Fort Worth, Texas, office of HKS Architects. The patient clinic facility was planned as a concierge-driven working platform, with a definite "hospitality" look and feel. Valet parking is offered upon arrival, and the main entry features a two-story open rotunda with a sweeping stainless steel and glass grand stair. The entry leads to an open, transparent registration area with private cubicles. Segmented waiting areas include registration, physician waiting, in-patient waiting, and in-patient/out-patient surgery. The rotunda carries a Class I occupancy while the adjacent facilities carry Class B occupancies, so particular attention was given to ensuring the floor plans complied with life-safety smoke and fire restrictions.

The main building addition added pre-admission areas for testing and screening, a 23-hour new-bed wing, new kitchen and dining facilities, and six new "high-intensity" operating rooms, which give doctors and surgeons a much higher level of operational flexibility. The second level of the main facility carries a Class B occupancy, and provides 24,000 square feet of new medical office building space, offering an ideal adjacency for patients and doctors.

The new facilities utilize a structural steel moment frame founded on drilled piers and grade beams. The buildings are clad with a complementary palette of Lueder's limestone, ACM composite metal panels, and portland-cement stucco, and are topped off with a pre-finished standing-seam roofing system.

The Texas Spine and Joint Hospital additions and renovations represent the second of four healthcare projects successfully completed by UEB for this client, typical of UEB's track record of maintaining an 85% repeat-customer standing. UEB is currently in negotiations to build a fifth medical facility for the same Owners.

Code	Division Name	%	S F Cost	Projected
00	Procurement and Contracting Require	0.69	1.61	186,119
01	General Requirements	27.71	64.65	7,486,079
03	Concrete	5.53	12.90	1,493,050
04	Masonry	0.62	1.45	168,097
05	Metals	10.71	24.99	2,894,147
06	Wood, Plastics, and Composites	0.45	1.06	122,715
07	Thermal and Moisture Protection	7.16	16.70	1,933,373
08	Openings	6.63	15.46	1,790,274
09	Finishes	11.85	27.65	3,201,464
10	Specialties	0.96	2.25	259,797
13	Special Construction	0.23	0.54	61,987
21	Fire Suppression	0.76	1.78	206,347
22	Plumbing	5.35	12.47	1,444,397
23	HVAC	11.76	27.44	3,176,342
26	Electrical	9.59	22.38	2,591,293
	Total Building Costs	100.00	233.31	27,015,480

COST PER SQUARE FOOT = $233.31

© Copyright 2020. For a more in-depth report on this building or additional case studies contact DC&D

File 42:

The construction of this clinic in this area has been a goal of UNMH and the Near North Valley Neighborhood Association (NNVNA) for a number of years. Until now, this area had little medical care available to residents.

It was the intention of the entire project team to provide a beautiful new structure that would benefit this neighborhood for decades to come.

This clinic is the newest addition to the 4th Street Corridor in Albuquerque. The 16,500-square-foot, 97-room multi-disciplinary primary care clinic includes: Blood Draw, Pharmacy, Radiology Lab with digital Wi-Fi X-ray, Resident's Room, and a Community/Conference Room. The clinic was built on the site of Larry's Drive-In, a local landmark that is commemorated inside the new building.

UNM Hospital contractually agreed to follow the City's existing corridor plan for the 4th Street area. Throughout the planning and construction process, UNMH and its contractors met regularly with NNVNA, which helped immensely with communication between agencies. UNMH and the architects involved the community by presenting a selection of exterior styles at a neighborhood meeting and at the St. Therese Parish Fiesta. The project team continued to attend neighborhood association meetings to update on progress, as well as inviting NNVNA delegates to attend weekly construction meetings. The clinic is committed to working with both nearby schools on health education and health career opportunities.

Layout was more than a typical office – after the slab was poured, but before the structural steel was installed, Richardson & Richardson laid out the unusual floor tile pattern angles, walls and openings. By using concrete dye to snap lines, the project team was able to clarify locations for all workers involved and prevent conflicts while the components of the building were installed.

The building was divided into seven areas for the purpose of work leveling, the idea being each craft would complete a section entirely before moving on to the next area. This Lean Construction technique allowed the reliable release of work to the trades to maximize productivity.

The project punch list (final quality check) was able to start in the first areas finished, while the building was still being completed in the latter areas of construction. This resulted in a continuous workflow and a minimal touch-up type punch list.

© Copyright 2020. For a more in-depth report on this building or additional case studies contact DC&D
@ 800-533-5680, or www.DCD.com

Code	Division Name	%	S F Cost	Projected
00	Procurement and Contracting Require	1.53	4.28	70,706
01	General Requirements	3.36	9.36	154,434
03	Concrete	5.44	15.18	250,511
04	Masonry	2.73	7.62	125,828
05	Metals	4.42	12.35	203,781
06	Wood, Plastics, and Composites	6.94	19.36	319,531
07	Thermal and Moisture Protection	4.47	12.49	206,083
08	Openings	5.92	16.52	272,547
09	Finishes	17.08	47.65	786,215
10	Specialties	1.31	3.66	60,465
12	Furnishings	0.27	0.76	12,505
21	Fire Suppression	2.19	6.12	100,897
22	Plumbing	6.61	18.45	304,552
23	HVAC	17.27	48.19	795,120
26	Electrical	20.43	57.00	940,559
	Total Building Costs	100.00	279.02	4,603,736

COST PER SQUARE FOOT = $279.02

© Copyright 2020. For a more in-depth report on this building or additional case studies contact DC&D @ 800-533-5680, or www.DCD.com

File 43:

When Sanford Health decided to perfect the patient process, they called on JLG to re-imagine healthcare clinical delivery in the 21st century. This grand undertaking led to a new prototype for the Sanford Health Clinical Model and the construction of a new 49,250-square-foot, $11.2 million facility to serve the people of Moorhead and the surrounding Minnesota communities.

The first of its kind in the Sanford system, Moorhead Clinic follows a collaborative, onstage-offstage care delivery model that makes clinic visits more efficient for the providers and less time consuming for the patient. The project includes 48 exam rooms organized into separate, flexible neighborhoods that each contain a procedure room and all staff work spaces. In addition, there is space shelled for a future exam room neighborhood, giving the owner flexibility to expand as the market dictates. Furthermore, there is a large diagnostic wing dedicated to laboratory spaces, a radiology suite, and a large pharmacy. The building's exterior articulation reflects the "Sanford Look," and the interior design creates well-defined yet efficient and understated spaces that promote well-being and healing.

Using a patient concierge, patients are assigned a particular exam room in the clinic when they pick up their RTLS tag. The staff is available to direct the patient towards their exam room, and intuitive wayfinding is incorporated into the building's interior design (color coded bulkheads and carpet tiles), directing patients to their destination. Respite areas throughout the clinic offer opportunities for families or patients to sit down. In addition, each exam room is equipped with a scale, blood pressure monitoring, etc. to take patient vitals in their own room prior to an exam.

The standard model for the clinic physician office model was a 120-square-foot office that was closed off and private from the rest of the clinical staff. However, in an effort to improve collaboration and efficiencies, the Moorhead clinic developed pods of "touch down" physician work stations that allowed for providers to have a space to answer emails, take calls, dictate patient information, etc., while still being connected to the staff and other physicians for collaborative purposes at "flow stations" in the offstage area. These modular stations can be reconfigured as needs change over time, offering the ultimate flexibility.

Code	Division Name	%	S F Cost	Projected
01	General Requirements	8.72	21.30	1,048,722
03	Concrete	4.81	11.75	578,894
04	Masonry	8.35	20.39	1,004,031
05	Metals	12.32	30.10	1,482,060
06	Wood & Plastics	5.30	12.95	638,062
07	Thermal & Moisture Protection	5.02	12.27	604,250
08	Doors & Windows	5.15	12.57	619,174
09	Finishes	14.24	34.79	1,713,048
10	Specialties	0.64	1.57	77,411
12	Furnishings	0.16	0.39	18,956
14	Conveying Systems	0.68	1.65	81,253
15	Mechanical	22.36	54.62	2,690,021
16	Electrical	12.26	29.95	1,475,071
	Total Building Costs	100.00	244.28	12,030,951

COST PER SQUARE FOOT = $244.28

© Copyright 2020. For a more in-depth report on this building or additional case studies contact DC&D @ 800-533-5680, or www.DCD.com

File 44:

This refurbished space is a 9,696-square-foot facility transformed from a hotel and night club into a new medical treatment facility – a building that symbolizes that the process of transformation and recovery is possible.

This administration building was created to enhance the performance of the neighboring Florida Recovery Center, a drug and alcohol rehabilitation facility. As the importance of overcoming addiction has become emphasized by the community, it recognized the need to set up and develop a modern facility to combat this growing disease. The construction and complete renovation of the building by BBI Construction Management Inc. started in March of 2018 and lasted 10 months.

Construction of this new UF Health expansion consists of two floors. The first floor has a large conference room and numerous meeting rooms, along with an auditorium seating over 170 occupants whose express purpose is to invite guest speakers and house group activities. The second floor has added many new offices and a new home for the UF Department of Psychiatry and the UF Health Addiction Medicine Florida Recovery Center.

Among the many improvements, the interior of the building was completely changed, with new construction that turned the building from a night club to a modern and appealing haven where people can come and receive treatment for a wide range of addiction disorders. The exterior of the building also saw drastic improvements: a revitalized brick façade, new roofing, exterior windows, and awnings. Even the parking lot was updated with new asphalt and exterior lighting.

The renovated medical facility took some creative engineering in order to change a building with a checkered past into a place where UF Health and its doctors can aid those who struggle from addiction and other ailments.

After almost $3 million in improvements, this open and inviting renovation offers needed hope, as only about one in 10 people in the U.S. with a substance-use disorder get the treatment they need. This expansion allows for continued clinical studies and serves as a resource for patients and their families. The newly renovated building provides a new environment that maximizes a chance at recovery from addiction for everyone – a new space that will change the lives of so many for years to come.

Code	Division Name	%	S F Cost	Projected
00	Procurement	0.52	1.70	16,510
01	General Requirements	22.39	72.93	707,086
03	Concrete	1.75	5.69	55,201
04	Masonry	0.55	1.79	17,330
05	Metals	2.39	7.79	75,560
06	Wood & Plastics	1.34	4.36	42,243
07	Thermal and Moisture	6.79	22.10	214,297
08	Openings	6.98	22.72	220,329
09	Finishes	12.74	41.48	402,190
10	Specialties	3.46	11.27	109,245
12	Furnishings	0.26	0.84	8,129
14	Conveying Systems	1.58	5.16	50,068
21	Fire Suppression	4.00	13.04	126,394
22	Plumbing	2.09	6.80	65,926
23	HVAC	17.55	57.17	554,355
26	Electrical	15.61	50.85	493,055
	Total Building Costs	100.00	325.69	3,157,919

COST PER SQUARE FOOT = $325.69

© Copyright 2020. For a more in-depth report on this building or additional case studies contact DC&D @ 800-533-5680, or www.DCD.com

File 45:

This new 118-unit assisted living community includes a 32-unit memory care neighborhood, and is in close proximity to world-class healthcare, cultural venues, shopping, and fine dining. This 96,283-square-foot community offers a luxurious lifestyle, with concierge services, chef-prepared meals, housekeeping and more. Various floor plans feature spacious one bedroom and one-bath units as well as deluxe two-bedroom and two-bath units.

For the design of Heritage Oaks, the interior spaces are configured for openness that promotes social interaction. Community spaces are intended to serve as the residents' family room. This innovative design provides indoor and outdoor spaces for meeting, entertaining, arts and crafts, wellness, dining, the development of computer skills, and recreation.

Heritage Oaks provides residents and their loved ones with comfort, security, and peace of mind. All spaces are designed with rich, durable materials designed to last. LED lighting is enhanced to create a warm, friendly, and sustainable environment. Healthy mental stimulation through environmental design – along with easy way finding for residents – contribute to a healthy, fearless, and meaningful lifestyle for the residents, visitors, and staff.

Having access to nature and the outdoors has long been considered therapeutic for the elderly residents. Research is beginning to confirm that spending time outdoors has many important health benefits, even to the point of increasing longevity.

With this in mind, the exterior landscape design includes looped walking paths and spaces that support continuous footsteps, plenty of shade to protect residents from overexposure to the sun, and comfortable seating which provides areas of rest.

Heritage Oaks has been planned to provide a well-designed, friendly, and relaxed community to fill every need of people looking for an assisted living or memory care residence.

© Copyright 2020. For a more in-depth report on this building or additional case studies contact DC&D @ 800-533-5680, or www.DCD.com

Code	Division Name	%	S F Cost	Projected
0	Procurement	2.69	5.93	570,939
1	General Requirements	12.28	27.11	2,610,520
3	Concrete	5.86	12.93	1,244,861
4	Masonry	3.94	8.70	838,111
5	Metals	1.83	4.03	388,189
6	Wood & Plastics	9.48	20.94	2,016,552
7	Thermal and Moisture	3.31	7.31	704,188
8	Openings	5.94	13.11	1,262,702
9	Finishes	20.06	44.29	4,264,031
10	Specialties	1.31	2.89	278,732
11	Equipment	2.24	4.95	476,991
13	Special Construction	0.30	0.66	63,704
14	Conveying Systems	1.40	3.09	297,876
21	Fire Suppression	1.23	2.72	261,433
22	Plumbing	7.17	15.84	1,524,988
23	HVAC	7.32	16.17	1,556,810
26	Electrical	13.08	28.87	2,779,648
28	Electronic Security	0.55	1.21	116,545
	Total Building Costs	100.00	220.77	21,256,820

COST PER SQUARE FOOT = $220.77

© Copyright 2020. For a more in-depth report on this building or additional case studies contact DC&D @ 800-533-5680, or www.DCD.com

File 46:

Texas Children's Bellaire Specialty Care opened its doors in April of 2017 offering services in otolaryngology, orthopedics, X-ray, and audiology. Within the 11,850 square feet, there are 12 standard Exam Rooms, two Radiology Rooms, a cast room, and five specialty rooms for audiology, including 2 sound booths and a hearing aid fitting room. The design team included HDR as the architect and WSP as the MEP engineer with DPR serving as the General Contractor.

Austin Specialty Care consists of build-out of a 23,000-square-foot floor of a new office building (excluding the core), with minor work on 2,000 square feet of an adjacent floor in preparation for future work. Vibrant colors for wayfinding and custom murals depicting Austin landmarks were incorporated throughout. Many corridors extend to the exterior window wall, providing abundant daylight deep into the facility and offering views of the surrounding neighborhood and treetops.

Through early research, the design team took advantage of a then-newly-released expedited review process with the City of Austin, and a permit was issued after just one week of review. Calvin Silva with McCarthy recalled, "The entire team had an all-in attitude from the start. It felt as if each team member was completely invested and committed to the successful completion of the project. We were faced with challenges – as with any construction project – but the team addressed them very quickly as they arose, with the best interest of the client in mind."

The project has already received an Outstanding Construction Award from the Austin Chapter of the Associated General Contractors of America (AGC).

The construction costs difference for the two facilities is just over one dollar per square foot, despite having been designed and built by different teams in different cities approximately 18 months apart. These similarities demonstrate the strength of Texas Children's Hospital's facility strategy of maintaining a cohesive brand by instilling design standards while simultaneously pushing for innovations on every project.

Code	Division Name	%	S F Cost	Projected
0	Procurement	4.87	11.17	279,328
1	General Requirements	11.32	25.95	648,759
5	Metals	0.42	0.97	24,156
6	Wood & Plastics	11.36	26.04	651,005
7	Thermal and Moisture	0.14	0.31	7,660
8	Openings	5.78	13.25	331,248
9	Finishes	16.97	38.88	972,082
10	Specialties	1.87	4.28	107,028
12	Furnishings	0.70	1.61	40,235
22	Plumbing	6.51	14.91	372,818
23	HVAC	8.87	20.33	508,329
26	Electrical	18.90	43.32	1,082,959
27	Communications	8.10	18.57	464,315
28	Electronic Security	4.18	9.57	239,321
	Total Building Costs	100.00	229.17	5,729,243

COST PER SQUARE FOOT = $229.17

© Copyright 2020. For a more in-depth report on this building or additional case studies contact DC&D @ 800-533-5680, or www.DCD.com

File 47:

The Central Association for the Blind and Visually Impaired (CABVI) has completed the construction of their state-of-the-art Vision Rehabilitation and Wellness center in downtown Utica.

This magnificent facility includes a therapeutic-recreational indoor swimming pool, fitness center, dorm/studio bedrooms for overnight accommodations, teaching kitchen, eye doctor's offices, vision store, therapy rooms, classrooms with smart technology, a conference room with a video wall, and much more.

The infrastructure of this facility is supported by green-technology, which includes a geothermal well system that uses ground energy to heat and cool the main building, garage/storage building and indoor swimming pool. In addition, the geothermal system heats the exterior concrete sidewalks for the outdoor walking loop. This allows the facility to conduct exterior mobility training all year long. Energy-efficient light fixtures, appliances, a TPO roofing system, and mechanical components were also purchased in an effort to provide environmental sustainability for years to come.

CABVI is extremely proud to be able to use this new facility to house the USA National Blind Hockey team when they're in the Utica area. They will also be using this facility for their camp program that they conduct for the blind and visually impaired children that they serve.

As a token of appreciation, a donor wall was incorporated into the grand entryway, which displays the names of all the financial contributors who supported this venture and made this incredible project possible.

© Copyright 2020. For a more in-depth report on this building or additional case studies contact DC&D @ 800-533-5680, or www.DCD.com

Code	Division Name	%	S F Cost	Projected
1	General Requirements	7.35	13.04	335,693
3	Concrete	3.48	6.17	158,705
4	Masonry	16.74	29.70	764,542
5	Metals	7.78	13.80	355,287
6	Wood & Plastics	3.43	6.08	156,499
7	Thermal and Moisture	9.53	16.91	435,202
8	Openings	5.23	9.28	238,886
9	Finishes	5.11	9.06	233,335
10	Specialties	0.74	1.32	34,075
11	Equipment	0.33	0.58	14,991
12	Furnishings	3.43	6.08	156,499
13	Special Construction	2.57	4.56	117,420
21	Fire Suppression	1.32	2.35	60,464
22	Plumbing	10.51	18.64	479,712
23	HVAC	10.50	18.63	479,463
26	Electrical	9.32	16.54	425,638
27	Communications	1.48	2.63	67,812
28	Electronic Security	1.15	2.04	52,568
	Total Building Costs	**100.00**	**177.41**	**4,566,791**

COST PER SQUARE FOOT = $177.41

© Copyright 2020. For a more in-depth report on this building or additional case studies contact DC&D
@ 800-533-5680, or www.DCD.com

File 48:

NorthCare's primary goal for the new campus was to consolidate its multiple metro locations into a one-stop solution for consumers' behavioral health needs.

The new Behavioral Health Focused Integrated Care Center is the second step in an effort to bring most of NorthCare's Oklahoma City facilities together on the same campus. The first step was a new 18,000-square-foot mental health crisis center that the community desperately needed.

The architecture of the new NorthCare campus challenges the stigma sometimes associated with mental health care facilities, normalizing patient and treatment areas to create a facility that supports wellness – a spectrum for patients, caregivers and visitors that covers social, emotional, environmental, intellectual, and physical wellness.

The main entrance to the new building is on the southeast corner of the campus. The two-story, 60,492-square-foot building features an airy lobby flooded with natural daylight, stacked-stone feature walls, and a landscaped courtyard. The open circulation space serves as reception for the entire building, waiting space for the pharmacy, and lobby space for the training center. Beyond the lobby is a large waiting room for the counseling area, the medical clinic, and the lab.

The therapy offices offer confidentiality and safety. Each of the offices has a solid wood door and a slender window running its entire height, to ensure patient privacy and contribute to increased building security. Transom windows bring natural light into those offices located in interior corridors. Each office accommodates three to four people – ample space for patients and members of their supportive network. Feature walls and chairs in the group rooms are clothed in bright, mood-lifting hues.

Materials include stacked stone feature walls. Two-tone stucco walls on the exterior include a custom black integral finish with shiny flecks. The lushly-landscaped northern courtyard has low seating walls made of rip-rap and topped with stained wood benches. The second floor is primarily administrative space overlooking the atrium lobby, and also includes meeting spaces and a roof terrace.

© Copyright 2020. For a more in-depth report on this building or additional case studies contact DC&D
@ 800-533-5680, or www.DCD.com

Code	Division Name	%	S F Cost	Projected
0	Bidding Requirements	1.32	3.66	221,063
1	General Requirements	13.30	36.78	2,223,827
3	Concrete	6.88	19.03	1,150,570
4	Masonry	1.42	3.93	237,418
5	Metals	14.58	40.32	2,438,080
6	Wood & Plastics	1.88	5.19	314,067
7	Thermal & Moisture	10.77	29.78	1,800,676
8	Doors & Windows	7.43	20.56	1,243,372
9	Finishes	12.67	35.04	2,118,626
10	Specialties	1.29	3.57	215,801
12	Furnishings	0.12	0.33	20,114
14	Conveying Systems	0.71	1.97	119,032
15	Mechanical	16.50	45.63	2,758,993
16	Electrical	11.12	30.76	1,859,676
	Total Building Costs	100.00	276.56	16,721,316

COST PER SQUARE FOOT = $276.56

© Copyright 2020. For a more in-depth report on this building or additional case studies contact DC&D @ 800-533-5680, or www.DCD.com

© Copyright 2020. For a more in-depth report on this building or additional case studies contact DC&D @ 800-533-5680, or www.DCD.com

Office

File 49:

The building program called for nearly 3,000 square feet of space for the Bothell Dental Office. An "L" shaped plan was laid out over the parking garage below. Two stairwells, one of which serves an entry lobby and the other a service stairwell, were located at each end of the "L". The entry lobby, main stairwell, and elevator can be accessed either from the parking area or from the front entry facing the street. The second floor main stairwell leads to a light-filled waiting area with large windows on both sides. Beyond the reception area are six operatories, followed by a lab and other service areas.

The building's look and configuration were further determined by fire preventive measures. Having the garage under the building resulted in the need for a non-combustible two-hour fire-rated floor under the offices and at supporting construction. To achieve this, CMU was chosen for the walls, and a pan deck with open web steel joists and rated acoustical tiles were chosen for the floor/ceiling assembly. Above it, the building is wood framed. Proximity to an adjacent property line called for a continuous one-hour fire-rating, a parapet, and limited openings. Walls surrounding the stairwells were either smoke barriers or one-hour rated to the underside of the roof sheathing.

On the exterior, a contemporary palette of materials was chosen to keep with the style of nearby residences and for ease of maintenance. Materials included: cement fiber lap siding, metal roofing, cased windows, and wood trellises. Aluminum storefront windows with cement board trim and horizontal trim bands give the building both a modern and traditional feel.

At the building base, CMU is used for both the building walls and the walls screening the parking. Natural colored CMU with one-sided ground face was installed on the single wythe walls in a random pattern to get a unique uniform look reminiscent of stone. Cedar trellises were added to the tops of the CMU screen walls for decoration and fall protection. Above, a generous metal roof has large overhangs on the south and east for sun control. It serves as a parapet to conceal rooftop mechanical equipment.

A Building Information Model was used for interior/exterior design documentation, consultant coordination, and 3D virtual walkthroughs used in client presentations.

Code	Division Name	%	S F Cost	Projected
00	Procurement and Contracting Require	5.54	8.79	46,591
01	General Requirements	16.21	25.73	136,402
03	Concrete	7.38	11.71	62,074
04	Masonry	9.29	14.74	78,163
05	Metals	7.98	12.67	67,151
06	Wood, Plastics, and Composites	14.53	23.07	122,326
07	Thermal and Moisture Protection	6.80	10.80	57,235
08	Openings	7.66	12.16	64,500
09	Finishes	6.05	9.60	50,918
10	Specialties	0.31	0.49	2,601
14	Conveying Systems	5.43	8.62	45,705
22	Plumbing	2.47	3.92	20,794
23	HVAC	2.83	4.50	23,817
26	Electrical	5.86	9.30	49,296
27	Communications	0.20	0.31	1,664
28	Electronic Safety and Security	1.46	2.31	12,256
	Total Building Costs	100.00	158.71	841,490

COST PER SQUARE FOOT = $158.71

© Copyright 2020. For a more in-depth report on this building or additional case studies contact DC&D
@ 800-533-5680, or www.DCD.com

FILE 50:

The 100 block of Adams Street in Fairmont, West Virginia, was long neglected. Omni Associates – Architects was selected by the WV GSA to convert this block into a 70,700-square-foot, five-story showcase office complex, while enhancing context of the city's historic downtown district. To that end, the building's exterior north, south, and west elevations feature historical forms of brick, precast stone, and glass fiber-reinforced concrete cornice. This is combined with modern features such as glass curtain wall openings and insulated metal panels. The building's east elevation with its simple geometric configuration provides a distinctive look which is easily identified when traveling to the city on its main connector from the interstate. The view from this elevation is the building's most dramatic, displaying a panoramic vista of the city's east side and the Tygart River. The design concept takes advantage of this by allowing all occupants to share this view, rather than having a select few offices with east-facing windows.

The building's structural steel on a caisson foundation will house 180 state employees from eight different state agencies.

In addition to the verification, coordination, and documentation of an extensive demolition package, Omni's design team provided a variety of other pre-construction services. They included site surveys and subsurface investigations of the site's extensive underground network to determine the current and remnant infrastructure systems and the remains of foundations from structures removed decades ago. This was crucial in the design development phase as plans were adapted to mitigate existing subsurface conditions. This was particularly true in evaluating foundations for stability and depth, as well as compliance with the Municipal Separate Storm Sewer System (MS4) which requires underground retainage.

This building, constructed by Pittsburgh-based P.J. Dick, Inc., was designed with the goal of achieving LEED® Silver Certification. This was easily obtainable with LEED design features such as interior and exterior LED lighting and thermal storage. Thermal storage used to make ice during low peak hours at night is then used for cooling during normal operating hours. This is an easy way to store energy and is a valuable energy cost-saving technology for building owners.

Code	Division Name	%	S F Cost	Projected
01	General Requirements	6.34	16.18	1,140,092
03	Concrete	9.25	23.59	1,661,289
04	Masonry	8.55	21.81	1,536,526
05	Metals	8.22	20.97	1,477,084
06	Wood, Plastics, and Composites	2.59	6.62	465,782
07	Thermal and Moisture Protection	7.60	19.38	1,365,628
08	Openings	5.54	14.12	994,449
09	Finishes	10.70	27.28	1,921,755
10	Specialties	0.76	1.93	136,407
11	Equipment	0.03	0.06	4,436
12	Furnishings	0.09	0.24	16,636
14	Conveying Systems	1.85	4.72	332,702
21	Fire Suppression	1.15	2.93	206,275
22	Plumbing	3.92	10.00	704,107
23	HVAC	19.06	48.61	3,424,607
25	Integrated Automation	0.69	1.76	124,167
26	Electrical	9.96	25.41	1,790,593
27	Communications	1.56	3.97	279,454
28	Electronic Safety and Security	2.14	5.46	384,222
	Total Building Costs	100.00	255.05	17,966,210

COST PER SQUARE FOOT = $255.05

© Copyright 2020. For a more in-depth report on this building or additional case studies contact DC&D @ 800-533-5680, or www.DCD.com

FILE 51:

The Evanston Medical Office is the new home for High Country Behavioral Health (HCBH) Out-Patient Services. The HCBH Out-Patient Facility accommodates a wide variety of clinical and medical services. The facility includes clinical offices, medical exam rooms, administrative offices, group treatment areas, recreation rooms, and a life skills education space. The facility also houses a short-term detention and stabilization center operated by the Evanston City Police, the Uinta County Sheriff, and the Lincoln County Sheriff. The detention center provides a reception desk, a monitoring area, a counseling office, and stabilization rooms for three individuals.

The project initially began in July of 2011. High Country Behavioral Health and Myers Anderson Architects evaluated the existing facilities. Myers Anderson worked closely with administration and staff to develop a master plan for consolidating their services onto one campus. HCBH utilized this planning information to engage in a public/private partnership with the City of Evanston to pursue a Community Readiness Grant. This grant provides the Evanston Economic Development Agency a tool to provide new jobs for the community. The City was awarded the grant in the fall of 2012.

The building is a single-story steel post and beam structure. The construction of the facility was slab on grade with structural steel curtain walls and masonry veneer. The building was designed with energy conservation in mind and with state-of-the art mechanical and electrical systems in order to keep annual utility costs at a minimum. The project budget was $2.3 million. The building is 9,157 square feet on a 1.5-acre site. The site is in an area of Evanston that the city plans to promote for future commercial development. As a cornerstone of growth in the area, the project set the standard for future design and construction in Evanston.

© Copyright 2020. For a more in-depth report on this building or additional case studies contact DC&D @ 800-533-5680, or www.DCD.com

Code	Division Name	%	S F Cost	Projected
01	General Requirements	9.37	23.99	219,673
03	Concrete	8.74	22.38	204,859
04	Masonry	2.03	5.20	47,614
05	Metals	10.98	28.11	257,322
06	Wood, Plastics, and Composites	6.86	17.57	160,885
07	Thermal and Moisture Protection	8.67	22.20	203,281
08	Openings	7.08	18.14	166,135
09	Finishes	16.15	41.35	378,625
10	Specialties	1.89	4.83	44,284
21	Fire Suppression	1.96	5.02	45,920
22	Plumbing	6.60	16.91	154,804
23	HVAC	6.29	16.11	147,528
26	Electrical	13.39	34.30	314,054
	Total Building Costs	100.00	256.09	2,344,983

COST PER SQUARE FOOT = $256.09

© Copyright 2020. For a more in-depth report on this building or additional case studies contact DC&D @ 800-533-5680, or www.DCD.com

FILE 52:

Six state agencies were designated to occupy this State Office Building. Due to volume of potential visitors, at-grade access was necessary for the Department of Motor Vehicles and Unemployment Program. Upper floors were designed to house various social services agencies, along with smaller regional offices with little public-facing impact.

The building was sited to take advantage of the slope, resulting in a five-story building on the east and a four-story building on the west, providing two at-grade entrances separated by a vertical height of 12 feet. The east entrance provides a public meeting room on the ground floor level that may be utilized by local/private entities without requiring access to the main floor. The west entrance provides at-grade access to the DMV and WorkForce. The two levels come together at the centrally-located elevator core and two-story space of the entry on the east.

The exterior building envelope consists of oversized red brick and structural clay tile that mimics sandstone in an ashlar pattern. The envelope is attached to a structural-steel frame and stud system, incorporating continuous insulation outboard of the structural frame.

The continuous insulation, along with spray-insulating foam in the steel stud cavity, creates an air- and vapor-resistant barrier, as well as an overall improved R-value for the entire building. The choice of the brick and stone-like façade topped with a vented aluminum cornice provides a traditional look that reflects the historic downtown district where the building is located.

The roof is a cool, white reflective SBS over insulating lightweight concrete, with an insulating value of R-20 through the roof alone.

The interior of the building has an efficiently designed floor plate and a central core with three elevators and public toilet rooms. The center of the building has a north/south circulation spine through the center of the building, connecting the core area with two remotely placed exit stairs.

Agency offices are placed on either side of the central spine, with open plan offices near the windows and private offices with demountable glazed and acoustical partitions looking through to the window walls.

© Copyright 2020. For a more in-depth report on this building or additional case studies contact DC&D @ 800-533-5680, or www.DCD.com

Code	Division Name	%	S F Cost	Projected
00	Procurement and Contracting Require	1.51	4.21	371,994
01	General Requirements	7.47	20.85	1,844,974
03	Concrete	7.89	22.04	1,950,662
04	Masonry	7.00	19.56	1,729,999
05	Metals	9.77	27.30	2,415,514
06	Wood, Plastics, and Composites	1.74	4.86	429,993
07	Thermal and Moisture Protection	6.75	18.86	1,669,355
08	Openings	4.42	12.35	1,092,200
09	Finishes	11.83	33.06	2,925,528
10	Specialties	7.17	20.02	1,771,324
11	Equipment	0.15	0.43	38,697
12	Furnishings	0.27	0.75	66,417
14	Conveying Systems	1.47	4.12	364,582
21	Fire Suppression	1.15	3.21	284,297
22	Plumbing	7.61	21.26	1,881,184
23	HVAC	7.13	19.92	1,762,674
26	Electrical	12.28	34.31	3,035,825
27	Communications	3.29	9.20	814,162
28	Electronic Safety and Security	0.82	2.29	202,751
44	Pollution Control Equipment	0.27	0.75	65,818
	Total Building Costs	100.00	279.33	24,717,950

COST PER SQUARE FOOT = $279.33

© Copyright 2020. For a more in-depth report on this building or additional case studies contact DC&D
@ 800-533-5680, or www.DCD.com

FILE 53:

Sitting on a prominent location at the corner of Lady and Huger Streets in the heart of Columbia's Vista, the Columbia Cigar and Candy Store and Warehouse had long remained forgotten, and excluded from its vibrant surroundings.

A new ownership group came along and made the decision to breathe new life into this forsaken building. While not on the National Register of Historic Places, the new owners still wanted to preserve the nature of the building, while converting it into a modern office space.

The renovation of the old Columbia Cigar and Candy Store and Warehouse would end up transforming the abandoned 1930s building into 29,000 square feet of prime modern office space.

In the process, several non-historical additions were demolished. A new stair lobby and a third-floor executive conference space (with a roof-top deck) were also added.

The original portion of the building consists of two major areas: a front office building along Huger Street and a warehouse portion between Geddes and Lady Streets. Originally independent of one another, badly-designed additions connected these two sections.

The original section of warehouse has unique 100-foot-long span trusses and a mezzanine. The mezzanine space is office and training space for one of the tenants. Part of the original mezzanine ramped up to a higher level, which created conflict with the trusses in regard to code-required head height.

This section was disassembled and rebuilt at the lower mezzanine level in order to capture that space. Even at the lower mezzanine level, the bottom of the roof trusses are only 7′10″ off the floor.

To complement the six existing skylights in the space, wall openings that had been bricked in were opened back up to allow natural light and views out of the space.

The existing vault, with its concrete ceiling and brick walls, was opened up with a glass storefront, and has become a collaborative sunlit area.

Much of the wood comprising the existing roof was salvaged and used to add character and tie the building to its past.

The front office building was converted back to its original use. Existing covered up wall openings were opened back up, paint was removed from the original brick walls, and a new wood floor was installed to create a warm and inviting executive office area.

The new stair tower and third floor is a modern glass and metal complement to the historic fabric of the existing building.

© **Copyright 2020. For a more in-depth report on this building or additional case studies contact DC&D**
@ **800-533-5680, or www.DCD.com**

Code	Division Name	%	S F Cost	Projected
00	Bidding Requirements	4.48	11.26	336,130
01	General Requirements	31.16	78.43	2,339,406
03	Concrete	2.38	5.99	178,747
04	Masonry	1.96	4.94	147,460
05	Metals	9.07	22.82	680,714
06	Wood & Plastics	2.26	5.70	170,027
07	Thermal & Moisture Protection	7.31	18.39	548,344
08	Doors & Windows	9.34	23.51	701,236
09	Finishes	8.49	21.37	637,557
10	Specialties	0.10	0.26	7,604
14	Conveying Systems	2.28	5.74	171,255
15	Mechanical	12.84	32.32	964,220
16	Electrical	8.32	20.95	624,756
	Total Building Costs	100.00	251.68	7,507,455

COST PER SQUARE FOOT = $251.68

© Copyright 2020. For a more in-depth report on this building or additional case studies contact DC&D

@ 800-533-5680, or www.DCD.com

File 54:

This 42,000-square-foot, two-story shell building was constructed as the second phase of a two-phase building development program. The design called for strict architectural guidelines to maintain high property values for the surrounding residential areas. The architect was also called upon to emphasize views of the city and surrounding mountain ranges.

The building is sited in the center of a 500-acre planned community. It is located on the southwest side of the intersection of two roadways, with a golf course adjacent on the south side. Site work included native plant and low-water-maintenance landscaping, site walls, site lighting, and retention and detention basins. The foundation is CMU, and exterior walls are EIFS. Interior walls are drywall over metal studs. The facility features both parking lots and a covered parking area.

The placement of the building on the site was planned to enhance its function. The building pads are flat and elevated above the adjoining streets, making the building highly visible from the road. The building's location on the site also enhances the view of the mountains to the north and the city and golf course to the south. There are no structures, existing or planned, that would obstruct these views in the future.

The floor sizes offer flexibility for a large, single tenant or for smaller, multi-tenant accommodations. Elevators, toilet rooms, mechanical rooms, and stairs are arranged in a convenient core for both single- and multi-tenant use.

Code	Division Name	%	S F Cost	Projected
00	Bidding Requirements	12.07	17.08	713,393
03	Concrete	8.51	12.042	502,869
04	Masonry	1.43	2.0215	84,516
05	Metals	20.33	28.776	1,201,375
06	Wood & Plastics	0.67	0.9405	39,536
07	Thermal & Moisture Protection	4.77	6.7454	281,798
08	Doors & Windows	8.70	12.313	513,997
09	Finishes	15.64	22.139	924,308
10	Specialties	1.19	1.6972	70,520
14	Conveying Systems	1.69	2.3998	100,070
15	Mechanical	13.59	19.242	803,357
16	Electrical	11.41	16.15	674,470
	Total Building Costs	100.00	141.56	5,910,208

COST PER SQUARE FOOT = $141.56

© Copyright 2020. For a more in-depth report on this building or additional case studies contact DC&D @ 800-533-5680, or www.DCD.com

File 55:

This office building is the first of two buildings to be constructed in an existing office complex. The site is adjacent to a major interstate and a city's water intake supply. These site conditions required attention to water quality and visibility. Retention ponds were included in the design to manage storm water runoff and provide an aesthetically pleasing landscape feature.

The building consists of a steel substructure under brick veneer accented with pre-cast concrete elements and aluminum windows. Old asphalt paving was recycled and used as fill under roads and parking areas and existing light poles were refurbished and reused.

The interior includes a two-story entrance lobby with Italian marble floors and a circular grand staircase. Extensive windows provide natural lighting for the interior. The building orientation and use of landscaping provide shade for the first floor.

Code	Division Name	%	S F Cost	Projected
01	General Requirements	9.54	13.88	1,246,275
03	Concrete	14.57	21.19	1,903,837
04	Masonry	5.06	7.35	660,810
05	Metals	17.41	25.32	2,274,572
06	Wood & Plastics	0.84	1.22	110,290
07	Thermal & Moisture Protection	2.79	4.04	363,888
08	Doors & Windows	9.53	13.85	1,245,058
09	Finishes	12.68	18.44	1,657,149
10	Specialties	0.76	1.10	98,707
12	Furnishings	0.46	0.67	59,669
14	Conveying Systems	1.95	2.83	254,654
15	Mechanical	17.04	24.78	2,226,394
16	Electrical	7.38	10.72	964,068
	Total Building Costs	100.00	145.39	13,065,375

COST PER SQUARE FOOT = $145.39

© Copyright 2020. For a more in-depth report on this building or additional case studies contact DC&D @ 800-533-5680, or www.DCD.com

File 56:

SNC-Lavalin's fitout of this Atlanta, GA office expansion space was a pilot implementation of a new design standard, developed to accommodate the work styles of five different organizations within the company, due to a recent merger.

This project consolidated suites on three different, non-contiguous floors down to two contiguous floors. The previous design standard consisted of 7½' x 7½' low-wall cubicles with an 8" top glass panel yielding 58-inch-high cubicle walls.

The new rollout incorporates a benching system offering a range of desk sizes all 6 feet wide, with 50-inch high front fabric privacy panels. The benching system introduced a modular kit of parts with varying return sizes, and the inclusion of mobile tables that can flex to support the various work styles of staff, from nomadic touchdown desks to extended workstations to support full size plan layouts.

The new standard also introduced more natural light, quiet rooms, a wider variety of technology-enabled collaborative spaces, and raised the dual monitors off the work surfaces on ergonomically adjustable monitor arms.

The pantry area was transformed into a work café, with plug-in capabilities to allow for staff to activate the space throughout the day as an alternative work environment. Lastly, the branding and overall color palette was modified to align with SNC-Lavalin's global branding guidelines.

The new 20,000-square-foot floor size provides 99 workstations and 16 offices, allowing SNC-Lavalin to:

- Increase space by 32%, but increase workstation capacity by 41%;

- Greatly improve the quantity and variety in choice of collaboration areas for employees;

- Improve plug-and-play technology offerings to encourage more movement about the space;

- Achieve multifactored increases in overall business functionality and employee well-being through the implementation of new design standards;

- Fitout the space at $36/square foot – approximately a 50% savings over similar type projects.

By implementing new design standards, SNC-Lavalin achieved a 50% cost savings in their buildout costs as compared to industry benchmarks.

© Copyright 2020. For a more in-depth report on this building or additional case studies contact DC&D @ 800-533-5680, or www.DCD.com

Code	Division Name	%	S F Cost	Projected
01	General Requirements	4.43	1.89	38,629
06	Wood & Plastics	6.24	2.66	54,302
07	Thermal and Moisture	1.55	0.66	13,420
08	Openings	8.72	3.72	75,760
09	Finishes	24.54	10.47	213,502
11	Equipment	0.87	0.37	7,447
21	Fire Suppression	1.85	0.79	16,010
22	Plumbing	2.48	1.06	21,594
23	HVAC	28.69	12.24	249,586
26	Electrical	20.63	8.80	179,523
	Total Building Costs	100.00	42.66	869,773

COST PER SQUARE FOOT = $42.66

© Copyright 2020. For a more in-depth report on this building or additional case studies contact DC&D @ 800-533-5680, or www.DCD.com

© Copyright 2020. For a more in-depth report on this building or additional case studies contact DC&D
@ 800-533-5680, or www.DCD.com

Recreational

© Copyright 2020. For a more in-depth report on this building or additional case studies contact DC&D
@ 800-533-5680, or www.DCD.com

FILE 57:

The new 9,500-seat, multi-purpose arena will host men's and women's basketball games, as well as concerts, special events, and day-to-day academic student activities.

The Athletics Foundation worked with AECOM to maximize opportunities for fan engagement, premium seating experiences, sustainable revenue sources, student involvement, and campus engagement.

Situated next to Vaught-Hemingway Stadium (which is undergoing an AECOM-designed expansion and renovation, as well), the Pavilion anchors an updated athletics complex near the Grove, which is the University's central open space, and renowned tailgating destination.

The scheme includes an adjacent 800-stall parking facility that houses the vertical circulation for the arena itself. Both the arena and parking garage reflect the architectural materiality and scale of the traditional campus brick and limestone buildings.

The proximity of the facilities is intended to build synergy between football and arena operations, as well as boost the game day experience for fans. Already, the broadcast TV facility in the complex is lauded as "best in SEC" by Ole Miss broadcast network partners.

Visitors enter through a covered courtyard from the north and arrive at a generous open area within the arena's main concourse that also serves as a daily food court facility for the University's students and faculty.

The main entry is marked by a series of Doric columns referencing the southern traditional architectural style of the Ole Miss campus.

In addition, a sweeping barrel roof affords a grand clerestory window wall. This brings natural lighting directly into the seating bowl, and defines the courtyard between the arena and football stadium that will be open to both basketball and football events.

The courtyard will be within the control lines of each facility event and, thus, extend the game-day experience beyond the current facades of both facilities.

Fans moving through the main concourse and mezzanine levels will have expansive views into the bowl – a rarity in college sports. Retractable lower seating allows for large group lectures and convocations on the event floor, and the north entry doubles as a food court on non-game days.

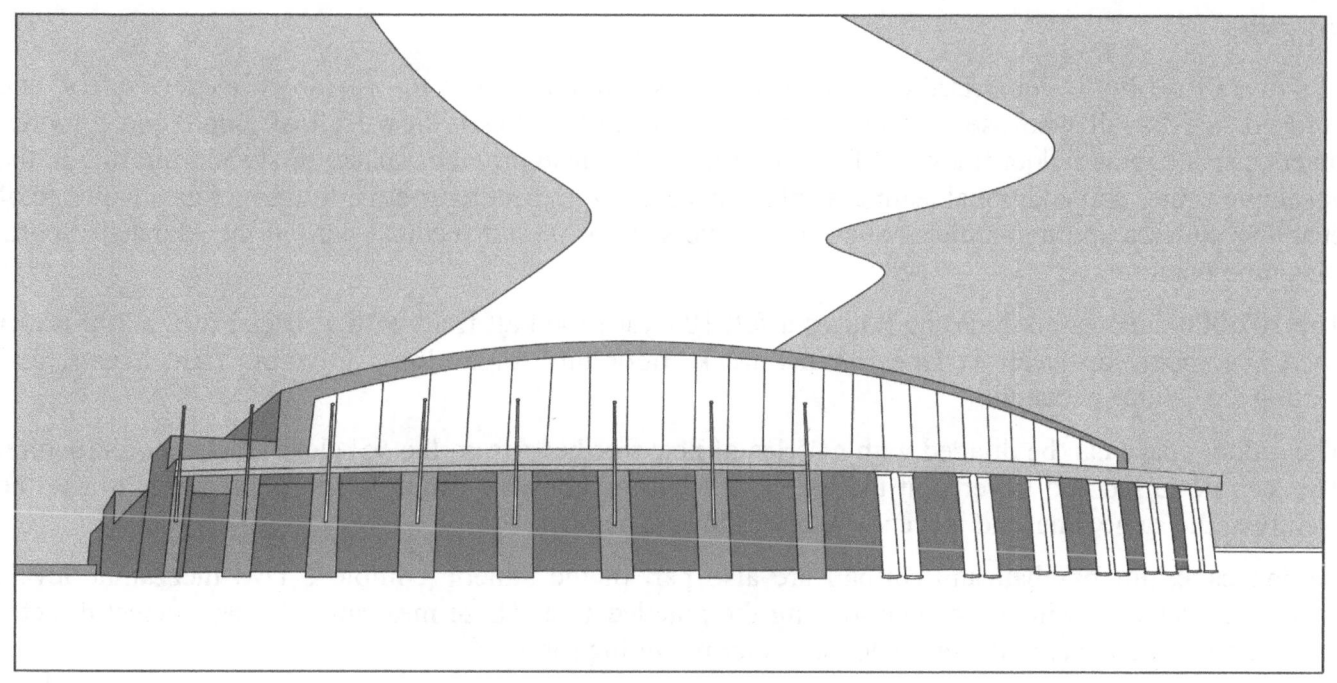

Code	Division Name	%	S F Cost	Projected
00	Procurement and Contracting Require	0.59	2.66	626,936
01	General Requirements	12.81	57.73	13,583,712
03	Concrete	12.95	58.34	13,727,316
04	Masonry	3.73	16.79	3,950,295
05	Metals	22.99	103.58	24,374,036
06	Wood, Plastics, and Composites	1.62	7.30	1,717,644
07	Thermal and Moisture Protection	6.23	28.06	6,603,028
08	Openings	2.44	10.98	2,584,414
09	Finishes	5.23	23.58	5,547,103
10	Specialties	0.41	1.83	428,962
11	Equipment	2.30	10.35	2,435,238
12	Furnishings	3.99	17.96	4,224,008
21	Fire Suppression	0.69	3.11	732,523
22	Plumbing	3.48	15.67	3,687,651
23	HVAC	9.04	40.71	9,578,860
26	Electrical	8.03	36.18	8,514,186
27	Communications	3.24	14.59	3,432,670
28	Electronic Safety and Security	0.23	1.05	247,438
	Total Building Costs	100.00	450.47	105,996,019

COST PER SQUARE FOOT = $450.47

© Copyright 2020. For a more in-depth report on this building or additional case studies contact DC&D
@ 800-533-5680, or www.DCD.com

FILE 58:

The overall facility is comprised of several buildings combined so as to provide efficiency, safety, and convenience for all who use it. The complex celebrates athletics with a Hall of Fame, and provides practice space in an indoor track and field environment. It also provides space for student tutoring in the academic center and additional team assembly space in large meeting rooms. It has met the challenge of enabling athletes and non-athletes alike to receive state-of-the-art medical care in the Marshall Sports Medicine Institute.

The 107,000-square-foot building houses a full 100-yard football field with artificial turf, a 300-meter NCAA competition-level six-lane running track, floor pits for multiple Olympic field events, and seating for 1,000 spectators.

The indoor space can be divided with a series of nets that hang from the 65' clear-height roof structure. This can be raised and lowered at the touch of a button, allowing multiple sports programs to use the facility at the same time, and in a comfortable and safe manner.

Batting cages for baseball and softball are also part of the athletic complex. Two mezzanine levels provide elevated viewing space overlooking the practice area. These mezzanine levels connect directly into the adjacent student-athlete academic center recruiting room.

The large volume of the indoor athletic facility component was pushed back off the street. It is fronted by smaller pedestrian-scaled structures that are specifically composed to work together with the existing weight-room structure, creating a coherent overall composition and architecturally framing a public plaza and parking area.

The area between the large building and the football stadium was landscaped and provided with ground-level power to enable tailgating and tenting for groups on football Saturdays.

The overall facility sits immediately adjacent to the existing Joan C. Edwards football stadium and weight room facilities on the edge of the Marshall University campus. This location provides entry to the Marshall Athletics department, and is an ideal spot for the multi-use facility, as this area of campus is already frequented by student-athletes on a daily basis for training and practice purposes. With the level of facilities becoming critical to recruitment, the IAF makes a bold statement within the greater campus.

Code	Division Name	%	S F Cost	Projected
00	Procurement and Contracting Require	1.15	1.70	182,613
01	General Requirements	5.61	8.24	886,292
03	Concrete	7.17	10.54	1,134,313
04	Masonry	3.99	5.87	631,378
05	Metals	7.39	10.85	1,167,037
06	Wood, Plastics, and Composites	0.20	0.29	31,907
07	Thermal and Moisture Protection	5.79	8.51	915,656
08	Openings	5.58	8.19	882,025
09	Finishes	5.05	7.43	799,202
10	Specialties	0.99	1.45	155,892
11	Equipment	5.55	8.16	877,790
12	Furnishings	0.06	0.09	8,799
13	Special Construction	24.35	35.78	3,848,769
21	Fire Suppression	1.26	1.85	199,227
22	Plumbing	3.36	4.94	531,946
23	HVAC	7.89	11.60	1,247,332
26	Electrical	14.60	21.46	2,308,393
	Total Building Costs	100.00	146.95	15,808,572

COST PER SQUARE FOOT = $146.95

© Copyright 2020. For a more in-depth report on this building or additional case studies contact DC&D @ 800-533-5680, or www.DCD.com

File 59:

The new Ann Arbor building and site have been designed to respect the adjacent residential neighborhood while providing a transitional buffer to the downtown. To fit with the residential environment, the building is scaled in brick with patterning and accents. It also steps back to the north and east as it gains height, to provide a more compatible scale. Large areas of glass accentuate the façades. Glass clerestories are reminiscent of cornices.

In response to MDEQ requirements related to flood paths, which limit ground floor area, the building rises four stories, plus mezzanine, above the ground with parking tucked below the building. Over half of the site is open and landscaped with native plantings, creating a natural park-like environment near the residential areas.

The first floor contains office, locker, and child-care spaces as well as an aquatic center with six 25-yard lanes, a lap pool and adjacent family pool with zero-depth entry, and a central whirlpool. There are separate women's/girls' and mens'/boys' locker areas, as well as family "cabanas", some with showers.

Off the main lobby is a reading room that overlooks the pools and a 4,700-square-foot childcare center for full-day and after-school care for children ages 2 - 11 years old. The center has a secured entrance, as well as dedicated and fenced playground area.

The 8,200-square-foot wellness center on the second floor offers cardiovascular machines, including treadmills, elipticals, stairclimbers, bicycles and rowing machines, strength training circuits and free weight equipment. To support the Y's extensive programs in the areas of dance, aerobics, martial arts, and yoga, five studios have been built around the specific space and configuration needs of these programs.

The third floor includes a full size gym and one-half size gym for basketball, gymnastics and volleyball. A three-lane elevated track circles the gym, offering a spectacular view of Ann Arbor.

Code	Division Name	%	S F Cost	Projected
00	Procurement and Contracting Require	16.52	43.89	3,659,201
01	General Requirements	1.92	5.11	426,323
03	Concrete	10.84	28.79	2,400,928
04	Masonry	6.57	17.46	1,455,776
05	Metals	9.47	25.15	2,097,501
06	Wood, Plastics, and Composites	2.01	5.34	445,235
07	Thermal and Moisture Protection	3.71	9.86	821,550
08	Openings	5.81	15.44	1,287,007
09	Finishes	6.29	16.69	1,392,360
10	Specialties	1.27	3.37	281,483
11	Equipment	0.42	1.12	93,554
13	Special Construction	5.73	15.23	1,269,493
14	Conveying Systems	0.80	2.13	177,260
21	Fire Suppression	1.58	4.21	350,106
22	Plumbing	4.93	13.11	1,092,941
23	HVAC	13.67	36.32	3,028,152
26	Electrical	8.45	22.44	1,871,292
	Total Building Costs	100.00	265.67	22,150,161

COST PER SQUARE FOOT = $265.67

© Copyright 2020. For a more in-depth report on this building or additional case studies contact DC&D
@ 800-533-5680, or www.DCD.com

File 60:

The David D. Hunting YMCA emerges from the landscape along US 131 to offer a tangible manifestation of the YMCA's emphasis on community. Designed to be a "destination" Y, this structure radiates energy and excitement by physically and visually connecting people and spaces both within the facility and to passersby.

This building's simple, uncomplicated form responds to both function and setting, filling its location on a fringe urban site with its east, west, and south edges abutting adjacent streets. The footprint, with its arched north and south facades, is derived from the third floor indoor running circuit.

Glass curtainwalls support passive solar strategies and combine with zinc panels and Renaissance stone to express an image of a solid, long-term community resident. The contrast created by mixing solidity and transparency establishes a kinetic and highly animated experience, while respecting the YMCA's traditional urban construction.

The lobby entrance immerses visitors in activity, offering views through the first floor aquatic center to the Grand Valley State University Campus and beyond. The nondenominational chapel, central to the YMCA mission, floats above the circulation desk, offering an inward focus and oasis of quiet in the midst of activity. While the pools anchor the main floor, an open staircase urges members and visitors upward to second and third floor fitness areas.

As one of the largest urban YMCAs in the nation, the 159,000-square-foot David D. Hunting YMCA serves a diverse population, from downtown business people to inner city families. They were challenged to create a building that would be a realization of the YMCA mission to build strong kids, strong families and strong communities. This building, with its open, interconnected spaces, works together to create a sense of community, as well as opportunities for interaction, as members naturally flow from one activity to another. The two full-court basketball floors can be sectioned off for other activities, while the 1/7th mile running track around the perimeter of the building offers unobstructed views of the city as well as activities taking place within the building. There are numerous conversation areas present opportunities to catch your breath or catch up with a friend.

Corporate YMCA offices overlook the third floor activities, providing staff with a visual touch-stone for the focus of their efforts. While the large open space supports community, smaller, intimate workout zones are created within the open areas, allowing users to focus on their personal goals or on the cityscape vista.

The decision to seek LEED® certification, the first Y in the nation to do so, came at the urging of the Hunting family, whose $5,000,000 gift in honor of their father, David D. Hunting, provided the foundation for the fundraising effort. Sustainable components range from low/no VOC off-gassing finishes to photovoltaic solar roof panels. The result is an elegant facility that reflects the vision and passion of David D. Hunting, a Steelcase founder, to unite the community of Grand Rapids. The building of community is evident as everyone, regardless of income, age, ability, race or religion, is welcome. Since its opening, membership has grown from 8,945 to 18,008 – an increase of over 200%.

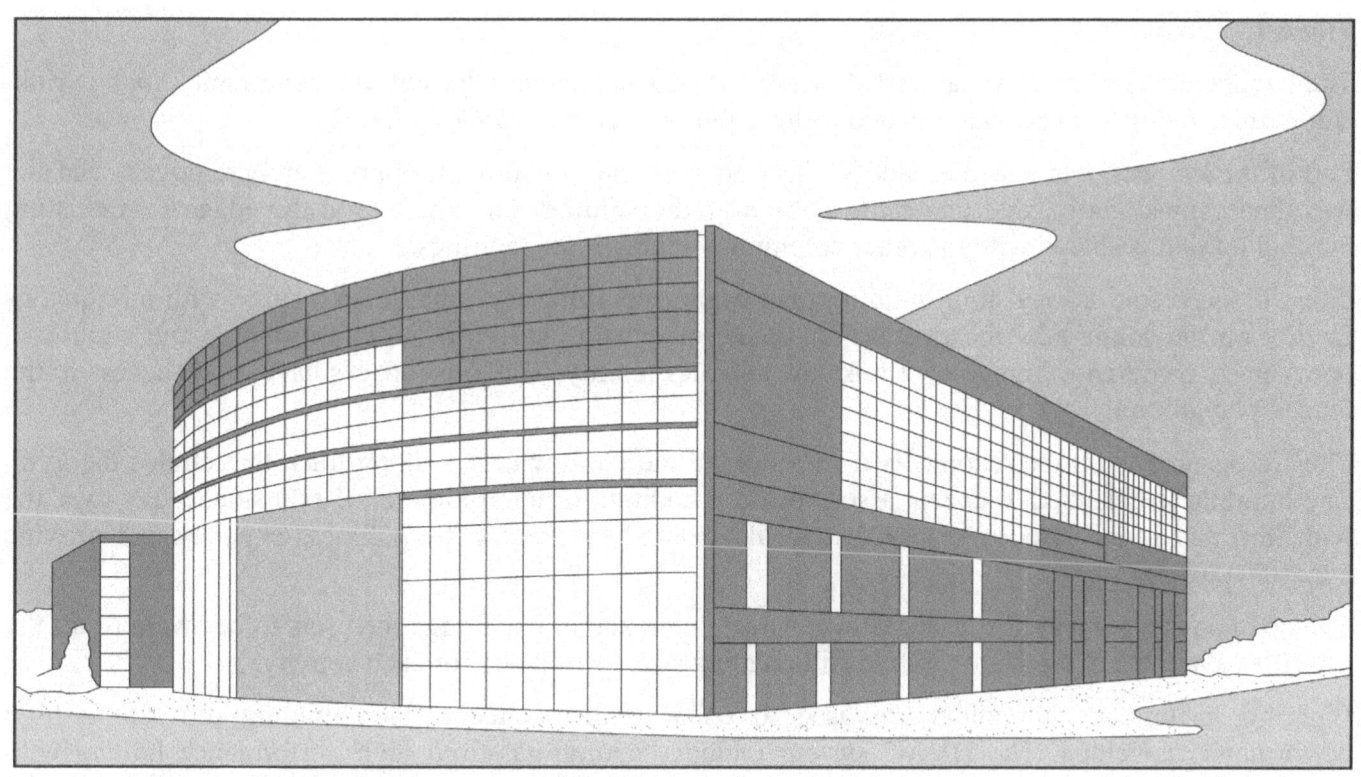

Code	Division Name	%	S F Cost	Projected
00	Bidding Requirements	6.51	13.74	2,239,053
01	General Requirements	9.13	19.27	3,140,332
03	Concrete	14.61	30.84	5,025,417
04	Masonry	5.44	11.49	1,871,590
05	Metals	6.51	13.73	2,237,709
06	Wood & Plastics	2.28	4.81	784,139
07	Thermal & Moisture Protection	1.26	2.65	432,915
08	Doors & Windows	9.48	20.01	3,261,444
09	Finishes	10.57	22.31	3,635,693
10	Specialties	2.28	4.81	783,497
11	Equipment	0.69	1.44	235,780
12	Furnishings	0.00	0.00	0
13	Special Construction	8.96	18.91	3,081,372
14	Conveying Systems	1.14	2.41	393,552
15	Mechanical	15.95	33.67	5,486,782
16	Electrical	5.18	10.92	1,779,932
	Total Building Costs	100.00	211.01	34,389,207

COST PER SQUARE FOOT = $211.01

© Copyright 2020. For a more in-depth report on this building or additional case studies contact DC&D @ 800-533-5680, or www.DCD.com

File 61:

The site for the Greater Nashua YMCA was a City-owned parcel adjacent to a community hockey rink, community football/soccer stadium and historic public park with walking trails.

Part of the site was over a former landfill that had to be monitored while appropriately removed. The site was then capped and vented under the slab-on-grade building. The site was at the edge of an existing parking lot that is shared with the other community recreational facilities.

The site suggested a long, thin building plan organized along a double-loaded spine with an aquatics facility on the south side, the gymnasium at the other end, and with the locker rooms and studios in between. A conference/lounge overlooks the aquatics facility. The kids' spaces have direct access to the fenced playground.

The fitness area is on the second level overlooking the pool, with a walking track that circles the gym. The building is designed to accept a second floor addition of approximately 5,600 square feet over the Kid Stop and multi-purpose spaces that would expand the second floor fitness capacity and provide additional offices.

The open concept is an effort to maximize natural light and to encourage the users to be aware of all the activities available at the facility while still creating a sense of place for each activity.

Lighting, materials, and colors are used to enhance this concept. The building provides a high performance envelope. The HVAC system includes natural-gas-fired high performance boilers with water source heat pumps, cooling tower and remote ERV ventilation. The aquatics center is treated with a dehumidifier and large ceiling fan.

Code	Division Name	%	S F Cost	Projected
00	Procurement and Contracting Require	2.92	5.76	287,749
01	General Requirements	5.50	10.83	541,773
03	Concrete	4.60	9.08	453,542
04	Masonry	6.35	12.52	625,614
05	Metals	10.89	21.46	1,072,462
06	Wood, Plastics, and Composites	4.52	8.90	444,867
07	Thermal and Moisture Protection	11.75	23.17	1,157,852
08	Openings	6.49	12.79	638,996
09	Finishes	11.07	21.83	1,090,889
10	Specialties	1.15	2.28	113,703
11	Equipment	0.56	1.10	54,913
12	Furnishings	0.13	0.24	12,397
13	Special Construction	9.31	18.34	916,715
14	Conveying Systems	0.71	1.41	69,968
23	HVAC	16.64	32.79	1,638,953
26	Electrical	7.41	14.60	729,772
	Total Building Costs	100.00	197.08	9,850,163

COST PER SQUARE FOOT = $197.08

© Copyright 2020. For a more in-depth report on this building or additional case studies contact DC&D @ 800-533-5680, or www.DCD.com

File 62:

The New Holland Recreation Center is an example of taking a tired, old space and converting it into a newer and fresher facility.

The warehouse that currently contains the New Holland Recreation Center was previously owned by Good's Furniture, which was subsequently purchased by Breuner's Furniture. Richard Good, owner of the warehouse, offered to sell a portion of the warehouse to the New Holland Recreation Center, to which they agreed.

Prior to this agreement, a group of building committee members along with representatives from Cornerstone Design-Architects toured the facility in order to evaluate the surrounding site and interior space. Ultimately, it was decided that the space could indeed meet the needs of the program, and also offer a competitive value for the property on which it would be located.

The recreation center contains a wellness area, junior-high regulation-size gymnasium, men's, women's, and family room lockers, indoor leisure pool, walking track, aerobics room, childcare area, a classroom, game area, and office/administration areas.

The design includes a curving, main corridor connecting the main entrance to the gymnasium and pool areas along with the walking track. The walking track is integrated with the public circulation as a concept to reduce program area by integrating the corridors and walking track together.

The design of the exterior included adding a base course of a split-face masonry veneer, along with adding storefront window openings to allow natural light to penetrate the interior spaces of the facility. The exterior siding was painted with graphics to dress up the front elevations. A large steel canopy was also added to accentuate the main entrance of the facility and guide visitors to the front door.

This project, however, shared a number of challenges within the existing structure. In planning space within the existing pre-engineered building, special care needed to be taken in locating larger spaces such as the gymnasium and indoor leisure pool.

The gymnasium was delegated to be located within the largest bay of the facility, to accommodate the junior-high regulation-size court. Additionally, the indoor leisure pool was interwoven around existing steel columns, and one of the columns was engaged into the design of the pool and became a bench feature within the pool itself.

Another challenge in working with an existing pre-engineered structure was the inability to locate and support any building element requiring structural support from the pre-engineered structure above. This affected the selected location of mechanical equipment within the shell of the building. To solve this problem, the design team created an equipment platform located between the indoor leisure pool and gymnasium areas. This equipment platform was centrally located to feed ductwork to the main areas of the facility.

The project has also been envisioned for future growth, with some of the plans to include an elevated running track and a climbing wall structure.

The project has been considered a success, and the recreation center has already surpassed their expectations for membership in the New Holland area of Lancaster County.

© Copyright 2020. For a more in-depth report on this building or additional case studies contact DC&D @ 800-533-5680, or www.DCD.com

Code	Division Name	%	S F Cost	Projected
00	Procurement and Contracting Require	15.44	21.07	1,080,022
03	Concrete	1.75	2.39	122,270
04	Masonry	3.60	4.92	251,819
05	Metals	2.56	3.50	179,061
06	Wood, Plastics, and Composites	2.77	3.77	193,731
07	Thermal and Moisture Protection	1.48	2.02	103,625
08	Openings	3.37	4.61	235,538
09	Finishes	13.87	18.93	970,068
10	Specialties	0.95	1.30	66,549
11	Equipment	0.14	0.19	10,015
13	Special Construction	11.89	16.23	831,695
21	Fire Suppression	2.55	3.47	178,413
22	Plumbing	4.62	6.31	323,130
23	HVAC	20.19	27.54	1,411,937
26	Electrical	14.82	20.21	1,036,370
	Total Building Costs	100.00	136.47	6,994,243

COST PER SQUARE FOOT = $136.47

© Copyright 2020. For a more in-depth report on this building or additional case studies contact DC&D @ 800-533-5680, or www.DCD.com

File 63:

A 33-acre, triangular site located directly off Interstate 64 on the west side of Fairview Heights was chosen for The Recreation Complex, a perfect spot to attract metro-east commuters from both sides of the Mississippi River.

In October of 2017, Holland Construction Services and the City of Fairview Heights broke ground on the $17.1 million dollar recreation complex. Construction of The REC was completed on schedule and within budget in March of 2019, with a grand opening in May of 2019.

The decision was made to dedicate 12,000 square feet of the recreation center to an indoor aquatic facility with a 25-yard multi-lane lap pool, children's spray ground, slides, sprays, lazy river, and a vortex. The center also features a 6,000-square-foot fitness center, with areas for free weights, floor exercise, aerobic and group fitness; a gymnasium; a climbing structure; elevated running tracks; a 400-meter, six-lane running track; a game area for billiards, cards and table tennis; locker rooms; multi-purpose and party rooms; and administration offices. Outdoor soccer fields, a dog park, pavilions, playgrounds, and a 1.5-mile walking path and nature trail are also part of the development.

The decision to stack the walking track above the basketball courts was made to provide an efficient space planning solution while also providing access to both members and non-members on the upper floor. The Clip and Climb feature also needed to be available for each of the users, because non-members will have the ability to use just that element without purchasing access to the other amenities, so placement of the structure near the front on the upper level was an obvious requirement.

Glass was chosen to overlook the pool from the open lounge, circulation paths were created to open the views of the cardio fitness areas, and access to the walking track was placed next to the reception area in order to provide understanding for orientation within the building no matter what activity you plan to tackle first.

Outdoors, the exterior materials of brick, glass and insulated metal panels became the palette that would paint the story of an iconic transparency that defines The REC.

© Copyright 2020. For a more in-depth report on this building or additional case studies contact DC&D @ 800-533-5680, or www.DCD.com

Code	Division Name	%	S F Cost	Projected
0	Procurement	0.01	0.03	1,887
1	General Requirements	29.41	95.62	5,572,929
3	Concrete	9.24	30.04	1,750,935
4	Masonry	5.22	16.98	989,889
5	Metals	7.62	24.78	1,444,092
6	Wood & Plastics	3.72	12.10	705,416
7	Thermal and Moisture	5.62	18.26	1,063,991
8	Openings	4.08	13.27	773,408
9	Finishes	5.32	17.29	1,007,490
10	Specialties	0.30	0.99	57,971
11	Equipment	0.22	0.71	41,492
12	Furnishings	0.40	1.30	75,506
13	Special Construction	9.97	32.40	1,888,316
14	Conveying Systems	0.66	2.15	125,408
21	Fire Suppression	1.04	3.37	196,254
22	Plumbing	3.45	11.22	653,723
23	HVAC	6.08	19.76	1,151,690
26	Electrical	7.65	24.86	1,449,002
	Total Building Costs	100.00	325.13	18,949,399

COST PER SQUARE FOOT = $325.13

© Copyright 2020. For a more in-depth report on this building or additional case studies contact DC&D @ 800-533-5680, or www.DCD.com

FILE 64:

Located on the shores of Lake Beulah, Wisconsin, Edwards YMCA Camp & Retreat Center is a branch of the Golden Corridor Family YMCA. Its 132 acres of forest, marshland, and prairie have offered youth and adult camp programs since 1929. The Seigle Welcome Center is the first stop in the wilderness as new campers arrive.

The new building is rustic and designed to fit well with the existing campground buildings. The log-look exterior met the energy efficiency goals of the project – important for a year-round campground that experiences frigid Wisconsin winters. The operable windows provide ample ventilation during the summer time, and the transoms allow for higher light transmission.

The interior design is warm and inviting. Children who are away from their parents for the first time are welcomed in the comfortable and homey lobby. Rustic accents, like the stone fireplace and pine window frames, set the mood for a complete away-from-home camp and retreat.

Beyond the lobby and reception area are the administrative offices and a conference room. The other wing houses the multi-bed infirmary, with the nurse's apartment adjacent to the infirmary. This small residence offers a living room with kitchenette, one bedroom, and one bathroom.

Camp Edwards serves approximately 1,260 youths in its summer resident camp, and 4,500 in environmental education. The new building will increase logistical capacity and camper capacity of both the camp and retreat center.

Code	Division Name	%	S F Cost	Projected
1	General Requirements	26.67	50.79	177,759
3	Concrete	8.04	15.31	53,570
4	Masonry	2.09	3.98	13,946
6	Wood & Plastics	19.88	37.86	132,520
7	Thermal and Moisture	2.84	5.41	18,945
8	Openings	5.26	10.01	35,023
9	Finishes	12.20	23.23	81,315
10	Specialties	0.99	1.89	6,630
12	Furnishings	0.55	1.05	3,664
22	Plumbing	4.34	8.27	28,948
23	HVAC	5.72	10.89	38,130
26	Electrical	11.41	21.72	76,013
	Total Building Costs	100.00	190.42	666,464

COST PER SQUARE FOOT = $190.42

© Copyright 2020. For a more in-depth report on this building or additional case studies contact DC&D @ 800-533-5680, or www.DCD.com

© Copyright 2020. For a more in-depth report on this building or additional case studies contact DC&D @ 800-533-5680, or www.DCD.com

Religious

File 65:

Turner Duran Architects chose to base the design on a Spanish Colonial concept, a design with which the people of the parish would be familiar and comfortable. This use of an historic theme follows in the tradition of American Christian architecture by which English "Georgian" Colonial, Central European Gothic, Italian Renaissance, and other design expressions would accompany newcomers to America and help them follow their faith in a familiar environment. White stucco walls, tile and metal red roofing, along with walls and windows with Spanish baroque decorative motifs in relief, are a featured part of the magnificent design. Stone arches create a covered loggia linking to exterior spaces, and all converge to produce an architectural composition of timelessness and cultural appropriateness.

A plaza for gathering and celebrations is essential. In Mexico, towns and villages are centered around a church and square in which community activities occur. This same sort of public space is integral here for the congregation to conduct the broad range of fellowship and devotional activities which flow from worship. The expansive plaza is focused on the main entry to the worship space, and is also bounded by other church facilities that feed directly into the space. All of the elements drawn from the Spanish baroque architectural heritage are incorporated into the design, including: hardscape ground surface, landscape providing shade and color, and flowing water.

The worship space must be visually expressive of the Mexican-American culture of the congregation. Not only would the design need to draw upon the historical themes mentioned above, it would need to use materials and colors that are at home in a North American context and that introduce visual energy into the space. This was achieved by means of the shrine incorporated near the altar table and the "sunburst" of gold leaf on the backdrop wall. It was also accomplished with a stunning, soaring dome that gives this relatively modestly-sized church of 650 seats a cathedral-like presence. Native timber structural framing and stone flooring complete the assemblage.

The result is a design of visual power and feeling that belies the modest size of the overall structure. By drawing upon a few historic and cultural connections desired by the client, a design was devised that not only achieved the specific goals set forth by the client, but ended up reaching well beyond the specifics of its location to communicate the pride and Christian devotion of its congregation.

© Copyright 2020. For a more in-depth report on this building or additional case studies contact DC&D @ 800-533-5680, or www.DCD.com

Code	Division Name	%	S F Cost	Projected
00	Procurement and Contracting Require	1.49	6.28	81,099
01	General Requirements	15.81	66.75	861,727
03	Concrete	6.34	26.78	345,640
04	Masonry	0.60	2.52	32,522
05	Metals	14.82	62.59	808,077
06	Wood, Plastics, and Composites	6.66	28.12	363,015
07	Thermal and Moisture Protection	9.94	41.96	541,821
08	Openings	4.05	17.09	220,659
09	Finishes	18.88	79.72	1,029,257
10	Specialties	1.16	4.90	63,207
21	Fire Suppression	2.43	10.26	132,493
22	Plumbing	2.80	11.83	152,642
23	HVAC	6.02	25.44	328,418
26	Electrical	8.51	35.92	463,687
28	Electronic Safety and Security	0.49	2.08	26,736
	Total Building Costs	100.00	422.23	5,451,000

COST PER SQUARE FOOT = $422.23

© Copyright 2020. For a more in-depth report on this building or additional case studies contact DC&D @ 800-533-5680, or www.DCD.com

FILE 66:

The roomy theater-style space seats 1,200 people, and shares its roof with a new two-story administrative and education wing. The six-story-tall glass-enclosed entrance greets congregants and visitors alike to this multi-building campus.

The original master plan envisioned that the Worship Center would be on the same location on the property, but growth needs forced the addition of offices, classrooms, and nursery spaces to the scope of the project. As a result, an auditorium-style worship space was wrapped on two sides by the ancillary spaces. However, this provided the opportunity to go vertical with the structure, and to emphasize the curvilinear shape of the space on the exterior architectural expression.

The basic structure forms the essence of the architecture. The steel roof structure in the worship space displays a radial pattern, fanning out from a center point to envelop the entire assembly, and aids in focusing attention on the proceedings taking place on the main stage. State-of-the-art audio/visual and sound systems assist in this purpose, and "cloud" panels nestled within the principal structural elements provide an optimal mix of acoustical reflection. The sprawling stage contains space sufficient for preaching, events, choirs, and bands.

Access to the entire building is provided by means of the generous arcing lobby stretching the entire building length, featuring full-height glass walls, allowing a good view of the new city springing up all around. A variety of luxury vinyl flooring materials in an arresting array of shapes and patterns provides contrast with the coffered ceilings and cast stone wall and column facings.

The soaring entry tower is capped off with copper-coated metal roofing, and also features a copper-coated cross reaching almost four stories in height, highlighted against a vast stretch of curtainwall. Brick masonry complements the existing campus structures, and cast stone completes the exterior composition.

A "partnering" approach was utilized to deliver the project. The general contractor was pre-selected in a competitive qualifications and proposal process; the principal mechanical, electrical, and plumbing subcontractors provided design/build systems, as did the sound and A/V system provider. For convenience and accountability, the construction and FF&E systems were all delivered under a single contract.

Code	Division Name	%	S F Cost	Projected
00	Procurement and Contracting Require	2.34	7.28	298,354
01	General Requirements	10.60	32.94	1,350,345
03	Concrete	7.98	24.80	1,016,690
04	Masonry	4.87	15.13	620,441
05	Metals	16.84	52.33	2,145,748
06	Wood, Plastics, and Composites	2.87	8.91	365,250
07	Thermal and Moisture Protection	6.90	21.44	879,066
08	Openings	4.82	14.99	614,773
09	Finishes	13.26	41.22	1,690,065
10	Specialties	2.15	6.68	273,777
12	Furnishings	1.61	5.01	205,041
14	Conveying Systems	0.80	2.50	102,332
21	Fire Suppression	1.18	3.65	149,837
22	Plumbing	2.67	8.31	340,925
23	HVAC	7.80	24.26	994,424
26	Electrical	8.66	26.93	1,104,006
27	Communications	3.97	12.36	506,409
28	Electronic Safety and Security	0.71	2.22	90,724
	Total Building Costs	100.00	310.84	12,745,392

COST PER SQUARE FOOT = $310.84

© Copyright 2020. For a more in-depth report on this building or additional case studies contact DC&D
@ 800-533-5680, or www.DCD.com

File 67:

This 7,600-square-foot, one-story church is located on a 10-acre, previously undeveloped site.

Construction consisted of three phases. In phase I, a 234-seat facility was constructed. In phase II, an education wing is to be built. In phase III, a permanently dedicated worship space is to be added and the initial multipurpose space will be converted to a social hall.

The initial building is situated in a meadow in view of a neighboring highway. The facility is serviced by an existing well and a new septic field.

Phase I maintained the site's natural landscaping, with wooded areas in the rear and the landscaped meadow flanking the other three façades. A proposed plaza, which will separate the building from the parking lot, is to be built when funds are available. This plaza will use exposed aggregate concrete to match the interior floors and will be enclosed with shrubbery.

The building's foundation is CMU. The exterior skin combines brick veneer to an eight-foot-high overhang with cement boards at the gabled ends and fascia. Roofing consists of 40-year heavy asphalt shingles and standard ridge vents over plywood sheathing. The entrance lies beneath the eight-foot overhang and leads directly into an open narthex.

Two wood structural systems were used to construct phase I. Glue-laminated arches over the high, open worship space and stick-built wood frame exterior bearing walls support factory-built wood trusses that form wings. The full volume of the building is expressed inside the main worship space, while the remaining attic areas are used to house the heating and cooling system. The tower was stick built on the ground and hoisted into place.

Quality and simplicity are emphasized in the interior finish through the use of exposed aggregate concrete floors, custom wood doors and windows, wood paneling and trim, and tongue and groove wood ceilings.

Plain wooden seating flanks the central pulpit area on three sides. Skylights and drop lighting provide both natural and artificial light to the interior, while exposed wood trusses add a rustic aesthetic dimension.

In phases II and III, corridors will lead off the central narthex in both directions, providing space for classrooms, a nursery, a kitchen, bathrooms, and office space. Simplicity and economy will be emphasized in the classrooms and support spaces by the use of ceramic and VCT flooring, carpet, gypsum board, and acoustic tile. The catering kitchen will be equipped to serve prepared meals. The facility is equipped with fire extinguishers.

Code	Division Name	%	S F Cost	Projected
00	Procurement and Contracting Require	8.44	17.86	135,734
01	General Requirements	2.21	4.68	35,593
03	Concrete	9.31	19.70	149,729
04	Masonry	3.16	6.69	50,902
05	Metals	0.12	0.27	1,997
06	Wood, Plastics, and Composites	31.11	65.87	500,525
07	Thermal and Moisture Protection	6.08	12.85	97,751
08	Openings	8.34	17.65	134,201
09	Finishes	6.19	13.10	99,527
10	Specialties	1.24	2.63	19,926
21	Fire Suppression	0.07	0.14	1,136
22	Plumbing	3.11	6.58	50,044
23	HVAC	10.26	21.72	165,029
26	Electrical	10.35	21.91	166,548
	Total Building Costs	100.00	211.67	1,608,652

COST PER SQUARE FOOT = $211.67

© Copyright 2020. For a more in-depth report on this building or additional case studies contact DC&D
@ 800-533-5680, or www.DCD.com

File 68:

This 29,000-square-foot church was designed to seat 1,200 to 1,500 people in a new sanctuary added onto the church's existing location.

The church committee wanted clear sight lines within the sanctuary with no obstructions of the pulpit area. Expandability and flexibility were seen to be key elements, as administration and classroom spaces will make up a future construction phase. A bright, open space with lots of windows was also thought to be a key design element. The committee ultimately settled upon a "fan shape" building option.

The architect was challenged to work with the city on a number of issues, such as the annexation of church property into the city limits and the granting of a variance on the building height. Stormwater drainage requirements and the supply of fresh water to the property were other issues that had to be worked out.

The structure utilizes a cast-in-place concrete foundation and clad metal roof. The building exterior features a traditional masonry look of brick, split-faced block, and arched windows, combined with a contemporary styling of synthetic stucco applied in a variety of shapes and levels.

The west elevation consists of three tall, slender, arch-topped windows which give natural light to the spacious choir area, above which sits a large conventionally built cupola and a very tall steeple. This creates a landmark for the surrounding community. A large foyer was constructed between the new sanctuary and the existing building and serves as a gathering space for church members.

Two formal entries flank opposite sides of the building, joined by a connecting hallway adjacent to the sanctuary. Subtle variations of blue and white used throughout the facility create a smooth transition from one area to another.

Two multi-purpose areas to be used for classrooms, counseling, or meetings are situated next to the worship area.

The most outstanding feature of the new addition is the worship area and sanctuary. The originally planned loge and balcony seating were removed, as were the temporary rooms to the rear of the sanctuary. This allowed the entire area to be opened up for seating on one main level, angled slightly to face the raised pulpit area.

The choir practice area is located behind the pulpit area and lit by the three exterior arched windows. Theatrical lighting in the sanctuary is designed to accommodate church pageants and other theatrical and musical performances.

The sanctuary is equipped with large video screens and an audio and lighting control booth in the rear of the room. The interior features white gypsum walls with carpeted flooring. The building is fully sprinklered with a fire suppression system.

Code	Division Name	%	S F Cost	Projected
00	Bidding Requirements	0.30	0.64	18,890
01	General Requirements	9.42	20.07	588,165
03	Concrete	5.25	11.19	327,804
04	Masonry	3.36	7.17	209,835
05	Metals	20.88	44.49	1,303,370
06	Wood & Plastics	1.48	3.15	92,174
07	Thermal & Moisture Protection	7.42	15.82	463,298
08	Doors & Windows	2.78	5.92	173,482
09	Finishes	21.06	44.87	1,314,510
10	Specialties	0.59	1.25	36,957
11	Equipment	1.25	2.66	78,081
13	Special Construction	2.72	5.79	169,929
15	Mechanical	12.36	26.33	771,603
16	Electrical	11.12	23.71	694,438
	Total Building Costs	100.00	213.09	6,242,534

COST PER SQUARE FOOT = $213.09

© Copyright 2020. For a more in-depth report on this building or additional case studies contact DC&D
@ 800-533-5680, or www.DCD.com

File 69:

Creating a surprising communal experience, the spiritual journey at Keystone Community Church in Ada, Michigan, begins upon first glimpse of the building.

Natural materials, clear windows and a distinct lack of Christian symbolism set it apart from its contemporary and traditional brethren. With a goal of "monstrous community focus, function and efficiency" the church is designed to be "a welcoming and dynamic community where people can connect with God, with others, and with opportunities to make a difference in our world."

Early in the design process, Keystone decided to seek USGBC LEED® Certification, as it reflected their respect for the land and their commitment to be good stewards of God's universe. The result is an efficient, flexible space, maximizing recycled materials, filled with fresh air and natural light.

The Keystone Church building uses a variety of sustainable strategies in its design and construction. The structure is sited in an existing field near a wooded north boundary. This boundary helps protect the auditorium and adjacent common and classroom spaces from the prevailing winter winds.

The main entry, offices, and common area face south, capturing sunlight for morning and evening services. The covered south porch controls the midday sun and shades the two-story glass curtainwall. Other elevations combine glass with locally fabricated brick and pre-cast concrete. Pre-finished fiber-reinforced siding adds additional texture to the low maintenance exterior material palette. Many spaces were designed to minimize the use of material and reduce the amount of finishing.

The interior is visually open with a commons connecting the major program elements. All occupied spaces offer exterior views in one or more directions. The commons is naturally lit from the south, east, and north, and from a translucent skylight. The classrooms have a variety of window sizes placed and scaled for child-sized views. Operable classroom windows allow natural ventilation on temperate days.

Stained concrete creates the durable commons floor without additional materials. The double height auditorium is clad in pre-cast panels that can be reused in future expansions. All paints are low-VOC products for minimal impact on air quality. Water use is reduced by low-flow fixtures, waterless urinals, and the omission of site irrigation. Energy consumption is reduced by using fluorescent light fixtures to efficiently illuminate spaces when conditions require. Radiant floor perimeter heat increases comfort at glass curtainwalls and eliminates high-velocity air requirements.

In addition to promoting practices that reduced the resources required to construct their building, the Keystone community is initiating a recycling program that will trickle down into the daily practices of their members and friends.

To encourage the use of alternate means of transportation, van-accessible parking spaces are provided, bicycle racks are available, and electric car recharging stations are provided close to the building. Additional efforts to expand the sustainable focus beyond the building include the addition of trees in the parking lot and stormwater management via a system of swales and settling basins to minimize the amount of silt which will be transported to local bodies of water.

© Copyright 2020. For a more in-depth report on this building or additional case studies contact DC&D @ 800-533-5680, or www.DCD.com

Code	Division Name	%	S F Cost	Projected
01	General Requirements	7.50	11.30	336,203
03	Concrete	13.63	20.52	611,112
04	Masonry	3.58	5.38	160,440
05	Metals	10.77	16.23	483,121
06	Wood, Plastics, and Composites	4.82	7.26	216,323
07	Thermal and Moisture Protection	4.18	6.29	187,480
08	Openings	9.20	13.86	412,817
09	Finishes	8.72	13.13	391,184
10	Specialties	1.13	1.70	50,475
11	Equipment	0.26	0.40	11,717
14	Conveying Systems	1.85	2.79	82,924
21	Fire Suppression	0.96	1.45	43,265
22	Plumbing	3.54	5.33	158,637
23	HVAC	14.67	22.10	657,983
26	Electrical	15.19	22.88	681,417
	Total Building Costs	100.00	150.64	4,485,096

COST PER SQUARE FOOT = $150.64

© Copyright 2020. For a more in-depth report on this building or additional case studies contact DC&D @ 800-533-5680, or www.DCD.com

File 70:

Good Shepherd Catholic Church and the St. Joseph Diocese of Kansas City hired HMN with Castrop Design Group to design a new church for the parish relocation.

Creating a master plan for the 32-acre site was the first step. It included space for the church, chapel, school, gym, daycare, outdoor recreation and rectory.

After completing the master plan, the HMN design team began designing the first phase. The clients' goal was to create a building that was historically symbolic, utilizing traditional ecclesiastic design elements.

It features a 70-foot bell tower, 500-seat church, a fellowship narthex (foyer), offices, parish hall with a commercial kitchen, as well as School of Religion classrooms. Design features include a column-free basement of long-span composite concrete floor, which is a stiffer and less expensive approach. The worship space is expandable to 700 seats. A future 70-seat adoration apse was included in the design.

The project team encountered several challenges on the project. The first was obtaining utilities economically. HMN negotiated with the city for shared costs of public infrastructure. Another challenge was the integration of multiple construction systems. Concrete block, heavy timber, steel and formed concrete were used to achieve the design the client desired, without being cost prohibitive.

© Copyright 2020. For a more in-depth report on this building or additional case studies contact DC&D
@ 800-533-5680, or www.DCD.com

Code	Division Name	%	S F Cost	Projected
00	Procurement and Contracting Require	0.84	1.68	41,535
01	General Requirements	10.49	20.90	518,519
03	Concrete	10.54	20.98	520,623
04	Masonry	8.36	16.66	413,261
05	Metals	9.99	19.90	493,892
06	Wood, Plastics, and Composites	8.06	16.05	398,394
07	Thermal and Moisture Protection	5.83	11.60	287,869
08	Openings	4.97	9.90	245,682
09	Finishes	12.22	24.33	603,693
10	Specialties	0.39	0.78	19,097
14	Conveying Systems	0.80	1.60	39,533
21	Fire Suppression	0.90	1.81	44,643
22	Plumbing	2.92	5.82	144,266
23	HVAC	13.24	26.35	654,045
26	Electrical	10.45	20.81	516,389
	Total Building Costs	100.00	199.17	4,941,441

COST PER SQUARE FOOT = $199.17

© Copyright 2020. For a more in-depth report on this building or additional case studies contact DC&D @ 800-533-5680, or www.DCD.com

File 71:

With a youth group numbering between 200 and 300 students and growing, the staff of the West Park Baptist Church in Knoxville, Tennessee expressed a need for a "home" for the youth ministry.

This new home would accomplish some important goals: First, the students would have a single area that could be their own, enabling the large group to be easily supervised, providing greater safety. Second, the ministers could have their offices and support spaces together, helping to improve the staff efficiency ministering to students. Lastly, it was of utmost importance to have a single space where all of the youth could gather for worship and fellowship; a unique space designed for their particular worship expressions and styles.

The building program presented many design challenges. Fellowship, worship, offices, food service and the ubiquitous mechanical systems all had to be accommodated. The combination of the many programmed uses created building code issues to be overcome during the design process.

As with many church buildings, the wise use of money was of deep concern. The architects, contractors and church staff spent many hours in meetings and in design charettes to integrate all of the needs and wants with the code requirements and within monetary limitations.

The result is an exciting building the whole of which far exceeds the sum of its parts. The most dramatic exterior element is the sloping, cantilevered canopy over an outdoor stage. West Park offers many activities for the surrounding neighborhoods and the outdoor stage provides the perfect focus for those events, as well as drawing attention to the building from the street.

Along the front and sides is a covered walkway which serves to connect two parts of the campus as well as reduce the scale of the building.

The 11,700-square-foot building is divided roughly in half. The first half is called "The Hub" and includes indoor recreation, cafe, offices and toilets, and also functions as the main entrance.

A dramatic 18-foot-high north-facing glass wall along the rear allows the space to flow to an outside fellowship area without incurring glare inside. This room also acts as a small assembly room with separate sound and video systems. A meandering, multi-color radius wall provides spatial interest and visually subdivides the room. Behind the radius wall are the offices and support spaces for the cafe.

The second half contains the worship center, designed specifically for the youth with state-of-the-art video and media capability, two rear-projection screens, sound system and theatrical lighting.

Seating consists of movable chairs and fixed restaurant-style booths, allowing the room to also be used for small-group activities. A 50- by 20-foot platform provides room for live bands, drama, and the worship leaders, and the rear wall of the platform can be opened directly to the outdoor stage.

Through careful planning, creative architecture and good construction management, the facility was completed within budget and on time. It is highly praised by the students, staff and parents who use it a number of times a week.

© Copyright 2020. For a more in-depth report on this building or additional case studies contact DC&D

 @ 800-533-5680, or www.DCD.com

Code	Division Name	%	S F Cost	Projected
01	General Requirements	3.85	9.37	109,577
03	Concrete	8.91	21.67	253,553
04	Masonry	5.17	12.58	147,140
05	Metals	13.09	31.82	372,460
06	Wood, Plastics, and Composites	1.32	3.22	37,627
07	Thermal and Moisture Protection	10.15	24.69	288,785
08	Openings	8.14	19.80	231,721
09	Finishes	16.09	39.13	457,831
10	Specialties	1.40	3.41	39,820
12	Furnishings	0.15	0.38	4,393
22	Plumbing	6.87	16.71	195,457
23	HVAC	9.47	23.04	269,570
26	Electrical	14.98	36.44	426,369
28	Electronic Safety and Security	0.40	0.95	11,255
	Total Building Costs	100.00	243.21	2,845,556

COST PER SQUARE FOOT = $243.21

© Copyright 2020. For a more in-depth report on this building or additional case studies contact DC&D @ 800-533-5680, or www.DCD.com

File 72:

Recognizing a need to serve the youth of the community, East Side Baptist Church constructed a 25,000-square-foot youth outreach building to provide a safe environment for after-school activities to students as well as providing additional space for the church's existing ministry programs. The Center is located near an elementary school and a junior high school and is also adjacent to a branch of the Fort Smith Public Library. The Center was constructed on the south end of the church's property and away from the existing buildings on campus in order for the building to retain its own image, separate from the other buildings on campus.

The program called for an auditorium space to accommodate 400 people in addition to a basketball court, which can be converted to a multi-purpose space seating 200 people at tables with chairs, a 26-foot-high indoor climbing wall, full service kitchen, electronic games area, an Internet café, full service snack bar, outdoor dining area, and an administrative office area. The exterior design was chosen to provide a contrast to the existing buildings on campus. Materials include utility-sized brick veneer, composite aluminum panels, metal wall panels, curtain wall framing with tinted, low E glass, and cementitious wall panels. The interior design palette consists of stained, polished concrete floors, painted exposed structure, bright painted colors and bold wall graphics.

Code	Division Name	%	S F Cost	Projected
01	General Requirements	5.58	15.22	380,742
03	Concrete	6.17	16.83	420,980
04	Masonry	1.46	3.98	99,434
05	Metals	6.65	18.16	454,008
06	Wood, Plastics, and Composites	2.11	5.77	144,225
07	Thermal and Moisture Protection	22.29	60.82	1,520,443
08	Openings	2.48	6.77	169,378
09	Finishes	9.77	26.66	666,271
10	Specialties	0.60	1.63	40,717
11	Equipment	9.75	26.59	665,011
12	Furnishings	13.28	36.25	906,306
21	Fire Suppression	1.67	4.55	113,735
22	Plumbing	2.80	7.63	190,836
23	HVAC	8.97	24.50	612,232
26	Electrical	6.42	17.51	437,796
	Total Building Costs	100.00	272.89	6,822,115

COST PER SQUARE FOOT = $272.89

© Copyright 2020. For a more in-depth report on this building or additional case studies contact DC&D
@ 800-533-5680, or www.DCD.com

© Copyright 2020. For a more in-depth report on this building or additional case studies contact DC&D @ 800-533-5680, or www.DCD.com

Residential

© Copyright 2020. For a more in-depth report on this building or additional case studies contact DC&D @ 800-533-5680, or www.DCD.com

FILE 73:

Designed as a contiguous structure, the building twists and turns along the site. Developing the parking areas along the travel route allowed for the building to hug the river and provide exciting vistas from all angles. The interplay of the apartment blocks allows those living here privacy and respite, while aiding in forging a complete community.

The architecture reflects the coastal nature of the site. Broad overhangs, large windows to enjoy the views, dormers reminiscent of historic beach cottages, and the casual colors of the project all combine to create a design that feels at home with the beach.

The building footprint meanders along the site, allowing for the majority of units to enjoy the surrounding natural environment. Using a concrete podium design under a portion of the building allowed for the parking field to be greatly reduced, therefore increasing access of the remaining portions of the site to the environment. The site plan is extremely efficient, with double-loaded drive aisles and head-in parking along the roadside portion of the site. Entrances dispersed around the perimeter allow for easy entry, while providing the necessary security. The efficiency of the site layout allows for a higher density, while decreasing the impervious area. The recreation area is sited to take advantage of the natural sun path, and allows for the pool area to receive the maximum amount of sunlight during the day.

Building materials were selected for their durability and economics. The base of the building utilizes a split-face CMU veneer, which grounds the building and provides the durability and protection needed to withstand the climate. Above this veneer, the planar design dictates the use of materials around the façade. Using mostly durable synthetic materials, the façade is designed to withstand days of bright sunlight while staying in place during a hurricane.

Taking advantage of the roof area on the top floor, the uppermost apartments utilize an open loft to create warmth and volume. This volume – when combined with the dormers – is unique in our area, and allows one to go back in time when ceiling shape was a leading design tool.

© Copyright 2020. For a more in-depth report on this building or additional case studies contact DC&D @ 800-533-5680, or www.DCD.com

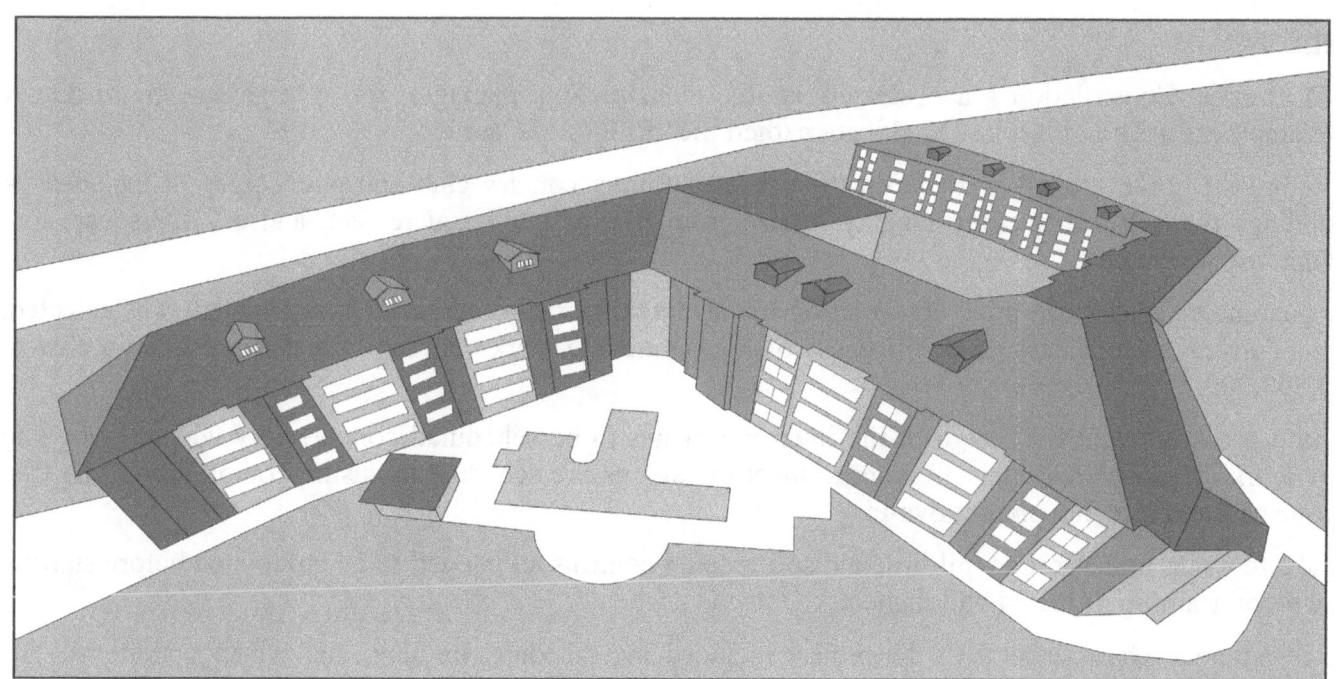

Code	Division Name	%	S F Cost	Projected
00	Procurement and Contracting Require	6.88	6.82	2,263,535
01	General Requirements	11.79	11.69	3,877,319
03	Concrete	5.02	4.97	1,647,728
04	Masonry	2.93	2.91	963,045
05	Metals	2.20	2.18	723,148
06	Wood, Plastics, and Composites	22.65	22.44	7,442,711
07	Thermal and Moisture Protection	4.01	3.98	1,320,470
08	Openings	1.69	1.68	556,533
09	Finishes	11.74	11.63	3,856,616
10	Specialties	0.81	0.80	265,476
11	Equipment	3.93	3.89	1,291,475
12	Furnishings	0.34	0.34	110,615
13	Special Construction	0.60	0.59	196,811
14	Conveying Systems	0.60	0.59	198,921
21	Fire Suppression	1.69	1.68	554,459
22	Plumbing	5.49	5.44	1,802,898
23	HVAC	7.01	6.95	2,305,119
26	Electrical	10.61	10.52	3,489,564
	Total Building Costs	100.00	99.10	32,866,444

COST PER SQUARE FOOT = $99.10

© Copyright 2020. For a more in-depth report on this building or additional case studies contact DC&D @ 800-533-5680, or www.DCD.com

FILE 74:

CD Barnes Construction was selected as the construction manager for a high-end multi-family development in Grand Rapids, Michigan, named the "Ridges of Cascade."

The project broke ground in 2013, on the site of a former country club and golf course. It included 24 buildings (with 10 units each), ranging in size from 831 to 1,415 square feet, and a 7,403-square-foot clubhouse/pool area.

A guaranteed maximum-price construction management at risk contract delivery system was selected. This delivery system was needed because of a separate site work contract which approached a cost of $3,500,000.

The process allowed for design of the interior finishes to be scheduled concurrently with the ongoing site work. This was necessary in order to meet the aggressive schedule to ensure completion of the first group of buildings for spring move-ins.

The site work, underground utilities, and soil erosion controls all needed to be completed before starting the wood framing of the 24 buildings.

A few unique characteristics of the project included the schedule, framing, and winter conditions. The schedule was the most critical function, as a new building had to be started every two weeks and finished in six months.

The new community is owned and managed by the LaCati Group – a local firm known in the Grand Rapids area for their multi-family development and management, custom home building, brokerage, and transitional living.

Chad Cassiday, President and Owner of the LaCati Group, shared, "People are changing the way they live; they want time, flexibility, and first-class amenities that they don't have to manage. We took a country club setting and provided the location and product the community desires." Cassiday added, "The Ridges provides luxury condo quality in a rental option that gives you freedom, yet requires no capital."

The Ridges of Cascade is now Grand Rapids' premier apartment community – offering one-, two-, and three-bedroom apartment homes. Each unit features an attached garage, private entrance, quartz countertops, stainless steel appliances, stone tile backsplashes, full-size washer and dryer, nine-foot ceilings, bar and island kitchens, custom cabinetry, private balcony or patio, and hardwood grain flooring.

Tenants also have access to a resort-style pool surrounded by palm trees, hot tub, sundeck, fire pit, fitness center, business center, 24-hour pet spa, and a community room with bar, flat screen televisions, and billiards table.

Code	Division Name	%	S F Cost	Projected
01	General Requirements	10.22	10.71	2,996,879
03	Concrete	8.71	9.12	2,552,897
04	Masonry	4.32	4.53	1,265,349
05	Metals	0.82	0.85	238,640
06	Wood, Plastics, and Composites	30.48	31.93	8,929,591
07	Thermal and Moisture Protection	4.90	5.13	1,437,392
08	Openings	4.53	4.75	1,326,397
09	Finishes	9.22	9.66	2,702,741
10	Specialties	0.34	0.36	99,896
11	Equipment	2.27	2.38	665,973
12	Furnishings	5.68	5.96	1,664,933
21	Fire Suppression	2.27	2.38	665,973
22	Plumbing	5.94	6.23	1,742,630
23	HVAC	4.92	5.16	1,442,942
26	Electrical	5.36	5.62	1,570,587
	Total Building Costs	100.00	104.78	29,302,822

COST PER SQUARE FOOT = $104.78

© Copyright 2020. For a more in-depth report on this building or additional case studies contact DC&D @ 800-533-5680, or www.DCD.com

FILE 75:

Motivated to create an affordable, as well as innovative, senior residential neighborhood, the architect and owner orchestrated their planning centered around "Pocket Neighborhoods," to encourage casual interactions between neighbors that bring richness to their lives. Positioning apartments to face sidewalks and to locate the cars and drives behind the buildings are key elements.

Each apartment has a covered front porch at the front entrance which is intended to function as an extension of the living room. This provides an outdoor space for people to spend time and interact with their neighbors.

Attention is given to human scale and the architectural "cottage" detailing common in Springfield. Each living unit has an attached one-car garage to the rear, with one exterior parking space for visitors. Exterior building design features a steep slope roof and dimensional shingles, heavy-duty vinyl siding, and man-made stone veneer.

Shakes and siding were installed on the gables for emphasis. The windows are single-hung vinyl windows with simulated divided lights, and porches have exposed timbers as a decorative wood trim.

Community Gardens stands in sharp contrast to typical subsidized housing projects. The pocket community is comprised of 50 apartments on a roughly 7-acre site. The modest size apartments are each 1,216 square feet. Each apartment contains 2 bedrooms, an attached garage, and a front porch. All apartments have a living area of 925 square feet, with an attached garage of an additional 292 square feet. Each has its own 175-square-foot covered front porch. There is an additional 400 square-foot utility building on the property to serve the 13 apartment buildings housing the 50 apartments.

Each unit may easily be converted to comply with the Americans with Disabilities Act. Some units are also sensory compatible groups in duplex, triplex, 4-plex, and 6-plex apartment buildings. All kitchen cabinetry has 9-inch-tall toe kicks, and many gliding drawers and shelves. Drop-in stoves were added to maintain ADA heights and contain kitchen cook hoods with exterior exhaust. In the bathroom, the 5-foot shower is a roll-in unit with hand-held shower wand and fold-down seat. The lavatory has adjacent built-in shelving, since the lavatory is wall mounted. The floor is low-pile carpet and vinyl luxury tile to promote a clean home with ease of maintenance.

Code	Division Name	%	S F Cost	Projected
00	Procurement	0.43	0.39	25,865
01	General Requirements	15.38	14.01	917,937
03	Concrete	9.49	8.64	566,246
06	Wood & Plastics	22.33	20.34	1,331,954
07	Thermal and Moisture	10.65	9.70	635,597
08	Openings	6.46	5.88	384,974
09	Finishes	9.16	8.34	546,550
10	Specialties	1.79	1.63	106,999
11	Equipment	2.24	2.04	133,704
12	Furnishings	0.35	0.32	20,694
22	Plumbing	7.31	6.66	436,042
23	HVAC	6.07	5.53	362,329
26	Electrical	8.02	7.30	477,901
28	Electronic Security	0.30	0.27	17,988
	Total Building Costs	100.00	91.07	5,964,779

COST PER SQUARE FOOT = $91.07

© Copyright 2020. For a more in-depth report on this building or additional case studies contact DC&D @ 800-533-5680, or www.DCD.com

File 76:

The affluent area of West Palm Beach, Florida had a need for affordable housing for senior citizens. The project was geared to working class residents ages 62 and older, with priority to military veterans and widows.

Corwil Architects, Inc. designed the new development with a mission of creating a beautiful, relaxing residential community with indoor/outdoor amenities conducive to Florida's climate and including high-end finishes not typically found in market rate housing.

The 125-unit apartment complex includes four residential buildings with garden-style apartments that surround a central plaza with benches, shaded pathways and lush, tropical landscaping. On-site parking, a palm-tree-lined perimeter, and outdoor hallways that take advantage of Florida's attractive weather are also incorporated. Construction was completed in 14 months.

The modern residential complex includes two one-story buildings, one three-story building and one four-story building, all with reinforced construction to meet Florida's stringent hurricane building codes. There are 75 one bedroom and 50 two-bedroom units with a contemporary design, high-end finishes and energy-efficient appliances. Because the property is geared to senior citizens, materials were selected for longevity and low maintenance.

The crown jewel of the development is a cosmopolitan clubhouse, an airy, welcoming recreation center meant to bring residents together as a needed social outlet. With sleek, coastal-influenced décor in a light-filled, high ceilinged space, the clubhouse includes a food preparation area, restrooms, and small seating areas that can be regrouped to accommodate large or small gatherings. Avant-garde lighting and art accentuate the space and floor-to-ceiling windows look over the plaza, which can be incorporated into the indoor/outdoor gatherings so popular in the Sunshine State.

Adjacent to the clubhouse is a state-of-the-art fitness center with expansive windows also overlooking the plaza and green. A business center, computer room, administrative offices and support services also are part of the development.

Code	Division Name	%	S F Cost	Projected
01	General Requirements	7.80	15.02	1,877,161
03	Concrete	24.10	46.41	5,801,534
04	Masonry	5.64	10.86	1,357,691
05	Metals	3.09	5.96	745,012
06	Wood & Plastics	3.45	6.65	831,606
07	Thermal and Moisture	2.36	4.54	567,982
08	Openings	4.94	9.52	1,190,561
09	Finishes	17.40	33.51	4,188,683
10	Specialties	0.98	1.89	236,506
11	Equipment	0.24	0.46	57,388
12	Furnishings	0.20	0.39	48,381
14	Conveying Systems	2.33	4.48	560,072
21	Fire Suppression	1.58	3.05	380,879
22	Plumbing	6.99	13.47	1,683,981
23	HVAC	5.17	9.95	1,244,285
26	Electrical	11.93	22.97	2,871,570
27	Communications	0.42	0.81	100,681
28	Electronic Security	1.38	2.65	330,808
	Total Building Costs	100.00	192.60	24,074,779

COST PER SQUARE FOOT = $192.60

© Copyright 2020. For a more in-depth report on this building or additional case studies contact DC&D @ 800-533-5680, or www.DCD.com

File 77:

In designing this single-family home, porches were placed at each level on the front to capture the views of Chesapeake Bay. A porch from the main level at the rear features a view of the lake and screened areas at both the front and rear, and offers outdoor space that can be used year round.

The first floor of this 2,600-square-foot home features a game room with a pool table and leads out to the rear screened porch. A craft room is set in the front for creative projects and gazing at the bay.

Wormy chestnut hardwood flooring throughout creates warmth not typically captured in new construction. The second floor opens up to the main living space with an open concept kitchen and family room.

The kitchen island includes seating that can be enjoyed by sharing this great space with people in both rooms. A gas fireplace flanked by custom built-ins adds a beautiful architectural feature to the space.

The nine-foot folding door enables the family room to open up and draw in the outdoor space of the massive second floor porch. The master suite, on the second level, includes a spacious bedroom, walk-in closet and bathroom complete with stylish barn doors. The third floor is home to two bedrooms and a loft that leads to the third-floor porch. The design and finishes of this home establish a combination of comfort and sophistication everyone would want in their retirement home.

Code	Division Name	%	S F Cost	Projected
00	Procurement	2.97	7.61	23,833
01	General Requirements	13.63	34.93	109,400
03	Concrete	2.66	6.83	21,390
04	Masonry	2.27	5.82	18,229
06	Wood & Plastics	37.45	95.99	300,634
07	Thermal and Moisture	1.97	5.04	15,790
08	Openings	6.89	17.67	55,333
09	Finishes	12.46	31.95	100,064
11	Equipment	3.87	9.91	31,039
22	Plumbing	5.37	13.76	43,101
23	HVAC	4.48	11.48	35,951
26	Electrical	5.33	13.65	42,760
27	Communications	0.66	1.68	5,275
	Total Building Costs	100.00	256.32	802,798

COST PER SQUARE FOOT = $256.32

© Copyright 2020. For a more in-depth report on this building or additional case studies contact DC&D
@ 800-533-5680, or www.DCD.com

File 78:

A blend of historical correctness and current design is evident in this single-family home located in the Historic Overlay District of Cape Charles, Virginia. All the exterior elements were designed to be consistent with District guidelines.

The traditional front porch is a welcoming sight as you approach the home, complete with a "legacy" bench constructed from the very pecan tree that was cut down to build the house. The second floor media room empties to a space directly over the front door designed to capture the magnificent view of Chesapeake Bay.

As you enter the 2,500-square-foot home you're treated to an open-concept first floor with a vaulted kitchen and dining room, punctuated by a two-story stone fireplace. The family room has two walls of windows offering natural light and the best views possible. The spacious master suite includes a large bedroom with a custom-built master closet. The large barn door leads to a beautifully designed master bath complete with a massive tiled shower and comfortably placed soaking tub. Each are flanked by a "his" and "hers" vanity capped off by a private toilet room.

As you gaze down from the second-floor balcony, you're treated to an expansive view of the kitchen and dining room. This feature offers the volume and atmosphere so important in today's lifestyle. On one side of the balcony is the media room, the site of informal entertaining. On the other side we find two bedrooms with a hall bath conveniently situated between them. This design makes it a perfect place for family to grow or for visiting guests to stay.

The finished home serves as a retirement residence, with enough space for the owners to entertain company and enjoy the unique Cape Charles atmosphere.

Code	Division Name	%	S F Cost	Projected
00	Procurement	3.65	8.89	23,743
01	General Requirements	19.58	47.65	127,309
03	Concrete	1.94	4.71	12,587
04	Masonry	1.94	4.73	12,627
06	Wood & Plastics	23.03	56.05	149,756
07	Thermal and Moisture	4.86	11.83	31,612
08	Openings	5.11	12.44	33,234
09	Finishes	11.53	28.06	74,971
10	Specialties	10.00	24.33	65,022
11	Equipment	2.02	4.92	13,159
12	Furnishings	2.40	5.85	15,643
22	Plumbing	4.91	11.95	31,941
23	HVAC	5.26	12.81	34,228
26	Electrical	3.74	9.11	24,348
	Total Building Costs	100.00	243.33	650,178

COST PER SQUARE FOOT = $243.33

© Copyright 2020. For a more in-depth report on this building or additional case studies contact DC&D
@ 800-533-5680, or www.DCD.com

FILE 79:

Mowery Construction is a cutting-edge construction firm based in Mechanicsburg, Pennsylvania. Mowery was recently challenged with the task of completing its first "Passive House" building. Passive house construction is popular in European countries, and slowly making its way to the United States. Buildings which are built to Passive House design and construction standards can perform anywhere from 75% to 95% more efficiently than conventional buildings built to code. The concept of Passive House is simple: The more airtight the building, the less the HVAC system must work, and the lower the monthly energy bill.

The project's lengthy design process began in 2014. Numerous rounds of mechanical system reviews and changes, architectural detail reviews, and product selection followed. In addition, Mowery worked closely with the design team to estimate and tune the pricing to ensure the final product was as cost effective as possible.

Through close attention to detail, Mowery was able to follow the design flawlessly and execute to the degree that all of Mowery's clients have come to expect. PHIUS, Passive House Institute of United States, performed several air-leakage tests of the building and was shocked to see Windy Hill's results as the lowest ever seen by the PHIUS organization – a truly remarkable feat.

The heating/cooling system consists of four HRV units, one on each floor, which utilize 100% outside air to supply comfortable air temperatures throughout the building. HRVs are complex units which treat the air prior to its distribution to the individual AC/Heating units, allowing the individual units to be smaller and extremely cost effective. This approach, accompanied by highly rated insulation and air leakage control, is what keeps Windy Hill II's monthly energy bill lower than the average building.

The Windy Hill II facility is in the final stages of review through the PHIUS rating company. It is an extremely prestigious and small group. Many buildings do not make it to final stage, but Windy Hill II is there, and Mowery expects the project to join a growing group of Passive House Buildings in America.

Code	Division Name	%	S F Cost	Projected
00	Procurement	4.86	7.44	398,886
01	General Requirements	13.45	20.61	1,104,953
03	Concrete	1.98	3.04	163,126
04	Masonry	3.09	4.73	253,864
05	Metals	0.64	0.98	52,516
06	Wood & Plastics	13.97	21.40	1,147,637
07	Thermal and Moisture	10.30	15.78	846,235
08	Openings	5.05	7.73	414,516
09	Finishes	10.17	15.58	835,336
10	Specialties	1.23	1.88	100,820
11	Equipment	1.49	2.29	123,021
12	Furnishings	0.10	0.16	8,399
14	Conveying Systems	2.91	4.46	239,262
21	Fire Suppression	1.34	2.06	110,547
22	Plumbing	5.09	7.79	417,733
23	HVAC	11.09	16.99	911,030
26	Electrical	13.21	20.24	1,085,477
	Total Building Costs	100.00	153.18	8,213,358

COST PER SQUARE FOOT = $153.18

© Copyright 2020. For a more in-depth report on this building or additional case studies contact DC&D
@ 800-533-5680, or www.DCD.com

FILE 80:

Bringing eighty new units of senior (55+) affordable housing apartments to the edge of downtown, the Eleanor Apartments also brought new life to an underused corner of the city. The apartments include features designed to engage people within the urban environment, and to support and promote healthy living and social interaction. Owner Mercy Housing is committed to a holistic approach, and blends amenities and resident services into its mission of housing vulnerable communities. The project responds by integrating four distinct strategies that are accomplished or reinforced through design and building features:

Encourage Social Interaction, Health and Well-Being: features include a pea patch; open stair; walking route; tall windows for daylight; outdoor and indoor gathering spaces; ground-floor front doors and small gardens; bike storage; and the units are pet-friendly. A small office and exam room on the ground floor accommodates visiting medical professionals, and signage guides residents to wellness opportunities throughout the building.

Inspire Sense of Identity, Pride & Belonging: high quality materials; distinctive colors to help identify buildings and floors; personalized entries; common spaces to encourage interaction, including mail room lobby, fourth-floor deck and spacious community room.

Protect Environment, Conserve Resources: 99.9 kw photovoltaic array; triple-pane windows; durable, solid-surface countertops; rain garden; bus stop; bike storage. These features help the building meet Evergreen Sustainable Development Standards.

Enhance Urban Fabric and Invite Pedestrians: positive street presence on all sides; building respects urban setting by abutting the street at the corner with a commercial-like presence; ground-floor units step back and are elevated with stoops and small fenced front garden. Green edge on opposite side of the building addresses the "drive by" experience; strong corners reinforce character. The building's large lineal mass is articulated to echo the rhythm of a downtown street. Window bays project from the façade and vibrant color is used to emphasize the form and enliven the street. The building brings masonry down to the pedestrian level and provides steel canopies for weather protection and a strong urban feel.

© Copyright 2020. For a more in-depth report on this building or additional case studies contact DC&D @ 800-533-5680, or www.DCD.com

Code	Division Name	%	S F Cost	Projected
00	Bidding Requirements	0.04	0.07	4,982
01	General Requirements	16.42	30.53	2,111,324
03	Concrete	4.23	7.86	543,371
04	Masonry	1.74	3.24	223,998
05	Metals	2.76	5.14	355,336
06	Wood & Plastics	10.53	19.58	1,354,194
07	Thermal & Moisture	7.05	13.10	905,887
08	Doors & Windows	10.54	19.60	1,355,642
09	Finishes	14.00	26.02	1,799,070
10	Specialties	2.38	4.43	306,596
11	Equipment	1.28	2.38	164,843
12	Furnishings	3.16	5.87	406,177
14	Conveying Systems	2.10	3.91	270,386
15	Mechanical	12.39	23.04	1,593,176
16	Electrical	11.37	21.13	1,460,860
	Total Building Costs	100.00	185.91	12,855,843

COST PER SQUARE FOOT = $185.91

© Copyright 2020. For a more in-depth report on this building or additional case studies contact DC&D @ 800-533-5680, or www.DCD.com

Section Two
Unit-In-Place Costs

DATA YOU CAN TRUST

	Unit	Man-Hrs	Material	Labor	Total

01210.01 ALLOWANCES

ALLOWANCES
  Overhead
    $20,000 project

	Unit	Man-Hrs	Material	Labor	Total
Minimum	PCT				15.00
Average	PCT				20.00
Maximum	PCT				40.00

    $100,000 project

	Unit	Man-Hrs	Material	Labor	Total
Minimum	PCT				12.00
Average	PCT				15.00
Maximum	PCT				25.00

    $500,000 project

	Unit	Man-Hrs	Material	Labor	Total
Minimum	PCT				10.00
Average	PCT				12.00
Maximum	PCT				20.00

    $1,000,000 project

	Unit	Man-Hrs	Material	Labor	Total
Minimum	PCT				6.00
Average	PCT				10.00
Maximum	PCT				12.00

    $10,000,000 project

	Unit	Man-Hrs	Material	Labor	Total
Minimum	PCT				1.50
Average	PCT				5.00
Maximum	PCT				8.00

  Profit
    $20,000 project

	Unit	Man-Hrs	Material	Labor	Total
Minimum	PCT				10.00
Average	PCT				15.00
Maximum	PCT				25.00

    $100,000 project

	Unit	Man-Hrs	Material	Labor	Total
Minimum	PCT				10.00
Average	PCT				12.00
Maximum	PCT				20.00

    $500,000 project

	Unit	Man-Hrs	Material	Labor	Total
Minimum	PCT				5.00
Average	PCT				10.00
Maximum	PCT				15.00

    $1,000,000 project

	Unit	Man-Hrs	Material	Labor	Total
Minimum	PCT				3.00
Average	PCT				8.00
Maximum	PCT				15.00

  Professional fees
  Architectural
    $100,000 project

	Unit	Man-Hrs	Material	Labor	Total
Minimum	PCT				5.00
Average	PCT				10.00
Maximum	PCT				20.00

    $500,000 project

	Unit	Man-Hrs	Material	Labor	Total
Minimum	PCT				5.00
Average	PCT				8.00
Maximum	PCT				12.00

    $1,000,000 project

	Unit	Man-Hrs	Material	Labor	Total
Minimum	PCT				3.50
Average	PCT				7.00
Maximum	PCT				10.00

  Structural engineering

	Unit	Man-Hrs	Material	Labor	Total
Minimum	PCT				2.00
Average	PCT				3.00
Maximum	PCT				5.00

  Mechanical engineering

	Unit	Man-Hrs	Material	Labor	Total
Minimum	PCT				4.00
Average	PCT				5.00
Maximum	PCT				15.00

  Electrical engineering

	Unit	Man-Hrs	Material	Labor	Total
Minimum	PCT				3.00
Average	PCT				5.00

	Unit	Man-Hrs	Material	Labor	Total

01210.01 ALLOWANCES (Cont.)

Electrical engineering

Maximum	PCT				12.00

Taxes

Sales tax

Minimum	PCT				4.00
Average	PCT				5.00
Maximum	PCT				10.00

Unemployment

Minimum	PCT				3.00
Average	PCT				6.50
Maximum	PCT				8.00
Social security (FICA)	PCT				7.85

01311.30 FIELD STAFF

FIELD STAFF

Superintendent

Minimum	YEAR				102,115.10
Average	YEAR				127,661.52
Maximum	YEAR				153,347.79

Field engineer

Minimum	YEAR				100,717.88
Average	YEAR				115,601.04
Maximum	YEAR				132,857.79

Foreman

Minimum	YEAR				67,872.31
Average	YEAR				108,544.37
Maximum	YEAR				127,084.16

Bookkeeper/timekeeper

Minimum	YEAR				39,260.73
Average	YEAR				51,269.89
Maximum	YEAR				66,332.67

Watchman

Minimum	YEAR				29,253.09
Average	YEAR				39,132.43
Maximum	YEAR				49,396.67

01321.30 SCHEDULING

SCHEDULING

Scheduling for

$100,000 project

Minimum	PCT				1.02
Average	PCT				2.05
Maximum	PCT				5.12

$500,000 project

Minimum	PCT				0.51
Average	PCT				1.02
Maximum	PCT				2.05

$1,000,000 project

Minimum	PCT				0.34
Average	PCT				0.77
Maximum	PCT				1.53

Scheduling software

Minimum	EA				690.00
Average	EA				3,970.00
Maximum	EA				79,410.00

01322.30 SURVEYING

SURVEYING

Surveying

Small crew	DAY				1,010.00
Average crew	DAY				1,520.00
Large crew	DAY				2,000.00

Lot lines and boundaries

Minimum	ACRE				730.00
Average	ACRE				1,520.00
Maximum	ACRE				2,480.00

© 2020 BNi Publications, Inc.

	Unit	Man-Hrs	Material	Labor	Total

01323.30 JOB REQUIREMENTS

JOB REQUIREMENTS
Job photographs, small jobs

	Unit	Man-Hrs	Material	Labor	Total
Minimum	EA				130.00
Average	EA				200.00
Maximum	EA				460.00

Large projects

	Unit	Man-Hrs	Material	Labor	Total
Minimum	EA				660.00
Average	EA				990.00
Maximum	EA				3,310.00

01452.30 TESTING

TESTING
Testing concrete, per test

	Unit	Man-Hrs	Material	Labor	Total
Minimum	EA				23.50
Average	EA				39.25
Maximum	EA				78.00

Soil, per test

	Unit	Man-Hrs	Material	Labor	Total
Minimum	EA				48.00
Average	EA				120.00
Maximum	EA				320.00

Welding, per test

	Unit	Man-Hrs	Material	Labor	Total
Minimum	EA				23.50
Average	EA				39.25
Maximum	EA				160.00

01521.90 SANITARY FACILITIES

SANITARY FACILITIES
Porta Potty

	Unit	Man-Hrs	Material	Labor	Total
Rental per Day minimum	EA				70.00
Rental per Day Maximum	EA				180.00
Rental per Month minimum	EA				200.00
Rental per Month Maximum	EA				350.00

Specialized, ADA

	Unit	Man-Hrs	Material	Labor	Total
Rental per Day minimum	EA				120.00
Rental per Day Max	EA				180.00
Rental per Month, minimum	EA				350.00
Rental per Month, Maximum	EA				580.00
Purchase prices, minimum	EA				820.00

01540.01 CONSTRUCTION AIDS

CONSTRUCTION AIDS
Scaffolding/staging, rent per month
Measured by lineal feet of base

	Unit	Man-Hrs	Material	Labor	Total
10' high	LF				14.50
20' high	LF				26.50
30' high	LF				37.00
40' high	LF				42.75
50' high	LF				51.00

Measured by square foot of surface

	Unit	Man-Hrs	Material	Labor	Total
Minimum	SF				0.64
Average	SF				1.11
Maximum	SF				1.99

Safety nets, heavy duty, per job

	Unit	Man-Hrs	Material	Labor	Total
Minimum	SF				0.43
Average	SF				0.52
Maximum	SF				1.14

Tarpaulins, fabric, per job

	Unit	Man-Hrs	Material	Labor	Total
Minimum	SF				0.30
Average	SF				0.51
Maximum	SF				1.32

01540.08 MOBILIZATION

MOBILIZATION
Equipment mobilization
Bulldozer

	Unit	Man-Hrs	Material	Labor	Total
Minimum	EA				220.00
Average	EA				460.00

	Unit	Man-Hrs	Material	Labor	Total

01540.08 MOBILIZATION (Cont.)

Bulldozer
Maximum	EA				780.00

Backhoe/front-end loader
Minimum	EA				130.00
Average	EA				230.00
Maximum	EA				510.00

Crane, crawler type
Minimum	EA				2,440.00
Average	EA				6,000.00
Maximum	EA				12,880.00

Truck crane
Minimum	EA				560.00
Average	EA				860.00
Maximum	EA				1,490.00

Pile driving rig
Minimum	EA				11,100.00
Average	EA				22,210.00
Maximum	EA				39,970.00

01540.09 EQUIPMENT

EQUIPMENT
Air compressor
60 cfm
By day	EA				110.00
By week	EA				320.00
By month	EA				980.00

300 cfm
By day	EA				230.00
By week	EA				700.00
By month	EA				2,140.00

600 cfm
By day	EA				620.00
By week	EA				1,860.00
By month	EA				5,630.00

Air tools, per compressor, per day
Minimum	EA				44.50
Average	EA				56.00
Maximum	EA				78.00

Generators, 5 kw
By day	EA				110.00
By week	EA				330.00
By month	EA				1,020.00

Heaters, salamander type, per week
Minimum	EA				130.00
Average	EA				190.00
Maximum	EA				400.00

Pumps, submersible
50 gpm
By day	EA				89.00
By week	EA				270.00
By month	EA				800.00

100 gpm
By day	EA				110.00
By week	EA				330.00
By month	EA				1,000.00

500 gpm
By day	EA				180.00
By week	EA				530.00
By month	EA				1,600.00

Diaphragm pump, by week
Minimum	EA				160.00
Average	EA				270.00
Maximum	EA				550.00

© 2020 BNi Publications, Inc.

	Unit	Man-Hrs	Material	Labor	Total

01540.09 EQUIPMENT (Cont.)

Pickup truck

By day	EA				170.00
By week	EA				490.00
By month	EA				1,510.00

Dump truck

6 c.y. truck

By day	EA				440.00
By week	EA				1,330.00
By month	EA				4,010.00

10 c.y. truck

By day	EA				550.00
By week	EA				1,670.00
By month	EA				5,010.00

16 c.y. truck

By day	EA				890.00
By week	EA				2,670.00
By month	EA				8,020.00

Backhoe, track mounted

1/2 c.y. capacity

By day	EA				910.00
By week	EA				2,780.00
By month	EA				8,240.00

1 c.y. capacity

By day	EA				1,450.00
By week	EA				4,340.00
By month	EA				13,030.00

2 c.y. capacity

By day	EA				2,450.00
By week	EA				7,350.00
By month	EA				22,050.00

3 c.y. capacity

By day	EA				4,680.00
By week	EA				14,030.00
By month	EA				42,100.00

Backhoe/loader, rubber tired

1/2 c.y. capacity

By day	EA				550.00
By week	EA				1,670.00
By month	EA				5,010.00

3/4 c.y. capacity

By day	EA				670.00
By week	EA				2,000.00
By month	EA				6,010.00

Bulldozer

75 hp

By day	EA				780.00
By week	EA				2,340.00
By month	EA				7,020.00

200 hp

By day	EA				2,230.00
By week	EA				6,680.00
By month	EA				20,050.00

400 hp

By day	EA				3,310.00
By week	EA				9,920.00
By month	EA				29,780.00

Cranes, crawler type

15 ton capacity

By day	EA				1,000.00
By week	EA				3,010.00
By month	EA				9,020.00

25 ton capacity

By day	EA				1,220.00
By week	EA				3,670.00

	Unit	Man-Hrs	Material	Labor	Total
01540.09 EQUIPMENT (Cont.)					
25 ton capacity					
By month	EA				11,020.00
50 ton capacity					
By day	EA				2,230.00
By week	EA				6,680.00
By month	EA				20,050.00
100 ton capacity					
By day	EA				3,340.00
By week	EA				10,020.00
By month	EA				30,170.00
Truck mounted, hydraulic					
15 ton capacity					
By day	EA				940.00
By week	EA				2,840.00
By month	EA				8,190.00
Loader, rubber tired					
1 c.y. capacity					
By day	EA				670.00
By week	EA				2,000.00
By month	EA				6,020.00
2 c.y. capacity					
By day	EA				1,000.00
By week	EA				3,900.00
By month	EA				11,690.00
3 c.y. capacity					
By day	EA				1,780.00
By week	EA				5,350.00
By month	EA				16,040.00
01562.30 TEMPORARY FACILITIES					
TEMPORARY FACILITIES					
Barricades, temporary					
Highway					
Concrete	LF	0.080	14.75	5.10	19.85
Wood	LF	0.032	5.10	2.04	7.14
Steel	LF	0.027	5.29	1.70	6.99
Pedestrian barricades					
Plywood	SF	0.027	4.54	1.70	6.24
Chain link fence	SF	0.027	3.85	1.70	5.55
Trailers, general office type, per month					
Minimum	EA				250.00
Average	EA				410.00
Maximum	EA				820.00
Crew change trailers, per month					
Minimum	EA				150.00
Average	EA				160.00
Maximum	EA				250.00
01581.30 SIGNS					
SIGNS					
Construction signs, temporary					
Signs, 2' x 4'					
Minimum	EA				41.75
Average	EA				100.00
Maximum	EA				350.00
Signs, 4' x 8'					
Minimum	EA				88.00
Average	EA				230.00
Maximum	EA				980.00
Signs, 8' x 8'					
Minimum	EA				110.00
Average	EA				350.00
Maximum	EA				3,540.00

© 2020 BNi Publications, Inc.

	Unit	Man-Hrs	Material	Labor	Total

01783.30 BONDS

BONDS
Performance bonds

	Unit	Man-Hrs	Material	Labor	Total
Minimum	PCT				0.62
Average	PCT				1.93
Maximum	PCT				3.07

	Unit	Man-Hrs	Material	Labor	Total
02321.30 SOIL BORING					
SOIL BORING					
Borings, uncased, stable earth					
2-1/2" dia.					
Minimum	LF	0.200		23.75	23.75
Average	LF	0.300		35.75	35.75
Maximum	LF	0.480		57.00	57.00
4" dia.					
Minimum	LF	0.218		26.00	26.00
Average	LF	0.343		40.75	40.75
Maximum	LF	0.600		71.00	71.00
Cased, including samples					
2-1/2" dia.					
Minimum	LF	0.240		28.50	28.50
Average	LF	0.400		47.50	47.50
Maximum	LF	0.800		95.00	95.00
4" dia.					
Minimum	LF	0.480		57.00	57.00
Average	LF	0.686		81.00	81.00
Maximum	LF	0.960		110.00	110.00
Drilling in rock					
No sampling					
Minimum	LF	0.436		52.00	52.00
Average	LF	0.632		75.00	75.00
Maximum	LF	0.857		100.00	100.00
With casing and sampling					
Minimum	LF	0.600		71.00	71.00
Average	LF	0.800		95.00	95.00
Maximum	LF	1.200		140.00	140.00
Test pits					
Light soil					
Minimum	EA	3.000		360.00	360.00
Average	EA	4.000		480.00	480.00
Maximum	EA	8.000		950.00	950.00
Heavy soil					
Minimum	EA	4.800		570.00	570.00
Average	EA	6.000		710.00	710.00
Maximum	EA	12.000		1,430.00	1,430.00
02411.31 CATCH BASIN / MANHOLE DEMOLITION					
CATCH BASIN / MANHOLE DEMOLITION					
Abandon catch basin or manhole (fill with sand)					
Minimum	EA	3.000		360.00	360.00
Average	EA	4.800		570.00	570.00
Maximum	EA	8.000		950.00	950.00
Remove and reset frame and cover					
Minimum	EA	1.600		190.00	190.00
Average	EA	2.400		290.00	290.00
Maximum	EA	4.000		480.00	480.00
Remove catch basin, to 10' deep					
Masonry					
Minimum	EA	4.800		570.00	570.00
Average	EA	6.000		710.00	710.00
Maximum	EA	8.000		950.00	950.00
Concrete					
Minimum	EA	6.000		710.00	710.00
Average	EA	8.000		950.00	950.00
Maximum	EA	9.600		1,140.00	1,140.00
02411.32 FENCE DEMOLITION					
FENCE DEMOLITION					
Remove fencing					
Chain link, 8' high					
For disposal	LF	0.040		2.55	2.55
For reuse	LF	0.100		6.38	6.38

© 2020 BNi Publications, Inc.

	Unit	Man-Hrs	Material	Labor	Total
02411.32 FENCE DEMOLITION (Cont.)					
Remove fencing					
Wood					
4' high	SF	0.027		1.70	1.70
6' high	SF	0.032		2.04	2.04
8' high	SF	0.040		2.55	2.55
Masonry					
8" thick					
4' high	SF	0.080		5.10	5.10
6' high	SF	0.100		6.38	6.38
8' high	SF	0.114		7.29	7.29
12" thick					
4' high	SF	0.133		8.51	8.51
6' high	SF	0.160		10.25	10.25
8' high	SF	0.200		12.75	12.75
12' high	SF	0.267		17.00	17.00
02411.33 CURB & GUTTER DEMOLITION					
CURB & GUTTER DEMOLITION					
Curb removal					
Concrete, unreinforced					
Minimum	LF	0.048		5.70	5.70
Average	LF	0.060		7.12	7.12
Maximum	LF	0.075		8.90	8.90
Reinforced					
Minimum	LF	0.077		9.19	9.19
Average	LF	0.086		10.25	10.25
Maximum	LF	0.096		11.50	11.50
Combination curb and 2' gutter					
Unreinforced					
Minimum	LF	0.063		7.50	7.50
Average	LF	0.083		9.82	9.82
Maximum	LF	0.120		14.25	14.25
Reinforced					
Minimum	LF	0.100		11.75	11.75
Average	LF	0.133		15.75	15.75
Maximum	LF	0.240		28.50	28.50
Granite curb					
Minimum	LF	0.069		8.14	8.14
Average	LF	0.080		9.50	9.50
Maximum	LF	0.092		11.00	11.00
Asphalt curb					
Minimum	LF	0.040		4.75	4.75
Average	LF	0.048		5.70	5.70
Maximum	LF	0.057		6.78	6.78
02421.32 GUARDRAIL DEMOLITION					
GUARDRAIL DEMOLITION					
Remove standard guardrail					
Steel					
Minimum	LF	0.060		7.12	7.12
Average	LF	0.080		9.50	9.50
Maximum	LF	0.120		14.25	14.25
Wood					
Minimum	LF	0.052		6.19	6.19
Average	LF	0.062		7.30	7.30
Maximum	LF	0.100		11.75	11.75
02431.33 HYDRANT DEMOLITION					
HYDRANT DEMOLITION					
Remove fire hydrant					
Minimum	EA	3.000		360.00	360.00
Average	EA	4.000		480.00	480.00
Maximum	EA	6.000		710.00	710.00
Remove and reset fire hydrant					
Minimum	EA	8.000		950.00	950.00
Average	EA	12.000		1,430.00	1,430.00
Maximum	EA	24.000		2,850.00	2,850.00

	Unit	Man-Hrs	Material	Labor	Total

02441.34 PAVEMENT AND SIDEWALK DEMOLITION

PAVEMENT AND SIDEWALK DEMOLITION

Bituminous pavement, up to 3" thick

On streets

	Unit	Man-Hrs	Material	Labor	Total
Minimum	SY	0.069		8.14	8.14
Average	SY	0.096		11.50	11.50
Maximum	SY	0.160		19.00	19.00

On pipe trench

	Unit	Man-Hrs	Material	Labor	Total
Minimum	SY	0.096		11.50	11.50
Average	SY	0.120		14.25	14.25
Maximum	SY	0.240		28.50	28.50

Concrete pavement, 6" thick

No reinforcement

	Unit	Man-Hrs	Material	Labor	Total
Minimum	SY	0.120		14.25	14.25
Average	SY	0.160		19.00	19.00
Maximum	SY	0.240		28.50	28.50

With wire mesh

	Unit	Man-Hrs	Material	Labor	Total
Minimum	SY	0.185		22.00	22.00
Average	SY	0.240		28.50	28.50
Maximum	SY	0.300		35.75	35.75

With rebars

	Unit	Man-Hrs	Material	Labor	Total
Minimum	SY	0.240		28.50	28.50
Average	SY	0.300		35.75	35.75
Maximum	SY	0.400		47.50	47.50

9" thick

No reinforcement

	Unit	Man-Hrs	Material	Labor	Total
Minimum	SY	0.160		19.00	19.00
Average	SY	0.200		23.75	23.75
Maximum	SY	0.240		28.50	28.50

With wire mesh

	Unit	Man-Hrs	Material	Labor	Total
Minimum	SY	0.253		30.00	30.00
Average	SY	0.300		35.75	35.75
Maximum	SY	0.369		43.75	43.75

With rebars

	Unit	Man-Hrs	Material	Labor	Total
Minimum	SY	0.320		38.00	38.00
Average	SY	0.400		47.50	47.50
Maximum	SY	0.533		63.00	63.00

12" thick

No reinforcement

	Unit	Man-Hrs	Material	Labor	Total
Minimum	SY	0.200		23.75	23.75
Average	SY	0.240		28.50	28.50
Maximum	SY	0.300		35.75	35.75

With wire mesh

	Unit	Man-Hrs	Material	Labor	Total
Minimum	SY	0.282		33.50	33.50
Average	SY	0.343		40.75	40.75
Maximum	SY	0.436		52.00	52.00

With rebars

	Unit	Man-Hrs	Material	Labor	Total
Minimum	SY	0.400		47.50	47.50
Average	SY	0.480		57.00	57.00
Maximum	SY	0.600		71.00	71.00

Sidewalk, 4" thick, with disposal

	Unit	Man-Hrs	Material	Labor	Total
Minimum	SY	0.057		6.78	6.78
Average	SY	0.080		9.50	9.50
Maximum	SY	0.114		13.50	13.50

Removal of pavement markings by waterblasting

	Unit	Man-Hrs	Material	Labor	Total
Minimum	SF	0.003		0.21	0.21
Average	SF	0.004		0.25	0.25
Maximum	SF	0.008		0.51	0.51

02451.34 DRAINAGE PIPING DEMOLITION

DRAINAGE PIPING DEMOLITION

Remove drainage pipe, not including excavation

12" dia.

	Unit	Man-Hrs	Material	Labor	Total
Minimum	LF	0.080		9.50	9.50
Average	LF	0.100		11.75	11.75
Maximum	LF	0.126		15.00	15.00

© 2020 BNi Publications, Inc.

	Unit	Man-Hrs	Material	Labor	Total

02451.34 DRAINAGE PIPING DEMOLITION (Cont.)

Remove drainage pipe, not including excavation

18" dia.
Minimum	LF	0.109		13.00	13.00
Average	LF	0.126		15.00	15.00
Maximum	LF	0.160		19.00	19.00

24" dia.
Minimum	LF	0.133		15.75	15.75
Average	LF	0.160		19.00	19.00
Maximum	LF	0.200		23.75	23.75

36" dia.
Minimum	LF	0.160		19.00	19.00
Average	LF	0.200		23.75	23.75
Maximum	LF	0.253		30.00	30.00

02461.34 GAS PIPING DEMOLITION

GAS PIPING DEMOLITION

Remove welded steel pipe, not including excavation

4" dia.
Minimum	LF	0.120		14.25	14.25
Average	LF	0.150		17.75	17.75
Maximum	LF	0.200		23.75	23.75

5" dia.
Minimum	LF	0.200		23.75	23.75
Average	LF	0.240		28.50	28.50
Maximum	LF	0.300		35.75	35.75

6" dia.
Minimum	LF	0.253		30.00	30.00
Average	LF	0.300		35.75	35.75
Maximum	LF	0.400		47.50	47.50

8" dia.
Minimum	LF	0.369		43.75	43.75
Average	LF	0.480		57.00	57.00
Maximum	LF	0.632		75.00	75.00

10" dia.
Minimum	LF	0.480		57.00	57.00
Average	LF	0.600		71.00	71.00
Maximum	LF	0.800		95.00	95.00

02471.34 SANITARY PIPING DEMOLITION

SANITARY PIPING DEMOLITION

Remove sewer pipe, not including excavation

4" dia.
Minimum	LF	0.067		7.91	7.91
Average	LF	0.096		11.50	11.50
Maximum	LF	0.160		19.00	19.00

6" dia.
Minimum	LF	0.075		8.90	8.90
Average	LF	0.109		13.00	13.00
Maximum	LF	0.200		23.75	23.75

8" dia.
Minimum	LF	0.080		9.50	9.50
Average	LF	0.120		14.25	14.25
Maximum	LF	0.240		28.50	28.50

10" dia.
Minimum	LF	0.086		10.25	10.25
Average	LF	0.126		15.00	15.00
Maximum	LF	0.267		31.75	31.75

12" dia.
Minimum	LF	0.092		11.00	11.00
Average	LF	0.133		15.75	15.75
Maximum	LF	0.300		35.75	35.75

15" dia.
Minimum	LF	0.100		11.75	11.75
Average	LF	0.141		16.75	16.75
Maximum	LF	0.343		40.75	40.75

	Unit	Man-Hrs	Material	Labor	Total

02471.34 SANITARY PIPING DEMOLITION (Cont.)

Remove sewer pipe, not including excavation

18" dia.

	Unit	Man-Hrs	Material	Labor	Total
Minimum	LF	0.109		13.00	13.00
Average	LF	0.160		19.00	19.00
Maximum	LF	0.400		47.50	47.50

24" dia.

Minimum	LF	0.120		14.25	14.25
Average	LF	0.200		23.75	23.75
Maximum	LF	0.480		57.00	57.00

30" dia.

Minimum	LF	0.133		15.75	15.75
Average	LF	0.240		28.50	28.50
Maximum	LF	0.600		71.00	71.00

36" dia.

Minimum	LF	0.160		19.00	19.00
Average	LF	0.300		35.75	35.75
Maximum	LF	0.800		95.00	95.00

02481.34 WATER PIPING DEMOLITION

WATER PIPING DEMOLITION

Remove water pipe, not including excavation

4" dia.

	Unit	Man-Hrs	Material	Labor	Total
Minimum	LF	0.096		11.50	11.50
Average	LF	0.109		13.00	13.00
Maximum	LF	0.126		15.00	15.00

6" dia.

Minimum	LF	0.100		11.75	11.75
Average	LF	0.114		13.50	13.50
Maximum	LF	0.133		15.75	15.75

8" dia.

Minimum	LF	0.109		13.00	13.00
Average	LF	0.126		15.00	15.00
Maximum	LF	0.150		17.75	17.75

10" dia.

Minimum	LF	0.114		13.50	13.50
Average	LF	0.133		15.75	15.75
Maximum	LF	0.160		19.00	19.00

12" dia.

Minimum	LF	0.120		14.25	14.25
Average	LF	0.141		16.75	16.75
Maximum	LF	0.171		20.25	20.25

14" dia.

Minimum	LF	0.126		15.00	15.00
Average	LF	0.150		17.75	17.75
Maximum	LF	0.185		22.00	22.00

16" dia.

Minimum	LF	0.133		15.75	15.75
Average	LF	0.160		19.00	19.00
Maximum	LF	0.200		23.75	23.75

18" dia.

Minimum	LF	0.141		16.75	16.75
Average	LF	0.171		20.25	20.25
Maximum	LF	0.218		26.00	26.00

20" dia.

Minimum	LF	0.150		17.75	17.75
Average	LF	0.185		22.00	22.00
Maximum	LF	0.240		28.50	28.50

Remove valves

6"	EA	1.200		140.00	140.00
10"	EA	1.333		160.00	160.00
14"	EA	1.500		180.00	180.00
18"	EA	2.000		240.00	240.00

© 2020 BNi Publications, Inc.

	Unit	Man-Hrs	Material	Labor	Total
02491.35 SAW CUTTING PAVEMENT					
SAW CUTTING PAVEMENT					
Pavement, bituminous					
2" thick	LF	0.016		2.21	2.21
3" thick	LF	0.020		2.76	2.76
4" thick	LF	0.025		3.40	3.40
5" thick	LF	0.027		3.68	3.68
6" thick	LF	0.029		3.95	3.95
Concrete pavement, with wire mesh					
4" thick	LF	0.031		4.25	4.25
5" thick	LF	0.033		4.61	4.61
6" thick	LF	0.036		5.03	5.03
8" thick	LF	0.040		5.53	5.53
10" thick	LF	0.044		6.14	6.14
Plain concrete, unreinforced					
4" thick	LF	0.027		3.68	3.68
5" thick	LF	0.031		4.25	4.25
6" thick	LF	0.033		4.61	4.61
8" thick	LF	0.036		5.03	5.03
10" thick	LF	0.040		5.53	5.53
02492.98 WALL, EXTERIOR, DEMOLITION					
WALL, EXTERIOR, DEMOLITION					
Concrete wall					
Light reinforcing					
6" thick	SF	0.120		14.25	14.25
8" thick	SF	0.126		15.00	15.00
10" thick	SF	0.133		15.75	15.75
12" thick	SF	0.150		17.75	17.75
Medium reinforcing					
6" thick	SF	0.126		15.00	15.00
8" thick	SF	0.133		15.75	15.75
10" thick	SF	0.150		17.75	17.75
12" thick	SF	0.171		20.25	20.25
Heavy reinforcing					
6" thick	SF	0.141		16.75	16.75
8" thick	SF	0.150		17.75	17.75
10" thick	SF	0.171		20.25	20.25
12" thick	SF	0.200		23.75	23.75
Masonry					
No reinforcing					
8" thick	SF	0.053		6.33	6.33
12" thick	SF	0.060		7.12	7.12
16" thick	SF	0.069		8.14	8.14
Horizontal reinforcing					
8" thick	SF	0.060		7.12	7.12
12" thick	SF	0.065		7.70	7.70
16" thick	SF	0.077		9.19	9.19
Vertical reinforcing					
8" thick	SF	0.077		9.19	9.19
12" thick	SF	0.089		10.50	10.50
16" thick	SF	0.109		13.00	13.00
Remove concrete headwall					
15" pipe	EA	1.714		200.00	200.00
18" pipe	EA	2.000		240.00	240.00
24" pipe	EA	2.182		260.00	260.00
30" pipe	EA	2.400		290.00	290.00
36" pipe	EA	2.667		320.00	320.00
48" pipe	EA	3.429		410.00	410.00
60" pipe	EA	4.800		570.00	570.00
02510.61 COMPLETE BUILDING DEMOLITION					
COMPLETE BUILDING DEMOLITION					
Building, complete with disposal					
Wood frame	CF	0.003		0.41	0.41
Concrete	CF	0.004		0.61	0.61
Steel frame	CF	0.005		0.82	0.82

DIVISION 02 SITE CONSTRUCTION

	Unit	Man-Hrs	Material	Labor	Total

02511.90 SELECTIVE BUILDING DEMOLITION

SELECTIVE BUILDING DEMOLITION
Partition removal
Concrete block partitions

	Unit	Man-Hrs	Material	Labor	Total
4" thick	SF	0.040		2.55	2.55
8" thick	SF	0.053		3.40	3.40
12" thick	SF	0.073		4.64	4.64

Brick masonry partitions

4" thick	SF	0.040		2.55	2.55
8" thick	SF	0.050		3.19	3.19
12" thick	SF	0.067		4.25	4.25
16" thick	SF	0.100		6.38	6.38

Cast-in-place concrete partitions
Unreinforced

6" thick	SF	0.160		19.00	19.00
8" thick	SF	0.171		20.25	20.25
10" thick	SF	0.200		23.75	23.75
12" thick	SF	0.240		28.50	28.50

Reinforced

6" thick	SF	0.185		22.00	22.00
8" thick	SF	0.240		28.50	28.50
10" thick	SF	0.267		31.75	31.75
12" thick	SF	0.320		38.00	38.00

Terra cotta

To 6" thick	SF	0.040		2.55	2.55

Stud partitions

Metal or wood, with drywall both sides	SF	0.040		2.55	2.55
Metal studs, both sides, lath and plaster	SF	0.053		3.40	3.40

Door and frame removal
Hollow metal in masonry wall
Single

2'6"x6'8"	EA	1.000		64.00	64.00
3'x7'	EA	1.333		85.00	85.00

Double

3'x7'	EA	1.600		100.00	100.00
4'x8'	EA	1.600		100.00	100.00

Wood in framed wall
Single

2'6"x6'8"	EA	0.571		36.50	36.50
3'x6'8"	EA	0.667		42.50	42.50

Double

2'6"x6'8"	EA	0.800		51.00	51.00
3'x6'8"	EA	0.889		57.00	57.00

Remove for re-use

Hollow metal	EA	2.000		130.00	130.00
Wood	EA	1.333		85.00	85.00

Floor removal

Brick flooring	SF	0.032		2.04	2.04
Ceramic or quarry tile	SF	0.018		1.13	1.13
Terrazzo	SF	0.036		2.27	2.27
Heavy wood	SF	0.021		1.36	1.36
Residential wood	SF	0.023		1.45	1.45
Resilient tile or linoleum	SF	0.008		0.51	0.51

Ceiling removal
Acoustical tile ceiling

Adhesive fastened	SF	0.008		0.51	0.51
Furred and glued	SF	0.007		0.42	0.42
Suspended grid	SF	0.005		0.31	0.31

Drywall ceiling

Furred and nailed	SF	0.009		0.56	0.56
Nailed to framing	SF	0.008		0.51	0.51

Plastered ceiling

Furred on framing	SF	0.020		1.27	1.27
Suspended system	SF	0.027		1.70	1.70

© 2020 BNi Publications, Inc.

	Unit	Man-Hrs	Material	Labor	Total

02511.90 SELECTIVE BUILDING DEMOLITION (Cont.)

	Unit	Man-Hrs	Material	Labor	Total
Roofing removal					
Steel frame					
Corrugated metal roofing	SF	0.016		1.02	1.02
Built-up roof on metal deck	SF	0.027		1.70	1.70
Wood frame					
Built-up roof on wood deck	SF	0.025		1.57	1.57
Roof shingles	SF	0.013		0.85	0.85
Roof tiles	SF	0.027		1.70	1.70
Concrete frame	CF	0.053		3.40	3.40
Concrete plank	SF	0.040		2.55	2.55
Built-up roof on concrete	SF	0.023		1.45	1.45
Cut-outs					
Concrete, elevated slabs, mesh reinforcing					
Under 5 cf	CF	0.800		51.00	51.00
Over 5 cf	CF	0.667		42.50	42.50
Bar reinforcing					
Under 5 cf	CF	1.333		85.00	85.00
Over 5 cf	CF	1.000		64.00	64.00
Window removal					
Metal windows, trim included					
2'x3'	EA	0.800		51.00	51.00
2'x4'	EA	0.889		57.00	57.00
2'x6'	EA	1.000		64.00	64.00
3'x4'	EA	1.000		64.00	64.00
3'x6'	EA	1.143		73.00	73.00
3'x8'	EA	1.333		85.00	85.00
4'x4'	EA	1.333		85.00	85.00
4'x6'	EA	1.600		100.00	100.00
4'x8'	EA	2.000		130.00	130.00
Wood windows, trim included					
2'x3'	EA	0.444		28.25	28.25
2'x4'	EA	0.471		30.00	30.00
2'x6'	EA	0.500		32.00	32.00
3'x4'	EA	0.533		34.00	34.00
3'x6'	EA	0.571		36.50	36.50
3'x8'	EA	0.615		39.25	39.25
6'x4'	EA	0.667		42.50	42.50
6'x6'	EA	0.727		46.50	46.50
6'x8'	EA	0.800		51.00	51.00
Walls, concrete, bar reinforcing					
Small jobs	CF	0.533		34.00	34.00
Large jobs	CF	0.444		28.25	28.25
Brick walls, not including toothing					
4" thick	SF	0.040		2.55	2.55
8" thick	SF	0.050		3.19	3.19
12" thick	SF	0.067		4.25	4.25
16" thick	SF	0.100		6.38	6.38
Concrete block walls, not including toothing					
4" thick	SF	0.044		2.83	2.83
6" thick	SF	0.047		3.00	3.00
8" thick	SF	0.050		3.19	3.19
10" thick	SF	0.057		3.64	3.64
12" thick	SF	0.067		4.25	4.25
Rubbish handling					
Load in dumpster or truck					
Minimum	CF	0.018		1.13	1.13
Maximum	CF	0.027		1.70	1.70
For use of elevators, add					
Minimum	CF	0.004		0.25	0.25
Maximum	CF	0.008		0.51	0.51
Rubbish hauling					
Hand loaded on trucks, 2 mile trip	CY	0.320		44.25	44.25
Machine loaded on trucks, 2 mile trip	CY	0.240		28.50	28.50

	Unit	Man-Hrs	Material	Labor	Total
02650.06 UNDERGROUND STORAGE TANK REMOVAL					
UNDERGROUND STORAGE TANK REMOVAL					
Remove underground storage tank, and backfill					
50 to 250 gals	EA	8.000		950.00	950.00
600 gals	EA	8.000		950.00	950.00
1000 gals	EA	12.000		1,430.00	1,430.00
4000 gals	EA	19.200		2,280.00	2,280.00
5000 gals	EA	19.200		2,280.00	2,280.00
10,000 gals	EA	32.000		3,800.00	3,800.00
12,000 gals	EA	40.000		4,750.00	4,750.00
15,000 gals	EA	48.000		5,700.00	5,700.00
20,000 gals	EA	60.000		7,130.00	7,130.00
02650.07 SEPTIC TANK REMOVAL					
SEPTIC TANK REMOVAL					
Remove septic tank					
1000 gals	EA	2.000		240.00	240.00
2000 gals	EA	2.400		290.00	290.00
5000 gals	EA	3.000		360.00	360.00
15,000 gals	EA	24.000		2,850.00	2,850.00
25,000 gals	EA	32.000		3,800.00	3,800.00
40,000 gals	EA	48.000		5,700.00	5,700.00
02820.01 ASBESTOS REMOVAL					
ASBESTOS REMOVAL					
Enclosure using wood studs & poly, install & remove	SF	0.020	530.00	1.27	531.27
Trailer (change room)	DAY				120.00
Disposal suits (4 suits per man day)	DAY				47.00
Type C respirator mask, includes hose & filters, per man	DAY				23.50
Respirator mask & filter, light contamination	DAY				9.39
Air monitoring test, 12 tests per day					
Off job testing	DAY				1,230.00
On the job testing	DAY				1,640.00
Asbestos vacuum with attachments	EA				710.00
Hydraspray piston pump	EA				950.00
Negative air pressure system	EA				950.00
Grade D breathing air equipment	EA				2,140.00
Glove bag, 44" x 60" x 6 mil plastic	EA				6.90
40 CY asbestos dumpster					
Weekly rental	EA				800.00
Pick up/delivery	EA				360.00
Asbestos dump fee	EA				230.00
02820.02 DUCT INSULATION REMOVAL					
DUCT INSULATION REMOVAL					
Remove duct insulation, duct size					
6" x 12"	LF	0.044	240.00	2.83	242.83
x 18"	LF	0.062	180.00	3.92	183.92
x 24"	LF	0.089	120.00	5.67	125.67
8" x 12"	LF	0.067	160.00	4.25	164.25
x 18"	LF	0.073	150.00	4.64	154.64
x 24"	LF	0.100	110.00	6.38	116.38
12" x 12"	LF	0.067	160.00	4.25	164.25
x 18"	LF	0.089	120.00	5.67	125.67
x 24"	LF	0.114	96.00	7.29	103.29
02820.03 PIPE INSULATION REMOVAL					
PIPE INSULATION REMOVAL					
Removal, asbestos insulation					
2" thick, pipe					
1" to 3" dia.	LF	0.067		4.25	4.25
4" to 6" dia.	LF	0.076		4.86	4.86
3" thick					
7" to 8" dia.	LF	0.080		5.10	5.10
9" to 10" dia.	LF	0.084		5.37	5.37
11" to 12" dia.	LF	0.089		5.67	5.67
13" to 14" dia.	LF	0.094		6.00	6.00
15" to 18" dia.	LF	0.100		6.38	6.38

	Unit	Man-Hrs	Material	Labor	Total
03013.01 CONCRETE REPAIR					
CONCRETE REPAIR					
Epoxy grout floor patch, 1/4" thick	SF	0.080	8.89	5.10	13.99
Grout, epoxy, 2 component system	CF				430.00
Epoxy sand	BAG				29.00
Epoxy modifier	GAL				190.00
Epoxy gel grout	SF	0.800	4.32	51.00	55.32
Injection valve, 1 way, threaded plastic	EA	0.160	12.00	10.25	22.25
Grout crack seal, 2 component	CF	0.800	1,000.00	51.00	1,051.00
Grout, non-shrink	CF	0.800	100.00	51.00	151.00
Concrete, epoxy modified					
Sand mix	CF	0.320	160.00	20.50	180.50
Gravel mix	CF	0.296	110.00	19.00	129.00
Concrete repair					
Soffit repair					
16" wide	LF	0.160	5.07	10.25	15.32
18" wide	LF	0.167	5.39	10.75	16.14
24" wide	LF	0.178	6.44	11.25	17.69
30" wide	LF	0.190	7.25	12.25	19.50
32" wide	LF	0.200	7.73	12.75	20.48
Edge repair					
2" spall	LF	0.200	2.41	12.75	15.16
3" spall	LF	0.211	2.41	13.50	15.91
4" spall	LF	0.216	2.57	13.75	16.32
6" spall	LF	0.222	2.66	14.25	16.91
8" spall	LF	0.235	2.82	15.00	17.82
9" spall	LF	0.267	2.89	17.00	19.89
Crack repair, 1/8" crack	LF	0.080	4.75	5.10	9.85
Reinforcing steel repair					
1 bar, 4 ft					
#4 bar	LF	0.100	0.74	8.32	9.06
#5 bar	LF	0.100	1.00	8.32	9.32
#6 bar	LF	0.107	1.22	8.88	10.10
#8 bar	LF	0.107	2.22	8.88	11.10
#9 bar	LF	0.114	2.83	9.51	12.34
#11 bar	LF	0.114	4.43	9.51	13.94
Form fabric, nylon					
18" diameter	LF				19.25
20" diameter	LF				19.50
24" diameter	LF				32.00
30" diameter	LF				32.75
36" diameter	LF				37.75
Pile repairs					
Polyethylene wrap					
30 mil thick					
60" wide	SF	0.267	20.75	17.00	37.75
72" wide	SF	0.320	22.75	20.50	43.25
60 mil thick					
60" wide	SF	0.267	24.50	17.00	41.50
80" wide	SF	0.364	28.50	23.25	51.75
Pile spall, average repair 3'					
18" x 18"	EA	0.667	64.00	42.50	106.50
20" x 20"	EA	0.800	85.00	51.00	136.00
03100.30 FORMWORK ACCESSORIES					
FORMWORK ACCESSORIES					
Column clamps					
Small, adjustable, 24"x24"	EA				87.00
Medium 36"x36"	EA				90.00
Large 60"x60"	EA				91.00
Forming hangers					
Iron 14 ga.	EA				2.81
22 ga.	EA				2.81
Snap ties					
Short-end with washers, 6" long	EA				1.73
12" long	EA				1.96

	Unit	Man-Hrs	Material	Labor	Total
03100.30 FORMWORK ACCESSORIES (Cont.)					
Short-end with washers, 6" long					
18" long	EA				2.34
24" long	EA				2.52
Long-end with washers, 6' long	EA				2.04
12" long	EA				2.26
18" long	EA				2.56
24" long	EA				2.87
Stakes					
Round, pre-drilled holes, 12" long	EA				6.14
18" long	EA				6.87
24" long	EA				8.90
30" long	EA				11.50
36" long	EA				13.75
48" long	EA				18.50
I beam type, 12" long	EA				5.05
18" long	EA				5.75
24" long	EA				8.73
30" long	EA				10.25
36" long	EA				13.00
48" long	EA				16.25
Taper ties					
50K, 1-1/4" to 1", 35" long	EA				85.00
45" long	EA				140.00
55" long	EA				170.00
Walers					
5" deep, 4' long	EA				240.00
8' long	EA				310.00
12' long	EA				510.00
16' long	EA				660.00
8" deep, 4' long	EA				320.00
8' long	EA				580.00
12' long	EA				840.00
16' long	EA				1,330.00
03111.30 BEAM FORMWORK					
BEAM FORMWORK					
Beam forms, job built					
Beam bottoms					
1 use	SF	0.133	5.27	10.75	16.02
2 uses	SF	0.127	3.10	10.25	13.35
3 uses	SF	0.123	2.38	10.00	12.38
4 uses	SF	0.118	1.97	9.59	11.56
5 uses	SF	0.114	1.80	9.32	11.12
Beam sides					
1 use	SF	0.089	3.77	7.24	11.01
2 uses	SF	0.084	2.24	6.86	9.10
3 uses	SF	0.080	1.97	6.52	8.49
4 uses	SF	0.076	1.81	6.21	8.02
5 uses	SF	0.073	1.60	5.93	7.53
03111.31 BOX CULVERT FORMWORK					
BOX CULVERT FORMWORK					
Box culverts, job built					
6' x 6'					
1 use	SF	0.080	3.84	6.52	10.36
2 uses	SF	0.076	2.09	6.21	8.30
3 uses	SF	0.073	1.74	5.93	7.67
4 uses	SF	0.070	1.47	5.67	7.14
5 uses	SF	0.067	1.28	5.43	6.71
8' x 12'					
1 use	SF	0.067	3.84	5.43	9.27
2 uses	SF	0.064	2.09	5.21	7.30
3 uses	SF	0.062	1.74	5.01	6.75
4 uses	SF	0.059	1.47	4.83	6.30
5 uses	SF	0.057	1.28	4.66	5.94

	Unit	Man-Hrs	Material	Labor	Total
03111.32 COLUMN FORMWORK					
COLUMN FORMWORK					
Column, square forms, job built					
8" x 8" columns					
1 use	SF	0.160	4.44	13.00	17.44
2 uses	SF	0.154	2.39	12.50	14.89
3 uses	SF	0.148	2.02	12.00	14.02
4 uses	SF	0.143	1.84	11.75	13.59
5 uses	SF	0.138	1.57	11.25	12.82
12" x 12" columns					
1 use	SF	0.145	4.05	11.75	15.80
2 uses	SF	0.140	2.25	11.50	13.75
3 uses	SF	0.136	1.80	11.00	12.80
4 uses	SF	0.131	1.57	10.75	12.32
5 uses	SF	0.127	1.32	10.25	11.57
16" x 16" columns					
1 use	SF	0.133	3.86	10.75	14.61
2 uses	SF	0.129	2.03	10.50	12.53
3 uses	SF	0.125	1.63	10.25	11.88
4 uses	SF	0.121	1.49	9.88	11.37
5 uses	SF	0.118	1.22	9.59	10.81
24" x 24" columns					
1 use	SF	0.123	3.86	10.00	13.86
2 uses	SF	0.119	1.80	9.73	11.53
3 uses	SF	0.116	1.50	9.45	10.95
4 uses	SF	0.113	1.22	9.18	10.40
5 uses	SF	0.110	1.12	8.93	10.05
36" x 36" columns					
1 use	SF	0.114	3.89	9.32	13.21
2 uses	SF	0.111	1.82	9.06	10.88
3 uses	SF	0.108	1.50	8.81	10.31
4 uses	SF	0.105	1.29	8.58	9.87
5 uses	SF	0.103	1.20	8.36	9.56
Round fiber forms, 1 use					
10" dia.	LF	0.160	5.79	13.00	18.79
12" dia.	LF	0.163	7.13	13.25	20.38
14" dia.	LF	0.170	9.36	14.00	23.36
16" dia.	LF	0.178	12.25	14.50	26.75
18" dia.	LF	0.190	20.00	15.50	35.50
24" dia.	LF	0.205	24.50	16.75	41.25
30" dia.	LF	0.222	36.75	18.00	54.75
36" dia.	LF	0.242	45.75	19.75	65.50
42" dia.	LF	0.267	83.00	21.75	104.75
03111.33 CURB FORMWORK					
CURB FORMWORK					
Curb forms					
Straight, 6" high					
1 use	LF	0.080	2.64	6.52	9.16
2 uses	LF	0.076	1.58	6.21	7.79
3 uses	LF	0.073	1.19	5.93	7.12
4 uses	LF	0.070	1.06	5.67	6.73
5 uses	LF	0.067	0.97	5.43	6.40
Curved, 6" high					
1 use	LF	0.100	2.86	8.15	11.01
2 uses	LF	0.094	1.80	7.67	9.47
3 uses	LF	0.089	1.37	7.24	8.61
4 uses	LF	0.085	1.25	6.94	8.19
5 uses	LF	0.082	1.16	6.65	7.81
03111.34 ELEVATED SLAB FORMWORK					
ELEVATED SLAB FORMWORK					
Elevated slab formwork					
Slab, with drop panels					
1 use	SF	0.064	4.75	5.21	9.96
2 uses	SF	0.062	2.75	5.01	7.76
3 uses	SF	0.059	2.13	4.83	6.96

	Unit	Man-Hrs	Material	Labor	Total

03111.34 ELEVATED SLAB FORMWORK (Cont.)

Slab, with drop panels

	Unit	Man-Hrs	Material	Labor	Total
4 uses	SF	0.057	1.89	4.66	6.55
5 uses	SF	0.055	1.70	4.49	6.19

Floor slab, hung from steel beams

	Unit	Man-Hrs	Material	Labor	Total
1 use	SF	0.062	3.82	5.01	8.83
2 uses	SF	0.059	2.09	4.83	6.92
3 uses	SF	0.057	1.91	4.66	6.57
4 uses	SF	0.055	1.64	4.49	6.13
5 uses	SF	0.053	1.40	4.34	5.74

Floor slab, with pans or domes

	Unit	Man-Hrs	Material	Labor	Total
1 use	SF	0.073	6.82	5.93	12.75
2 uses	SF	0.070	4.43	5.67	10.10
3 uses	SF	0.067	4.13	5.43	9.56
4 uses	SF	0.064	3.85	5.21	9.06
5 uses	SF	0.062	3.41	5.01	8.42

Equipment curbs, 12" high

	Unit	Man-Hrs	Material	Labor	Total
1 use	LF	0.080	3.51	6.52	10.03
2 uses	LF	0.076	2.26	6.21	8.47
3 uses	LF	0.073	1.96	5.93	7.89
4 uses	LF	0.070	1.77	5.67	7.44
5 uses	LF	0.067	1.53	5.43	6.96

03111.35 EQUIPMENT PAD FORMWORK

EQUIPMENT PAD FORMWORK

Equipment pad, job built

	Unit	Man-Hrs	Material	Labor	Total
1 use	SF	0.100	4.61	8.15	12.76
2 uses	SF	0.094	2.77	7.67	10.44
3 uses	SF	0.089	2.22	7.24	9.46
4 uses	SF	0.084	1.73	6.86	8.59
5 uses	SF	0.080	1.37	6.52	7.89

03111.36 FOOTING FORMWORK

FOOTING FORMWORK

Wall footings, job built, continuous

	Unit	Man-Hrs	Material	Labor	Total
1 use	SF	0.080	2.14	6.52	8.66
2 uses	SF	0.076	1.51	6.21	7.72
3 uses	SF	0.073	1.24	5.93	7.17
4 uses	SF	0.070	1.10	5.67	6.77
5 uses	SF	0.067	0.95	5.43	6.38

Column footings, spread

	Unit	Man-Hrs	Material	Labor	Total
1 use	SF	0.100	2.27	8.15	10.42
2 uses	SF	0.094	1.69	7.67	9.36
3 uses	SF	0.089	1.20	7.24	8.44
4 uses	SF	0.084	1.01	6.86	7.87
5 uses	SF	0.080	0.92	6.52	7.44

03111.37 GRADE BEAM FORMWORK

GRADE BEAM FORMWORK

Grade beams, job built

	Unit	Man-Hrs	Material	Labor	Total
1 use	SF	0.080	3.38	6.52	9.90
2 uses	SF	0.076	1.89	6.21	8.10
3 uses	SF	0.073	1.48	5.93	7.41
4 uses	SF	0.070	1.23	5.67	6.90
5 uses	SF	0.067	1.02	5.43	6.45

03111.38 PILE CAP FORMWORK

PILE CAP FORMWORK

Pile cap forms, job built

Square

	Unit	Man-Hrs	Material	Labor	Total
1 use	SF	0.100	3.83	8.15	11.98
2 uses	SF	0.094	2.21	7.67	9.88
3 uses	SF	0.089	1.75	7.24	8.99
4 uses	SF	0.084	1.55	6.86	8.41
5 uses	SF	0.080	1.28	6.52	7.80

Triangular

	Unit	Man-Hrs	Material	Labor	Total
1 use	SF	0.114	4.07	9.32	13.39
2 uses	SF	0.107	2.68	8.69	11.37

© 2020 BNi Publications, Inc.

	Unit	Man-Hrs	Material	Labor	Total
03111.38 PILE CAP FORMWORK (Cont.)					
Triangular					
3 uses	SF	0.100	2.14	8.15	10.29
4 uses	SF	0.094	1.75	7.67	9.42
5 uses	SF	0.089	1.39	7.24	8.63
03111.39 SLAB / MAT FORMWORK					
SLAB / MAT FORMWORK					
Mat foundations, job built					
1 use	SF	0.100	3.35	8.15	11.50
2 uses	SF	0.094	1.94	7.67	9.61
3 uses	SF	0.089	1.42	7.24	8.66
4 uses	SF	0.084	1.20	6.86	8.06
5 uses	SF	0.080	0.97	6.52	7.49
Edge forms					
6" high					
1 use	LF	0.073	3.38	5.93	9.31
2 uses	LF	0.070	1.94	5.67	7.61
3 uses	LF	0.067	1.43	5.43	6.86
4 uses	LF	0.064	1.21	5.21	6.42
5 uses	LF	0.062	0.97	5.01	5.98
12" high					
1 use	LF	0.080	3.18	6.52	9.70
2 uses	LF	0.076	1.81	6.21	8.02
3 uses	LF	0.073	1.32	5.93	7.25
4 uses	LF	0.070	1.10	5.67	6.77
5 uses	LF	0.067	0.89	5.43	6.32
Formwork for openings					
1 use	SF	0.160	4.56	13.00	17.56
2 uses	SF	0.145	2.63	11.75	14.38
3 uses	SF	0.133	2.20	10.75	12.95
4 uses	SF	0.123	1.69	10.00	11.69
5 uses	SF	0.114	1.42	9.32	10.74
03111.40 STAIR FORMWORK					
STAIR FORMWORK					
Stairway forms, job built					
1 use	SF	0.160	5.27	13.00	18.27
2 uses	SF	0.145	2.95	11.75	14.70
3 uses	SF	0.133	2.29	10.75	13.04
4 uses	SF	0.123	2.10	10.00	12.10
5 uses	SF	0.114	1.76	9.32	11.08
Stairs, elevated					
1 use	SF	0.160	6.36	13.00	19.36
2 uses	SF	0.133	3.38	10.75	14.13
3 uses	SF	0.114	2.95	9.32	12.27
4 uses	SF	0.107	2.54	8.69	11.23
5 uses	SF	0.100	2.10	8.15	10.25
03111.41 WALL FORMWORK					
WALL FORMWORK					
Wall forms, exterior, job built					
Up to 8' high wall					
1 use	SF	0.080	3.61	6.52	10.13
2 uses	SF	0.076	1.99	6.21	8.20
3 uses	SF	0.073	1.75	5.93	7.68
4 uses	SF	0.070	1.51	5.67	7.18
5 uses	SF	0.067	1.32	5.43	6.75
Over 8' high wall					
1 use	SF	0.100	3.96	8.15	12.11
2 uses	SF	0.094	2.26	7.67	9.93
3 uses	SF	0.089	2.06	7.24	9.30
4 uses	SF	0.084	1.88	6.86	8.74
5 uses	SF	0.080	1.62	6.52	8.14
Over 16' high wall					
1 use	SF	0.114	4.16	9.32	13.48
2 uses	SF	0.107	2.49	8.69	11.18

	Unit	Man-Hrs	Material	Labor	Total

03111.41 WALL FORMWORK (Cont.)

Over 16' high wall

	Unit	Man-Hrs	Material	Labor	Total
3 uses	SF	0.100	2.26	8.15	10.41
4 uses	SF	0.094	2.06	7.67	9.73
5 uses	SF	0.089	1.88	7.24	9.12

Radial wall forms

	Unit	Man-Hrs	Material	Labor	Total
1 use	SF	0.123	3.88	10.00	13.88
2 uses	SF	0.114	2.32	9.32	11.64
3 uses	SF	0.107	2.15	8.69	10.84
4 uses	SF	0.100	1.95	8.15	10.10
5 uses	SF	0.094	1.75	7.67	9.42

Retaining wall forms

	Unit	Man-Hrs	Material	Labor	Total
1 use	SF	0.089	3.35	7.24	10.59
2 uses	SF	0.084	1.78	6.86	8.64
3 uses	SF	0.080	1.54	6.52	8.06
4 uses	SF	0.076	1.34	6.21	7.55
5 uses	SF	0.073	1.14	5.93	7.07

Radial retaining wall forms

	Unit	Man-Hrs	Material	Labor	Total
1 use	SF	0.133	3.55	10.75	14.30
2 uses	SF	0.123	2.18	10.00	12.18
3 uses	SF	0.114	1.87	9.32	11.19
4 uses	SF	0.107	1.77	8.69	10.46
5 uses	SF	0.100	1.52	8.15	9.67

Column pier and pilaster

	Unit	Man-Hrs	Material	Labor	Total
1 use	SF	0.160	3.96	13.00	16.96
2 uses	SF	0.145	2.34	11.75	14.09
3 uses	SF	0.133	2.18	10.75	12.93
4 uses	SF	0.123	1.99	10.00	11.99
5 uses	SF	0.114	1.78	9.32	11.10

Interior wall forms

Up to 8' high

	Unit	Man-Hrs	Material	Labor	Total
1 use	SF	0.073	3.61	5.93	9.54
2 uses	SF	0.070	2.01	5.67	7.68
3 uses	SF	0.067	1.78	5.43	7.21
4 uses	SF	0.064	1.52	5.21	6.73
5 uses	SF	0.062	1.28	5.01	6.29

Over 8' high

	Unit	Man-Hrs	Material	Labor	Total
1 use	SF	0.089	3.96	7.24	11.20
2 uses	SF	0.084	2.26	6.86	9.12
3 uses	SF	0.080	2.06	6.52	8.58
4 uses	SF	0.076	1.88	6.21	8.09
5 uses	SF	0.073	1.64	5.93	7.57

Over 16' high

	Unit	Man-Hrs	Material	Labor	Total
1 use	SF	0.100	4.15	8.15	12.30
2 uses	SF	0.094	2.49	7.67	10.16
3 uses	SF	0.089	2.26	7.24	9.50
4 uses	SF	0.084	2.06	6.86	8.92
5 uses	SF	0.080	1.88	6.52	8.40

Radial wall forms

	Unit	Man-Hrs	Material	Labor	Total
1 use	SF	0.107	3.88	8.69	12.57
2 uses	SF	0.100	2.32	8.15	10.47
3 uses	SF	0.094	2.15	7.67	9.82
4 uses	SF	0.089	1.95	7.24	9.19
5 uses	SF	0.084	1.75	6.86	8.61

Curved wall forms, 24" sections

	Unit	Man-Hrs	Material	Labor	Total
1 use	SF	0.160	3.71	13.00	16.71
2 uses	SF	0.145	2.21	11.75	13.96
3 uses	SF	0.133	2.05	10.75	12.80
4 uses	SF	0.123	1.87	10.00	11.87
5 uses	SF	0.114	1.67	9.32	10.99

PVC form liner, per side, smooth finish

	Unit	Man-Hrs	Material	Labor	Total
1 use	SF	0.067	9.32	5.43	14.75
2 uses	SF	0.064	5.12	5.21	10.33
3 uses	SF	0.062	4.33	5.01	9.34
4 uses	SF	0.057	3.34	4.66	8.00
5 uses	SF	0.053	2.66	4.34	7.00

© 2020 BNi Publications, Inc.

	Unit	Man-Hrs	Material	Labor	Total

03112.42 MISCELLANEOUS FORMWORK

MISCELLANEOUS FORMWORK

Keyway forms (5 uses)

	Unit	Man-Hrs	Material	Labor	Total
2 x 4	LF	0.040	0.30	3.26	3.56
2 x 6	LF	0.044	0.44	3.62	4.06

Bulkheads

Walls, with keyways

	Unit	Man-Hrs	Material	Labor	Total
2 piece	LF	0.073	5.09	5.93	11.02
3 piece	LF	0.080	6.44	6.52	12.96

Elevated slab, with keyway

	Unit	Man-Hrs	Material	Labor	Total
2 piece	LF	0.067	5.84	5.43	11.27
3 piece	LF	0.073	8.60	5.93	14.53

Ground slab, with keyway

	Unit	Man-Hrs	Material	Labor	Total
2 piece	LF	0.057	6.03	4.66	10.69
3 piece	LF	0.062	7.37	5.01	12.38

Chamfer strips

Wood

	Unit	Man-Hrs	Material	Labor	Total
1/2" wide	LF	0.018	0.29	1.44	1.73
3/4" wide	LF	0.018	0.37	1.44	1.81
1" wide	LF	0.018	0.50	1.44	1.94

PVC

	Unit	Man-Hrs	Material	Labor	Total
1/2" wide	LF	0.018	1.29	1.44	2.73
3/4" wide	LF	0.018	1.40	1.44	2.84
1" wide	LF	0.018	2.03	1.44	3.47

Radius

	Unit	Man-Hrs	Material	Labor	Total
1"	LF	0.019	1.51	1.55	3.06
1-1/2"	LF	0.019	2.73	1.55	4.28

Reglets

	Unit	Man-Hrs	Material	Labor	Total
Galvanized steel, 24 ga.	LF	0.032	1.96	2.60	4.56

Metal formwork

Straight edge forms

	Unit	Man-Hrs	Material	Labor	Total
4" high	LF	0.050	23.50	4.07	27.57
6" high	LF	0.053	25.75	4.34	30.09
8" high	LF	0.057	35.25	4.66	39.91
12" high	LF	0.062	41.00	5.01	46.01
16" high	LF	0.067	48.25	5.43	53.68

Curb form, S-shape

12" x

	Unit	Man-Hrs	Material	Labor	Total
1'-6"	LF	0.114	52.00	9.32	61.32
2'	LF	0.107	57.00	8.69	65.69
2'-6"	LF	0.100	62.00	8.15	70.15
3'	LF	0.089	67.00	7.24	74.24

03150.01 CONCRETE ACCESSORIES

CONCRETE ACCESSORIES

Expansion joint, poured

Asphalt

	Unit	Man-Hrs	Material	Labor	Total
1/2" x 1"	LF	0.016	0.90	1.02	1.92
1" x 2"	LF	0.017	2.82	1.11	3.93

Liquid neoprene, cold applied

	Unit	Man-Hrs	Material	Labor	Total
1/2" x 1"	LF	0.016	3.52	1.04	4.56
1" x 2"	LF	0.018	14.50	1.13	15.63

Polyurethane, 2 parts

	Unit	Man-Hrs	Material	Labor	Total
1/2" x 1"	LF	0.027	3.37	1.70	5.07
1" x 2"	LF	0.029	13.25	1.85	15.10

Rubberized asphalt, cold

	Unit	Man-Hrs	Material	Labor	Total
1/2" x 1"	LF	0.016	0.86	1.02	1.88
1" x 2"	LF	0.017	2.59	1.11	3.70

Hot, fuel resistant

	Unit	Man-Hrs	Material	Labor	Total
1/2" x 1"	LF	0.016	1.56	1.02	2.58
1" x 2"	LF	0.017	7.53	1.11	8.64

Expansion joint, premolded, in slabs

Asphalt

	Unit	Man-Hrs	Material	Labor	Total
1/2" x 6"	LF	0.020	1.00	1.27	2.27
1" x 12"	LF	0.027	1.67	1.70	3.37

	Unit	Man-Hrs	Material	Labor	Total
03150.01 CONCRETE ACCESSORIES (Cont.)					
Expansion joint, premolded, in slabs					
Cork					
1/2" x 6"	LF	0.020	1.99	1.27	3.26
1" x 12"	LF	0.027	7.56	1.70	9.26
Neoprene sponge					
1/2" x 6"	LF	0.020	2.93	1.27	4.20
1" x 12"	LF	0.027	10.75	1.70	12.45
Polyethylene foam					
1/2" x 6"	LF	0.020	1.13	1.27	2.40
1" x 12"	LF	0.027	5.21	1.70	6.91
Polyurethane foam					
1/2" x 6"	LF	0.020	1.49	1.27	2.76
1" x 12"	LF	0.027	3.29	1.70	4.99
Polyvinyl chloride foam					
1/2" x 6"	LF	0.020	3.19	1.27	4.46
1" x 12"	LF	0.027	6.89	1.70	8.59
Rubber, gray sponge					
1/2" x 6"	LF	0.020	4.97	1.27	6.24
1" x 12"	LF	0.027	21.50	1.70	23.20
Asphalt felt control joints or bond breaker, screed joints					
4" slab	LF	0.016	1.34	1.02	2.36
6" slab	LF	0.018	1.68	1.13	2.81
8" slab	LF	0.020	2.19	1.27	3.46
10" slab	LF	0.023	3.09	1.45	4.54
Keyed cold expansion and control joints, 24 ga.					
4" slab	LF	0.050	1.09	3.19	4.28
5" slab	LF	0.050	1.45	3.19	4.64
6" slab	LF	0.053	1.68	3.40	5.08
8" slab	LF	0.057	2.04	3.64	5.68
10" slab	LF	0.062	2.24	3.92	6.16
Waterstops					
Polyvinyl chloride					
Ribbed					
3/16" thick x					
4" wide	LF	0.040	1.59	2.55	4.14
6" wide	LF	0.044	2.42	2.83	5.25
1/2" thick x					
9" wide	LF	0.050	6.43	3.19	9.62
Ribbed with center bulb					
3/16" thick x 9" wide	LF	0.050	5.40	3.19	8.59
3/8" thick x 9" wide	LF	0.050	6.35	3.19	9.54
Dumbbell type, 3/8" thick x 6" wide	LF	0.044	6.43	2.83	9.26
Plain, 3/8" thick x 9" wide	LF	0.050	8.54	3.19	11.73
Center bulb, 3/8" thick x 9" wide	LF	0.050	10.25	3.19	13.44
Rubber					
Flat dumbbell					
3/8" thick x					
6" wide	LF	0.044	7.91	2.83	10.74
9" wide	LF	0.050	8.54	3.19	11.73
Center bulb					
3/8" thick x					
6" wide	LF	0.044	8.88	2.83	11.71
9" wide	LF	0.050	11.00	3.19	14.19
Vapor barrier					
4 mil polyethylene	SF	0.003	0.05	0.17	0.22
6 mil polyethylene	SF	0.003	0.08	0.17	0.25
Gravel porous fill, under floor slabs, 3/4" stone	CY	1.333	22.25	85.00	107.25
Reinforcing accessories					
Beam bolsters					
1-1/2" high, plain	LF	0.008	0.59	0.66	1.25
Galvanized	LF	0.008	1.30	0.66	1.96
3" high					
Plain	LF	0.010	0.84	0.83	1.67
Galvanized	LF	0.010	2.08	0.83	2.91

© 2020 BNi Publications, Inc.

	Unit	Man-Hrs	Material	Labor	Total

03150.01 CONCRETE ACCESSORIES (Cont.)

Reinforcing accessories
Slab bolsters
1" high

	Unit	Man-Hrs	Material	Labor	Total
Plain	LF	0.004	0.63	0.33	0.96
Galvanized	LF	0.004	1.27	0.33	1.60

2" high

Plain	LF	0.004	0.70	0.37	1.07
Galvanized	LF	0.004	1.49	0.37	1.86

Chairs, high chairs
3" high

Plain	EA	0.020	1.70	1.66	3.36
Galvanized	EA	0.020	1.87	1.66	3.53

5" high

Plain	EA	0.021	1.75	1.75	3.50
Galvanized	EA	0.021	3.52	1.75	5.27

8" high

Plain	EA	0.023	2.87	1.90	4.77
Galvanized	EA	0.023	4.88	1.90	6.78

12" high

Plain	EA	0.027	5.20	2.22	7.42
Galvanized	EA	0.027	9.93	2.22	12.15

Continuous, high chair
3" high

Plain	LF	0.005	2.36	0.44	2.80
Galvanized	LF	0.005	2.92	0.44	3.36

5" high

Plain	LF	0.006	2.54	0.47	3.01
Galvanized	LF	0.006	3.58	0.47	4.05

8" high

Plain	LF	0.006	2.92	0.51	3.43
Galvanized	LF	0.006	3.79	0.51	4.30

12" high

Plain	LF	0.007	3.76	0.55	4.31
Galvanized	LF	0.007	4.88	0.55	5.43

Spirals or Stirrups

8" to 24"	TON	20.000	3,050.00	1,660.00	4,710.00
24" to 48"	TON	17.778	3,050.00	1,480.00	4,530.00
48" to 84"	TON	16.000	3,050.00	1,330.00	4,380.00

03210.01 BEAM REINFORCING

BEAM REINFORCING
Beam-girders

#3 - #4	TON	20.000	1,880.00	1,660.00	3,540.00
#5 - #6	TON	16.000	1,650.00	1,330.00	2,980.00
#7 - #8	TON	13.333	1,570.00	1,110.00	2,680.00
#9 - #10	TON	11.429	1,570.00	950.00	2,520.00
#11	TON	10.667	1,570.00	890.00	2,460.00
#14	TON	10.000	1,570.00	830.00	2,400.00

Galvanized

#3 - #4	TON	20.000	3,190.00	1,660.00	4,850.00
#5 - #6	TON	16.000	3,020.00	1,330.00	4,350.00
#7 - #8	TON	13.333	2,900.00	1,110.00	4,010.00
#9 - #10	TON	11.429	2,900.00	950.00	3,850.00
#11	TON	10.667	2,900.00	890.00	3,790.00
#14	TON	10.000	2,900.00	830.00	3,730.00

Epoxy coated

#3 - #4	TON	22.857	2,760.00	1,900.00	4,660.00
#5 - #6	TON	17.778	2,590.00	1,480.00	4,070.00
#7 - #8	TON	14.545	2,510.00	1,210.00	3,720.00
#9 - #10	TON	12.308	2,510.00	1,020.00	3,530.00
#11	TON	11.429	2,510.00	950.00	3,460.00
#14	TON	10.667	2,510.00	890.00	3,400.00

Bond Beams

#3 - #4	TON	26.667	1,880.00	2,220.00	4,100.00
#5 - #6	TON	20.000	1,650.00	1,660.00	3,310.00

	Unit	Man-Hrs	Material	Labor	Total
03210.01 BEAM REINFORCING (Cont.)					
Bond Beams					
#7 - #8	TON	17.778	1,570.00	1,480.00	3,050.00
Galvanized					
#3 - #4	TON	26.667	3,060.00	2,220.00	5,280.00
#5 - #6	TON	20.000	3,020.00	1,660.00	4,680.00
#7 - #8	TON	17.778	2,900.00	1,480.00	4,380.00
Epoxy coated					
#3 - #4	TON	32.000	2,760.00	2,660.00	5,420.00
#5 - #6	TON	22.857	2,590.00	1,900.00	4,490.00
#7 - #8	TON	20.000	2,510.00	1,660.00	4,170.00
03210.02 BOX CULVERT REINFORCING					
BOX CULVERT REINFORCING					
Box culverts					
#3 - #4	TON	10.000	1,880.00	830.00	2,710.00
#5 - #6	TON	8.889	1,650.00	740.00	2,390.00
#7 - #8	TON	8.000	1,570.00	670.00	2,240.00
#9 - #10	TON	7.273	1,570.00	610.00	2,180.00
#11	TON	6.667	1,570.00	550.00	2,120.00
Galvanized					
#3 - #4	TON	10.000	3,060.00	830.00	3,890.00
#5 - #6	TON	8.889	3,020.00	740.00	3,760.00
#7 - #8	TON	8.000	2,900.00	670.00	3,570.00
#9 - #10	TON	7.273	2,900.00	610.00	3,510.00
#11	TON	6.667	2,900.00	550.00	3,450.00
Epoxy coated					
#3 - #4	TON	10.667	2,760.00	890.00	3,650.00
#5 - #6	TON	9.412	2,590.00	780.00	3,370.00
#7 - #8	TON	8.421	2,510.00	700.00	3,210.00
#9 - #10	TON	7.619	2,510.00	630.00	3,140.00
#11	TON	6.957	2,510.00	580.00	3,090.00
03210.03 COLUMN REINFORCING					
COLUMN REINFORCING					
Columns					
#3 - #4	TON	22.857	1,880.00	1,900.00	3,780.00
#5 - #6	TON	17.778	1,650.00	1,480.00	3,130.00
#7 - #8	TON	16.000	1,570.00	1,330.00	2,900.00
#9 - #10	TON	14.545	1,570.00	1,210.00	2,780.00
#11	TON	13.333	1,570.00	1,110.00	2,680.00
#14	TON	12.308	1,570.00	1,020.00	2,590.00
#18	TON	11.429	1,570.00	950.00	2,520.00
Galvanized					
#3 - #4	TON	22.857	3,190.00	1,900.00	5,090.00
#5 - #6	TON	17.778	3,020.00	1,480.00	4,500.00
#7 - #8	TON	16.000	2,900.00	1,330.00	4,230.00
#9 - #10	TON	14.545	2,900.00	1,210.00	4,110.00
#11	TON	13.333	2,900.00	1,110.00	4,010.00
#14	TON	12.308	2,900.00	1,020.00	3,920.00
#18	TON	11.429	2,900.00	950.00	3,850.00
Epoxy coated					
#3 - #4	TON	26.667	2,760.00	2,220.00	4,980.00
#5 - #6	TON	20.000	2,590.00	1,660.00	4,250.00
#7 - #8	TON	17.778	2,510.00	1,480.00	3,990.00
#9 - #10	TON	16.000	2,510.00	1,330.00	3,840.00
#11	TON	14.545	2,510.00	1,210.00	3,720.00
#14	TON	13.333	2,510.00	1,110.00	3,620.00
#18	TON	12.308	2,510.00	1,020.00	3,530.00
03210.04 ELEVATED SLAB REINFORCING					
ELEVATED SLAB REINFORCING					
Elevated slab					
#3 - #4	TON	10.000	1,880.00	830.00	2,710.00
#5 - #6	TON	8.889	1,650.00	740.00	2,390.00
#7 - #8	TON	8.000	1,570.00	670.00	2,240.00
#9 - #10	TON	7.273	1,570.00	610.00	2,180.00

© 2020 BNi Publications, Inc.

	Unit	Man-Hrs	Material	Labor	Total

03210.04 ELEVATED SLAB REINFORCING (Cont.)

Elevated slab

	Unit	Man-Hrs	Material	Labor	Total
#11	TON	6.667	1,570.00	550.00	2,120.00

Galvanized

	Unit	Man-Hrs	Material	Labor	Total
#3 - #4	TON	10.000	3,060.00	830.00	3,890.00
#5 - #6	TON	8.889	3,020.00	740.00	3,760.00
#7 - #8	TON	8.000	2,900.00	670.00	3,570.00
#9 - #10	TON	7.273	2,900.00	610.00	3,510.00
#11	TON	6.667	2,900.00	550.00	3,450.00

Epoxy coated

	Unit	Man-Hrs	Material	Labor	Total
#3 - #4	TON	10.667	2,760.00	890.00	3,650.00
#5 - #6	TON	9.412	2,590.00	780.00	3,370.00
#7 - #8	TON	8.421	2,510.00	700.00	3,210.00
#9 - #10	TON	7.619	2,510.00	630.00	3,140.00
#11	TON	6.957	2,510.00	580.00	3,090.00

03210.05 EQUIP. PAD REINFORCING

EQUIP. PAD REINFORCING

Equipment pad

	Unit	Man-Hrs	Material	Labor	Total
#3 - #4	TON	16.000	1,880.00	1,330.00	3,210.00
#5 - #6	TON	14.545	1,650.00	1,210.00	2,860.00
#7 - #8	TON	13.333	1,570.00	1,110.00	2,680.00
#9 - #10	TON	12.308	1,570.00	1,020.00	2,590.00
#11	TON	11.429	1,570.00	950.00	2,520.00

03210.06 FOOTING REINFORCING

FOOTING REINFORCING

Footings

Grade 50

	Unit	Man-Hrs	Material	Labor	Total
#3 - #4	TON	13.333	1,880.00	1,110.00	2,990.00
#5 - #6	TON	11.429	1,650.00	950.00	2,600.00
#7 - #8	TON	10.000	1,570.00	830.00	2,400.00
#9 - #10	TON	8.889	1,570.00	740.00	2,310.00

Grade 60

	Unit	Man-Hrs	Material	Labor	Total
#3 - #4	TON	13.333	1,880.00	1,110.00	2,990.00
#5 - #6	TON	11.429	1,650.00	950.00	2,600.00
#7 - #8	TON	10.000	1,570.00	830.00	2,400.00
#9 - #10	TON	8.889	1,570.00	740.00	2,310.00

Grade 70

	Unit	Man-Hrs	Material	Labor	Total
#3 - #4	TON	13.333	1,880.00	1,110.00	2,990.00
#5 - #6	TON	11.429	1,650.00	950.00	2,600.00
#7 - #8	TON	10.000	1,570.00	830.00	2,400.00
#9 - #10	TON	8.889	1,570.00	740.00	2,310.00
#11	TON	8.000	1,570.00	670.00	2,240.00

Straight dowels, 24" long

	Unit	Man-Hrs	Material	Labor	Total
1" dia. (#8)	EA	0.020	5.82	1.66	7.48
3/4" dia. (#6)	EA	0.019	5.24	1.54	6.78
5/8" dia. (#5)	EA	0.017	4.53	1.44	5.97
1/2" dia. (#4)	EA	0.016	3.41	1.33	4.74

03210.07 FOUNDATION REINFORCING

FOUNDATION REINFORCING

Foundations

	Unit	Man-Hrs	Material	Labor	Total
#3 - #4	TON	13.333	1,880.00	1,110.00	2,990.00
#5 - #6	TON	11.429	1,650.00	950.00	2,600.00
#7 - #8	TON	10.000	1,570.00	830.00	2,400.00
#9 - #10	TON	8.889	1,570.00	740.00	2,310.00
#11	TON	8.000	1,570.00	670.00	2,240.00

Galvanized

	Unit	Man-Hrs	Material	Labor	Total
#3 - #4	TON	13.333	3,210.00	1,110.00	4,320.00
#5 - #6	TON	11.429	3,030.00	950.00	3,980.00
#7 - #8	TON	10.000	2,910.00	830.00	3,740.00
#9 - #10	TON	8.889	2,910.00	740.00	3,650.00
#11	TON	8.000	2,910.00	670.00	3,580.00

Epoxy Coated

	Unit	Man-Hrs	Material	Labor	Total
#3 - #4	TON	14.545	2,770.00	1,210.00	3,980.00
#5 - #6	TON	12.308	2,600.00	1,020.00	3,620.00

	Unit	Man-Hrs	Material	Labor	Total
03210.07 FOUNDATION REINFORCING (Cont.)					
Epoxy Coated					
#7 - #8	TON	10.667	2,520.00	890.00	3,410.00
#9 - #10	TON	9.412	2,520.00	780.00	3,300.00
#11	TON	8.421	2,520.00	700.00	3,220.00
03210.08 GRADE BEAM REINFORCING					
GRADE BEAM REINFORCING					
Grade beams					
#3 - #4	TON	12.308	1,880.00	1,020.00	2,900.00
#5 - #6	TON	10.667	1,660.00	890.00	2,550.00
#7 - #8	TON	9.412	1,570.00	780.00	2,350.00
#9 - #10	TON	8.421	1,570.00	700.00	2,270.00
#11	TON	7.619	1,570.00	630.00	2,200.00
Galvanized					
#3 - #4	TON	12.308	3,210.00	1,020.00	4,230.00
#5 - #6	TON	10.667	3,030.00	890.00	3,920.00
#7 - #8	TON	9.412	2,910.00	780.00	3,690.00
#9 - #10	TON	8.421	2,910.00	700.00	3,610.00
#11	TON	7.619	2,910.00	630.00	3,540.00
Epoxy coated					
#3 - #4	TON	13.333	2,770.00	1,110.00	3,880.00
#5 - #6	TON	11.429	2,600.00	950.00	3,550.00
#7 - #8	TON	10.000	2,520.00	830.00	3,350.00
#9 - #10	TON	8.889	2,520.00	740.00	3,260.00
#11	TON	8.000	2,520.00	670.00	3,190.00
03210.09 SLAB / MAT REINFORCING					
SLAB / MAT REINFORCING					
Bars, slabs					
#3 - #4	TON	13.333	1,880.00	1,110.00	2,990.00
#5 - #6	TON	11.429	1,660.00	950.00	2,610.00
#7 - #8	TON	10.000	1,570.00	830.00	2,400.00
#9 - #10	TON	8.889	1,570.00	740.00	2,310.00
#11	TON	8.000	1,570.00	670.00	2,240.00
Galvanized					
#3 - #4	TON	13.333	3,210.00	1,110.00	4,320.00
#5 - #6	TON	11.429	3,030.00	950.00	3,980.00
#7 - #8	TON	10.000	2,910.00	830.00	3,740.00
#9 - #10	TON	8.889	2,910.00	740.00	3,650.00
#11	TON	8.000	2,910.00	670.00	3,580.00
Epoxy coated					
#3 - #4	TON	14.545	2,770.00	1,210.00	3,980.00
#5 - #6	TON	12.308	2,600.00	1,020.00	3,620.00
#7 - #8	TON	10.667	2,520.00	890.00	3,410.00
#9 - #10	TON	9.412	2,520.00	780.00	3,300.00
#11	TON	8.421	2,520.00	700.00	3,220.00
Wire mesh, slabs					
Galvanized					
4x4					
W1.4xW1.4	SF	0.005	0.46	0.44	0.90
W2.0xW2.0	SF	0.006	0.60	0.47	1.07
W2.9xW2.9	SF	0.006	0.85	0.51	1.36
W4.0xW4.0	SF	0.007	1.25	0.55	1.80
6x6					
W1.4xW1.4	SF	0.004	0.43	0.33	0.76
W2.0xW2.0	SF	0.004	0.60	0.37	0.97
W2.9xW2.9	SF	0.005	0.82	0.39	1.21
W4.0xW4.0	SF	0.005	0.88	0.44	1.32
Standard					
2x2					
W.9xW.9	SF	0.005	0.46	0.44	0.90
4x4					
W1.4xW1.4	SF	0.005	0.31	0.44	0.75
W2.0xW2.0	SF	0.006	0.40	0.47	0.87
W2.9xW2.9	SF	0.006	0.55	0.51	1.06
W4.0xW4.0	SF	0.007	0.85	0.55	1.40

© 2020 BNi Publications, Inc.

	Unit	Man-Hrs	Material	Labor	Total
03210.09 SLAB / MAT REINFORCING (Cont.)					
Standard					
6x6					
W1.4xW1.4	SF	0.004	0.20	0.33	0.53
W2.0xW2.0	SF	0.004	0.27	0.37	0.64
W2.9xW2.9	SF	0.005	0.40	0.39	0.79
W4.0xW4.0	SF	0.005	0.57	0.44	1.01
03210.10 STAIR REINFORCING					
STAIR REINFORCING					
Stairs					
#3 - #4	TON	16.000	1,880.00	1,330.00	3,210.00
#5 - #6	TON	13.333	1,660.00	1,110.00	2,770.00
#7 - #8	TON	11.429	1,570.00	950.00	2,520.00
#9 - #10	TON	10.000	1,570.00	830.00	2,400.00
Galvanized					
#3 - #4	TON	16.000	3,210.00	1,330.00	4,540.00
#5 - #6	TON	13.333	3,030.00	1,110.00	4,140.00
#7 - #8	TON	11.429	2,910.00	950.00	3,860.00
#9 - #10	TON	10.000	2,910.00	830.00	3,740.00
Epoxy coated					
#3 - #4	TON	17.778	2,770.00	1,480.00	4,250.00
#5 - #6	TON	14.545	2,600.00	1,210.00	3,810.00
#7 - #8	TON	12.308	2,520.00	1,020.00	3,540.00
#9 - #10	TON	10.667	2,520.00	890.00	3,410.00
Stair Nosing, Steel, Galvanized					
3' long	EA	0.044	18.25	3.70	21.95
4' long	EA	0.053	24.75	4.44	29.19
5 ' long	EA	0.067	36.75	5.55	42.30
03210.11 WALL REINFORCING					
WALL REINFORCING					
Walls					
#3 - #4	TON	11.429	1,880.00	950.00	2,830.00
#5 - #6	TON	10.000	1,660.00	830.00	2,490.00
#7 - #8	TON	8.889	1,570.00	740.00	2,310.00
#9 - #10	TON	8.000	1,570.00	670.00	2,240.00
Galvanized					
#3 - #4	TON	11.429	3,210.00	950.00	4,160.00
#5 - #6	TON	10.000	3,030.00	830.00	3,860.00
#7 - #8	TON	8.889	2,910.00	740.00	3,650.00
#9 - #10	TON	8.000	2,910.00	670.00	3,580.00
Epoxy coated					
#3 - #4	TON	12.308	2,770.00	1,020.00	3,790.00
#5 - #6	TON	10.667	2,600.00	890.00	3,490.00
#7 - #8	TON	9.412	2,520.00	780.00	3,300.00
#9 - #10	TON	8.421	2,520.00	700.00	3,220.00
Masonry wall (horizontal)					
#3 - #4	TON	32.000	1,880.00	2,660.00	4,540.00
#5 - #6	TON	26.667	1,660.00	2,220.00	3,880.00
Galvanized					
#3 - #4	TON	32.000	3,210.00	2,660.00	5,870.00
#5 - #6	TON	26.667	3,030.00	2,220.00	5,250.00
Masonry wall (vertical)					
#3 - #4	TON	40.000	1,880.00	3,330.00	5,210.00
#5 - #6	TON	32.000	1,660.00	2,660.00	4,320.00
Galvanized					
#3 - #4	TON	40.000	3,210.00	3,330.00	6,540.00
#5 - #6	TON	32.000	3,030.00	2,660.00	5,690.00
03210.16 PILE CAP REINFORCING					
PILE CAP REINFORCING					
Pile caps					
#3 - #4	TON	20.000	1,880.00	1,660.00	3,540.00
#5 - #6	TON	17.778	1,660.00	1,480.00	3,140.00
#7 - #8	TON	16.000	1,570.00	1,330.00	2,900.00
#9 - #10	TON	14.545	1,570.00	1,210.00	2,780.00

	Unit	Man-Hrs	Material	Labor	Total
03210.16 PILE CAP REINFORCING (Cont.)					
Pile caps					
#11	TON	13.333	1,570.00	1,110.00	2,680.00
Galvanized					
#3 - #4	TON	20.000	3,210.00	1,660.00	4,870.00
#5 - #6	TON	17.778	3,030.00	1,480.00	4,510.00
#7 - #8	TON	16.000	2,910.00	1,330.00	4,240.00
#9 - #10	TON	14.545	2,910.00	1,210.00	4,120.00
#11	TON	13.333	2,910.00	1,110.00	4,020.00
Epoxy coated					
#3 - #4	TON	22.857	2,770.00	1,900.00	4,670.00
#5 - #6	TON	20.000	2,600.00	1,660.00	4,260.00
#7 - #8	TON	17.778	2,520.00	1,480.00	4,000.00
#9 - #10	TON	16.000	2,520.00	1,330.00	3,850.00
#11	TON	14.545	2,520.00	1,210.00	3,730.00
03305.31 CONCRETE ADMIXTURES					
CONCRETE ADMIXTURES					
Concrete admixtures					
Water reducing admixture	GAL				12.25
Set retarder	GAL				26.75
Air entraining agent	GAL				11.75
03310.01 BEAM CONCRETE					
BEAM CONCRETE					
Beams and girders					
2500# or 3000# concrete					
By crane	CY	0.960	140.00	100.00	240.00
By pump	CY	0.873	140.00	94.00	234.00
By hand buggy	CY	0.800	140.00	51.00	191.00
3500# or 4000# concrete					
By crane	CY	0.960	150.00	100.00	250.00
By pump	CY	0.873	150.00	94.00	244.00
By hand buggy	CY	0.800	150.00	51.00	201.00
5000# concrete					
By crane	CY	0.960	160.00	100.00	260.00
By pump	CY	0.873	160.00	94.00	254.00
By hand buggy	CY	0.800	160.00	51.00	211.00
Bond beam, 3000# concrete					
By pump					
8" high					
4" wide	LF	0.019	0.38	2.06	2.44
6" wide	LF	0.022	0.92	2.34	3.26
8" wide	LF	0.024	1.17	2.58	3.75
10" wide	LF	0.027	1.56	2.86	4.42
12" wide	LF	0.030	2.09	3.22	5.31
16" high					
8" wide	LF	0.030	2.88	3.22	6.10
10" wide	LF	0.034	3.87	3.68	7.55
12" wide	LF	0.040	5.13	4.30	9.43
By crane					
8" high					
4" wide	LF	0.021	0.47	2.24	2.71
6" wide	LF	0.023	0.87	2.45	3.32
8" wide	LF	0.024	1.11	2.58	3.69
10" wide	LF	0.027	1.45	2.86	4.31
12" wide	LF	0.030	1.97	3.22	5.19
16" high					
8" wide	LF	0.030	2.73	3.22	5.95
10" wide	LF	0.032	3.65	3.44	7.09
12" wide	LF	0.037	4.85	3.97	8.82
03310.02 COLUMN CONCRETE					
COLUMN CONCRETE					
Columns					
2500# or 3000# concrete					
By crane	CY	0.873	140.00	94.00	234.00
By pump	CY	0.800	140.00	86.00	226.00

	Unit	Man-Hrs	Material	Labor	Total

03310.02 COLUMN CONCRETE (Cont.)

Columns
3500# or 4000# concrete

	Unit	Man-Hrs	Material	Labor	Total
By crane	CY	0.873	150.00	94.00	244.00
By pump	CY	0.800	150.00	86.00	236.00

5000# concrete

	Unit	Man-Hrs	Material	Labor	Total
By crane	CY	0.873	160.00	94.00	254.00
By pump	CY	0.800	160.00	86.00	246.00

03310.03 ELEVATED SLAB CONCRETE

ELEVATED SLAB CONCRETE
Elevated slab
2500# or 3000# concrete

	Unit	Man-Hrs	Material	Labor	Total
By crane	CY	0.480	140.00	52.00	192.00
By pump	CY	0.369	140.00	39.75	179.75
By hand buggy	CY	0.800	140.00	51.00	191.00

3500# or 4000# concrete

	Unit	Man-Hrs	Material	Labor	Total
By crane	CY	0.480	150.00	52.00	202.00
By pump	CY	0.369	150.00	39.75	189.75
By hand buggy	CY	0.800	150.00	51.00	201.00

5000# concrete

	Unit	Man-Hrs	Material	Labor	Total
By crane	CY	0.480	160.00	52.00	212.00
By pump	CY	0.369	160.00	39.75	199.75
By hand buggy	CY	0.800	160.00	51.00	211.00

Topping
2500# or 3000# concrete

	Unit	Man-Hrs	Material	Labor	Total
By crane	CY	0.480	140.00	52.00	192.00
By pump	CY	0.369	140.00	39.75	179.75
By hand buggy	CY	0.800	140.00	51.00	191.00

3500# or 4000# concrete

	Unit	Man-Hrs	Material	Labor	Total
By crane	CY	0.480	150.00	52.00	202.00
By pump	CY	0.369	150.00	39.75	189.75
By hand buggy	CY	0.800	150.00	51.00	201.00

5000# concrete

	Unit	Man-Hrs	Material	Labor	Total
By crane	CY	0.480	160.00	52.00	212.00
By pump	CY	0.369	160.00	39.75	199.75
By hand buggy	CY	0.800	160.00	51.00	211.00

03310.04 EQUIPMENT PAD CONCRETE

EQUIPMENT PAD CONCRETE
Equipment pad
2500# or 3000# concrete

	Unit	Man-Hrs	Material	Labor	Total
By chute	CY	0.267	140.00	17.00	157.00
By pump	CY	0.686	140.00	74.00	214.00
By crane	CY	0.800	140.00	86.00	226.00

3500# or 4000# concrete

	Unit	Man-Hrs	Material	Labor	Total
By chute	CY	0.267	140.00	17.00	157.00
By pump	CY	0.686	140.00	74.00	214.00
By crane	CY	0.800	140.00	86.00	226.00

5000# concrete

	Unit	Man-Hrs	Material	Labor	Total
By chute	CY	0.267	160.00	17.00	177.00
By pump	CY	0.686	160.00	74.00	234.00
By crane	CY	0.800	160.00	86.00	246.00

03310.05 FOOTING CONCRETE

FOOTING CONCRETE
Continuous footing
2500# or 3000# concrete

	Unit	Man-Hrs	Material	Labor	Total
By chute	CY	0.267	140.00	17.00	157.00
By pump	CY	0.600	140.00	65.00	205.00
By crane	CY	0.686	140.00	74.00	214.00

3500# or 4000# concrete

	Unit	Man-Hrs	Material	Labor	Total
By chute	CY	0.267	140.00	17.00	157.00
By pump	CY	0.600	140.00	65.00	205.00
By crane	CY	0.686	140.00	74.00	214.00

5000# concrete

	Unit	Man-Hrs	Material	Labor	Total
By chute	CY	0.267	160.00	17.00	177.00
By pump	CY	0.600	160.00	65.00	225.00

	Unit	Man-Hrs	Material	Labor	Total

03310.05 FOOTING CONCRETE (Cont.)

5000# concrete

By crane	CY	0.686	160.00	74.00	234.00

Spread footing

2500# or 3000# concrete

Under 5 c.y.

By chute	CY	0.267	140.00	17.00	157.00
By pump	CY	0.640	140.00	69.00	209.00
By crane	CY	0.738	140.00	79.00	219.00

Over 5 c.y.

By chute	CY	0.200	140.00	12.75	152.75
By pump	CY	0.565	140.00	61.00	201.00
By crane	CY	0.640	140.00	69.00	209.00

3500# or 4000# concrete

Under 5 c.y.

By chute	CY	0.267	150.00	17.00	167.00
By pump	CY	0.640	140.00	69.00	209.00
By crane	CY	0.738	140.00	79.00	219.00

Over 5 c.y.

By chute	CY	0.200	140.00	12.75	152.75
By pump	CY	0.565	140.00	61.00	201.00
By crane	CY	0.640	140.00	69.00	209.00

5000# concrete

Under 5 c.y.

By chute	CY	0.267	150.00	17.00	167.00
By pump	CY	0.640	150.00	69.00	219.00
By crane	CY	0.738	150.00	79.00	229.00

Over 5 c.y.

By chute	CY	0.200	150.00	12.75	162.75
By pump	CY	0.565	150.00	61.00	211.00
By crane	CY	0.640	150.00	69.00	219.00

03310.06 GRADE BEAM CONCRETE

GRADE BEAM CONCRETE

Grade beam

2500# or 3000# concrete

By chute	CY	0.267	140.00	17.00	157.00
By crane	CY	0.686	140.00	74.00	214.00
By pump	CY	0.600	140.00	65.00	205.00
By hand buggy	CY	0.800	140.00	51.00	191.00

3500# or 4000# concrete

By chute	CY	0.267	150.00	17.00	167.00
By crane	CY	0.686	150.00	74.00	224.00
By pump	CY	0.600	150.00	65.00	215.00
By hand buggy	CY	0.800	150.00	51.00	201.00

5000# concrete

By chute	CY	0.267	160.00	17.00	177.00
By crane	CY	0.686	160.00	74.00	234.00
By pump	CY	0.600	160.00	65.00	225.00
By hand buggy	CY	0.800	160.00	51.00	211.00

03310.07 PILE CAP CONCRETE

PILE CAP CONCRETE

Pile cap

2500# or 3000 concrete

By chute	CY	0.267	140.00	17.00	157.00
By crane	CY	0.800	140.00	86.00	226.00
By pump	CY	0.686	140.00	74.00	214.00
By hand buggy	CY	0.800	140.00	51.00	191.00

3500# or 4000# concrete

By chute	CY	0.267	150.00	17.00	167.00
By crane	CY	0.800	150.00	86.00	236.00
By pump	CY	0.686	150.00	74.00	224.00
By hand buggy	CY	0.800	150.00	51.00	201.00

5000# concrete

By chute	CY	0.267	160.00	17.00	177.00
By crane	CY	0.800	160.00	86.00	246.00

© 2020 BNi Publications, Inc.

	Unit	Man-Hrs	Material	Labor	Total
03310.07 PILE CAP CONCRETE (Cont.)					
5000# concrete					
By pump	CY	0.686	160.00	74.00	234.00
By hand buggy	CY	0.800	160.00	51.00	211.00
03310.08 SLAB / MAT CONCRETE					
SLAB / MAT CONCRETE					
Slab on grade					
2500# or 3000# concrete					
By chute	CY	0.200	140.00	12.75	152.75
By crane	CY	0.400	140.00	43.00	183.00
By pump	CY	0.343	140.00	37.00	177.00
By hand buggy	CY	0.533	140.00	34.00	174.00
3500# or 4000# concrete					
By chute	CY	0.200	150.00	12.75	162.75
By crane	CY	0.400	150.00	43.00	193.00
By pump	CY	0.343	150.00	37.00	187.00
By hand buggy	CY	0.533	150.00	34.00	184.00
5000# concrete					
By chute	CY	0.200	160.00	12.75	172.75
By crane	CY	0.400	160.00	43.00	203.00
By pump	CY	0.343	160.00	37.00	197.00
By hand buggy	CY	0.533	160.00	34.00	194.00
Foundation mat					
2500# or 3000# concrete, over 20 c.y.					
By chute	CY	0.160	140.00	10.25	150.25
By crane	CY	0.343	140.00	37.00	177.00
By pump	CY	0.300	140.00	32.25	172.25
By hand buggy	CY	0.400	140.00	25.50	165.50
03310.09 WALL CONCRETE					
WALL CONCRETE					
Walls					
2500# or 3000# concrete					
To 4'					
By chute	CY	0.229	140.00	14.50	154.50
By crane	CY	0.800	140.00	86.00	226.00
By pump	CY	0.738	140.00	79.00	219.00
To 8'					
By crane	CY	0.873	140.00	94.00	234.00
By pump	CY	0.800	140.00	86.00	226.00
To 16'					
By crane	CY	0.960	140.00	100.00	240.00
By pump	CY	0.873	140.00	94.00	234.00
Over 16'					
By crane	CY	1.067	140.00	110.00	250.00
By pump	CY	0.960	140.00	100.00	240.00
3500# or 4000# concrete					
To 4'					
By chute	CY	0.229	150.00	14.50	164.50
By crane	CY	0.800	150.00	86.00	236.00
By pump	CY	0.738	150.00	79.00	229.00
To 8'					
By crane	CY	0.873	150.00	94.00	244.00
By pump	CY	0.800	150.00	86.00	236.00
To 16'					
By crane	CY	0.960	150.00	100.00	250.00
By pump	CY	0.873	150.00	94.00	244.00
Over 16'					
By crane	CY	1.067	150.00	110.00	260.00
By pump	CY	0.960	150.00	100.00	250.00
5000# concrete					
To 4'					
By chute	CY	0.229	160.00	14.50	174.50
By crane	CY	0.800	160.00	86.00	246.00
By pump	CY	0.738	160.00	79.00	239.00

	Unit	Man-Hrs	Material	Labor	Total

03310.09 WALL CONCRETE (Cont.)

5000# concrete
To 8'

	Unit	Man-Hrs	Material	Labor	Total
By crane	CY	0.873	160.00	94.00	254.00
By pump	CY	0.800	160.00	86.00	246.00

To 16'

	Unit	Man-Hrs	Material	Labor	Total
By crane	CY	0.960	160.00	100.00	260.00
By pump	CY	0.873	160.00	94.00	254.00

Filled block (CMU)
3000# concrete, by pump

	Unit	Man-Hrs	Material	Labor	Total
4" wide	SF	0.034	0.53	3.68	4.21
6" wide	SF	0.040	1.19	4.30	5.49
8" wide	SF	0.048	1.86	5.16	7.02
10" wide	SF	0.056	2.49	6.07	8.56
12" wide	SF	0.069	3.21	7.37	10.58
Pilasters, 3000# concrete	CF	0.960	7.28	100.00	107.28
Wall cavity, 2" thick, 3000# concrete	SF	0.032	1.35	3.44	4.79

03310.11 STAIR CONCRETE

STAIR CONCRETE
Stairs
2500# or 3000# concrete

	Unit	Man-Hrs	Material	Labor	Total
By chute	CY	0.267	140.00	17.00	157.00
By crane	CY	0.800	140.00	86.00	226.00
By pump	CY	0.686	140.00	74.00	214.00
By hand buggy	CY	0.800	140.00	51.00	191.00

3500# or 4000# concrete

	Unit	Man-Hrs	Material	Labor	Total
By chute	CY	0.267	150.00	17.00	167.00
By crane	CY	0.800	150.00	86.00	236.00
By pump	CY	0.686	150.00	74.00	224.00
By hand buggy	CY	0.800	150.00	51.00	201.00

5000# concrete

	Unit	Man-Hrs	Material	Labor	Total
By chute	CY	0.267	160.00	17.00	177.00
By crane	CY	0.800	160.00	86.00	246.00
By pump	CY	0.686	160.00	74.00	234.00
By hand buggy	CY	0.800	160.00	51.00	211.00

03350.01 CONCRETE FINISHES

CONCRETE FINISHES
Floor finishes

	Unit	Man-Hrs	Material	Labor	Total
Broom	SF	0.011		0.72	0.72
Screed	SF	0.010		0.63	0.63
Darby	SF	0.010		0.63	0.63
Steel float	SF	0.013		0.85	0.85

Granolithic topping

	Unit	Man-Hrs	Material	Labor	Total
1/2" thick	SF	0.036	0.48	2.32	2.80
1" thick	SF	0.040	0.88	2.55	3.43
2" thick	SF	0.044	1.06	2.83	3.89

Wall finishes

	Unit	Man-Hrs	Material	Labor	Total
Burlap rub, with cement paste	SF	0.013	0.13	0.85	0.98
Float finish	SF	0.020	0.13	1.27	1.40
Etch with acid	SF	0.013	0.42	0.85	1.27

Sandblast

	Unit	Man-Hrs	Material	Labor	Total
Minimum	SF	0.016	0.14	1.36	1.50
Maximum	SF	0.016	0.52	1.36	1.88

Bush hammer

	Unit	Man-Hrs	Material	Labor	Total
Green concrete	SF	0.040		2.55	2.55
Cured concrete	SF	0.062		3.92	3.92
Break ties and patch holes	SF	0.016		1.02	1.02

Carborundum

	Unit	Man-Hrs	Material	Labor	Total
Dry rub	SF	0.027		1.70	1.70
Wet rub	SF	0.040		2.55	2.55

Floor hardeners
Metallic

	Unit	Man-Hrs	Material	Labor	Total
Light service	SF	0.010	0.44	0.63	1.07
Heavy service	SF	0.013	1.34	0.85	2.19

© 2020 BNi Publications, Inc.

	Unit	Man-Hrs	Material	Labor	Total
03350.01 CONCRETE FINISHES (Cont.)					
Floor hardeners					
Non-metallic					
Light service	SF	0.010	0.22	0.63	0.85
Heavy service	SF	0.013	0.93	0.85	1.78
Rusticated concrete finish					
Beveled edge	LF	0.044	0.43	2.83	3.26
Square edge	LF	0.057	0.61	3.64	4.25
Solid board concrete finish					
Standard	SF	0.067	1.10	4.25	5.35
Rustic	SF	0.080	1.02	5.10	6.12
03371.90 PNEUMATIC CONCRETE					
PNEUMATIC CONCRETE					
Pneumatic applied concrete (gunite)					
2" thick	SF	0.030	6.55	3.56	10.11
3" thick	SF	0.040	8.04	4.75	12.79
4" thick	SF	0.048	9.81	5.70	15.51
Finish surface					
Minimum	SF	0.040		3.26	3.26
Maximum	SF	0.080		6.52	6.52
03390.01 CURING CONCRETE					
CURING CONCRETE					
Sprayed membrane					
Slabs	SF	0.002	0.06	0.10	0.16
Walls	SF	0.002	0.09	0.12	0.21
Curing paper					
Slabs	SF	0.002	0.09	0.13	0.22
Walls	SF	0.002	0.09	0.15	0.24
Burlap					
7.5 oz.	SF	0.003	0.07	0.17	0.24
12 oz.	SF	0.003	0.10	0.18	0.28
03410.01 PRECAST BEAMS					
PRECAST BEAMS					
Prestressed, double tee, 24" deep, 8' wide					
35' span					
115 psf	SF	0.008	14.00	1.41	15.41
140 psf	SF	0.008	14.75	1.41	16.16
40' span					
80 psf	SF	0.009	13.25	1.52	14.77
143 psf	SF	0.009	14.00	1.52	15.52
45' span					
50 psf	SF	0.007	12.50	1.30	13.80
70 psf	SF	0.007	13.25	1.30	14.55
100 psf	SF	0.007	13.50	1.30	14.80
130 psf	SF	0.007	15.25	1.30	16.55
50' span					
75 psf	SF	0.007	12.50	1.18	13.68
100 psf	SF	0.007	13.50	1.18	14.68
Precast beams, girders and joists					
1000 lb/lf live load					
10' span	LF	0.160	110.00	28.50	138.50
20' span	LF	0.096	120.00	17.00	137.00
30' span	LF	0.080	150.00	14.25	164.25
3000 lb/lf live load					
10' span	LF	0.160	120.00	28.50	148.50
20' span	LF	0.096	140.00	17.00	157.00
30' span	LF	0.080	180.00	14.25	194.25
5000 lb/lf live load					
10' span	LF	0.160	120.00	28.50	148.50
20' span	LF	0.096	160.00	17.00	177.00
30' span	LF	0.080	200.00	14.25	214.25

	Unit	Man-Hrs	Material	Labor	Total

03410.02 PRECAST COLUMNS

PRECAST COLUMNS

Prestressed concrete columns

10" x 10"

	Unit	Man-Hrs	Material	Labor	Total
10' long	EA	0.960	330.00	170.00	500.00
15' long	EA	1.000	500.00	180.00	680.00
20' long	EA	1.067	660.00	190.00	850.00
25' long	EA	1.143	860.00	200.00	1,060.00
30' long	EA	1.200	1,030.00	210.00	1,240.00

12" x 12"

	Unit	Man-Hrs	Material	Labor	Total
20' long	EA	1.200	920.00	210.00	1,130.00
25' long	EA	1.297	1,110.00	230.00	1,340.00
30' long	EA	1.371	1,420.00	240.00	1,660.00

16" x 16"

	Unit	Man-Hrs	Material	Labor	Total
20' long	EA	1.200	1,420.00	210.00	1,630.00
25' long	EA	1.297	2,090.00	230.00	2,320.00
30' long	EA	1.371	2,470.00	240.00	2,710.00

20" x 20"

	Unit	Man-Hrs	Material	Labor	Total
20' long	EA	1.263	2,550.00	220.00	2,770.00
25' long	EA	1.333	3,480.00	240.00	3,720.00
30' long	EA	1.412	3,990.00	250.00	4,240.00

24" x 24"

	Unit	Man-Hrs	Material	Labor	Total
20' long	EA	1.333	3,890.00	240.00	4,130.00
25' long	EA	1.412	4,730.00	250.00	4,980.00
30' long	EA	1.500	5,840.00	270.00	6,110.00

28" x 28"

	Unit	Man-Hrs	Material	Labor	Total
20' long	EA	1.500	5,290.00	270.00	5,560.00
25' long	EA	1.600	6,400.00	280.00	6,680.00
30' long	EA	1.714	7,930.00	300.00	8,230.00

32" x 32"

	Unit	Man-Hrs	Material	Labor	Total
20' long	EA	1.600	6,680.00	280.00	6,960.00
25' long	EA	1.714	8,630.00	300.00	8,930.00
30' long	EA	1.846	9,880.00	330.00	10,210.00

36" x 36"

	Unit	Man-Hrs	Material	Labor	Total
20' long	EA	1.714	8,350.00	300.00	8,650.00
25' long	EA	1.846	10,430.00	330.00	10,760.00
30' long	EA	2.000	12,520.00	350.00	12,870.00

03410.03 PRECAST SLABS

PRECAST SLABS

Prestressed flat slab

6" thick, 4' wide

20' span

	Unit	Man-Hrs	Material	Labor	Total
80 psf	SF	0.020	20.25	3.54	23.79
110 psf	SF	0.020	20.25	3.54	23.79

25' span

	Unit	Man-Hrs	Material	Labor	Total
80 psf	SF	0.019	20.75	3.40	24.15

Cored slab

6" thick, 4' wide

20' span

	Unit	Man-Hrs	Material	Labor	Total
80 psf	SF	0.020	10.75	3.54	14.29
100 psf	SF	0.020	11.00	3.54	14.54
130 psf	SF	0.020	11.25	3.54	14.79

8" thick, 4' wide

25' span

	Unit	Man-Hrs	Material	Labor	Total
70 psf	SF	0.019	10.50	3.40	13.90
125 psf	SF	0.019	11.25	3.40	14.65
170 psf	SF	0.019	11.25	3.40	14.65

30' span

	Unit	Man-Hrs	Material	Labor	Total
70 psf	SF	0.016	10.50	2.83	13.33
90 psf	SF	0.016	11.00	2.83	13.83

35' span

	Unit	Man-Hrs	Material	Labor	Total
70 psf	SF	0.015	11.00	2.66	13.66

© 2020 BNi Publications, Inc.

	Unit	Man-Hrs	Material	Labor	Total

03410.03 PRECAST SLABS (Cont.)

Cored slab
  10" thick, 4' wide

	Unit	Man-Hrs	Material	Labor	Total
30' span					
75 psf	SF	0.016	11.00	2.83	13.83
100 psf	SF	0.016	11.25	2.83	14.08
130 psf	SF	0.016	11.75	2.83	14.58
35' span					
60 psf	SF	0.015	11.25	2.66	13.91
80 psf	SF	0.015	11.50	2.66	14.16
120 psf	SF	0.015	12.00	2.66	14.66
40' span					
65 psf	SF	0.012	12.25	2.12	14.37
Slabs, roof and floor members, 4' wide					
6" thick, 25' span	SF	0.019	9.73	3.40	13.13
8" thick, 30' span	SF	0.015	11.25	2.58	13.83
10" thick, 40' span	SF	0.013	13.75	2.30	16.05
Tee members					
Multiple tee, roof and floor					
Minimum	SF	0.012	12.50	2.12	14.62
Maximum	SF	0.024	15.75	4.25	20.00
Double tee wall member					
Minimum	SF	0.014	11.75	2.43	14.18
Maximum	SF	0.027	14.75	4.73	19.48
Single tee					
Short span, roof members					
Minimum	SF	0.015	13.00	2.58	15.58
Maximum	SF	0.030	16.00	5.32	21.32
Long span, roof members					
Minimum	SF	0.012	16.50	2.12	18.62
Maximum	SF	0.024	19.75	4.25	24.00

03450.01 PRECAST WALLS

PRECAST WALLS
  Wall panel, 8' x 20'

	Unit	Man-Hrs	Material	Labor	Total
Gray cement					
Liner finish					
4" wall	SF	0.014	15.50	2.43	17.93
5" wall	SF	0.014	16.75	2.50	19.25
6" wall	SF	0.015	19.25	2.58	21.83
8" wall	SF	0.015	19.25	2.66	21.91
Sandblast finish					
4" wall	SF	0.014	18.00	2.43	20.43
5" wall	SF	0.014	19.75	2.50	22.25
6" wall	SF	0.015	21.50	2.58	24.08
8" wall	SF	0.015	22.50	2.66	25.16
White cement					
Liner finish					
4" wall	SF	0.014	19.00	2.43	21.43
5" wall	SF	0.014	20.00	2.50	22.50
6" wall	SF	0.015	22.00	2.58	24.58
8" wall	SF	0.015	23.25	2.66	25.91
Sandblast finish					
4" wall	SF	0.014	20.25	2.43	22.68
5" wall	SF	0.014	21.50	2.50	24.00
6" wall	SF	0.015	22.00	2.58	24.58
8" wall	SF	0.015	24.50	2.66	27.16
Double tee wall panel, 24" deep					
Gray cement					
Liner finish	SF	0.016	11.00	2.83	13.83
Sandblast finish	SF	0.016	13.50	2.83	16.33
White cement					
Form liner finish	SF	0.016	15.25	2.83	18.08
Sandblast finish	SF	0.016	19.75	2.83	22.58

	Unit	Man-Hrs	Material	Labor	Total

03450.01 PRECAST WALLS (Cont.)

Wall panel, 8' x 20'
Partition panels

	Unit	Man-Hrs	Material	Labor	Total
4" wall	SF	0.016	16.50	2.83	19.33
5" wall	SF	0.016	17.75	2.83	20.58
6" wall	SF	0.016	19.50	2.83	22.33
8" wall	SF	0.016	21.25	2.83	24.08

Cladding panels

	Unit	Man-Hrs	Material	Labor	Total
4" wall	SF	0.017	16.25	3.04	19.29
5" wall	SF	0.017	17.75	3.04	20.79
6" wall	SF	0.017	19.75	3.04	22.79
8" wall	SF	0.017	21.25	3.04	24.29

Sandwich panel, 2.5" cladding panel, 2" insulation

	Unit	Man-Hrs	Material	Labor	Total
5" wall	SF	0.017	24.00	3.04	27.04
6" wall	SF	0.017	25.25	3.04	28.29
8" wall	SF	0.017	26.50	3.04	29.54

03480.01 PRECAST SPECIALTIES

PRECAST SPECIALTIES
Precast concrete, coping, 4' to 8' long

	Unit	Man-Hrs	Material	Labor	Total
12" wide	LF	0.060	11.00	7.12	18.12
10" wide	LF	0.069	9.76	8.14	17.90
Splash block, 30"x12"x4"	EA	0.400	16.75	47.50	64.25
Stair unit, per riser	EA	0.400	110.00	47.50	157.50

Sun screen and trellis, 8' long, 12" high

	Unit	Man-Hrs	Material	Labor	Total
4" thick blades	EA	0.300	120.00	35.75	155.75
5" thick blades	EA	0.300	140.00	35.75	175.75
6" thick blades	EA	0.320	180.00	38.00	218.00
8" thick blades	EA	0.320	230.00	38.00	268.00

Bearing pads for precast members, 2" wide strips

	Unit	Man-Hrs	Material	Labor	Total
1/8" thick	LF	0.003	0.39	0.20	0.59
1/4" thick	LF	0.003	0.51	0.20	0.71
1/2" thick	LF	0.003	0.58	0.20	0.78
3/4" thick	LF	0.004	1.14	0.23	1.37
1" thick	LF	0.004	1.18	0.25	1.43
1-1/2" thick	LF	0.004	1.51	0.25	1.76

03530.01 CONCRETE TOPPINGS

CONCRETE TOPPINGS
Gypsum fill

	Unit	Man-Hrs	Material	Labor	Total
2" thick	SF	0.005	2.16	0.53	2.69
2-1/2" thick	SF	0.005	2.46	0.54	3.00
3" thick	SF	0.005	3.03	0.56	3.59
3-1/2" thick	SF	0.005	3.46	0.57	4.03
4" thick	SF	0.006	4.05	0.64	4.69

Formboard
Mineral fiber board

	Unit	Man-Hrs	Material	Labor	Total
1" thick	SF	0.020	1.94	1.27	3.21
1-1/2" thick	SF	0.023	5.09	1.45	6.54

Cement fiber board

	Unit	Man-Hrs	Material	Labor	Total
1" thick	SF	0.027	1.51	1.70	3.21
1-1/2" thick	SF	0.031	1.94	1.96	3.90

Glass fiber board

	Unit	Man-Hrs	Material	Labor	Total
1" thick	SF	0.020	2.38	1.27	3.65
1-1/2" thick	SF	0.023	3.23	1.45	4.68

Poured deck
Vermiculite or perlite

	Unit	Man-Hrs	Material	Labor	Total
1 to 4 mix	CY	0.800	210.00	86.00	296.00
1 to 6 mix	CY	0.738	180.00	79.00	259.00

Vermiculite or perlite
2" thick

	Unit	Man-Hrs	Material	Labor	Total
1 to 4 mix	SF	0.005	1.94	0.54	2.48
1 to 6 mix	SF	0.005	1.41	0.49	1.90

3" thick

	Unit	Man-Hrs	Material	Labor	Total
1 to 4 mix	SF	0.007	2.64	0.79	3.43
1 to 6 mix	SF	0.007	2.09	0.73	2.82

© 2020 BNi Publications, Inc.

	Unit	Man-Hrs	Material	Labor	Total
03530.01 CONCRETE TOPPINGS (Cont.)					
Concrete plank, lightweight					
2" thick	SF	0.024	10.50	4.25	14.75
2-1/2" thick	SF	0.024	10.75	4.25	15.00
3-1/2" thick	SF	0.027	11.25	4.73	15.98
4" thick	SF	0.027	11.75	4.73	16.48
Channel slab, lightweight, straight					
2-3/4" thick	SF	0.024	8.49	4.25	12.74
3-1/2" thick	SF	0.024	8.74	4.25	12.99
3-3/4" thick	SF	0.024	9.43	4.25	13.68
4-3/4" thick	SF	0.027	12.00	4.73	16.73
Gypsum plank					
2" thick	SF	0.024	3.92	4.25	8.17
3" thick	SF	0.024	4.12	4.25	8.37
Cement fiber, T & G planks					
1" thick	SF	0.022	2.16	3.87	6.03
1-1/2" thick	SF	0.022	2.30	3.87	6.17
2" thick	SF	0.024	2.74	4.25	6.99
2-1/2" thick	SF	0.024	2.91	4.25	7.16
3" thick	SF	0.024	3.78	4.25	8.03
3-1/2" thick	SF	0.027	4.37	4.73	9.10
4" thick	SF	0.027	4.80	4.73	9.53
03610.01 GROUTING					
GROUTING					
Grouting for bases					
Non-shrink					
Metallic grout					
1" deep	SF	0.160	8.87	13.50	22.37
2" deep	SF	0.178	16.75	15.00	31.75
Non-metallic grout					
1" deep	SF	0.160	6.68	13.50	20.18
2" deep	SF	0.178	12.75	15.00	27.75
Fluid type					
Non-metallic					
1" deep	SF	0.160	6.83	13.50	20.33
2" deep	SF	0.178	12.00	15.00	27.00
Grouting for joints					
Portland cement grout (1 cement to 3 sand)					
1/2" joint thickness					
6" wide joints	LF	0.027	0.22	2.26	2.48
8" wide joints	LF	0.032	0.25	2.72	2.97
1" joint thickness					
4" wide joints	LF	0.025	0.25	2.12	2.37
6" wide joints	LF	0.028	0.41	2.34	2.75
8" wide joints	LF	0.033	0.51	2.83	3.34
Non-shrink, non-metallic grout					
1/2" joint thickness					
4" wide joint	LF	0.023	1.20	1.94	3.14
6" wide joint	LF	0.027	1.58	2.26	3.84
8" wide joint	LF	0.032	2.06	2.72	4.78
1" joint thickness					
4" wide joint	LF	0.025	2.06	2.12	4.18
6" wide joint	LF	0.028	3.12	2.34	5.46
8" wide joint	LF	0.033	4.23	2.83	7.06
03821.31 CORE DRILLING					
CORE DRILLING					
Concrete					
6" thick					
3" dia.	EA	0.571		48.50	48.50
4" dia.	EA	0.667		57.00	57.00
6" dia.	EA	0.800		68.00	68.00
8" dia.	EA	1.333		110.00	110.00
8" thick					
3" dia.	EA	0.800		68.00	68.00
4" dia.	EA	1.000		85.00	85.00

	Unit	Man-Hrs	Material	Labor	Total
03821.31 CORE DRILLING (Cont.)					
8" thick					
6" dia.	EA	1.143		97.00	97.00
8" dia.	EA	1.600		140.00	140.00
10" thick					
3" dia.	EA	1.000		85.00	85.00
4" dia.	EA	1.143		97.00	97.00
6" dia.	EA	1.333		110.00	110.00
8" dia.	EA	2.000		170.00	170.00
12" thick					
3" dia.	EA	1.333		110.00	110.00
4" dia.	EA	1.600		140.00	140.00
6" dia.	EA	2.000		170.00	170.00
8" dia.	EA	2.667		230.00	230.00

© 2020 BNi Publications, Inc.

	Unit	Man-Hrs	Material	Labor	Total

04012.01 RESTORATION AND CLEANING

RESTORATION AND CLEANING

Masonry cleaning

Washing brick

	Unit	Man-Hrs	Material	Labor	Total
Smooth surface	SF	0.013	0.26	1.03	1.29
Rough surface	SF	0.018	0.36	1.38	1.74

Steam clean masonry

Smooth face

	Unit	Man-Hrs	Material	Labor	Total
Minimum	SF	0.010	0.56	0.85	1.41
Maximum	SF	0.015	0.90	1.23	2.13

Rough face

	Unit	Man-Hrs	Material	Labor	Total
Minimum	SF	0.013	0.82	1.13	1.95
Maximum	SF	0.020	1.21	1.70	2.91

Sandblast masonry

	Unit	Man-Hrs	Material	Labor	Total
Minimum	SF	0.016	0.50	1.36	1.86
Maximum	SF	0.027	0.76	2.26	3.02

Pointing masonry

	Unit	Man-Hrs	Material	Labor	Total
Brick	SF	0.032	1.37	2.48	3.85
Concrete block	SF	0.023	0.60	1.77	2.37

Cut and repoint

Brick

	Unit	Man-Hrs	Material	Labor	Total
Minimum	SF	0.040	0.47	3.11	3.58
Maximum	SF	0.080	0.81	6.22	7.03
Stone work	LF	0.062	1.24	4.78	6.02

Cut and recaulk

	Unit	Man-Hrs	Material	Labor	Total
Oil base caulks	LF	0.053	1.59	4.14	5.73
Butyl caulks	LF	0.053	1.40	4.14	5.54
Polysulfides and acrylics	LF	0.053	2.71	4.14	6.85
Silicones	LF	0.053	3.17	4.14	7.31

Cement and sand grout on walls, to 1/8" thick

	Unit	Man-Hrs	Material	Labor	Total
Minimum	SF	0.032	0.78	2.48	3.26
Maximum	SF	0.040	1.98	3.11	5.09

Brick removal and replacement

	Unit	Man-Hrs	Material	Labor	Total
Minimum	EA	0.100	0.82	7.77	8.59
Average	EA	0.133	1.07	10.25	11.32
Maximum	EA	0.400	2.17	31.00	33.17

04051.61 MASONRY GROUT

MASONRY GROUT

	Unit	Man-Hrs	Material	Labor	Total
Grout, non-shrink, non-metallic, trowelable	CF	0.016	5.94	1.90	7.84

Grout door frame, hollow metal

	Unit	Man-Hrs	Material	Labor	Total
Single	EA	0.600	14.50	71.00	85.50
Double	EA	0.632	20.50	75.00	95.50

Grout-filled concrete block (CMU)

	Unit	Man-Hrs	Material	Labor	Total
4" wide	SF	0.020	0.43	2.37	2.80
6" wide	SF	0.022	1.12	2.59	3.71
8" wide	SF	0.024	1.65	2.85	4.50
12" wide	SF	0.025	2.71	3.00	5.71

Grout-filled individual CMU cells

	Unit	Man-Hrs	Material	Labor	Total
4" wide	LF	0.012	0.36	1.42	1.78
6" wide	LF	0.012	0.48	1.42	1.90
8" wide	LF	0.012	0.64	1.42	2.06
10" wide	LF	0.014	0.80	1.62	2.42
12" wide	LF	0.014	0.97	1.62	2.59

Bond beams or lintels, 8" deep

	Unit	Man-Hrs	Material	Labor	Total
6" thick	LF	0.022	0.97	2.34	3.31
8" thick	LF	0.024	1.28	2.58	3.86
10" thick	LF	0.027	1.61	2.86	4.47
12" thick	LF	0.030	1.93	3.22	5.15

Cavity walls

	Unit	Man-Hrs	Material	Labor	Total
2" thick	SF	0.032	1.07	3.44	4.51
3" thick	SF	0.032	1.61	3.44	5.05
4" thick	SF	0.034	2.14	3.68	5.82
6" thick	SF	0.040	3.21	4.30	7.51

04052.31 MASONRY ACCESSORIES

	Unit	Man-Hrs	Material	Labor	Total
MASONRY ACCESSORIES					
Foundation vents	EA	0.320	26.25	24.75	51.00
Bar reinforcing					
Horizontal					
#3 - #4	LB	0.032	0.63	2.48	3.11
#5 - #6	LB	0.027	0.63	2.07	2.70
Vertical					
#3 - #4	LB	0.040	0.63	3.11	3.74
#5 - #6	LB	0.032	0.63	2.48	3.11
Horizontal joint reinforcing					
Truss type					
4" wide, 6" wall	LF	0.003	0.20	0.24	0.44
6" wide, 8" wall	LF	0.003	0.20	0.25	0.45
8" wide, 10" wall	LF	0.003	0.25	0.27	0.52
10" wide, 12" wall	LF	0.004	0.25	0.28	0.53
12" wide, 14" wall	LF	0.004	0.30	0.29	0.59
Ladder type					
4" wide, 6" wall	LF	0.003	0.15	0.24	0.39
6" wide, 8" wall	LF	0.003	0.17	0.25	0.42
8" wide, 10" wall	LF	0.003	0.18	0.27	0.45
10" wide, 12" wall	LF	0.003	0.22	0.27	0.49
Rectangular wall ties					
3/16" dia., galvanized					
2" x 6"	EA	0.013	0.38	1.03	1.41
2" x 8"	EA	0.013	0.40	1.03	1.43
2" x 10"	EA	0.013	0.47	1.03	1.50
2" x 12"	EA	0.013	0.53	1.03	1.56
4" x 6"	EA	0.016	0.44	1.24	1.68
4" x 8"	EA	0.016	0.49	1.24	1.73
4" x 10"	EA	0.016	0.63	1.24	1.87
4" x 12"	EA	0.016	0.73	1.24	1.97
1/4" dia., galvanized					
2" x 6"	EA	0.013	0.71	1.03	1.74
2" x 8"	EA	0.013	0.80	1.03	1.83
2" x 10"	EA	0.013	0.91	1.03	1.94
2" x 12"	EA	0.013	1.04	1.03	2.07
4" x 6"	EA	0.016	0.82	1.24	2.06
4" x 8"	EA	0.016	0.91	1.24	2.15
4" x 10"	EA	0.016	1.04	1.24	2.28
4" x 12"	EA	0.016	1.08	1.24	2.32
Z-type wall ties, galvanized					
6" long					
1/8" dia.	EA	0.013	0.34	1.03	1.37
3/16" dia.	EA	0.013	0.36	1.03	1.39
1/4" dia.	EA	0.013	0.38	1.03	1.41
8" long					
1/8" dia.	EA	0.013	0.36	1.03	1.39
3/16" dia.	EA	0.013	0.38	1.03	1.41
1/4" dia.	EA	0.013	0.40	1.03	1.43
10" long					
1/8" dia.	EA	0.013	0.38	1.03	1.41
3/16" dia.	EA	0.013	0.44	1.03	1.47
1/4" dia.	EA	0.013	0.49	1.03	1.52
Dovetail anchor slots					
Galvanized steel, filled					
24 ga.	LF	0.020	1.17	1.55	2.72
20 ga.	LF	0.020	2.46	1.55	4.01
16 oz. copper, foam filled	LF	0.020	3.53	1.55	5.08
Dovetail anchors					
16 ga.					
3-1/2" long	EA	0.013	0.39	1.03	1.42
5-1/2" long	EA	0.013	0.48	1.03	1.51
12 ga.					
3-1/2" long	EA	0.013	0.52	1.03	1.55
5-1/2" long	EA	0.013	0.86	1.03	1.89

© 2020 BNi Publications, Inc.

	Unit	Man-Hrs	Material	Labor	Total

04052.31 MASONRY ACCESSORIES (Cont.)

Dovetail, triangular galvanized ties, 12 ga.

	Unit	Man-Hrs	Material	Labor	Total
3" x 3"	EA	0.013	0.88	1.03	1.91
5" x 5"	EA	0.013	0.95	1.03	1.98
7" x 7"	EA	0.013	1.07	1.03	2.10
7" x 9"	EA	0.013	1.14	1.03	2.17

Brick anchors
  Corrugated, 3-1/2" long

	Unit	Man-Hrs	Material	Labor	Total
16 ga.	EA	0.013	0.57	1.03	1.60
12 ga.	EA	0.013	0.66	1.03	1.69

  Non-corrugated, 3-1/2" long

	Unit	Man-Hrs	Material	Labor	Total
16 ga.	EA	0.013	0.47	1.03	1.50
12 ga.	EA	0.013	0.85	1.03	1.88

Cavity wall anchors, corrugated, galvanized
  5" long

	Unit	Man-Hrs	Material	Labor	Total
16 ga.	EA	0.013	0.95	1.03	1.98
12 ga.	EA	0.013	1.43	1.03	2.46

  7" long

	Unit	Man-Hrs	Material	Labor	Total
28 ga.	EA	0.013	1.05	1.03	2.08
24 ga.	EA	0.013	1.33	1.03	2.36
22 ga.	EA	0.013	1.36	1.03	2.39
16 ga.	EA	0.013	1.55	1.03	2.58

Mesh ties, 16 ga., 3" wide

	Unit	Man-Hrs	Material	Labor	Total
8" long	EA	0.013	1.28	1.03	2.31
12" long	EA	0.013	1.43	1.03	2.46
20" long	EA	0.013	1.96	1.03	2.99
24" long	EA	0.013	2.16	1.03	3.19

04052.32 MASONRY CONTROL JOINTS

MASONRY CONTROL JOINTS

	Unit	Man-Hrs	Material	Labor	Total
Control joint, cross shaped PVC	LF	0.020	2.38	1.55	3.93

Closed cell joint filler

	Unit	Man-Hrs	Material	Labor	Total
1/2"	LF	0.020	0.41	1.55	1.96
3/4"	LF	0.020	0.85	1.55	2.40

Rubber, for

	Unit	Man-Hrs	Material	Labor	Total
4" wall	LF	0.020	2.75	1.55	4.30
6" wall	LF	0.021	3.40	1.63	5.03
8" wall	LF	0.022	4.10	1.72	5.82

PVC, for

	Unit	Man-Hrs	Material	Labor	Total
4" wall	LF	0.020	1.43	1.55	2.98
6" wall	LF	0.021	2.41	1.63	4.04
8" wall	LF	0.022	3.65	1.72	5.37

04052.35 MASONRY FLASHING

MASONRY FLASHING
  Through-wall flashing

	Unit	Man-Hrs	Material	Labor	Total
5 oz. coated copper	SF	0.067	4.18	5.18	9.36
0.030" elastomeric	SF	0.053	1.32	4.14	5.46

04211.31 BRICK MASONRY

BRICK MASONRY
  Standard size brick, running bond
  Face brick, red (6.4/sf)

	Unit	Man-Hrs	Material	Labor	Total
Veneer	SF	0.133	5.66	10.25	15.91
Cavity wall	SF	0.114	5.66	8.88	14.54
9" solid wall	SF	0.229	11.25	17.75	29.00

Common brick (6.4/sf)

	Unit	Man-Hrs	Material	Labor	Total
Select common for veneers	SF	0.133	3.69	10.25	13.94

Back-up

	Unit	Man-Hrs	Material	Labor	Total
4" thick	SF	0.100	3.32	7.77	11.09
8" thick	SF	0.160	6.65	12.50	19.15

Firewall

	Unit	Man-Hrs	Material	Labor	Total
12" thick	SF	0.267	10.75	20.75	31.50
16" thick	SF	0.364	14.25	28.25	42.50

Glazed brick (7.4/sf)

	Unit	Man-Hrs	Material	Labor	Total
Veneer	SF	0.145	15.25	11.25	26.50

	Unit	Man-Hrs	Material	Labor	Total

04211.31 BRICK MASONRY (Cont.)

Standard size brick, running bond

Buff or gray face brick (6.4/sf)

	Unit	Man-Hrs	Material	Labor	Total
Veneer	SF	0.133	6.58	10.25	16.83
Cavity wall	SF	0.114	6.58	8.88	15.46

Jumbo or oversize brick (3/sf)

	Unit	Man-Hrs	Material	Labor	Total
4" veneer	SF	0.080	4.76	6.22	10.98
4" back-up	SF	0.067	4.76	5.18	9.94
8" back-up	SF	0.114	5.52	8.88	14.40
12" firewall	SF	0.200	7.42	15.50	22.92
16" firewall	SF	0.267	10.50	20.75	31.25

Norman brick, red face (4.5/sf)

	Unit	Man-Hrs	Material	Labor	Total
4" veneer	SF	0.100	7.88	7.77	15.65
Cavity wall	SF	0.089	7.88	6.91	14.79

Chimney, standard brick, including flue

	Unit	Man-Hrs	Material	Labor	Total
16" x 16"	LF	0.800	32.00	62.00	94.00
16" x 20"	LF	0.800	54.00	62.00	116.00
16" x 24"	LF	0.800	58.00	62.00	120.00
20" x 20"	LF	1.000	45.00	78.00	123.00
20" x 24"	LF	1.000	61.00	78.00	139.00
20" x 32"	LF	1.143	68.00	89.00	157.00
Window sill, face brick on edge	LF	0.200	3.59	15.50	19.09

04212.31 STRUCTURAL TILE

STRUCTURAL TILE

Structural glazed tile

6T series, 5-1/2" x 12"

Glazed on one side

	Unit	Man-Hrs	Material	Labor	Total
2" thick	SF	0.080	11.00	6.22	17.22
4" thick	SF	0.080	13.25	6.22	19.47
6" thick	SF	0.089	20.75	6.91	27.66
8" thick	SF	0.100	25.50	7.77	33.27

Glazed on two sides

	Unit	Man-Hrs	Material	Labor	Total
4" thick	SF	0.100	19.25	7.77	27.02
6" thick	SF	0.114	26.50	8.88	35.38

Special shapes

	Unit	Man-Hrs	Material	Labor	Total
Group 1	SF	0.160	11.25	12.50	23.75
Group 2	SF	0.160	14.25	12.50	26.75
Group 3	SF	0.160	18.75	12.50	31.25
Group 4	SF	0.160	37.75	12.50	50.25
Group 5	SF	0.160	46.00	12.50	58.50

Fire rated

	Unit	Man-Hrs	Material	Labor	Total
4" thick, 1 hr rating	SF	0.080	18.00	6.22	24.22
6" thick, 2 hr rating	SF	0.089	25.25	6.91	32.16

8W series, 8" x 16"

Glazed on one side

	Unit	Man-Hrs	Material	Labor	Total
2" thick	SF	0.053	12.50	4.14	16.64
4" thick	SF	0.053	13.25	4.14	17.39
6" thick	SF	0.062	22.00	4.78	26.78
8" thick	SF	0.062	24.00	4.78	28.78

Glazed on two sides

	Unit	Man-Hrs	Material	Labor	Total
4" thick	SF	0.067	21.00	5.18	26.18
6" thick	SF	0.080	29.25	6.22	35.47
8" thick	SF	0.080	35.50	6.22	41.72

Special shapes

	Unit	Man-Hrs	Material	Labor	Total
Group 1	SF	0.114	18.75	8.88	27.63
Group 2	SF	0.114	23.00	8.88	31.88
Group 3	SF	0.114	25.25	8.88	34.13
Group 4	SF	0.114	42.00	8.88	50.88
Group 5	SF	0.114	53.00	8.88	61.88

Fire rated

	Unit	Man-Hrs	Material	Labor	Total
4" thick, 1 hr rating	SF	0.114	31.50	8.88	40.38
6" thick, 2 hr rating	SF	0.114	43.25	8.88	52.13

© 2020 BNi Publications, Inc.

04220.01 CONCRETE MASONRY UNITS

	Unit	Man-Hrs	Material	Labor	Total
CONCRETE MASONRY UNITS					
Hollow, load bearing					
4"	SF	0.059	1.62	4.60	6.22
6"	SF	0.062	2.38	4.78	7.16
8"	SF	0.067	2.73	5.18	7.91
10"	SF	0.073	3.77	5.65	9.42
12"	SF	0.080	4.34	6.22	10.56
Solid, load bearing					
4"	SF	0.059	2.55	4.60	7.15
6"	SF	0.062	2.86	4.78	7.64
8"	SF	0.067	3.91	5.18	9.09
10"	SF	0.073	4.16	5.65	9.81
12"	SF	0.080	6.19	6.22	12.41
Back-up block, 8" x 16"					
2"	SF	0.046	1.70	3.55	5.25
4"	SF	0.047	1.78	3.65	5.43
6"	SF	0.050	2.60	3.88	6.48
8"	SF	0.053	2.99	4.14	7.13
10"	SF	0.057	4.13	4.44	8.57
12"	SF	0.062	4.75	4.78	9.53
Foundation wall, 8" x 16"					
6"	SF	0.057	2.60	4.44	7.04
8"	SF	0.062	2.99	4.78	7.77
10"	SF	0.067	4.13	5.18	9.31
12"	SF	0.073	4.76	5.65	10.41
Solid					
6"	SF	0.062	3.15	4.78	7.93
8"	SF	0.067	4.30	5.18	9.48
10"	SF	0.073	4.57	5.65	10.22
12"	SF	0.080	6.79	6.22	13.01
Exterior, styrofoam inserts, std weight, 8" x 16"					
6"	SF	0.062	4.57	4.78	9.35
8"	SF	0.067	4.93	5.18	10.11
10"	SF	0.073	6.40	5.65	12.05
12"	SF	0.080	8.77	6.22	14.99
Lightweight					
6"	SF	0.062	5.09	4.78	9.87
8"	SF	0.067	5.73	5.18	10.91
10"	SF	0.073	6.08	5.65	11.73
12"	SF	0.080	8.04	6.22	14.26
Acoustical slotted block					
4"	SF	0.073	5.31	5.65	10.96
6"	SF	0.073	5.56	5.65	11.21
8"	SF	0.080	6.94	6.22	13.16
Filled cavities					
4"	SF	0.089	5.69	6.91	12.60
6"	SF	0.094	6.55	7.31	13.86
8"	SF	0.100	8.40	7.77	16.17
Hollow, split face					
4"	SF	0.059	3.64	4.60	8.24
6"	SF	0.062	4.21	4.78	8.99
8"	SF	0.067	4.42	5.18	9.60
10"	SF	0.073	4.95	5.65	10.60
12"	SF	0.080	5.28	6.22	11.50
Split rib profile					
4"	SF	0.073	4.42	5.65	10.07
6"	SF	0.073	5.13	5.65	10.78
8"	SF	0.080	5.58	6.22	11.80
10"	SF	0.080	6.12	6.22	12.34
12"	SF	0.080	6.63	6.22	12.85
High strength block, 3500 psi					
2"	SF	0.059	1.71	4.60	6.31
4"	SF	0.062	2.14	4.78	6.92
6"	SF	0.062	2.56	4.78	7.34

	Unit	Man-Hrs	Material	Labor	Total

04220.01 CONCRETE MASONRY UNITS (Cont.)

High strength block, 3500 psi

	Unit	Man-Hrs	Material	Labor	Total
8"	SF	0.067	2.90	5.18	8.08
10"	SF	0.073	3.38	5.65	9.03
12"	SF	0.080	4.00	6.22	10.22

Solar screen concrete block

4" thick

	Unit	Man-Hrs	Material	Labor	Total
6" x 6"	SF	0.178	4.29	13.75	18.04
8" x 8"	SF	0.160	5.12	12.50	17.62
12" x 12"	SF	0.123	5.24	9.56	14.80

8" thick

	Unit	Man-Hrs	Material	Labor	Total
8" x 16"	SF	0.114	5.24	8.88	14.12

Glazed block

	Unit	Man-Hrs	Material	Labor	Total
Cove base, glazed 1 side, 2"	LF	0.089	11.00	6.91	17.91
4"	LF	0.089	11.25	6.91	18.16
6"	LF	0.100	11.50	7.77	19.27
8"	LF	0.100	12.50	7.77	20.27

Single face

	Unit	Man-Hrs	Material	Labor	Total
2"	SF	0.067	11.50	5.18	16.68
4"	SF	0.067	14.25	5.18	19.43
6"	SF	0.073	15.25	5.65	20.90
8"	SF	0.080	16.00	6.22	22.22
10"	SF	0.089	18.00	6.91	24.91
12"	SF	0.094	19.25	7.31	26.56

Double face

	Unit	Man-Hrs	Material	Labor	Total
4"	SF	0.084	17.25	6.54	23.79
6"	SF	0.089	20.25	6.91	27.16
8"	SF	0.100	21.25	7.77	29.02

Corner or bullnose

	Unit	Man-Hrs	Material	Labor	Total
2"	EA	0.100	18.25	7.77	26.02
4"	EA	0.114	23.50	8.88	32.38
6"	EA	0.114	28.75	8.88	37.63
8"	EA	0.133	31.25	10.25	41.50
10"	EA	0.145	34.00	11.25	45.25
12"	EA	0.160	36.50	12.50	49.00

Gypsum unit masonry

Partition blocks (12"x30")

Solid

	Unit	Man-Hrs	Material	Labor	Total
2"	SF	0.032	1.41	2.48	3.89

Hollow

	Unit	Man-Hrs	Material	Labor	Total
3"	SF	0.032	1.42	2.48	3.90
4"	SF	0.033	1.63	2.59	4.22
6"	SF	0.036	1.74	2.82	4.56

Vertical reinforcing

    4' o.c., add 5% to labor

    2'8" o.c., add 15% to labor

Interior partitions, add 10% to labor

04220.09 BOND BEAMS & LINTELS

BOND BEAMS & LINTELS

Bond beam, no grout or reinforcement

8" x 16" x

	Unit	Man-Hrs	Material	Labor	Total
4" thick	LF	0.062	1.85	4.78	6.63
6" thick	LF	0.064	2.83	4.97	7.80
8" thick	LF	0.067	3.24	5.18	8.42
10" thick	LF	0.070	4.01	5.40	9.41
12" thick	LF	0.073	4.56	5.65	10.21

Beam lintel, no grout or reinforcement

8" x 16" x

	Unit	Man-Hrs	Material	Labor	Total
10" thick	LF	0.080	8.85	6.22	15.07
12" thick	LF	0.089	9.42	6.91	16.33

Precast masonry lintel

6 lf, 8" high x

	Unit	Man-Hrs	Material	Labor	Total
4" thick	LF	0.133	7.80	10.25	18.05
6" thick	LF	0.133	9.96	10.25	20.21
8" thick	LF	0.145	11.25	11.25	22.50

© 2020 BNi Publications, Inc.

	Unit	Man-Hrs	Material	Labor	Total
04220.09 BOND BEAMS & LINTELS (Cont.)					
6 lf, 8" high x					
10" thick	LF	0.145	13.50	11.25	24.75
10 lf, 8" high x					
4" thick	LF	0.080	9.80	6.22	16.02
6" thick	LF	0.080	12.00	6.22	18.22
8" thick	LF	0.089	13.50	6.91	20.41
10" thick	LF	0.089	18.25	6.91	25.16
Steel angles and plates					
Minimum	LB	0.011	1.46	0.88	2.34
Maximum	LB	0.020	2.15	1.55	3.70
Various size angle lintels					
1/4" stock					
3" x 3"	LF	0.050	7.54	3.88	11.42
3" x 3-1/2"	LF	0.050	8.30	3.88	12.18
3/8" stock					
3" x 4"	LF	0.050	13.00	3.88	16.88
3-1/2" x 4"	LF	0.050	13.75	3.88	17.63
4" x 4"	LF	0.050	15.00	3.88	18.88
5" x 3-1/2"	LF	0.050	16.00	3.88	19.88
6" x 3-1/2"	LF	0.050	18.00	3.88	21.88
1/2" stock					
6" x 4"	LF	0.050	19.75	3.88	23.63
04230.01 GLASS BLOCK					
GLASS BLOCK					
Glass block, 4" thick					
6" x 6"	SF	0.267	38.25	20.75	59.00
8" x 8"	SF	0.200	24.25	15.50	39.75
12" x 12"	SF	0.160	30.75	12.50	43.25
04240.01 CLAY TILE					
CLAY TILE					
Hollow clay tile, for back-up, 12" x 12"					
Scored face					
Load bearing					
4" thick	SF	0.057	7.22	4.44	11.66
6" thick	SF	0.059	8.42	4.60	13.02
8" thick	SF	0.062	10.50	4.78	15.28
10" thick	SF	0.064	13.00	4.97	17.97
12" thick	SF	0.067	22.00	5.18	27.18
Non-load bearing					
3" thick	SF	0.055	5.85	4.28	10.13
4" thick	SF	0.057	6.77	4.44	11.21
6" thick	SF	0.059	7.84	4.60	12.44
8" thick	SF	0.062	9.99	4.78	14.77
12" thick	SF	0.067	17.75	5.18	22.93
Partition, 12" x 12"					
In walls					
3" thick	SF	0.067	5.85	5.18	11.03
4" thick	SF	0.067	6.78	5.18	11.96
6" thick	SF	0.070	7.48	5.40	12.88
8" thick	SF	0.073	9.81	5.65	15.46
10" thick	SF	0.076	11.75	5.92	17.67
12" thick	SF	0.080	17.00	6.22	23.22
Clay tile floors					
4" thick	SF	0.044	6.77	3.45	10.22
6" thick	SF	0.047	8.42	3.65	12.07
8" thick	SF	0.050	10.50	3.88	14.38
10" thick	SF	0.053	13.00	4.14	17.14
12" thick	SF	0.057	19.25	4.44	23.69
Terra cotta					
Coping, 10" or 12" wide, 3" thick	LF	0.160	16.00	12.50	28.50

	Unit	Man-Hrs	Material	Labor	Total

04430.01 STONE

STONE
  Rubble stone
    Walls set in mortar

	Unit	Man-Hrs	Material	Labor	Total
8" thick	SF	0.200	17.50	15.50	33.00
12" thick	SF	0.320	21.00	24.75	45.75
18" thick	SF	0.400	28.00	31.00	59.00
24" thick	SF	0.533	35.00	41.50	76.50

    Dry set wall

	Unit	Man-Hrs	Material	Labor	Total
8" thick	SF	0.133	19.50	10.25	29.75
12" thick	SF	0.200	22.25	15.50	37.75
18" thick	SF	0.267	30.50	20.75	51.25
24" thick	SF	0.320	37.25	24.75	62.00

  Cut stone
   Imported marble
    Facing panels

	Unit	Man-Hrs	Material	Labor	Total
3/4" thick	SF	0.320	45.25	24.75	70.00
1-1/2" thick	SF	0.364	64.00	28.25	92.25
2-1/4" thick	SF	0.444	77.00	34.50	111.50

    Base
     1" thick

	Unit	Man-Hrs	Material	Labor	Total
4" high	LF	0.400	20.50	31.00	51.50
6" high	LF	0.400	24.75	31.00	55.75

    Columns, solid

	Unit	Man-Hrs	Material	Labor	Total
Plain faced	CF	5.333	150.00	410.00	560.00
Fluted	CF	5.333	420.00	410.00	830.00
Flooring, travertine, minimum	SF	0.123	20.75	9.56	30.31
Average	SF	0.160	27.75	12.50	40.25
Maximum	SF	0.178	51.00	13.75	64.75

   Domestic marble
    Facing panels

	Unit	Man-Hrs	Material	Labor	Total
7/8" thick	SF	0.320	42.50	24.75	67.25
1-1/2" thick	SF	0.364	64.00	28.25	92.25
2-1/4" thick	SF	0.444	77.00	34.50	111.50

    Stairs

	Unit	Man-Hrs	Material	Labor	Total
12" treads	LF	0.400	38.00	31.00	69.00
6" risers	LF	0.267	28.25	20.75	49.00

    Thresholds, 7/8" thick, 3' long, 4" to 6" wide

	Unit	Man-Hrs	Material	Labor	Total
Plain	EA	0.667	34.50	52.00	86.50
Beveled	EA	0.667	38.25	52.00	90.25

    Window sill

	Unit	Man-Hrs	Material	Labor	Total
6" wide, 2" thick	LF	0.320	19.25	24.75	44.00

    Stools

	Unit	Man-Hrs	Material	Labor	Total
5" wide, 7/8" thick	LF	0.320	25.75	24.75	50.50

   Limestone panels up to 12' x 5', smooth finish

	Unit	Man-Hrs	Material	Labor	Total
2" thick	SF	0.096	29.50	11.50	41.00
3" thick	SF	0.096	34.50	11.50	46.00
4" thick	SF	0.096	49.25	11.50	60.75

   Miscellaneous limestone items

	Unit	Man-Hrs	Material	Labor	Total
Steps, 14" wide, 6" deep	LF	0.533	63.00	41.50	104.50
Coping, smooth finish	CF	0.267	88.00	20.75	108.75
Sills, lintels, jambs, smooth finish	CF	0.320	88.00	24.75	112.75

   Granite veneer facing panels, polished
    7/8" thick

	Unit	Man-Hrs	Material	Labor	Total
Black	SF	0.320	48.25	24.75	73.00
Gray	SF	0.320	38.00	24.75	62.75

    Base

	Unit	Man-Hrs	Material	Labor	Total
4" high	LF	0.160	20.25	12.50	32.75
6" high	LF	0.178	24.50	13.75	38.25
Curbing, straight, 6" x 16"	LF	0.400	22.50	47.50	70.00
Radius curbs, radius over 5'	LF	0.533	27.50	63.00	90.50

   Ashlar veneer

	Unit	Man-Hrs	Material	Labor	Total
4" thick, random	SF	0.320	34.00	24.75	58.75

   Pavers, 4" x 4" split

	Unit	Man-Hrs	Material	Labor	Total
Gray	SF	0.160	33.25	12.50	45.75
Pink	SF	0.160	32.75	12.50	45.25

© 2020 BNi Publications, Inc.

	Unit	Man-Hrs	Material	Labor	Total
04430.01 STONE (Cont.)					
Pavers, 4" x 4" split					
Black	SF	0.160	32.25	12.50	44.75
Slate, panels					
1" thick	SF	0.320	27.50	24.75	52.25
2" thick	SF	0.364	37.25	28.25	65.50
Sills or stools					
1" thick					
6" wide	LF	0.320	12.75	24.75	37.50
10" wide	LF	0.348	20.75	27.00	47.75
2" thick					
6" wide	LF	0.364	21.00	28.25	49.25
10" wide	LF	0.400	34.75	31.00	65.75
04510.01 FLUE LINERS					
FLUE LINERS					
Flue liners					
Rectangular					
8" x 12"	LF	0.133	10.50	10.25	20.75
12" x 12"	LF	0.145	13.25	11.25	24.50
12" x 18"	LF	0.160	23.25	12.50	35.75
16" x 16"	LF	0.178	25.00	13.75	38.75
18" x 18"	LF	0.190	31.00	14.75	45.75
20" x 20"	LF	0.200	52.00	15.50	67.50
24" x 24"	LF	0.229	62.00	17.75	79.75
Round					
18" dia.	LF	0.190	47.75	14.75	62.50
24" dia.	LF	0.229	94.00	17.75	111.75
04710.01 SIMULATED BRICK AND STONE					
SIMULATED BRICK AND STONE					
Brick Veneer Panel 48" x 33"					
Antique	EA	0.400	140.00	31.00	171.00
Baked Clay	EA	0.400	120.00	31.00	151.00
Brick Cream Caramel	EA	0.400	140.00	31.00	171.00
Dusky Evening	EA	0.400	140.00	31.00	171.00
Glacier	EA	0.400	120.00	31.00	151.00
Merlot	EA	0.400	140.00	31.00	171.00
Mixed Twilight	EA	0.400	120.00	31.00	151.00
Mocha	EA	0.400	140.00	31.00	171.00
Spiced	EA	0.400	120.00	31.00	151.00
Cast stone					
6" Window/Door Molding	LF	0.080	20.75	6.22	26.97
12" Dia. Column	LF	0.200	88.00	15.50	103.50
12" x 12" Quoins	EA	0.100	61.00	7.77	68.77
6" Base Molding	LF	0.080	16.50	6.22	22.72
10" Wallcap	LF	0.080	18.75	6.22	24.97
3 Piece baluster system	LF	0.100	100.00	7.77	107.77
24" x 24" x 1-1/2" Paver	SF	0.020	11.00	1.55	12.55
Simulated Stone					
Slate, 43-1/4" Wide × 8-1/2" High × approx. 1-3/4" Thick					
Arizona Red	EA	0.027	29.50	2.07	31.57
Brunswick Brown	EA	0.027	29.50	2.07	31.57
Midnight Ash	EA	0.027	29.50	2.07	31.57
Onyx	EA	0.027	29.50	2.07	31.57
Pewter	EA	0.027	29.50	2.07	31.57
Rocky Mountain Graphite	EA	0.027	29.50	2.07	31.57
Sahara	EA	0.027	29.50	2.07	31.57
Stacked Stone 49-1/4" Wide x 25" High 2" Thick					
Birchwood	EA	0.400	110.00	31.00	141.00
Earth	EA	0.400	110.00	31.00	141.00
Honey	EA	0.400	110.00	31.00	141.00
Espresso	EA	0.400	110.00	31.00	141.00
Spice	EA	0.400	110.00	31.00	141.00
Potomac	EA	0.400	110.00	31.00	141.00
Ponderosa	EA	0.400	110.00	31.00	141.00
Tudor	EA	0.400	110.00	31.00	141.00

	Unit	Man-Hrs	Material	Labor	Total

04710.01 SIMULATED BRICK AND STONE (Cont.)

Stacked Stone 49-1/4" Wide x 25" High 2" Thick

	Unit	Man-Hrs	Material	Labor	Total
Riviera	EA	0.400	110.00	31.00	141.00
White	EA	0.400	110.00	31.00	141.00

Corners 15-1/2 x 14-1/2 x 25" High x 2-1/4" Thick

	Unit	Man-Hrs	Material	Labor	Total
Birchwood	EA	0.100	65.00	7.77	72.77
Earth	EA	0.100	65.00	7.77	72.77
Honey	EA	0.100	65.00	7.77	72.77
Espresso	EA	0.100	65.00	7.77	72.77
Spice	EA	0.100	65.00	7.77	72.77
Potomac	EA	0.100	65.00	7.77	72.77
Ponderosa	EA	0.100	65.00	7.77	72.77
Tudor	EA	0.100	65.00	7.77	72.77
Riviera	EA	0.100	65.00	7.77	72.77
White	EA	0.100	65.00	7.77	72.77

Ledgers 48" Wide x 3-1/2" Deep x 3-5/8" High

	Unit	Man-Hrs	Material	Labor	Total
Birchwood	EA	0.267	33.00	20.75	53.75
Earth	EA	0.267	33.00	20.75	53.75
Honey	EA	0.267	33.00	20.75	53.75
Espresso	EA	0.267	33.00	20.75	53.75
Spice	EA	0.267	33.00	20.75	53.75
Potomac	EA	0.267	33.00	20.75	53.75
Ponderosa	EA	0.267	33.00	20.75	53.75
Tudor	EA	0.267	33.00	20.75	53.75
Riviera	EA	0.267	33.00	20.75	53.75
White	EA	0.267	33.00	20.75	53.75

© 2020 BNi Publications, Inc.

	Unit	Man-Hrs	Material	Labor	Total
05052.31 STRUCTURAL WELDING					
STRUCTURAL WELDING					
Welding					
Single pass					
1/8"	LF	0.040	0.33	3.60	3.93
3/16"	LF	0.053	0.55	4.80	5.35
1/4"	LF	0.067	0.77	6.00	6.77
Miscellaneous steel shapes					
Plain	LB	0.002	1.44	0.14	1.58
Galvanized	LB	0.003	1.80	0.24	2.04
Plates					
Plain	LB	0.002	1.29	0.18	1.47
Galvanized	LB	0.003	1.66	0.28	1.94
05052.39 METAL FASTENINGS					
METAL FASTENINGS					
Powder Actuated Anchors					
Loads					
Single Shot					
.22 Cal Green	EA				0.07
.22 Cal Yellow	EA				0.11
.22 Cal Red	EA				0.12
Strip					
.27 Cal Green	EA				0.18
.27 Cal Yellow	EA				0.17
.27 Cal Red	EA				0.17
Pins					
.145 Dia. x Length 300 Head					
1/2"	EA				0.18
5/8"	EA				0.25
3/4"	EA				0.29
1"	EA				0.37
1-1/4"	EA				0.38
1-1/2"	EA				0.44
2"	EA				0.46
2-1/2"	EA				0.49
3"	EA				0.52
Anchor bolts, material only					
3/8" x					
8" long	EA				1.11
10" long	EA				1.21
12" long	EA				1.31
1/2" x					
8" long	EA				1.65
10" long	EA				1.76
12" long	EA				1.93
18" long	EA				2.10
5/8" x					
8" long	EA				1.54
10" long	EA				1.70
12" long	EA				1.81
18" long	EA				1.93
24" long	EA				2.10
3/4" x					
8" long	EA				2.20
12" long	EA				2.48
18" long	EA				3.41
24" long	EA				4.52
7/8" x					
8" long	EA				2.20
12" long	EA				2.48
18" long	EA				3.41
24" long	EA				4.52
1" x					
12" long	EA				4.41
18" long	EA				5.51

	Unit	Man-Hrs	Material	Labor	Total
05052.39 METAL FASTENINGS (Cont.)					
1" x					
24" long	EA				6.61
36" long	EA				9.93
Expansion shield					
1/4"	EA				0.68
3/8"	EA				1.14
1/2"	EA				2.25
5/8"	EA				3.26
3/4"	EA				3.99
1"	EA				5.40
Non-drilling anchor					
1/4"	EA				0.71
3/8"	EA				0.88
1/2"	EA				1.35
5/8"	EA				2.22
3/4"	EA				3.81
Self-drilling anchor					
1/4"	EA				1.79
5/16"	EA				2.23
3/8"	EA				2.68
1/2"	EA				3.58
5/8"	EA				6.80
3/4"	EA				8.92
7/8"	EA				12.50
Add 25% for galvanized anchor bolts					
Channel door frame, with anchors	LB	0.009	1.96	0.80	2.76
Corner guard angle, with anchors	LB	0.013	1.75	1.20	2.95
05052.40 METAL LINTELS					
METAL LINTELS					
Lintels, steel					
Plain	LB	0.020	1.33	1.80	3.13
Galvanized	LB	0.020	2.00	1.80	3.80
05120.01 BEAMS, GIRDERS, COLUMNS, TRUSSES					
BEAMS, GIRDERS, COLUMNS, TRUSSES					
Beams and girders, A-36					
Welded	TON	4.800	3,160.00	850.00	4,010.00
Bolted	TON	4.364	3,070.00	770.00	3,840.00
Columns					
Pipe					
6" dia.	LB	0.005	1.61	0.85	2.46
12" dia.	LB	0.004	1.37	0.70	2.07
Purlins and girts					
Welded	TON	8.000	3,010.00	1,420.00	4,430.00
Bolted	TON	6.857	2,960.00	1,220.00	4,180.00
Column base plates					
Up to 150 lb each	LB	0.005	1.73	0.48	2.21
Over 150 lb each	LB	0.007	1.41	0.60	2.01
Structural pipe					
3" to 5" o.d.	TON	9.600	3,250.00	1,700.00	4,950.00
6" to 12" o.d.	TON	6.857	3,010.00	1,220.00	4,230.00
Structural tube					
6" square					
Light sections	TON	9.600	3,770.00	1,700.00	5,470.00
Heavy sections	TON	6.857	3,530.00	1,220.00	4,750.00
6" wide rectangular					
Light sections	TON	8.000	3,770.00	1,420.00	5,190.00
Heavy sections	TON	6.000	3,530.00	1,060.00	4,590.00
Greater than 6" wide rectangular					
Light sections	TON	8.000	4,010.00	1,420.00	5,430.00
Heavy sections	TON	6.000	3,780.00	1,060.00	4,840.00
Miscellaneous structural shapes					
Steel angle	TON	12.000	2,680.00	2,130.00	4,810.00
Steel plate	TON	8.000	3,040.00	1,420.00	4,460.00

© 2020 BNi Publications, Inc.

	Unit	Man-Hrs	Material	Labor	Total
05120.01 BEAMS, GIRDERS, COLUMNS, TRUSSES (Cont.)					
Trusses, field welded					
60 lb/lf	TON	6.000	4,090.00	1,060.00	5,150.00
100 lb/lf	TON	4.800	3,580.00	850.00	4,430.00
150 lb/lf	TON	4.000	3,370.00	710.00	4,080.00
Bolted					
60 lb/lf	TON	5.333	4,040.00	950.00	4,990.00
100 lb/lf	TON	4.364	3,530.00	770.00	4,300.00
150 lb/lf	TON	3.692	3,350.00	650.00	4,000.00
Add for galvanizing	TON				830.00
05150.11 WIRE ROPE					
WIRE ROPE					
Galvanized Cable					
1/16"	LF				0.30
1/8"	LF				1.01
3/16"	LF				1.33
1/4"	LF				1.67
5/16"	LF				2.33
3/8"	LF				2.78
1/2"	LF				3.03
5/8"	LF				3.41
3/4"	LF				5.62
1-1/4"	LF				14.75
Stainless					
1/16"	LF				0.34
1/8"	LF				1.12
3/16"	LF				1.47
1/4"	LF				1.85
5/16"	LF				2.58
3/8"	LF				3.09
1/2"	LF				3.36
5/8"	LF				4.11
3/4"	LF				6.23
1-1/4"	LF				16.25
Coated					
1/16"	LF				0.58
1/8"	LF				1.25
3/16"	LF				2.00
Clips					
1/16"	EA				1.37
1/8"	EA				1.52
3/16"	EA				1.57
1/4"	EA				1.56
5/16"	EA				2.68
3/8"	EA				1.89
1/2"	EA				2.32
5/8"	EA				4.04
3/4"	EA				6.30
1-1/4"	EA				10.50
Thimbles					
3/16"	EA				0.75
1/4"	EA				1.00
5/16"	EA				1.07
3/8"	EA				1.47
1/2"	EA				1.83
5/8"	EA				4.95
3/4"	EA				4.85
1-1/4"	EA				13.50
Sleeves (Swage type)					
1/16"	EA				0.29
1/8"	EA				0.74
3/16"	EA				0.69
1/4"	EA				0.85
5/16"	EA				1.76
3/8"	EA				1.90

	Unit	Man-Hrs	Material	Labor	Total
05150.11 WIRE ROPE (Cont.)					
Sleeves (Swage type)					
1/2"	EA				1.95
5/8"	EA				2.11
3/4"	EA				2.21
1-1/4"	EA				2.32
05210.01 METAL JOISTS					
METAL JOISTS					
Joist					
DLH series	TON	3.200	1,960.00	570.00	2,530.00
K series	TON	3.200	2,030.00	570.00	2,600.00
LH series	TON	3.200	1,960.00	570.00	2,530.00
05310.01 METAL DECKING					
METAL DECKING					
Roof, 1-1/2" deep, non-composite					
16 ga.					
Primed	SF	0.008	4.91	1.41	6.32
Galvanized	SF	0.008	5.15	1.41	6.56
18 ga.					
Primed	SF	0.008	3.84	1.41	5.25
Galvanized	SF	0.008	4.21	1.41	5.62
20 ga.					
Primed	SF	0.008	2.82	1.41	4.23
Galvanized	SF	0.008	3.35	1.41	4.76
22 ga.					
Primed	SF	0.008	2.29	1.41	3.70
Galvanized	SF	0.008	2.57	1.41	3.98
Open type decking, galvanized					
1-1/2" deep					
18 ga.	SF	0.008	3.69	1.41	5.10
20 ga.	SF	0.008	2.82	1.41	4.23
22 ga.	SF	0.008	2.43	1.41	3.84
3" deep					
16 ga.	SF	0.009	5.73	1.54	7.27
18 ga.	SF	0.009	5.39	1.54	6.93
20 ga.	SF	0.009	4.08	1.54	5.62
22 ga.	SF	0.009	3.96	1.54	5.50
4-1/2" deep					
16 ga.	SF	0.010	8.50	1.70	10.20
18 ga.	SF	0.010	7.03	1.70	8.73
6" deep					
16 ga.	SF	0.011	11.75	1.89	13.64
18 ga.	SF	0.011	10.25	1.89	12.14
7-1/2" deep					
16 ga.	SF	0.011	12.75	1.98	14.73
18 ga.	SF	0.011	12.00	1.98	13.98
Cellular type					
1-1/2" deep, galvanized					
18-18 ga.	SF	0.010	10.25	1.70	11.95
22-18 ga.	SF	0.010	9.23	1.70	10.93
3" deep, galvanized					
16-16 ga.	SF	0.011	14.50	1.89	16.39
18-16 ga.	SF	0.011	13.50	1.89	15.39
18-18 ga.	SF	0.011	12.50	1.89	14.39
20-18 ga.	SF	0.011	11.00	1.89	12.89
4-1/2" deep, galvanized					
16-16 ga.	SF	0.011	21.75	2.02	23.77
18-16 ga.	SF	0.011	20.00	2.02	22.02
18-18 ga.	SF	0.011	19.00	2.02	21.02
20-18 ga.	SF	0.011	17.25	2.02	19.27
Composite deck, non-cellular, galvanized					
1-1/2" deep					
18 ga.	SF	0.009	3.41	1.54	4.95
20 ga.	SF	0.009	3.11	1.54	4.65
22 ga.	SF	0.009	2.52	1.54	4.06

© 2020 BNi Publications, Inc.

	Unit	Man-Hrs	Material	Labor	Total
05310.01 METAL DECKING (Cont.)					
Composite deck, non-cellular, galvanized					
3" deep					
18 ga.	SF	0.009	4.80	1.63	6.43
20 ga.	SF	0.009	3.11	1.63	4.74
22 ga.	SF	0.009	2.52	1.63	4.15
Slab form floor deck					
9/16" deep					
28 ga.	SF	0.009	1.53	1.54	3.07
1-5/16" deep					
24 ga.	SF	0.009	2.24	1.60	3.84
22 ga.	SF	0.009	2.69	1.60	4.29
05410.01 METAL FRAMING					
METAL FRAMING					
Furring channel, galvanized					
Beams and columns, 3/4"					
12" o.c.	SF	0.080	0.44	7.20	7.64
16" o.c.	SF	0.073	0.34	6.54	6.88
Walls, 3/4"					
12" o.c.	SF	0.040	0.44	3.60	4.04
16" o.c.	SF	0.033	0.34	3.00	3.34
24" o.c.	SF	0.027	0.24	2.40	2.64
1-1/2"					
12" o.c.	SF	0.040	0.72	3.60	4.32
16" o.c.	SF	0.033	0.55	3.00	3.55
24" o.c.	SF	0.027	0.37	2.40	2.77
Stud, load bearing					
16" o.c.					
16 ga.					
2-1/2"	SF	0.036	1.33	3.20	4.53
3-5/8"	SF	0.036	1.57	3.20	4.77
4"	SF	0.036	1.63	3.20	4.83
6"	SF	0.040	2.05	3.60	5.65
18 ga.					
2-1/2"	SF	0.036	1.08	3.20	4.28
3-5/8"	SF	0.036	1.33	3.20	4.53
4"	SF	0.036	1.39	3.20	4.59
6"	SF	0.040	1.76	3.60	5.36
8"	SF	0.040	2.12	3.60	5.72
20 ga.					
2-1/2"	SF	0.036	0.60	3.20	3.80
3-5/8"	SF	0.036	0.72	3.20	3.92
4"	SF	0.036	0.79	3.20	3.99
6"	SF	0.040	0.96	3.60	4.56
8"	SF	0.040	1.15	3.60	4.75
24" o.c.					
16 ga.					
2-1/2"	SF	0.031	0.91	2.76	3.67
3-5/8"	SF	0.031	1.08	2.76	3.84
4"	SF	0.031	1.15	2.76	3.91
6"	SF	0.033	1.39	3.00	4.39
8"	SF	0.033	1.76	3.00	4.76
18 ga.					
2-1/2"	SF	0.031	0.72	2.76	3.48
3-5/8"	SF	0.031	0.84	2.76	3.60
4"	SF	0.031	0.91	2.76	3.67
6"	SF	0.033	1.15	3.00	4.15
8"	SF	0.033	1.39	3.00	4.39
20 ga.					
2-1/2"	SF	0.031	0.44	2.76	3.20
3-5/8"	SF	0.031	0.49	2.76	3.25
4"	SF	0.031	0.55	2.76	3.31
6"	SF	0.033	0.71	3.00	3.71
8"	SF	0.033	0.88	3.00	3.88

	Unit	Man-Hrs	Material	Labor	Total
05510.01 STAIRS					
STAIRS					
Stock unit, steel, complete, per riser					
Tread					
3'-6" wide	EA	1.000	240.00	90.00	330.00
4' wide	EA	1.143	280.00	100.00	380.00
5' wide	EA	1.333	330.00	120.00	450.00
Metal pan stair, cement filled, per riser					
3'-6" wide	EA	0.800	260.00	72.00	332.00
4' wide	EA	0.889	300.00	80.00	380.00
5' wide	EA	1.000	340.00	90.00	430.00
Landing, steel pan	SF	0.200	100.00	18.00	118.00
Cast iron tread, steel stringers, stock units, per riser					
Tread					
3'-6" wide	EA	1.000	460.00	90.00	550.00
4' wide	EA	1.143	530.00	100.00	630.00
5' wide	EA	1.333	640.00	120.00	760.00
Stair treads, abrasive, 12" x 3'-6"					
Cast iron					
3/8"	EA	0.400	220.00	36.00	256.00
1/2"	EA	0.400	280.00	36.00	316.00
Cast aluminum					
5/16"	EA	0.400	250.00	36.00	286.00
3/8"	EA	0.400	270.00	36.00	306.00
1/2"	EA	0.400	320.00	36.00	356.00
05513.31 LADDERS					
LADDERS					
Ladder, 18" wide					
With cage	LF	0.533	110.00	48.00	158.00
Without cage	LF	0.400	70.00	36.00	106.00
05521.31 RAILINGS					
RAILINGS					
Railing, pipe					
1-1/4" diameter, welded steel					
2-rail					
Primed	LF	0.160	31.75	14.50	46.25
Galvanized	LF	0.160	40.75	14.50	55.25
3-rail					
Primed	LF	0.200	40.75	18.00	58.75
Galvanized	LF	0.200	53.00	18.00	71.00
Wall mounted, single rail, welded steel					
Primed	LF	0.123	21.25	11.00	32.25
Galvanized	LF	0.123	27.50	11.00	38.50
1-1/2" diameter, welded steel					
2-rail					
Primed	LF	0.160	34.50	14.50	49.00
Galvanized	LF	0.160	44.75	14.50	59.25
3-rail					
Primed	LF	0.200	43.25	18.00	61.25
Galvanized	LF	0.200	56.00	18.00	74.00
Wall mounted, single rail, welded steel					
Primed	LF	0.123	21.75	11.00	32.75
Galvanized	LF	0.123	28.50	11.00	39.50
2" diameter, welded steel					
2-rail					
Primed	LF	0.178	41.25	16.00	57.25
Galvanized	LF	0.178	54.00	16.00	70.00
3-rail					
Primed	LF	0.229	52.00	20.50	72.50
Galvanized	LF	0.229	68.00	20.50	88.50
Wall mounted, single rail, welded steel					
Primed	LF	0.133	23.75	12.00	35.75
Galvanized	LF	0.133	30.75	12.00	42.75

© 2020 BNi Publications, Inc.

	Unit	Man-Hrs	Material	Labor	Total

05530.01 METAL GRATING

METAL GRATING

Floor plate, checkered, steel

1/4"

Primed	SF	0.011	11.75	1.02	12.77
Galvanized	SF	0.011	18.00	1.02	19.02

3/8"

Primed	SF	0.012	17.25	1.10	18.35
Galvanized	SF	0.012	27.25	1.10	28.35

Aluminum grating, pressure-locked bearing bars

3/4" x 1/8"	SF	0.020	28.75	1.80	30.55
1" x 1/8"	SF	0.020	32.25	1.80	34.05
1-1/4" x 1/8"	SF	0.020	46.00	1.80	47.80
1-1/4" x 3/16"	SF	0.020	48.25	1.80	50.05
1-1/2" x 1/8"	SF	0.020	63.00	1.80	64.80
1-3/4" x 3/16"	SF	0.020	35.75	1.80	37.55

Miscellaneous expenses

Cutting

Minimum	LF	0.053		4.80	4.80
Maximum	LF	0.080		7.20	7.20

Banding

Minimum	LF	0.133		12.00	12.00
Maximum	LF	0.160		14.50	14.50

Toe plates

Minimum	LF	0.160		14.50	14.50
Maximum	LF	0.200		18.00	18.00

Steel grating, primed

3/4" x 1/8"	SF	0.027	9.98	2.40	12.38
1" x 1/8"	SF	0.027	10.25	2.40	12.65
1-1/4" x 1/8"	SF	0.027	11.50	2.40	13.90
1-1/4" x 3/16"	SF	0.027	15.25	2.40	17.65
1-1/2" x 1/8"	SF	0.027	14.00	2.40	16.40
1-3/4" x 3/16"	SF	0.027	20.00	2.40	22.40

Galvanized

3/4" x 1/8"	SF	0.027	12.50	2.40	14.90
1" x 1/8"	SF	0.027	13.00	2.40	15.40
1-1/4" x 1/8"	SF	0.027	14.25	2.40	16.65
1-1/4" x 3/16"	SF	0.027	19.00	2.40	21.40
1-1/2" x 1/8"	SF	0.027	17.50	2.40	19.90
1-3/4" x 3/16"	SF	0.027	24.75	2.40	27.15

Miscellaneous expenses

Cutting

Minimum	LF	0.057		5.14	5.14
Maximum	LF	0.089		8.00	8.00

Banding

Minimum	LF	0.145		13.00	13.00
Maximum	LF	0.178		16.00	16.00

Toe plates

Minimum	LF	0.178		16.00	16.00
Maximum	LF	0.229		20.50	20.50

05560.01 CASTINGS

CASTINGS

Miscellaneous castings

Light sections	LB	0.016	8.84	1.44	10.28
Heavy sections	LB	0.011	6.47	1.02	7.49

Manhole covers and frames

Regular, city type

18" dia.

100 lb	EA	1.600	410.00	140.00	550.00

24" dia.

200 lb	EA	1.600	380.00	140.00	520.00
300 lb	EA	1.778	390.00	160.00	550.00
400 lb	EA	1.778	410.00	160.00	570.00
26" dia., 475 lb	EA	2.000	500.00	180.00	680.00
30" dia., 600 lb	EA	2.286	640.00	210.00	850.00

	Unit	Man-Hrs	Material	Labor	Total
05560.01 CASTINGS (Cont.)					
Regular, city type					
8" square, 75 lb	EA	0.320	180.00	28.75	208.75
24" square					
126 lb	EA	1.600	400.00	140.00	540.00
500 lb	EA	2.000	640.00	180.00	820.00
Watertight type					
20" dia., 200 lb	EA	2.000	330.00	180.00	510.00
24" dia., 350 lb	EA	2.667	570.00	240.00	810.00
Steps, cast iron					
7" x 9"	EA	0.160	18.75	14.50	33.25
8" x 9"	EA	0.178	26.50	16.00	42.50
Manhole covers and frames, aluminum					
12" x 12"	EA	0.320	91.00	28.75	119.75
18" x 18"	EA	0.320	94.00	28.75	122.75
24" x 24"	EA	0.400	100.00	36.00	136.00
Corner protection					
Steel angle guard with anchors					
2" x 2" x 3/16"	LF	0.114	17.50	10.25	27.75
2" x 3" x 1/4"	LF	0.114	19.75	10.25	30.00
3" x 3" x 5/16"	LF	0.114	23.00	10.25	33.25
3" x 4" x 5/16"	LF	0.123	27.75	11.00	38.75
4" x 4" x 5/16"	LF	0.123	28.75	11.00	39.75
05590.01 METAL SPECIALTIES					
METAL SPECIALTIES					
Kick plate					
4" high x 1/4" thick					
Primed	LF	0.160	8.89	14.50	23.39
Galvanized	LF	0.160	10.00	14.50	24.50
6" high x 1/4" thick					
Primed	LF	0.178	10.00	16.00	26.00
Galvanized	LF	0.178	12.00	16.00	28.00
05730.01 ORNAMENTAL METAL					
ORNAMENTAL METAL					
Railings, square bars, 6" o.c., shaped top rails					
Steel	LF	0.400	97.00	36.00	133.00
Aluminum	LF	0.400	120.00	36.00	156.00
Bronze	LF	0.533	240.00	48.00	288.00
Stainless steel	LF	0.533	250.00	48.00	298.00
Laminated metal or wood handrails					
2-1/2" round or oval shape	LF	0.400	290.00	36.00	326.00

© 2020 BNi Publications, Inc.

	Unit	Man-Hrs	Material	Labor	Total

06052.31 ACCESSORIES

ACCESSORIES

Column/post base, cast aluminum

	Unit	Man-Hrs	Material	Labor	Total
4" x 4"	EA	0.200	19.75	16.25	36.00
6" x 6"	EA	0.200	27.50	16.25	43.75

Bridging, metal, per pair

	Unit	Man-Hrs	Material	Labor	Total
12" o.c.	EA	0.080	2.68	6.52	9.20
16" o.c.	EA	0.073	2.47	5.93	8.40

Anchors

Bolts, threaded two ends, with nuts and washers

1/2" dia.

	Unit	Man-Hrs	Material	Labor	Total
4" long	EA	0.050	3.13	4.07	7.20
7-1/2" long	EA	0.050	3.64	4.07	7.71

3/4" dia.

	Unit	Man-Hrs	Material	Labor	Total
7-1/2" long	EA	0.050	6.91	4.07	10.98
15" long	EA	0.050	10.50	4.07	14.57

Framing anchors

	Unit	Man-Hrs	Material	Labor	Total
10 gauge	EA	0.067	1.23	5.43	6.66

Bolts, carriage

	Unit	Man-Hrs	Material	Labor	Total
1/4 x 4	EA	0.080	0.81	6.52	7.33
5/16 x 6	EA	0.084	1.84	6.86	8.70
3/8 x 6	EA	0.084	3.72	6.86	10.58
1/2 x 6	EA	0.084	5.19	6.86	12.05

Joist and beam hangers

18 ga.

	Unit	Man-Hrs	Material	Labor	Total
2 x 4	EA	0.080	1.50	6.52	8.02
2 x 6	EA	0.080	1.80	6.52	8.32
2 x 8	EA	0.080	2.10	6.52	8.62
2 x 10	EA	0.089	2.26	7.24	9.50
2 x 12	EA	0.100	2.93	8.15	11.08

16 ga.

	Unit	Man-Hrs	Material	Labor	Total
3 x 6	EA	0.089	5.26	7.24	12.50
3 x 8	EA	0.089	6.39	7.24	13.63
3 x 10	EA	0.094	7.21	7.67	14.88
3 x 12	EA	0.107	8.12	8.69	16.81
3 x 14	EA	0.114	8.79	9.32	18.11
4 x 6	EA	0.089	9.02	7.24	16.26
4 x 8	EA	0.089	10.50	7.24	17.74
4 x 10	EA	0.094	12.00	7.67	19.67
4 x 12	EA	0.107	15.50	8.69	24.19
4 x 14	EA	0.114	16.25	9.32	25.57

Rafter anchors, 18 ga., 1-1/2" wide

	Unit	Man-Hrs	Material	Labor	Total
5-1/4" long	EA	0.067	1.13	5.43	6.56
10-3/4" long	EA	0.067	1.68	5.43	7.11

Shear plates

	Unit	Man-Hrs	Material	Labor	Total
2-5/8" dia.	EA	0.062	4.02	5.01	9.03
4" dia.	EA	0.067	8.37	5.43	13.80

Sill anchors

	Unit	Man-Hrs	Material	Labor	Total
Embedded in concrete	EA	0.080	2.96	6.52	9.48

Split rings

	Unit	Man-Hrs	Material	Labor	Total
2-1/2" dia.	EA	0.089	2.43	7.24	9.67
4" dia.	EA	0.100	4.48	8.15	12.63

Strap ties, 14 ga., 1-3/8" wide

	Unit	Man-Hrs	Material	Labor	Total
12" long	EA	0.067	3.04	5.43	8.47
18" long	EA	0.073	3.27	5.93	9.20
24" long	EA	0.080	4.86	6.52	11.38
36" long	EA	0.089	6.69	7.24	13.93

Toothed rings

	Unit	Man-Hrs	Material	Labor	Total
2-5/8" dia.	EA	0.133	2.81	10.75	13.56
4" dia.	EA	0.160	3.27	13.00	16.27

06057.31 WOOD TREATMENT

WOOD TREATMENT

Creosote preservative treatment

	Unit	Man-Hrs	Material	Labor	Total
8 lb/cf	BF				0.74
10 lb/cf	BF				0.88

	Unit	Man-Hrs	Material	Labor	Total
06057.31 WOOD TREATMENT (Cont.)					
Salt preservative treatment					
Oil borne					
Minimum	BF				0.67
Maximum	BF				0.95
Water borne					
Minimum	BF				0.47
Maximum	BF				0.74
Fire retardant treatment					
Minimum	BF				0.95
Maximum	BF				1.15
Kiln dried, softwood, add to framing costs					
1" thick	BF				0.34
2" thick	BF				0.47
3" thick	BF				0.60
4" thick	BF				0.74
06110.01 BLOCKING					
BLOCKING					
Steel construction					
Walls					
2x4	LF	0.053	0.54	4.34	4.88
2x6	LF	0.062	0.82	5.01	5.83
2x8	LF	0.067	1.08	5.43	6.51
2x10	LF	0.073	1.44	5.93	7.37
2x12	LF	0.080	1.86	6.52	8.38
Ceilings					
2x4	LF	0.062	0.54	5.01	5.55
2x6	LF	0.073	0.82	5.93	6.75
2x8	LF	0.080	1.08	6.52	7.60
2x10	LF	0.089	1.44	7.24	8.68
2x12	LF	0.100	1.86	8.15	10.01
Wood construction					
Walls					
2x4	LF	0.044	0.60	3.62	4.22
2x6	LF	0.050	0.91	4.07	4.98
2x8	LF	0.053	1.20	4.34	5.54
2x10	LF	0.057	1.60	4.66	6.26
2x12	LF	0.062	2.07	5.01	7.08
Ceilings					
2x4	LF	0.050	0.60	4.07	4.67
2x6	LF	0.057	0.91	4.66	5.57
2x8	LF	0.062	1.20	5.01	6.21
2x10	LF	0.067	1.60	5.43	7.03
2x12	LF	0.073	2.07	5.93	8.00
06110.02 CEILING FRAMING					
CEILING FRAMING					
Ceiling joists					
12" o.c.					
2x4	SF	0.019	0.89	1.55	2.44
2x6	SF	0.020	1.28	1.63	2.91
2x8	SF	0.021	1.89	1.71	3.60
2x10	SF	0.022	2.15	1.81	3.96
2x12	SF	0.024	3.96	1.91	5.87
16" o.c.					
2x4	SF	0.015	0.72	1.25	1.97
2x6	SF	0.016	1.08	1.30	2.38
2x8	SF	0.017	1.53	1.35	2.88
2x10	SF	0.017	1.72	1.41	3.13
2x12	SF	0.018	3.23	1.48	4.71
24" o.c.					
2x4	SF	0.013	0.52	1.03	1.55
2x6	SF	0.013	0.86	1.08	1.94
2x8	SF	0.014	1.28	1.14	2.42
2x10	SF	0.015	1.53	1.20	2.73
2x12	SF	0.016	3.88	1.27	5.15

© 2020 BNi Publications, Inc.

	Unit	Man-Hrs	Material	Labor	Total
06110.02 CEILING FRAMING (Cont.)					
Headers and nailers					
2x4	LF	0.026	0.60	2.10	2.70
2x6	LF	0.027	0.91	2.17	3.08
2x8	LF	0.029	1.20	2.33	3.53
2x10	LF	0.031	1.60	2.50	4.10
2x12	LF	0.033	1.97	2.71	4.68
Sister joists for ceilings					
2x4	LF	0.057	0.60	4.66	5.26
2x6	LF	0.067	0.91	5.43	6.34
2x8	LF	0.080	1.20	6.52	7.72
2x10	LF	0.100	1.60	8.15	9.75
2x12	LF	0.133	1.97	10.75	12.72
06110.03 FLOOR FRAMING					
FLOOR FRAMING					
Floor joists					
12" o.c.					
2x6	SF	0.016	1.09	1.30	2.39
2x8	SF	0.016	1.61	1.33	2.94
2x10	SF	0.017	2.23	1.35	3.58
2x12	SF	0.017	3.27	1.41	4.68
2x14	SF	0.017	4.99	1.35	6.34
3x6	SF	0.017	3.70	1.38	5.08
3x8	SF	0.017	4.82	1.41	6.23
3x10	SF	0.018	6.03	1.48	7.51
3x12	SF	0.019	7.24	1.55	8.79
3x14	SF	0.020	8.26	1.63	9.89
4x6	SF	0.017	4.82	1.35	6.17
4x8	SF	0.017	6.19	1.41	7.60
4x10	SF	0.018	7.92	1.48	9.40
4x12	SF	0.019	9.64	1.55	11.19
4x14	SF	0.020	11.25	1.63	12.88
16" o.c.					
2x6	SF	0.013	0.94	1.08	2.02
2x8	SF	0.014	1.33	1.10	2.43
2x10	SF	0.014	1.61	1.12	2.73
2x12	SF	0.014	2.01	1.16	3.17
2x14	SF	0.015	4.48	1.20	5.68
3x6	SF	0.014	3.09	1.12	4.21
3x8	SF	0.014	3.96	1.16	5.12
3x10	SF	0.015	4.99	1.20	6.19
3x12	SF	0.015	6.03	1.25	7.28
3x14	SF	0.016	7.14	1.30	8.44
4x6	SF	0.014	3.96	1.12	5.08
4x8	SF	0.014	5.43	1.16	6.59
4x10	SF	0.015	6.71	1.20	7.91
4x12	SF	0.015	7.92	1.25	9.17
4x14	SF	0.016	9.47	1.30	10.77
Sister joists for floors					
2x4	LF	0.050	0.60	4.07	4.67
2x6	LF	0.057	0.91	4.66	5.57
2x8	LF	0.067	1.20	5.43	6.63
2x10	LF	0.080	1.60	6.52	8.12
2x12	LF	0.100	2.07	8.15	10.22
3x6	LF	0.080	3.01	6.52	9.53
3x8	LF	0.089	3.70	7.24	10.94
3x10	LF	0.100	4.90	8.15	13.05
3x12	LF	0.114	5.93	9.32	15.25
4x6	LF	0.080	3.88	6.52	10.40
4x8	LF	0.089	5.16	7.24	12.40
4x10	LF	0.100	6.71	8.15	14.86
4x12	LF	0.114	7.48	9.32	16.80

DIVISION 06 WOOD AND PLASTICS

	Unit	Man-Hrs	Material	Labor	Total

06110.03 FLOOR FRAMING (Cont.)

Plywood Web Joists, 16" o.c.
  3/8" plywood web and 1-3/4" top & bottom chord

	Unit	Man-Hrs	Material	Labor	Total
9-1/2" depth	SF	0.014	1.78	1.12	2.90
11-7/8" depth	SF	0.016	1.84	1.30	3.14
14" depth	SF	0.018	2.26	1.44	3.70
16" depth	SF	0.020	3.39	1.63	5.02

Wood Trussed Floor Joists
  2" x 4" chord and truss members

	Unit	Man-Hrs	Material	Labor	Total
11-1/4" depth	SF	0.016	5.73	1.30	7.03
14" depth	SF	0.018	6.15	1.44	7.59
16" depth	SF	0.020	6.31	1.63	7.94
18" depth	SF	0.023	6.63	1.86	8.49

06110.04 FURRING

FURRING
Furring, wood strips
Walls
On masonry or concrete walls
1x2 furring

	Unit	Man-Hrs	Material	Labor	Total
12" o.c.	SF	0.025	0.48	2.03	2.51
16" o.c.	SF	0.023	0.41	1.86	2.27
24" o.c.	SF	0.021	0.39	1.71	2.10

1x3 furring

	Unit	Man-Hrs	Material	Labor	Total
12" o.c.	SF	0.025	0.60	2.03	2.63
16" o.c.	SF	0.023	0.54	1.86	2.40
24" o.c.	SF	0.021	0.42	1.71	2.13

On wood walls
1x2 furring

	Unit	Man-Hrs	Material	Labor	Total
12" o.c.	SF	0.018	0.48	1.44	1.92
16" o.c.	SF	0.016	0.41	1.30	1.71
24" o.c.	SF	0.015	0.38	1.18	1.56

1x3 furring

	Unit	Man-Hrs	Material	Labor	Total
12" o.c.	SF	0.018	0.61	1.44	2.05
16" o.c.	SF	0.016	0.52	1.30	1.82
24" o.c.	SF	0.015	0.42	1.18	1.60

Ceilings
On masonry or concrete ceilings
1x2 furring

	Unit	Man-Hrs	Material	Labor	Total
12" o.c.	SF	0.044	0.48	3.62	4.10
16" o.c.	SF	0.040	0.41	3.26	3.67
24" o.c.	SF	0.036	0.38	2.96	3.34

1x3 furring

	Unit	Man-Hrs	Material	Labor	Total
12" o.c.	SF	0.044	0.60	3.62	4.22
16" o.c.	SF	0.040	0.52	3.26	3.78
24" o.c.	SF	0.036	0.42	2.96	3.38

On wood ceilings
1x2 furring

	Unit	Man-Hrs	Material	Labor	Total
12" o.c.	SF	0.030	0.48	2.41	2.89
16" o.c.	SF	0.027	0.41	2.17	2.58
24" o.c.	SF	0.024	0.38	1.97	2.35

1x3

	Unit	Man-Hrs	Material	Labor	Total
12" o.c.	SF	0.030	0.60	2.41	3.01
16" o.c.	SF	0.027	0.52	2.17	2.69
24" o.c.	SF	0.024	0.42	1.97	2.39

06110.05 ROOF FRAMING

ROOF FRAMING
Roof framing
Rafters, gable end
0-2 pitch (flat to 2-in-12)
12" o.c.

	Unit	Man-Hrs	Material	Labor	Total
2x4	SF	0.017	0.86	1.35	2.21
2x6	SF	0.017	1.20	1.41	2.61
2x8	SF	0.018	1.72	1.48	3.20
2x10	SF	0.019	2.15	1.55	3.70
2x12	SF	0.020	3.96	1.63	5.59

© 2020 BNi Publications, Inc.

06110.05 ROOF FRAMING (Cont.)

	Unit	Man-Hrs	Material	Labor	Total
0-2 pitch (flat to 2-in-12)					
16" o.c.					
2x6	SF	0.014	1.08	1.16	2.24
2x8	SF	0.015	1.52	1.20	2.72
2x10	SF	0.015	1.72	1.25	2.97
2x12	SF	0.016	3.18	1.30	4.48
24" o.c.					
2x6	SF	0.012	0.60	0.98	1.58
2x8	SF	0.013	1.26	1.01	2.27
2x10	SF	0.013	1.46	1.05	2.51
2x12	SF	0.013	2.57	1.08	3.65
4-6 pitch (4-in-12 to 6-in-12)					
12" o.c.					
2x4	SF	0.017	0.86	1.41	2.27
2x6	SF	0.018	1.28	1.48	2.76
2x8	SF	0.019	1.97	1.55	3.52
2x10	SF	0.020	2.23	1.63	3.86
2x12	SF	0.021	3.44	1.71	5.15
16" o.c.					
2x6	SF	0.015	1.08	1.20	2.28
2x8	SF	0.015	1.72	1.25	2.97
2x10	SF	0.016	1.97	1.30	3.27
2x12	SF	0.017	2.93	1.35	4.28
24" o.c.					
2x6	SF	0.013	0.86	1.01	1.87
2x8	SF	0.013	1.46	1.05	2.51
2x10	SF	0.014	1.54	1.12	2.66
2x12	SF	0.015	2.41	1.25	3.66
8-12 pitch (8-in-12 to 12-in-12)					
12" o.c.					
2x4	SF	0.018	0.94	1.48	2.42
2x6	SF	0.019	1.46	1.55	3.01
2x8	SF	0.020	2.07	1.63	3.70
2x10	SF	0.021	2.41	1.71	4.12
2x12	SF	0.022	3.70	1.81	5.51
16" o.c.					
2x6	SF	0.015	1.20	1.25	2.45
2x8	SF	0.016	1.93	1.30	3.23
2x10	SF	0.017	2.15	1.35	3.50
2x12	SF	0.017	3.09	1.41	4.50
24" o.c.					
2x6	SF	0.013	0.94	1.05	1.99
2x8	SF	0.013	1.53	1.08	2.61
2x10	SF	0.014	1.72	1.12	2.84
2x12	SF	0.014	2.75	1.16	3.91
Ridge boards					
2x6	LF	0.040	0.91	3.26	4.17
2x8	LF	0.044	1.20	3.62	4.82
2x10	LF	0.050	1.60	4.07	5.67
2x12	LF	0.057	2.07	4.66	6.73
Hip rafters					
2x6	LF	0.029	0.91	2.33	3.24
2x8	LF	0.030	1.20	2.41	3.61
2x10	LF	0.031	1.60	2.50	4.10
2x12	LF	0.032	2.07	2.60	4.67
Jack rafters					
4-6 pitch (4-in-12 to 6-in-12)					
16" o.c.					
2x6	SF	0.024	1.12	1.91	3.03
2x8	SF	0.024	1.72	1.97	3.69
2x10	SF	0.026	1.97	2.10	4.07
2x12	SF	0.027	2.93	2.17	5.10
24" o.c.					
2x6	SF	0.018	0.86	1.48	2.34
2x8	SF	0.019	1.46	1.51	2.97

	Unit	Man-Hrs	Material	Labor	Total

06110.05 ROOF FRAMING (Cont.)

24" o.c.

2x10	SF	0.020	1.72	1.59	3.31
2x12	SF	0.020	2.49	1.63	4.12

8-12 pitch (8-in-12 to 12-in-12)

16" o.c.

2x6	SF	0.025	1.72	2.03	3.75
2x8	SF	0.026	2.15	2.10	4.25
2x10	SF	0.027	3.09	2.17	5.26
2x12	SF	0.028	4.30	2.24	6.54

24" o.c.

2x6	SF	0.019	1.37	1.55	2.92
2x8	SF	0.020	1.72	1.59	3.31
2x10	SF	0.020	2.75	1.63	4.38
2x12	SF	0.021	3.96	1.67	5.63

Sister rafters

2x4	LF	0.057	0.60	4.66	5.26
2x6	LF	0.067	0.91	5.43	6.34
2x8	LF	0.080	1.20	6.52	7.72
2x10	LF	0.100	1.60	8.15	9.75
2x12	LF	0.133	2.07	10.75	12.82

Fascia boards

2x4	LF	0.040	0.60	3.26	3.86
2x6	LF	0.040	0.91	3.26	4.17
2x8	LF	0.044	1.20	3.62	4.82
2x10	LF	0.044	1.60	3.62	5.22
2x12	LF	0.050	2.07	4.07	6.14

Cant strips

Fiber

3x3	LF	0.023	0.48	1.86	2.34
4x4	LF	0.024	0.67	1.97	2.64

Wood

3x3	LF	0.024	2.49	1.97	4.46

06110.06 SLEEPERS

SLEEPERS

Sleepers, over concrete

12" o.c.

1x2	SF	0.018	0.29	1.48	1.77
1x3	SF	0.019	0.43	1.55	1.98
2x4	SF	0.022	0.94	1.81	2.75
2x6	SF	0.024	1.37	1.91	3.28

16" o.c.

1x2	SF	0.016	0.26	1.30	1.56
1x3	SF	0.016	0.37	1.30	1.67
2x4	SF	0.019	0.78	1.55	2.33
2x6	SF	0.020	1.15	1.63	2.78

06110.07 SOFFITS

SOFFITS

Soffit framing

2x3	LF	0.057	0.41	4.66	5.07
2x4	LF	0.062	0.50	5.01	5.51
2x6	LF	0.067	0.74	5.43	6.17
2x8	LF	0.073	1.05	5.93	6.98

06110.08 WALL FRAMING

WALL FRAMING

Framing wall, studs

12" o.c.

2x3	SF	0.015	0.53	1.20	1.73
2x4	SF	0.015	0.74	1.20	1.94
2x6	SF	0.016	1.08	1.30	2.38
2x8	SF	0.017	1.44	1.35	2.79

16" o.c.

2x3	SF	0.013	0.43	1.01	1.44
2x4	SF	0.013	0.60	1.01	1.61

© 2020 BNi Publications, Inc.

06110.08 WALL FRAMING (Cont.)

	Unit	Man-Hrs	Material	Labor	Total
16" o.c.					
2x6	SF	0.013	0.86	1.08	1.94
2x8	SF	0.014	1.36	1.12	2.48
24" o.c.					
2x3	SF	0.011	0.33	0.88	1.21
2x4	SF	0.011	0.45	0.88	1.33
2x6	SF	0.011	0.72	0.93	1.65
2x8	SF	0.012	0.94	0.95	1.89
Plates, top or bottom					
2x3	LF	0.024	0.41	1.91	2.32
2x4	LF	0.025	0.50	2.03	2.53
2x6	LF	0.027	0.74	2.17	2.91
2x8	LF	0.029	1.05	2.33	3.38
Headers, door or window					
2x6					
Single					
3' long	EA	0.400	2.44	32.50	34.94
6' long	EA	0.500	4.88	40.75	45.63
Double					
3' long	EA	0.444	4.89	36.25	41.14
6' long	EA	0.571	9.79	46.50	56.29
2x8					
Single					
4' long	EA	0.500	4.46	40.75	45.21
8' long	EA	0.615	8.92	50.00	58.92
Double					
4' long	EA	0.571	8.92	46.50	55.42
8' long	EA	0.727	18.00	59.00	77.00
2x10					
Single					
5' long	EA	0.615	6.75	50.00	56.75
10' long	EA	0.800	13.50	65.00	78.50
Double					
5' long	EA	0.667	13.50	54.00	67.50
10' long	EA	0.800	27.00	65.00	92.00
2x12					
Single					
6' long	EA	0.615	9.79	50.00	59.79
12' long	EA	0.800	19.25	65.00	84.25
Double					
6' long	EA	0.727	19.25	59.00	78.25
12' long	EA	0.889	38.50	72.00	110.50

06130.01 HEAVY TIMBER

	Unit	Man-Hrs	Material	Labor	Total
HEAVY TIMBER					
Mill framed structures					
Beams to 20' long					
Douglas fir					
6x8	LF	0.080	8.27	8.60	16.87
6x10	LF	0.083	9.77	8.90	18.67
6x12	LF	0.089	11.75	9.56	21.31
6x14	LF	0.092	14.00	9.93	23.93
6x16	LF	0.096	15.25	10.25	25.50
8x10	LF	0.083	13.00	8.90	21.90
8x12	LF	0.089	15.25	9.56	24.81
8x14	LF	0.092	17.50	9.93	27.43
8x16	LF	0.096	20.00	10.25	30.25
Southern yellow pine					
6x8	LF	0.080	6.56	8.60	15.16
6x10	LF	0.083	7.97	8.90	16.87
6x12	LF	0.089	10.25	9.56	19.81
6x14	LF	0.092	11.75	9.93	21.68
6x16	LF	0.096	13.00	10.25	23.25
8x10	LF	0.083	10.75	8.90	19.65
8x12	LF	0.089	13.25	9.56	22.81

	Unit	Man-Hrs	Material	Labor	Total
06130.01 HEAVY TIMBER (Cont.)					
Southern yellow pine					
8x14	LF	0.092	15.00	9.93	24.93
8x16	LF	0.096	17.50	10.25	27.75
Columns to 12' high					
Douglas fir					
6x6	LF	0.120	5.95	13.00	18.95
8x8	LF	0.120	10.25	13.00	23.25
10x10	LF	0.133	17.75	14.25	32.00
12x12	LF	0.133	22.00	14.25	36.25
Southern yellow pine					
6x6	LF	0.120	5.12	13.00	18.12
8x8	LF	0.120	8.61	13.00	21.61
10x10	LF	0.133	13.50	14.25	27.75
12x12	LF	0.133	18.75	14.25	33.00
Posts, treated					
4x4	LF	0.032	2.05	2.60	4.65
6x6	LF	0.040	5.95	3.26	9.21
06150.01 WOOD DECKING					
WOOD DECKING					
Decking, T&G solid					
Cedar					
3" thick	SF	0.020	11.50	1.63	13.13
4" thick	SF	0.021	14.50	1.73	16.23
Fir					
3" thick	SF	0.020	5.05	1.63	6.68
4" thick	SF	0.021	6.13	1.73	7.86
Southern yellow pine					
3" thick	SF	0.023	5.05	1.86	6.91
4" thick	SF	0.025	5.34	2.00	7.34
White pine					
3" thick	SF	0.020	6.13	1.63	7.76
4" thick	SF	0.021	8.30	1.73	10.03
06160.01 FLOOR SHEATHING					
FLOOR SHEATHING					
Sub-flooring, plywood, CDX					
1/2" thick	SF	0.010	0.60	0.81	1.41
5/8" thick	SF	0.011	0.87	0.93	1.80
3/4" thick	SF	0.013	1.60	1.08	2.68
Structural plywood					
1/2" thick	SF	0.010	0.95	0.81	1.76
5/8" thick	SF	0.011	1.52	0.93	2.45
3/4" thick	SF	0.012	1.60	1.00	2.60
Board type sub-flooring					
1x6					
Minimum	SF	0.018	1.45	1.44	2.89
Maximum	SF	0.020	1.84	1.63	3.47
1x8					
Minimum	SF	0.017	1.60	1.37	2.97
Maximum	SF	0.019	1.88	1.53	3.41
1x10					
Minimum	SF	0.016	2.24	1.30	3.54
Maximum	SF	0.018	2.41	1.44	3.85
Underlayment					
Hardboard, 1/4" tempered	SF	0.010	0.89	0.81	1.70
Plywood, CDX					
3/8" thick	SF	0.010	0.93	0.81	1.74
1/2" thick	SF	0.011	1.11	0.86	1.97
5/8" thick	SF	0.011	1.28	0.93	2.21
3/4" thick	SF	0.012	1.60	1.00	2.60

© 2020 BNi Publications, Inc.

	Unit	Man-Hrs	Material	Labor	Total
06160.02 ROOF SHEATHING					
ROOF SHEATHING					
Sheathing					
Plywood, CDX					
3/8" thick	SF	0.010	0.93	0.84	1.77
1/2" thick	SF	0.011	1.11	0.86	1.97
5/8" thick	SF	0.011	1.28	0.93	2.21
3/4" thick	SF	0.012	1.60	1.00	2.60
Structural plywood					
3/8" thick	SF	0.010	0.59	0.84	1.43
1/2" thick	SF	0.011	0.77	0.86	1.63
5/8" thick	SF	0.011	0.93	0.93	1.86
3/4" thick	SF	0.012	1.12	1.00	2.12
06160.03 WALL SHEATHING					
WALL SHEATHING					
Sheathing					
Plywood, CDX					
3/8" thick	SF	0.012	0.93	0.96	1.89
1/2" thick	SF	0.012	1.11	1.00	2.11
5/8" thick	SF	0.013	1.28	1.08	2.36
3/4" thick	SF	0.015	1.60	1.18	2.78
Waferboard					
3/8" thick	SF	0.012	0.59	0.96	1.55
1/2" thick	SF	0.012	0.77	1.00	1.77
5/8" thick	SF	0.013	0.93	1.08	2.01
3/4" thick	SF	0.015	1.02	1.18	2.20
Structural plywood					
3/8" thick	SF	0.012	0.93	0.96	1.89
1/2" thick	SF	0.012	1.11	1.00	2.11
5/8" thick	SF	0.013	1.28	1.08	2.36
3/4" thick	SF	0.015	1.11	1.18	2.29
Gypsum, 1/2" thick	SF	0.012	0.59	1.00	1.59
Asphalt impregnated fiberboard, 1/2" thick	SF	0.012	1.02	1.00	2.02
06175.31 WOOD TRUSSES					
WOOD TRUSSES					
Truss, fink, 2x4 members					
3-in-12 slope					
24' span	EA	0.686	120.00	74.00	194.00
26' span	EA	0.686	130.00	74.00	204.00
28' span	EA	0.727	140.00	78.00	218.00
30' span	EA	0.727	140.00	78.00	218.00
34' span	EA	0.774	150.00	83.00	233.00
38' span	EA	0.774	150.00	83.00	233.00
5-in-12 slope					
24' span	EA	0.706	130.00	76.00	206.00
28' span	EA	0.727	140.00	78.00	218.00
30' span	EA	0.750	150.00	81.00	231.00
32' span	EA	0.750	160.00	81.00	241.00
40' span	EA	0.800	210.00	86.00	296.00
Gable, 2x4 members					
5-in-12 slope					
24' span	EA	0.706	150.00	76.00	226.00
26' span	EA	0.706	160.00	76.00	236.00
28' span	EA	0.727	180.00	78.00	258.00
30' span	EA	0.750	190.00	81.00	271.00
32' span	EA	0.750	190.00	81.00	271.00
36' span	EA	0.774	210.00	83.00	293.00
40' span	EA	0.800	220.00	86.00	306.00
King post type, 2x4 members					
4-in-12 slope					
16' span	EA	0.649	90.00	70.00	160.00
18' span	EA	0.667	97.00	72.00	169.00
24' span	EA	0.706	100.00	76.00	176.00
26' span	EA	0.706	110.00	76.00	186.00
30' span	EA	0.750	140.00	81.00	221.00

	Unit	Man-Hrs	Material	Labor	Total
06175.31 WOOD TRUSSES (Cont.)					
4-in-12 slope					
34' span	EA	0.750	150.00	81.00	231.00
38' span	EA	0.774	180.00	83.00	263.00
42' span	EA	0.828	210.00	89.00	299.00
06181.31 LAMINATED BEAMS					
LAMINATED BEAMS					
Parallel strand beams 3-1/2" wide x					
9-1/2"	LF	0.034	12.25	3.68	15.93
11-1/4"	LF	0.036	13.00	3.82	16.82
11-7/8"	LF	0.037	13.75	3.97	17.72
14"	LF	0.044	17.25	4.69	21.94
16"	LF	0.048	20.50	5.16	25.66
18"	LF	0.053	24.25	5.73	29.98
Laminated veneer beams, 1-3/4" wide x					
11-7/8"	LF	0.037	8.27	3.97	12.24
14"	LF	0.044	10.25	4.69	14.94
16"	LF	0.048	10.25	5.16	15.41
18"	LF	0.053	13.00	5.73	18.73
Laminated strand beams, 1-3/4" wide x					
9-1/2"	LF	0.034	5.31	3.68	8.99
11-7/8"	LF	0.037	6.07	3.97	10.04
14"	LF	0.044	7.14	4.69	11.83
16"	LF	0.048	8.19	5.16	13.35
3-1/2" wide x					
9-1/2"	LF	0.034	9.34	3.68	13.02
11-7/8"	LF	0.037	12.25	3.97	16.22
14"	LF	0.044	14.25	4.69	18.94
16"	LF	0.048	17.00	5.16	22.16
Gluelam beam, 3-1/2" wide x					
10"	LF	0.034	14.25	3.68	17.93
12"	LF	0.040	16.75	4.30	21.05
15"	LF	0.046	19.75	4.91	24.66
5-1/2" wide x					
10"	LF	0.034	22.75	3.68	26.43
16"	LF	0.048	35.75	5.16	40.91
20"	LF	0.056	42.00	6.07	48.07
7-1/2" wide x					
10"	LF	0.037	30.50	3.97	34.47
12"	LF	0.051	48.00	5.43	53.43
15"	LF	0.060	57.00	6.45	63.45
18"	LF	0.064	68.00	6.88	74.88
9-1/2" wide x					
10"	LF	0.037	30.50	3.97	34.47
16"	LF	0.051	49.00	5.43	54.43
20"	LF	0.060	61.00	6.45	67.45
24"	LF	0.064	77.00	6.88	83.88
30"	LF	0.074	96.00	7.94	103.94
06202.31 FINISH CARPENTRY					
FINISH CARPENTRY					
Mouldings and trim					
Apron, flat					
9/16 x 2	LF	0.040	1.97	3.26	5.23
9/16 x 3-1/2	LF	0.042	4.55	3.43	7.98
Base					
Colonial					
7/16 x 2-1/4	LF	0.040	2.35	3.26	5.61
7/16 x 3	LF	0.040	3.04	3.26	6.30
7/16 x 3-1/4	LF	0.040	3.11	3.26	6.37
9/16 x 3	LF	0.042	3.04	3.43	6.47
9/16 x 3-1/4	LF	0.042	3.18	3.43	6.61
11/16 x 2-1/4	LF	0.044	3.34	3.62	6.96
Ranch					
7/16 x 2-1/4	LF	0.040	2.57	3.26	5.83
7/16 x 3-1/4	LF	0.040	3.04	3.26	6.30

© 2020 BNi Publications, Inc.

06202.31 FINISH CARPENTRY (Cont.)

	Unit	Man-Hrs	Material	Labor	Total
Ranch					
9/16 x 2-1/4	LF	0.042	2.80	3.43	6.23
9/16 x 3	LF	0.042	3.04	3.43	6.47
9/16 x 3-1/4	LF	0.042	3.11	3.43	6.54
Casing					
11/16 x 2-1/2	LF	0.036	2.42	2.96	5.38
11/16 x 3-1/2	LF	0.038	2.73	3.10	5.83
Chair rail					
9/16 x 2-1/2	LF	0.040	2.57	3.26	5.83
9/16 x 3-1/2	LF	0.040	3.56	3.26	6.82
Closet pole					
1-1/8" dia.	LF	0.053	1.74	4.34	6.08
1-5/8" dia.	LF	0.053	2.57	4.34	6.91
Cove					
9/16 x 1-3/4	LF	0.040	1.97	3.26	5.23
11/16 x 2-3/4	LF	0.040	3.04	3.26	6.30
Crown					
9/16 x 1-5/8	LF	0.053	2.57	4.34	6.91
9/16 x 2-5/8	LF	0.062	2.80	5.01	7.81
11/16 x 3-5/8	LF	0.067	3.04	5.43	8.47
11/16 x 4-1/4	LF	0.073	4.55	5.93	10.48
11/16 x 5-1/4	LF	0.080	5.08	6.52	11.60
Drip cap					
1-1/16 x 1-5/8	LF	0.040	2.73	3.26	5.99
Glass bead					
3/8 x 3/8	LF	0.050	0.98	4.07	5.05
1/2 x 9/16	LF	0.050	1.21	4.07	5.28
5/8 x 5/8	LF	0.050	1.29	4.07	5.36
3/4 x 3/4	LF	0.050	1.52	4.07	5.59
Half round					
1/2	LF	0.032	1.14	2.60	3.74
5/8	LF	0.032	1.52	2.60	4.12
3/4	LF	0.032	2.05	2.60	4.65
Lattice					
1/4 x 7/8	LF	0.032	0.91	2.60	3.51
1/4 x 1-1/8	LF	0.032	0.98	2.60	3.58
1/4 x 1-3/8	LF	0.032	1.05	2.60	3.65
1/4 x 1-3/4	LF	0.032	1.18	2.60	3.78
1/4 x 2	LF	0.032	1.36	2.60	3.96
Ogee molding					
5/8 x 3/4	LF	0.040	1.81	3.26	5.07
11/16 x 1-1/8	LF	0.040	4.25	3.26	7.51
11/16 x 1-3/8	LF	0.040	3.34	3.26	6.60
Parting bead					
3/8 x 7/8	LF	0.050	1.52	4.07	5.59
Quarter round					
1/4 x 1/4	LF	0.032	0.53	2.60	3.13
3/8 x 3/8	LF	0.032	0.76	2.60	3.36
1/2 x 1/2	LF	0.032	0.98	2.60	3.58
11/16 x 11/16	LF	0.035	0.98	2.83	3.81
3/4 x 3/4	LF	0.035	1.81	2.83	4.64
1-1/16 x 1-1/16	LF	0.036	1.43	2.96	4.39
Railings, balusters					
1-1/8 x 1-1/8	LF	0.080	4.86	6.52	11.38
1-1/2 x 1-1/2	LF	0.073	5.69	5.93	11.62
Screen moldings					
1/4 x 3/4	LF	0.067	1.21	5.43	6.64
5/8 x 5/16	LF	0.067	1.52	5.43	6.95
Shoe					
7/16 x 11/16	LF	0.032	1.52	2.60	4.12
Sash beads					
1/2 x 3/4	LF	0.067	1.74	5.43	7.17
1/2 x 7/8	LF	0.067	1.97	5.43	7.40
1/2 x 1-1/8	LF	0.073	2.12	5.93	8.05

	Unit	Man-Hrs	Material	Labor	Total
06202.31 FINISH CARPENTRY (Cont.)					
Sash beads					
5/8 x 7/8	LF	0.073	2.12	5.93	8.05
Stop					
5/8 x 1-5/8					
Colonial	LF	0.050	1.05	4.07	5.12
Ranch	LF	0.050	1.05	4.07	5.12
Stools					
11/16 x 2-1/4	LF	0.089	4.63	7.24	11.87
11/16 x 2-1/2	LF	0.089	4.86	7.24	12.10
11/16 x 5-1/4	LF	0.100	5.01	8.15	13.16
Exterior trim, casing, select pine, 1x3	LF	0.040	3.34	3.26	6.60
Douglas fir					
1x3	LF	0.040	1.59	3.26	4.85
1x4	LF	0.040	1.97	3.26	5.23
1x6	LF	0.044	2.57	3.62	6.19
1x8	LF	0.050	3.56	4.07	7.63
Cornices, white pine, #2 or better					
1x2	LF	0.040	0.98	3.26	4.24
1x4	LF	0.040	1.21	3.26	4.47
1x6	LF	0.044	1.97	3.62	5.59
1x8	LF	0.047	2.42	3.83	6.25
1x10	LF	0.050	3.11	4.07	7.18
1x12	LF	0.053	3.87	4.34	8.21
Shelving, pine					
1x8	LF	0.062	1.74	5.01	6.75
1x10	LF	0.064	2.28	5.21	7.49
1x12	LF	0.067	2.88	5.43	8.31
Plywood shelf, 3/4", with edge band, 12" wide	LF	0.080	3.11	6.52	9.63
Adjustable shelf, and rod, 12" wide					
3' to 4' long	EA	0.200	24.75	16.25	41.00
5' to 8' long	EA	0.267	46.50	21.75	68.25
Prefinished wood shelves with brackets and supports					
8" wide					
3' long	EA	0.200	73.00	16.25	89.25
4' long	EA	0.200	84.00	16.25	100.25
6' long	EA	0.200	120.00	16.25	136.25
10" wide					
3' long	EA	0.200	81.00	16.25	97.25
4' long	EA	0.200	120.00	16.25	136.25
6' long	EA	0.200	130.00	16.25	146.25
06220.01 MILLWORK					
MILLWORK					
Countertop, laminated plastic					
25" x 7/8" thick					
Minimum	LF	0.200	18.50	16.25	34.75
Average	LF	0.267	34.75	21.75	56.50
Maximum	LF	0.320	51.00	26.00	77.00
25" x 1-1/4" thick					
Minimum	LF	0.267	22.25	21.75	44.00
Average	LF	0.320	44.50	26.00	70.50
Maximum	LF	0.400	67.00	32.50	99.50
Add for cutouts	EA	0.500		40.75	40.75
Backsplash, 4" high, 7/8" thick	LF	0.160	24.50	13.00	37.50
Plywood, sanded, A-C					
1/4" thick	SF	0.027	1.58	2.17	3.75
3/8" thick	SF	0.029	1.71	2.33	4.04
1/2" thick	SF	0.031	1.94	2.50	4.44
A-D					
1/4" thick	SF	0.027	1.50	2.17	3.67
3/8" thick	SF	0.029	1.71	2.33	4.04
1/2" thick	SF	0.031	1.86	2.50	4.36
Base cabinet, 34-1/2" high, 24" deep, hardwood					
Minimum	LF	0.320	240.00	26.00	266.00
Average	LF	0.400	270.00	32.50	302.50

© 2020 BNi Publications, Inc.

	Unit	Man-Hrs	Material	Labor	Total
06220.01 MILLWORK (Cont.)					
Base cabinet, 34-1/2" high, 24" deep, hardwood					
Maximum	LF	0.533	310.00	43.50	353.50
Wall cabinets					
Minimum	LF	0.267	73.00	21.75	94.75
Average	LF	0.320	99.00	26.00	125.00
Maximum	LF	0.400	120.00	32.50	152.50
06260.01 PANEL WORK					
PANEL WORK					
Hardboard, tempered, 1/4" thick					
Natural faced	SF	0.020	1.14	1.63	2.77
Plastic faced	SF	0.023	1.71	1.86	3.57
Pegboard, natural	SF	0.020	1.43	1.63	3.06
Plastic faced	SF	0.023	1.71	1.86	3.57
Untempered, 1/4" thick					
Natural faced	SF	0.020	1.07	1.63	2.70
Plastic faced	SF	0.023	1.86	1.86	3.72
Pegboard, natural	SF	0.020	1.14	1.63	2.77
Plastic faced	SF	0.023	1.65	1.86	3.51
Plywood, unfinished, 1/4" thick					
Birch					
Natural	SF	0.027	1.22	2.17	3.39
Select	SF	0.027	1.79	2.17	3.96
Knotty pine	SF	0.027	2.37	2.17	4.54
Cedar (closet lining)					
Standard boards T&G	SF	0.027	2.94	2.17	5.11
Particle board	SF	0.027	1.79	2.17	3.96
Plywood, prefinished, 1/4" thick, premium grade					
Birch veneer	SF	0.032	4.30	2.60	6.90
Cherry veneer	SF	0.032	5.02	2.60	7.62
Chestnut veneer	SF	0.032	9.69	2.60	12.29
Lauan veneer	SF	0.032	1.86	2.60	4.46
Mahogany veneer	SF	0.032	4.95	2.60	7.55
Oak veneer (red)	SF	0.032	4.95	2.60	7.55
Pecan veneer	SF	0.032	6.24	2.60	8.84
Rosewood veneer	SF	0.032	9.69	2.60	12.29
Teak veneer	SF	0.032	6.39	2.60	8.99
Walnut veneer	SF	0.032	5.52	2.60	8.12
06431.31 STAIRWORK					
STAIRWORK					
Risers, 1x8, 42" wide					
White oak	EA	0.400	52.00	32.50	84.50
Pine	EA	0.400	46.00	32.50	78.50
Treads, 1-1/16" x 9-1/2" x 42"					
White oak	EA	0.500	62.00	40.75	102.75
06440.01 COLUMNS					
COLUMNS					
Column, hollow, round wood					
12" diameter					
10' high	EA	0.800	920.00	95.00	1,015.00
12' high	EA	0.857	1,130.00	100.00	1,230.00
14' high	EA	0.960	1,350.00	110.00	1,460.00
16' high	EA	1.200	1,680.00	140.00	1,820.00
24" diameter					
16' high	EA	1.200	3,830.00	140.00	3,970.00
18' high	EA	1.263	4,350.00	150.00	4,500.00
20' high	EA	1.263	5,350.00	150.00	5,500.00
22' high	EA	1.333	5,630.00	160.00	5,790.00
24' high	EA	1.333	6,150.00	160.00	6,310.00

	Unit	Man-Hrs	Material	Labor	Total
07110.01 DAMPPROOFING					
DAMPPROOFING					
Silicone dampproofing, sprayed on					
Concrete surface					
1 coat	SF	0.004	0.64	0.28	0.92
2 coats	SF	0.006	1.06	0.39	1.45
Concrete block					
1 coat	SF	0.005	0.64	0.34	0.98
2 coats	SF	0.007	1.06	0.46	1.52
Brick					
1 coat	SF	0.006	0.64	0.39	1.03
2 coats	SF	0.008	1.06	0.51	1.57
07111.31 BITUMINOUS DAMPPROOFING					
BITUMINOUS DAMPPROOFING					
Building paper, asphalt felt					
15 lb	SF	0.032	0.19	2.04	2.23
30 lb	SF	0.033	0.37	2.12	2.49
Asphalt, troweled, cold, primer plus					
1 coat	SF	0.027	0.68	1.70	2.38
2 coats	SF	0.040	1.43	2.55	3.98
3 coats	SF	0.050	2.04	3.19	5.23
Fibrous asphalt, hot troweled, primer plus					
1 coat	SF	0.032	0.68	2.04	2.72
2 coats	SF	0.044	1.43	2.83	4.26
3 coats	SF	0.057	2.04	3.64	5.68
Asphaltic paint dampproofing, per coat					
Brush on	SF	0.011	0.35	0.72	1.07
Spray on	SF	0.009	0.49	0.56	1.05
07111.61 PARGING / MASONRY PLASTER					
PARGING / MASONRY PLASTER					
Parging					
1/2" thick	SF	0.053	0.44	4.14	4.58
3/4" thick	SF	0.067	0.48	5.18	5.66
1" thick	SF	0.080	0.63	6.22	6.85
07130.01 WATERPROOFING					
WATERPROOFING					
Membrane waterproofing, elastomeric					
Butyl					
1/32" thick	SF	0.032	1.54	2.04	3.58
1/16" thick	SF	0.033	2.01	2.12	4.13
Butyl with nylon					
1/32" thick	SF	0.032	1.80	2.04	3.84
1/16" thick	SF	0.033	2.17	2.12	4.29
Neoprene					
1/32" thick	SF	0.032	2.64	2.04	4.68
1/16" thick	SF	0.033	3.78	2.12	5.90
Neoprene with nylon					
1/32" thick	SF	0.032	2.74	2.04	4.78
1/16" thick	SF	0.033	4.42	2.12	6.54
Bituminous membrane, asphalt felt, 15 lb.					
One ply	SF	0.020	0.91	1.27	2.18
Two ply	SF	0.024	1.08	1.54	2.62
Three ply	SF	0.029	1.33	1.82	3.15
Four ply	SF	0.033	1.54	2.12	3.66
Five ply	SF	0.042	1.64	2.68	4.32
Modified asphalt membrane, fibrous asphalt					
One ply	SF	0.033	0.57	2.12	2.69
Two ply	SF	0.040	1.17	2.55	3.72
Three ply	SF	0.044	1.82	2.83	4.65
Four ply	SF	0.053	2.42	3.40	5.82
Five ply	SF	0.064	2.91	4.08	6.99
Asphalt coated protective board					
1/8" thick	SF	0.020	0.54	1.27	1.81
1/4" thick	SF	0.020	0.73	1.27	2.00

© 2020 BNi Publications, Inc.

	Unit	Man-Hrs	Material	Labor	Total
07130.01 WATERPROOFING (Cont.)					
Asphalt coated protective board					
3/8" thick	SF	0.020	0.82	1.27	2.09
1/2" thick	SF	0.021	0.99	1.34	2.33
Cement protective board					
3/8" thick	SF	0.027	1.52	1.70	3.22
1/2" thick	SF	0.027	2.13	1.70	3.83
Fluid applied, neoprene					
50 mil	SF	0.027	2.13	1.70	3.83
90 mil	SF	0.027	3.53	1.70	5.23
Tab extended polyurethane					
.050" thick	SF	0.020	1.97	1.27	3.24
Fluid applied rubber based polyurethane					
6 mil	SF	0.025	1.26	1.59	2.85
15 mil	SF	0.020	2.39	1.27	3.66
Bentonite waterproofing, panels					
3/16" thick	SF	0.020	2.14	1.27	3.41
1/4" thick	SF	0.020	2.43	1.27	3.70
5/8" thick	SF	0.021	3.62	1.34	4.96
Granular admixtures, trowel on, 3/8" thick	SF	0.020	2.00	1.27	3.27
Metallic oxide, iron compound, troweled					
5/8" thick	SF	0.020	1.82	1.27	3.09
3/4" thick	SF	0.023	2.20	1.45	3.65
07211.31 BOARD INSULATION					
BOARD INSULATION					
Insulation, rigid					
Fiberglass, roof					
0.75" thick, R2.78	SF	0.007	0.55	0.46	1.01
1.06" thick, R4.17	SF	0.008	0.84	0.48	1.32
1.31" thick, R5.26	SF	0.008	1.13	0.51	1.64
1.63" thick, R6.67	SF	0.008	1.39	0.53	1.92
2.25" thick, R8.33	SF	0.009	1.53	0.56	2.09
Composite board, roof					
1-1/2" thick, R6.67	SF	0.008	1.20	0.51	1.71
1-5/8" thick, R7.69	SF	0.008	1.27	0.53	1.80
2" thick, R10.0	SF	0.009	2.29	0.56	2.85
2-1/4" thick, R12.50	SF	0.009	2.54	0.60	3.14
2-1/2" thick, R14.29	SF	0.010	2.76	0.63	3.39
2-3/4" thick, R16.67	SF	0.011	3.03	0.68	3.71
3-1/4" thick, R20.00	SF	0.011	3.90	0.72	4.62
Perlite board, roof					
1.00" thick, R2.78	SF	0.007	0.57	0.42	0.99
1.50" thick, R4.17	SF	0.007	0.90	0.44	1.34
2.00" thick, R5.92	SF	0.007	1.10	0.46	1.56
2.50" thick, R6.67	SF	0.008	1.35	0.48	1.83
3.00" thick, R8.33	SF	0.008	1.69	0.51	2.20
4.00" thick, R10.00	SF	0.008	1.88	0.53	2.41
5.25" thick, R14.29	SF	0.009	2.07	0.56	2.63
Rigid urethane					
Roof					
1" thick, R6.67	SF	0.007	1.09	0.42	1.51
1.20" thick, R8.33	SF	0.007	1.25	0.43	1.68
1.50" thick, R11.11	SF	0.007	1.49	0.44	1.93
2" thick, R14.29	SF	0.007	1.92	0.46	2.38
2.25" thick, R16.67	SF	0.008	2.52	0.48	3.00
Wall					
1" thick, R6.67	SF	0.008	1.09	0.53	1.62
1.5" thick, R11.11	SF	0.009	1.49	0.56	2.05
2" thick, R14.29	SF	0.009	1.97	0.60	2.57
Polystyrene					
Roof					
1.0" thick, R4.17	SF	0.007	0.41	0.42	0.83
1.5" thick, R6.26	SF	0.007	0.63	0.44	1.07
2.0" thick, R8.33	SF	0.007	0.78	0.46	1.24

	Unit	Man-Hrs	Material	Labor	Total

07211.31 BOARD INSULATION (Cont.)

Polystyrene
Wall

1.0" thick, R4.17	SF	0.008	0.41	0.53	0.94
1.5" thick, R6.26	SF	0.009	0.63	0.56	1.19
2.0" thick, R8.33	SF	0.009	0.78	0.60	1.38

Rigid board insulation, deck
Mineral fiberboard

1" thick, R3.0	SF	0.007	0.60	0.42	1.02
2" thick, R5.26	SF	0.007	1.33	0.46	1.79

Fiberglass

1" thick, R4.3	SF	0.007	1.03	0.42	1.45
2" thick, R8.5	SF	0.007	1.52	0.46	1.98

Polystyrene

1" thick, R5.4	SF	0.007	0.41	0.42	0.83
2" thick, R10.8	SF	0.007	1.05	0.46	1.51

Urethane

.75" thick, R5.4	SF	0.007	0.95	0.42	1.37
1" thick, R6.4	SF	0.007	1.13	0.42	1.55
1.5" thick, R10.7	SF	0.007	1.36	0.44	1.80
2" thick, R14.3	SF	0.007	1.55	0.46	2.01

Foamglass

1" thick, R1.8	SF	0.007	1.54	0.42	1.96
2" thick, R5.26	SF	0.007	1.96	0.46	2.42

Wood fiber

1" thick, R3.85	SF	0.007	1.74	0.42	2.16
2" thick, R7.7	SF	0.007	2.10	0.46	2.56

Particle board

3/4" thick, R2.08	SF	0.007	0.92	0.42	1.34
1" thick, R2.77	SF	0.007	0.96	0.42	1.38
2" thick, R5.50	SF	0.007	1.27	0.46	1.73

07211.61 BATT INSULATION

BATT INSULATION
Ceiling, fiberglass, unfaced

3-1/2" thick, R11	SF	0.009	0.45	0.60	1.05
6" thick, R19	SF	0.011	0.58	0.68	1.26
9" thick, R30	SF	0.012	1.15	0.78	1.93

Suspended ceiling, unfaced

3-1/2" thick, R11	SF	0.009	0.45	0.56	1.01
6" thick, R19	SF	0.010	0.58	0.63	1.21
9" thick, R30	SF	0.011	1.15	0.72	1.87

Crawl space, unfaced

3-1/2" thick, R11	SF	0.012	0.45	0.78	1.23
6" thick, R19	SF	0.013	0.58	0.85	1.43
9" thick, R30	SF	0.015	1.15	0.92	2.07

Wall, fiberglass
Paper backed

2" thick, R7	SF	0.008	0.34	0.53	0.87
3" thick, R8	SF	0.009	0.38	0.56	0.94
4" thick, R11	SF	0.009	0.62	0.60	1.22
6" thick, R19	SF	0.010	0.92	0.63	1.55

Foil backed, 1 side

2" thick, R7	SF	0.008	0.66	0.53	1.19
3" thick, R11	SF	0.009	0.71	0.56	1.27
4" thick, R14	SF	0.009	0.75	0.60	1.35
6" thick, R21	SF	0.010	0.98	0.63	1.61

Foil backed, 2 sides

2" thick, R7	SF	0.009	0.76	0.60	1.36
3" thick, R11	SF	0.010	0.97	0.63	1.60
4" thick, R14	SF	0.011	1.14	0.68	1.82
6" thick, R21	SF	0.011	1.23	0.72	1.95

Unfaced

2" thick, R7	SF	0.008	0.42	0.53	0.95
3" thick, R9	SF	0.009	0.48	0.56	1.04
4" thick, R11	SF	0.009	0.51	0.60	1.11

© 2020 BNi Publications, Inc.

	Unit	Man-Hrs	Material	Labor	Total
07211.61 BATT INSULATION (Cont.)					
Unfaced					
6" thick, R19	SF	0.010	0.66	0.63	1.29
Mineral wool batts					
Paper backed					
2" thick, R6	SF	0.008	0.36	0.53	0.89
4" thick, R12	SF	0.009	0.83	0.56	1.39
6" thick, R19	SF	0.010	1.03	0.63	1.66
Fasteners, self adhering, attached to ceiling deck					
2-1/2" long	EA	0.013	0.26	0.85	1.11
4-1/2" long	EA	0.015	0.29	0.92	1.21
Capped, self-locking washers	EA	0.008	0.26	0.51	0.77
07212.31 LOOSE FILL INSULATION					
LOOSE FILL INSULATION					
Blown-in type					
Fiberglass					
5" thick, R11	SF	0.007	0.41	0.42	0.83
6" thick, R13	SF	0.008	0.48	0.51	0.99
9" thick, R19	SF	0.011	0.58	0.72	1.30
Rockwool, attic application					
6" thick, R13	SF	0.008	0.38	0.51	0.89
8" thick, R19	SF	0.010	0.45	0.63	1.08
10" thick, R22	SF	0.012	0.53	0.78	1.31
12" thick, R26	SF	0.013	0.68	0.85	1.53
15" thick, R30	SF	0.016	0.82	1.02	1.84
Poured type					
Fiberglass					
1" thick, R4	SF	0.005	0.45	0.31	0.76
2" thick, R8	SF	0.006	0.84	0.36	1.20
3" thick, R12	SF	0.007	1.24	0.42	1.66
4" thick, R16	SF	0.008	1.63	0.51	2.14
Mineral wool					
1" thick, R3	SF	0.005	0.50	0.31	0.81
2" thick, R6	SF	0.006	0.92	0.36	1.28
3" thick, R9	SF	0.007	1.40	0.42	1.82
4" thick, R12	SF	0.008	1.63	0.51	2.14
Vermiculite or perlite					
2" thick, R4.8	SF	0.006	0.98	0.36	1.34
3" thick, R7.2	SF	0.007	1.39	0.42	1.81
4" thick, R9.6	SF	0.008	1.81	0.51	2.32
Masonry, poured vermiculite or perlite					
4" block	SF	0.004	0.57	0.25	0.82
6" block	SF	0.005	0.86	0.31	1.17
8" block	SF	0.006	1.25	0.36	1.61
10" block	SF	0.006	1.65	0.39	2.04
12" block	SF	0.007	2.05	0.42	2.47
07212.91 SPRAYED INSULATION					
SPRAYED INSULATION					
Foam, sprayed on					
Polystyrene					
1" thick, R4	SF	0.008	0.69	0.51	1.20
2" thick, R8	SF	0.011	1.34	0.68	2.02
Urethane					
1" thick, R4	SF	0.008	0.65	0.51	1.16
2" thick, R8	SF	0.011	1.24	0.68	1.92
07240.01 AGGREGATE COATED PANELS					
AGGREGATE COATED PANELS					
Dryvit type system					
1" thick	SF	0.027	3.31	2.40	5.71
1-1/2" thick	SF	0.029	3.45	2.57	6.02
2" thick	SF	0.033	3.91	3.00	6.91
07240.11 EXTERIOR INSULATION FINISH SYSTEM, EIFS					
EXTERIOR INSULATION FINISH SYSTEM, EIFS					
3" Thick	SF	0.010	5.08	0.63	5.71

	Unit	Man-Hrs	Material	Labor	Total
07240.11 EXTERIOR INSULATION FINISH SYSTEM, EIFS					
For Base & Finish Only	SF				1.83
07260.01 VAPOR BARRIERS					
VAPOR BARRIERS					
Vapor barrier, polyethylene					
2 mil	SF	0.004	0.02	0.25	0.27
6 mil	SF	0.004	0.07	0.25	0.32
8 mil	SF	0.004	0.08	0.28	0.36
10 mil	SF	0.004	0.09	0.28	0.37
07311.31 ASPHALT SHINGLES					
ASPHALT SHINGLES					
Standard asphalt shingles, strip shingles					
210 lb/square	SQ	0.800	95.00	62.00	157.00
235 lb/square	SQ	0.889	99.00	69.00	168.00
240 lb/square	SQ	1.000	100.00	78.00	178.00
260 lb/square	SQ	1.143	150.00	89.00	239.00
300 lb/square	SQ	1.333	160.00	100.00	260.00
385 lb/square	SQ	1.600	220.00	120.00	340.00
Roll roofing, mineral surface					
90 lb	SQ	0.571	55.00	44.50	99.50
110 lb	SQ	0.667	92.00	52.00	144.00
140 lb	SQ	0.800	95.00	62.00	157.00
07311.61 METAL SHINGLES					
METAL SHINGLES					
Aluminum, .020" thick					
Plain	SQ	1.600	280.00	120.00	400.00
Colors	SQ	1.600	310.00	120.00	430.00
Steel, galvanized					
26 ga.					
Plain	SQ	1.600	350.00	120.00	470.00
Colors	SQ	1.600	440.00	120.00	560.00
24 ga.					
Plain	SQ	1.600	400.00	120.00	520.00
Colors	SQ	1.600	510.00	120.00	630.00
Porcelain enamel, 22 ga.					
Minimum	SQ	2.000	870.00	160.00	1,030.00
Average	SQ	2.000	1,000.00	160.00	1,160.00
Maximum	SQ	2.000	1,120.00	160.00	1,280.00
07312.61 SLATE SHINGLES					
SLATE SHINGLES					
Slate shingles					
Pennsylvania					
Ribbon	SQ	4.000	600.00	310.00	910.00
Clear	SQ	4.000	770.00	310.00	1,080.00
Vermont					
Black	SQ	4.000	710.00	310.00	1,020.00
Gray	SQ	4.000	780.00	310.00	1,090.00
Green	SQ	4.000	800.00	310.00	1,110.00
Red	SQ	4.000	1,440.00	310.00	1,750.00
Replacement shingles					
Small jobs	EA	0.267	12.75	20.75	33.50
Large jobs	SF	0.133	9.94	10.25	20.19
07312.91 WOOD SHINGLES					
WOOD SHINGLES					
Wood shingles, on roofs					
White cedar, #1 shingles					
4" exposure	SQ	2.667	270.00	210.00	480.00
5" exposure	SQ	2.000	240.00	160.00	400.00
#2 shingles					
4" exposure	SQ	2.667	190.00	210.00	400.00
5" exposure	SQ	2.000	160.00	160.00	320.00
Resquared and rebutted					
4" exposure	SQ	2.667	240.00	210.00	450.00
5" exposure	SQ	2.000	200.00	160.00	360.00

© 2020 BNi Publications, Inc.

	Unit	Man-Hrs	Material	Labor	Total

07312.91 WOOD SHINGLES (Cont.)

On walls

White cedar, #1 shingles

	Unit	Man-Hrs	Material	Labor	Total
4" exposure	SQ	4.000	270.00	310.00	580.00
5" exposure	SQ	3.200	240.00	250.00	490.00
6" exposure	SQ	2.667	200.00	210.00	410.00

#2 shingles

	Unit	Man-Hrs	Material	Labor	Total
4" exposure	SQ	4.000	190.00	310.00	500.00
5" exposure	SQ	3.200	160.00	250.00	410.00
6" exposure	SQ	2.667	130.00	210.00	340.00
Add for fire retarding	SQ				120.00

07312.92 WOOD SHAKES

WOOD SHAKES

Shakes, hand split, 24" red cedar, on roofs

	Unit	Man-Hrs	Material	Labor	Total
5" exposure	SQ	4.000	300.00	310.00	610.00
7" exposure	SQ	3.200	280.00	250.00	530.00
9" exposure	SQ	2.667	260.00	210.00	470.00

On walls

	Unit	Man-Hrs	Material	Labor	Total
6" exposure	SQ	4.000	280.00	310.00	590.00
8" exposure	SQ	3.200	270.00	250.00	520.00
10" exposure	SQ	2.667	260.00	210.00	470.00
Add for fire retarding	SQ				78.00

07321.61 CONCRETE ROOF TILE

CONCRETE ROOF TILE

Concrete Roof Tile, Corrugated

	Unit	Man-Hrs	Material	Labor	Total
13"x16-1/2", 90/SQ, 950 LB/SQ Earthtone Colors	SQ	4.000	180.00	310.00	490.00
Custom Blues	SQ	4.000	390.00	310.00	700.00
Custom Greens	SQ	4.000	230.00	310.00	540.00

Concrete Roof Tile, Shakes

	Unit	Man-Hrs	Material	Labor	Total
13"x16-1/2", 90/SQ, 950 LB/SQ, Colors	SQ	4.000	240.00	310.00	550.00

07410.01 MANUFACTURED ROOFS

MANUFACTURED ROOFS

Aluminum roof panels, for steel framing

Corrugated

Unpainted finish

	Unit	Man-Hrs	Material	Labor	Total
.024"	SF	0.020	2.06	1.55	3.61
.030"	SF	0.020	3.35	1.55	4.90

Painted finish

	Unit	Man-Hrs	Material	Labor	Total
.024"	SF	0.020	2.61	1.55	4.16
.030"	SF	0.020	3.52	1.55	5.07

V-beam

Unpainted finish

	Unit	Man-Hrs	Material	Labor	Total
.032"	SF	0.020	2.96	1.55	4.51
.040"	SF	0.020	3.56	1.55	5.11
.050"	SF	0.020	4.48	1.55	6.03

Painted finish

	Unit	Man-Hrs	Material	Labor	Total
.032"	SF	0.020	3.85	1.55	5.40
.040"	SF	0.020	4.61	1.55	6.16
.050"	SF	0.020	5.51	1.55	7.06

Steel roof panels, for structural steel framing

Corrugated, painted

	Unit	Man-Hrs	Material	Labor	Total
18 ga.	SF	0.020	4.26	1.55	5.81
20 ga.	SF	0.020	3.97	1.55	5.52
22 ga.	SF	0.020	3.50	1.55	5.05

Box rib, painted

	Unit	Man-Hrs	Material	Labor	Total
18 ga.	SF	0.021	4.97	1.63	6.60
20 ga.	SF	0.021	4.09	1.63	5.72
22 ga.	SF	0.021	3.64	1.63	5.27

4" rib, painted

	Unit	Man-Hrs	Material	Labor	Total
18 ga.	SF	0.022	5.73	1.73	7.46
20 ga.	SF	0.022	4.85	1.73	6.58
22 ga.	SF	0.022	4.34	1.73	6.07

	Unit	Man-Hrs	Material	Labor	Total
07410.01 MANUFACTURED ROOFS (Cont.)					
Standing seam roof					
2" high seam, painted					
22 ga.	SF	0.032	5.55	2.49	8.04
24 ga.	SF	0.032	5.43	2.49	7.92
26 ga.	SF	0.032	5.26	2.49	7.75
07420.03 MANUFACTURED WALLS					
MANUFACTURED WALLS					
Sandwich panels with 1-1/2" fiberglass insulation					
Galvanized 18 ga. steel interior panels					
Exterior panels					
16 ga. aluminum	SF	0.107	7.26	9.60	16.86
18 ga. galvanized steel	SF	0.107	10.25	9.60	19.85
20 ga. painted steel	SF	0.107	10.50	9.60	20.10
20 ga. stainless steel	SF	0.107	10.75	9.60	20.35
Metal liner panels, 1-3/8" thick, 24" wide					
Galvanized					
22 ga.	SF	0.027	3.64	2.40	6.04
20 ga.	SF	0.027	4.01	2.40	6.41
18 ga.	SF	0.027	4.93	2.40	7.33
Primed					
22 ga.	SF	0.027	2.83	2.40	5.23
20 ga.	SF	0.027	3.26	2.40	5.66
18 ga.	SF	0.027	4.01	2.40	6.41
07420.05 METAL SIDING PANELS					
METAL SIDING PANELS					
Aluminum siding panels					
Corrugated					
Plain finish					
.024"	SF	0.032	2.23	2.88	5.11
.032"	SF	0.032	2.62	2.88	5.50
Painted finish					
.024"	SF	0.032	2.78	2.88	5.66
.032"	SF	0.032	3.19	2.88	6.07
V-beam					
Plain finish					
.032"	SF	0.032	3.37	2.88	6.25
.040"	SF	0.032	3.89	2.88	6.77
.050"	SF	0.032	4.93	2.88	7.81
Painted finish					
.032"	SF	0.032	4.15	2.88	7.03
.040"	SF	0.032	4.90	2.88	7.78
.050"	SF	0.032	6.97	2.88	9.85
4" rib					
Plain finish					
.032"	SF	0.036	3.09	3.27	6.36
.040"	SF	0.036	3.44	3.27	6.71
.050"	SF	0.036	4.19	3.27	7.46
Painted finish					
.032"	SF	0.036	4.01	3.27	7.28
.040"	SF	0.036	4.18	3.27	7.45
.050"	SF	0.036	4.78	3.27	8.05
Steel siding panels					
Corrugated					
22 ga.	SF	0.053	2.73	4.80	7.53
24 ga.	SF	0.053	2.49	4.80	7.29
26 ga.	SF	0.053	2.26	4.80	7.06
Box rib					
20 ga.	SF	0.053	4.08	4.80	8.88
22 ga.	SF	0.053	3.42	4.80	8.22
24 ga.	SF	0.053	3.01	4.80	7.81
26 ga.	SF	0.053	2.46	4.80	7.26
Ribbed, sheets, galvanized					
22 ga.	SF	0.032	3.42	2.88	6.30
24 ga.	SF	0.032	3.01	2.88	5.89

© 2020 BNi Publications, Inc.

	Unit	Man-Hrs	Material	Labor	Total
07420.05 METAL SIDING PANELS (Cont.)					
Ribbed, sheets, galvanized					
26 ga.	SF	0.032	2.46	2.88	5.34
28 ga.	SF	0.032	2.25	2.88	5.13
Primed					
24 ga.	SF	0.032	3.01	2.88	5.89
26 ga.	SF	0.032	2.46	2.88	5.34
28 ga.	SF	0.032	2.25	2.88	5.13
07462.31 WOOD SIDING					
WOOD SIDING					
Beveled siding, cedar					
A grade					
1/2 x 6	SF	0.040	4.89	3.26	8.15
1/2 x 8	SF	0.032	5.00	2.60	7.60
3/4 x 10	SF	0.027	6.43	2.17	8.60
Clear					
1/2 x 6	SF	0.040	5.44	3.26	8.70
1/2 x 8	SF	0.032	5.56	2.60	8.16
3/4 x 10	SF	0.027	7.45	2.17	9.62
B grade					
1/2 x 6	SF	0.040	5.26	3.26	8.52
1/2 x 8	SF	0.032	5.94	2.60	8.54
3/4 x 10	SF	0.027	5.60	2.17	7.77
Board and batten					
Cedar					
1x6	SF	0.040	6.84	3.26	10.10
1x8	SF	0.032	6.22	2.60	8.82
1x10	SF	0.029	5.62	2.33	7.95
1x12	SF	0.026	5.04	2.10	7.14
Pine					
1x6	SF	0.040	1.73	3.26	4.99
1x8	SF	0.032	1.69	2.60	4.29
1x10	SF	0.029	1.62	2.33	3.95
1x12	SF	0.026	1.49	2.10	3.59
Redwood					
1x6	SF	0.040	7.44	3.26	10.70
1x8	SF	0.032	6.93	2.60	9.53
1x10	SF	0.029	6.43	2.33	8.76
1x12	SF	0.026	5.93	2.10	8.03
Tongue and groove					
Cedar					
1x4	SF	0.044	6.43	3.62	10.05
1x6	SF	0.042	6.18	3.43	9.61
1x8	SF	0.040	5.80	3.26	9.06
1x10	SF	0.038	5.69	3.10	8.79
Pine					
1x4	SF	0.044	1.93	3.62	5.55
1x6	SF	0.042	1.82	3.43	5.25
1x8	SF	0.040	1.70	3.26	4.96
1x10	SF	0.038	1.62	3.10	4.72
Redwood					
1x4	SF	0.044	6.80	3.62	10.42
1x6	SF	0.042	6.55	3.43	9.98
1x8	SF	0.040	6.33	3.26	9.59
1x10	SF	0.038	6.04	3.10	9.14
07462.91 PLYWOOD SIDING					
PLYWOOD SIDING					
Rough sawn cedar, 3/8" thick	SF	0.027	2.16	2.17	4.33
Fir, 3/8" thick	SF	0.027	1.19	2.17	3.36
Texture 1-11, 5/8" thick					
Cedar	SF	0.029	2.92	2.33	5.25
Fir	SF	0.029	2.04	2.33	4.37
Redwood	SF	0.029	3.14	2.22	5.36
Southern Yellow Pine	SF	0.029	1.66	2.33	3.99

	Unit	Man-Hrs	Material	Labor	Total
07463.31 PLASTIC SIDING					
PLASTIC SIDING					
Horizontal vinyl siding, solid					
8" wide					
Standard	SF	0.031	1.35	2.50	3.85
Insulated	SF	0.031	1.64	2.50	4.14
10" wide					
Standard	SF	0.029	1.40	2.33	3.73
Insulated	SF	0.029	1.68	2.33	4.01
Vinyl moldings for doors and windows	LF	0.032	0.87	2.60	3.47
07464.61 WOOD FIBER CEMENT SIDING					
WOOD FIBER CEMENT SIDING					
Lap siding 5/16" x 8.25 x 12', 7" exposure	SF	0.031	1.32	2.50	3.82
Panel siding 4' x 8'	SF	0.029	0.99	2.33	3.32
Shingle siding 14-5/8" x 25-5/32" (per bundle)	EA				130.00
07511.31 BUILT-UP ASPHALT ROOFING					
BUILT-UP ASPHALT ROOFING					
Built-up roofing, asphalt felt, including gravel					
2 ply	SQ	2.000	88.00	160.00	248.00
3 ply	SQ	2.667	120.00	210.00	330.00
4 ply	SQ	3.200	170.00	250.00	420.00
Walkway, for built-up roofs					
3' x 3' x					
1/2" thick	SF	0.027	2.46	2.07	4.53
3/4" thick	SF	0.027	3.81	2.07	5.88
1" thick	SF	0.027	4.12	2.07	6.19
Roof bonds					
10 yrs	SQ				37.25
20 yrs	SQ				42.50
Cant strip, 4" x 4"					
Treated wood	LF	0.023	2.56	1.77	4.33
Foamglass	LF	0.020	2.20	1.55	3.75
Mineral fiber	LF	0.020	0.43	1.55	1.98
New gravel for built-up roofing, 400 lb/sq	SQ	1.600	44.50	120.00	164.50
Roof gravel (ballast)	CY	4.000	32.75	310.00	342.75
Aluminum coating, top surfacing, for built-up roofing	SQ	1.333	49.00	100.00	149.00
Remove 4-ply built-up roof (includes gravel)	SQ	4.000		310.00	310.00
Remove & replace gravel, includes flood coat	SQ	2.667	59.00	210.00	269.00
07530.01 SINGLE-PLY ROOFING					
SINGLE-PLY ROOFING					
Elastic sheet roofing					
Neoprene, 1/16" thick	SF	0.010	2.83	0.77	3.60
EPDM rubber					
45 mil	SF	0.010	1.78	0.77	2.55
60 mil	SF	0.010	2.44	0.77	3.21
PVC					
45 mil	SF	0.010	2.34	0.77	3.11
60 mil	SF	0.010	2.78	0.77	3.55
Flashing					
Pipe flashing, 90 mil thick					
1" pipe	EA	0.200	34.00	15.50	49.50
2" pipe	EA	0.200	36.50	15.50	52.00
3" pipe	EA	0.211	36.75	16.50	53.25
4" pipe	EA	0.211	40.00	16.50	56.50
5" pipe	EA	0.222	42.75	17.25	60.00
6" pipe	EA	0.222	46.50	17.25	63.75
8" pipe	EA	0.235	53.00	18.25	71.25
10" pipe	EA	0.267	61.00	20.75	81.75
12" pipe	EA	0.267	74.00	20.75	94.75
Neoprene flashing, 60 mil thick strip					
6" wide	LF	0.067	1.72	5.19	6.91
12" wide	LF	0.100	3.38	7.78	11.16
18" wide	LF	0.133	4.98	10.25	15.23
24" wide	LF	0.200	6.55	15.50	22.05

© 2020 BNi Publications, Inc.

	Unit	Man-Hrs	Material	Labor	Total
07530.01 SINGLE-PLY ROOFING (Cont.)					
Adhesives					
Mastic sealer, applied at joints only					
1/4" bead	LF	0.004	0.19	0.31	0.50
Fluid applied roofing					
Urethane, 2 part, elastomeric membrane					
1" thick	SF	0.013	4.97	1.03	6.00
Vinyl liquid roofing, 2 coats, 2 mils per coat	SF	0.011	7.07	0.88	7.95
Silicone roofing, 2 coats sprayed, 16 mil per coat	SF	0.013	5.28	1.03	6.31
Inverted roof system					
Insulated membrane with coarse gravel ballast					
3 ply with 2" polystyrene	SF	0.013	8.47	1.03	9.50
Ballast, 3/4" through 1-1/2" gravel, 100lb/sf	SF	0.008	0.52	0.62	1.14
Walkway for membrane roofs, 1/2" thick	SF	0.027	2.69	2.07	4.76
07610.01 METAL ROOFING					
METAL ROOFING					
Sheet metal roofing, copper, 16 oz, batten seam	SQ	5.333	1,800.00	420.00	2,220.00
Standing seam	SQ	5.000	1,760.00	390.00	2,150.00
Aluminum roofing, natural finish					
Corrugated, on steel frame					
.0175" thick	SQ	2.286	140.00	180.00	320.00
.0215" thick	SQ	2.286	180.00	180.00	360.00
.024" thick	SQ	2.286	210.00	180.00	390.00
.032" thick	SQ	2.286	260.00	180.00	440.00
V-beam, on steel frame					
.032" thick	SQ	2.286	270.00	180.00	450.00
.040" thick	SQ	2.286	290.00	180.00	470.00
.050" thick	SQ	2.286	370.00	180.00	550.00
Ridge cap					
.019" thick	LF	0.027	4.25	2.07	6.32
Corrugated galvanized steel roofing, on steel frame					
28 ga.	SQ	2.286	230.00	180.00	410.00
26 ga.	SQ	2.286	270.00	180.00	450.00
24 ga.	SQ	2.286	300.00	180.00	480.00
22 ga.	SQ	2.286	330.00	180.00	510.00
26 ga., factory insulated with 1" polystyrene	SQ	3.200	510.00	250.00	760.00
Ridge roll					
10" wide	LF	0.027	2.31	2.07	4.38
20" wide	LF	0.032	4.70	2.49	7.19
07620.01 FLASHING AND TRIM					
FLASHING AND TRIM					
Counter flashing					
Aluminum, .032"	SF	0.080	2.09	6.22	8.31
Stainless steel, .015"	SF	0.080	6.69	6.22	12.91
Copper					
16 oz.	SF	0.080	9.36	6.22	15.58
20 oz.	SF	0.080	11.00	6.22	17.22
24 oz.	SF	0.080	13.50	6.22	19.72
32 oz.	SF	0.080	16.50	6.22	22.72
Valley flashing					
Aluminum, .032"	SF	0.050	1.74	3.89	5.63
Stainless steel, .015	SF	0.050	5.56	3.89	9.45
Copper					
16 oz.	SF	0.050	9.36	3.89	13.25
20 oz.	SF	0.067	11.00	5.19	16.19
24 oz.	SF	0.050	13.50	3.89	17.39
32 oz.	SF	0.050	16.50	3.89	20.39
Base flashing					
Aluminum, .040"	SF	0.067	2.60	5.19	7.79
Stainless steel, .018"	SF	0.067	6.65	5.19	11.84
Copper					
16 oz.	SF	0.067	9.36	5.19	14.55
20 oz.	SF	0.050	11.00	3.89	14.89
24 oz.	SF	0.067	13.50	5.19	18.69
32 oz.	SF	0.067	16.50	5.19	21.69

	Unit	Man-Hrs	Material	Labor	Total
07620.01 FLASHING AND TRIM (Cont.)					
Waterstop, T section, 22 ga.					
1-1/2" x 3"	LF	0.040	3.25	3.11	6.36
2" x 2"	LF	0.040	3.60	3.11	6.71
4" x 3"	LF	0.040	4.41	3.11	7.52
6" x 4"	LF	0.040	4.67	3.11	7.78
8" x 4"	LF	0.040	5.79	3.11	8.90
Scupper outlets					
10" x 10" x 4"	EA	0.200	58.00	15.50	73.50
22" x 4" x 4"	EA	0.200	62.00	15.50	77.50
8" x 8" x 5"	EA	0.200	57.00	15.50	72.50
Flashing and trim, aluminum					
.019" thick	SF	0.057	1.28	4.44	5.72
.032" thick	SF	0.057	1.57	4.44	6.01
.040" thick	SF	0.062	2.69	4.79	7.48
Neoprene sheet flashing, .060" thick	SF	0.050	2.14	3.89	6.03
Copper, paper backed					
2 oz.	SF	0.080	2.75	6.22	8.97
5 oz.	SF	0.080	3.55	6.22	9.77
Drainage boots, roof, cast iron					
2 x 3	LF	0.100	120.00	7.78	127.78
3 x 4	LF	0.100	140.00	7.78	147.78
4 x 5	LF	0.107	160.00	8.30	168.30
4 x 6	LF	0.107	170.00	8.30	178.30
5 x 7	LF	0.114	190.00	8.89	198.89
Pitch pocket, copper, 16 oz.					
4 x 4	EA	0.200	140.00	15.50	155.50
6 x 6	EA	0.200	150.00	15.50	165.50
8 x 8	EA	0.200	200.00	15.50	215.50
8 x 10	EA	0.200	230.00	15.50	245.50
8 x 12	EA	0.200	270.00	15.50	285.50
Reglets, copper 10 oz.	LF	0.053	7.76	4.15	11.91
Stainless steel, .020"	LF	0.053	3.51	4.15	7.66
Gravel stop					
Aluminum, .032"					
4"	LF	0.027	2.04	2.07	4.11
6"	LF	0.027	3.01	2.07	5.08
8"	LF	0.031	4.04	2.39	6.43
10"	LF	0.031	5.05	2.39	7.44
Copper, 16 oz.					
4"	LF	0.027	6.52	2.07	8.59
6"	LF	0.027	9.72	2.07	11.79
8"	LF	0.031	13.00	2.39	15.39
10"	LF	0.031	16.25	2.39	18.64
07710.01 MANUFACTURED SPECIALTIES					
MANUFACTURED SPECIALTIES					
Moisture relief vent					
Aluminum	EA	0.114	23.25	8.89	32.14
Copper	EA	0.114	63.00	8.89	71.89
Expansion joint					
Aluminum					
Opening to 2.5"	LF	0.057	17.75	4.44	22.19
Opening to 3.5"	LF	0.062	17.50	4.79	22.29
Copper, 16 oz.					
Opening to 2.5"	LF	0.057	33.25	4.44	37.69
Opening to 3.5"	LF	0.062	41.25	4.79	46.04
Butyl or neoprene					
4" wide					
16 oz. copper bellows	LF	0.067	32.00	5.19	37.19
28 ga. stainless steel bellows	LF	0.067	20.00	5.19	25.19
6" wide					
Copper bellows	LF	0.073	35.25	5.66	40.91
Stainless steel					
Opening to 2.5"	LF	0.057	20.50	4.44	24.94
Opening to 3.5"	LF	0.062	26.00	4.79	30.79

© 2020 BNi Publications, Inc.

07710.01 MANUFACTURED SPECIALTIES (Cont.)

	Unit	Man-Hrs	Material	Labor	Total
Smoke vent, 48" x 48"					
Aluminum	EA	2.000	2,310.00	160.00	2,470.00
Galvanized steel	EA	2.000	2,030.00	160.00	2,190.00
Heat/smoke vent, 48" x 96"					
Aluminum	EA	2.667	3,240.00	210.00	3,450.00
Galvanized steel	EA	2.667	2,760.00	210.00	2,970.00
Ridge vent strips					
Mill finish	LF	0.053	3.90	4.15	8.05
Connectors	EA	0.200	3.85	15.50	19.35
End cap	EA	0.229	1.92	17.75	19.67
Soffit vents					
Mill finish					
2-1/2" wide	LF	0.032	0.49	2.49	2.98
3" wide	LF	0.032	0.60	2.49	3.09
6" wide	LF	0.032	1.04	2.49	3.53
Roof hatches					
Steel, plain, primed					
2'6" x 3'0"	EA	2.000	800.00	160.00	960.00
2'6" x 4'6"	EA	2.667	1,180.00	210.00	1,390.00
2'6" x 8'0"	EA	4.000	1,820.00	310.00	2,130.00
Galvanized steel					
2'6" x 3'0"	EA	2.000	820.00	160.00	980.00
2'6" x 4'6"	EA	2.667	1,240.00	210.00	1,450.00
2'6" x 8'0"	EA	4.000	1,940.00	310.00	2,250.00
Aluminum					
2'6" x 3'0"	EA	2.000	950.00	160.00	1,110.00
2'6" x 4'6"	EA	2.667	1,430.00	210.00	1,640.00
2'6" x 8'0"	EA	4.000	2,660.00	310.00	2,970.00
Ceiling access doors					
Swing up model, metal frame					
Steel door					
2'6" x 2'6"	EA	0.800	690.00	62.00	752.00
2'6" x 3'0"	EA	0.800	740.00	62.00	802.00
Aluminum door					
2'6" x 2'6"	EA	0.800	850.00	62.00	912.00
2'6" x 3'0"	EA	0.800	920.00	62.00	982.00
Swing down model, metal frame					
Steel door					
2'6" x 2'6"	EA	0.800	1,040.00	62.00	1,102.00
2'6" x 3'0"	EA	0.800	1,120.00	62.00	1,182.00
Aluminum door					
2'6" x 2'6"	EA	0.800	1,240.00	62.00	1,302.00
2'6" x 3'0"	EA	0.800	1,330.00	62.00	1,392.00
Gravity ventilators, with curb, base, damper and screen					
Stationary siphon					
6" dia.	EA	0.533	54.00	41.50	95.50
12" dia.	EA	0.533	93.00	41.50	134.50
24" dia.	EA	0.800	340.00	62.00	402.00
36" dia.	EA	0.800	720.00	62.00	782.00
Wind driven spinner					
6" dia.	EA	0.533	82.00	41.50	123.50
12" dia.	EA	0.533	110.00	41.50	151.50
24" dia.	EA	0.800	410.00	62.00	472.00
36" dia.	EA	0.800	840.00	62.00	902.00
Stationary mushroom					
16" dia.	EA	0.800	670.00	62.00	732.00
30" dia.	EA	1.000	1,510.00	78.00	1,588.00
36" dia.	EA	1.333	1,940.00	100.00	2,040.00
42" dia.	EA	1.600	2,900.00	120.00	3,020.00

07712.31 GUTTERS AND DOWNSPOUTS

	Unit	Man-Hrs	Material	Labor	Total
GUTTERS AND DOWNSPOUTS					
Copper gutter and downspout					
Downspouts, 16 oz. copper					
Round					
3" dia.	LF	0.053	12.50	4.15	16.65
4" dia.	LF	0.053	15.50	4.15	19.65
Rectangular, corrugated					
2" x 3"	LF	0.050	12.00	3.89	15.89
3" x 4"	LF	0.050	14.75	3.89	18.64
Rectangular, flat surface					
2" x 3"	LF	0.053	13.75	4.15	17.90
3" x 4"	LF	0.053	19.50	4.15	23.65
Lead-coated copper downspouts					
Round					
3" dia.	LF	0.050	16.25	3.89	20.14
4" dia.	LF	0.057	19.75	4.44	24.19
Rectangular, corrugated					
2" x 3"	LF	0.053	16.25	4.15	20.40
3" x 4"	LF	0.053	19.50	4.15	23.65
Rectangular, plain					
2" x 3"	LF	0.053	11.25	4.15	15.40
3" x 4"	LF	0.053	13.25	4.15	17.40
Gutters, 16 oz. copper					
Half round					
4" wide	LF	0.080	11.25	6.22	17.47
5" wide	LF	0.089	13.75	6.92	20.67
Type K					
4" wide	LF	0.080	12.50	6.22	18.72
5" wide	LF	0.089	13.00	6.92	19.92
Lead-coated copper gutters					
Half round					
4" wide	LF	0.080	13.50	6.22	19.72
6" wide	LF	0.089	18.50	6.92	25.42
Type K					
4" wide	LF	0.080	14.75	6.22	20.97
5" wide	LF	0.089	19.25	6.92	26.17
Aluminum gutter and downspout					
Downspouts					
2" x 3"	LF	0.053	1.45	4.15	5.60
3" x 4"	LF	0.057	2.00	4.44	6.44
4" x 5"	LF	0.062	2.31	4.79	7.10
Round					
3" dia.	LF	0.053	2.44	4.15	6.59
4" dia.	LF	0.057	3.13	4.44	7.57
Gutters, stock units					
4" wide	LF	0.084	2.26	6.55	8.81
5" wide	LF	0.089	2.69	6.92	9.61
Galvanized steel gutter and downspout					
Downspouts, round corrugated					
3" dia.	LF	0.053	2.09	4.15	6.24
4" dia.	LF	0.053	2.80	4.15	6.95
5" dia.	LF	0.057	4.18	4.44	8.62
6" dia.	LF	0.057	5.54	4.44	9.98
Rectangular					
2" x 3"	LF	0.053	1.89	4.15	6.04
3" x 4"	LF	0.050	2.70	3.89	6.59
4" x 4"	LF	0.050	3.38	3.89	7.27
Gutters, stock units					
5" wide					
Plain	LF	0.089	1.82	6.92	8.74
Painted	LF	0.089	1.98	6.92	8.90
6" wide					
Plain	LF	0.094	2.55	7.32	9.87
Painted	LF	0.094	2.86	7.32	10.18

© 2020 BNi Publications, Inc.

	Unit	Man-Hrs	Material	Labor	Total

07810.01 FIREPROOFING

FIREPROOFING

Sprayed on

1" thick

	Unit	Man-Hrs	Material	Labor	Total
On beams	SF	0.018	0.89	1.13	2.02
On columns	SF	0.016	0.91	1.02	1.93

On decks

	Unit	Man-Hrs	Material	Labor	Total
Flat surface	SF	0.008	0.91	0.51	1.42
Fluted surface	SF	0.010	1.15	0.63	1.78

1-1/2" thick

	Unit	Man-Hrs	Material	Labor	Total
On beams	SF	0.023	1.60	1.45	3.05
On columns	SF	0.020	1.81	1.27	3.08

On decks

	Unit	Man-Hrs	Material	Labor	Total
Flat surface	SF	0.010	1.36	0.63	1.99
Fluted surface	SF	0.013	1.60	0.85	2.45

07920.01 CAULKING

CAULKING

Caulk exterior, two component

	Unit	Man-Hrs	Material	Labor	Total
1/4 x 1/2	LF	0.040	0.43	3.26	3.69
3/8 x 1/2	LF	0.044	0.66	3.62	4.28
1/2 x 1/2	LF	0.050	0.90	4.07	4.97

Caulk interior, single component

	Unit	Man-Hrs	Material	Labor	Total
1/4 x 1/2	LF	0.038	0.29	3.10	3.39
3/8 x 1/2	LF	0.042	0.41	3.43	3.84
1/2 x 1/2	LF	0.047	0.54	3.83	4.37

Butyl rubber fillers

	Unit	Man-Hrs	Material	Labor	Total
1/4" x 1/4"	LF	0.016	0.83	1.30	2.13
1/2" x 1/2"	LF	0.027	1.21	2.17	3.38
1/2" x 3/4"	LF	0.032	1.85	2.60	4.45
3/4" x 3/4"	LF	0.032	2.43	2.60	5.03
1" x 1"	LF	0.036	2.85	2.89	5.74

Seals, O-ring type cord

	Unit	Man-Hrs	Material	Labor	Total
1/4" dia.	LF	0.020	0.91	1.63	2.54
1/2" dia.	LF	0.021	2.72	1.71	4.43
1" dia.	LF	0.022	9.64	1.81	11.45
1-1/4" dia.	LF	0.024	12.25	1.91	14.16
1-1/2" dia.	LF	0.025	16.25	2.03	18.28
1-3/4" dia.	LF	0.026	24.00	2.10	26.10
2" dia.	LF	0.027	31.00	2.17	33.17

Polyvinyl chloride, closed cell

	Unit	Man-Hrs	Material	Labor	Total
1/4" x 2"	LF	0.029	0.62	2.33	2.95
1/4" x 6"	LF	0.036	1.96	2.96	4.92

Silicone foam penetration seal

	Unit	Man-Hrs	Material	Labor	Total
1/4" x 1/2"	LF	0.010	0.24	0.81	1.05
1/2" x 1/2"	LF	0.013	0.41	1.08	1.49
1/2" x 3/4"	LF	0.016	0.64	1.30	1.94
3/4" x 3/4"	LF	0.020	0.96	1.63	2.59
1/8" x 1"	LF	0.010	0.24	0.81	1.05
1/8" x 3"	LF	0.016	0.64	1.30	1.94
1/4" x 3"	LF	0.020	1.27	1.63	2.90
1/4" x 6"	LF	0.027	2.61	2.17	4.78
1/2" x 6"	LF	0.062	5.14	5.01	10.15
1/2" x 9"	LF	0.100	7.72	8.15	15.87
1/2" x 12"	LF	0.145	10.25	11.75	22.00

Oil base sealants and caulking

	Unit	Man-Hrs	Material	Labor	Total
1/4" x 1/4"	LF	0.020	0.05	1.63	1.68
1/4" x 3/8"	LF	0.021	0.11	1.69	1.80
1/4" x 1/2"	LF	0.022	0.12	1.76	1.88
3/8" x 3/8"	LF	0.023	0.15	1.86	2.01
3/8" x 1/2"	LF	0.024	0.17	1.97	2.14
3/8" x 5/8"	LF	0.026	0.31	2.10	2.41
3/8" x 3/4"	LF	0.028	0.35	2.24	2.59
1/2" x 1/2"	LF	0.031	0.31	2.50	2.81
1/2" x 5/8"	LF	0.035	0.39	2.83	3.22
1/2" x 3/4"	LF	0.040	0.45	3.26	3.71

	Unit	Man-Hrs	Material	Labor	Total
07920.01 CAULKING (Cont.)					
Oil base sealants and caulking					
1/2" x 7/8"	LF	0.041	0.53	3.34	3.87
1/2" x 1"	LF	0.042	0.58	3.43	4.01
3/4" x 3/4"	LF	0.043	0.68	3.52	4.20
1" x 1"	LF	0.044	1.19	3.62	4.81
Polyurethane compounds					
1/4" x 1/4"	LF	0.020	0.24	1.63	1.87
1/4" x 3/8"	LF	0.021	0.43	1.69	2.12
1/4" x 1/2"	LF	0.022	0.54	1.76	2.30
3/8" x 3/8"	LF	0.023	0.60	1.86	2.46
3/8" x 1/2"	LF	0.024	0.77	1.97	2.74
3/8" x 5/8"	LF	0.026	0.96	2.10	3.06
3/8" x 3/4"	LF	0.028	1.16	2.24	3.40
1/2" x 1/2"	LF	0.031	1.11	2.50	3.61
1/2" x 5/8"	LF	0.035	1.21	2.83	4.04
1/2" x 3/4"	LF	0.040	1.39	3.26	4.65
1/2" x 7/8"	LF	0.041	1.77	3.34	5.11
1/2" x 1"	LF	0.044	2.24	3.62	5.86
3/4" x 3/4"	LF	0.043	2.28	3.52	5.80
3/4" x 1"	LF	0.044	2.49	3.62	6.11
Backer rod, polyethylene					
1/4"	LF	0.020	0.06	1.63	1.69
1/2"	LF	0.021	0.10	1.71	1.81
3/4"	LF	0.022	0.13	1.81	1.94
1"	LF	0.024	0.19	1.91	2.10
07950.01 EXPANSION JOINTS					
EXPANSION JOINTS					
Expansion joints with covers, floor assembly type					
With 1" space					
Aluminum	LF	0.133	31.25	12.00	43.25
Bronze	LF	0.133	65.00	12.00	77.00
Stainless steel	LF	0.133	51.00	12.00	63.00
With 2" space					
Aluminum	LF	0.133	33.75	12.00	45.75
Bronze	LF	0.133	60.00	12.00	72.00
Stainless steel	LF	0.133	53.00	12.00	65.00
Ceiling and wall assembly type					
With 1" space					
Aluminum	LF	0.160	17.50	14.50	32.00
Bronze	LF	0.160	60.00	14.50	74.50
Stainless steel	LF	0.160	54.00	14.50	68.50
With 2" space					
Aluminum	LF	0.160	19.25	14.50	33.75
Bronze	LF	0.160	65.00	14.50	79.50
Stainless steel	LF	0.160	57.00	14.50	71.50
Exterior roof and wall, aluminum					
Roof to roof					
With 1" space	LF	0.133	51.00	12.00	63.00
With 2" space	LF	0.133	55.00	12.00	67.00
Roof to wall					
With 1" space	LF	0.145	39.75	13.00	52.75
With 2" space	LF	0.145	47.25	13.00	60.25
Flat wall to wall					
With 1" space	LF	0.133	19.25	12.00	31.25
With 2" space	LF	0.133	21.00	12.00	33.00
Corner to flat wall					
With 1" space	LF	0.160	23.25	14.50	37.75
With 2" in space	LF	0.160	23.50	14.50	38.00

© 2020 BNi Publications, Inc.

	Unit	Man-Hrs	Material	Labor	Total

08111.31 METAL DOORS

METAL DOORS

Flush hollow metal, std. duty, 20 ga., 1-3/8" thick

	Unit	Man-Hrs	Material	Labor	Total
2-6 x 6-8	EA	0.889	370.00	72.00	442.00
2-8 x 6-8	EA	0.889	390.00	72.00	462.00
3-0 x 6-8	EA	0.889	420.00	72.00	492.00

1-3/4" thick

	Unit	Man-Hrs	Material	Labor	Total
2-6 x 6-8	EA	0.889	410.00	72.00	482.00
2-8 x 6-8	EA	0.889	510.00	72.00	582.00
3-0 x 6-8	EA	0.889	470.00	72.00	542.00
2-6 x 7-0	EA	0.889	450.00	72.00	522.00
2-8 x 7-0	EA	0.889	470.00	72.00	542.00
3-0 x 7-0	EA	0.889	500.00	72.00	572.00

Heavy duty, 20 ga., unrated, 1-3/4"

	Unit	Man-Hrs	Material	Labor	Total
2-8 x 6-8	EA	0.889	450.00	72.00	522.00
3-0 x 6-8	EA	0.889	490.00	72.00	562.00
2-8 x 7-0	EA	0.889	520.00	72.00	592.00
3-0 x 7-0	EA	0.889	500.00	72.00	572.00
3-4 x 7-0	EA	0.889	520.00	72.00	592.00

18 ga., 1-3/4", unrated door

	Unit	Man-Hrs	Material	Labor	Total
2-0 x 7-0	EA	0.889	480.00	72.00	552.00
2-4 x 7-0	EA	0.889	480.00	72.00	552.00
2-6 x 7-0	EA	0.889	480.00	72.00	552.00
2-8 x 7-0	EA	0.889	530.00	72.00	602.00
3-0 x 7-0	EA	0.889	490.00	72.00	562.00
3-4 x 7-0	EA	0.889	600.00	72.00	672.00

2", unrated door

	Unit	Man-Hrs	Material	Labor	Total
2-0 x 7-0	EA	1.000	530.00	82.00	612.00
2-4 x 7-0	EA	1.000	530.00	82.00	612.00
2-6 x 7-0	EA	1.000	530.00	82.00	612.00
2-8 x 7-0	EA	1.000	580.00	82.00	662.00
3-0 x 7-0	EA	1.000	600.00	82.00	682.00
3-4 x 7-0	EA	1.000	610.00	82.00	692.00

Galvanized metal door

	Unit	Man-Hrs	Material	Labor	Total
3-0 x 7-0	EA	1.000	620.00	82.00	702.00
For lead lining in doors	EA				1,120.00
For sound attenuation	EA				100.00

Vision glass

	Unit	Man-Hrs	Material	Labor	Total
8" x 8"	EA	1.000	130.00	82.00	212.00
8" x 48"	EA	1.000	200.00	82.00	282.00
Fixed metal louver	EA	0.800	290.00	65.00	355.00

For fire rating, add

	Unit	Man-Hrs	Material	Labor	Total
3 hr door	EA				490.00
1-1/2 hr door	EA				220.00
3/4 hr door	EA				110.00

1' extra height, add to material, 20%
1'6" extra height, add to material, 60%
For dutch doors with shelf, add to material, 100%

08111.34 METAL DOOR FRAMES

METAL DOOR FRAMES

Hollow metal, stock, 18 ga., 4-3/4" x 1-3/4"

	Unit	Man-Hrs	Material	Labor	Total
2-0 x 7-0	EA	1.000	160.00	82.00	242.00
2-4 x 7-0	EA	1.000	190.00	82.00	272.00
2-6 x 7-0	EA	1.000	190.00	82.00	272.00
2-8 x 7-0	EA	1.000	190.00	82.00	272.00
3-0 x 7-0	EA	1.000	190.00	82.00	272.00
4-0 x 7-0	EA	1.333	210.00	110.00	320.00
5-0 x 7-0	EA	1.333	220.00	110.00	330.00
6-0 x 7-0	EA	1.333	260.00	110.00	370.00

16 ga., 6-3/4" x 1-3/4"

	Unit	Man-Hrs	Material	Labor	Total
2-0 x 7-0	EA	1.000	190.00	90.00	280.00
2-4 x 7-0	EA	1.000	180.00	90.00	270.00
2-6 x 7-0	EA	1.000	180.00	90.00	270.00
2-8 x 7-0	EA	1.000	180.00	90.00	270.00
3-0 x 7-0	EA	1.000	200.00	90.00	290.00

	Unit	Man-Hrs	Material	Labor	Total

08111.34 METAL DOOR FRAMES (Cont.)

16 ga., 6-3/4" x 1-3/4"

	Unit	Man-Hrs	Material	Labor	Total
4-0 x 7-0	EA	1.333	230.00	120.00	350.00
6-0 x 7-0	EA	1.333	260.00	120.00	380.00
Transom frame					
3-4 x 1-6	EA	1.000	130.00	90.00	220.00
3-8 x 1-6	EA	1.000	130.00	90.00	220.00
6-4 x 1-6	EA	1.000	190.00	90.00	280.00
Transom sash					
3-0 x 1-4	EA	1.000	120.00	90.00	210.00
3-4 x 1-4	EA	1.000	130.00	90.00	220.00
6-0 x 1-4	EA	1.000	190.00	90.00	280.00
1' extension of frame, add	EA				24.75
14 ga. frame, add	EA				24.75
For fire rating, add					
3 hour	EA				67.00
1-1/2 hour	EA				54.00
3/4 hour	EA				47.00
Lead lining in frame, add	EA				140.00
Sidelights, complete					
1-0 x 7-2	EA	1.000	460.00	90.00	550.00
1-4 x 7-2	EA	1.000	510.00	90.00	600.00
1-0 x 8-8	EA	1.000	540.00	90.00	630.00
1-6 x 8-8	EA	1.000	560.00	90.00	650.00
16 ga., 4-3/4" x 1-3/4"					
2-0 x 7-0	EA	1.000	170.00	90.00	260.00
2-4 x 7-0	EA	1.000	170.00	90.00	260.00
2-6 x 7-0	EA	1.000	170.00	90.00	260.00
2-8 x 7-0	EA	1.000	170.00	90.00	260.00
3-0 x 7-0	EA	1.000	180.00	90.00	270.00
4-0 x 7-0	EA	1.333	180.00	120.00	300.00
6-0 x 7-0	EA	1.333	190.00	120.00	310.00
Transom frame					
3-4 x 1-6	EA	1.000	120.00	90.00	210.00
3-8 x 1-6	EA	1.000	120.00	90.00	210.00
6-4 x 1-6	EA	1.000	160.00	90.00	250.00
Transom sash					
3-0 x 1-4	EA	1.000	100.00	90.00	190.00
3-4 x 1-4	EA	1.000	110.00	90.00	200.00
6-0 x 1-4	EA	1.000	160.00	90.00	250.00
1' extension of door frame, add	EA				24.75
14 ga., metal frame, add	EA				24.75
For fire rating, add					
3 hour	EA				64.00
1-1/2 hour	EA				51.00
3/4 hour	EA				44.75
Lead lining in frame, add	EA				140.00
Sidelights, complete					
1-0 x 7-2	EA	1.000	440.00	90.00	530.00
1-4 x 7-2	EA	1.000	460.00	90.00	550.00
1-0 x 8-8	EA	1.000	500.00	90.00	590.00
1-4 x 8-8	EA	1.000	510.00	90.00	600.00
16 ga., 5-3/4" x 1-3/4"					
2-0 x 7-0	EA	1.000	170.00	82.00	252.00
2-4 x 7-0	EA	1.000	180.00	82.00	262.00
2-6 x 7-0	EA	1.000	180.00	82.00	262.00
2-8 x 7-0	EA	1.000	190.00	82.00	272.00
3-0 x 7-0	EA	1.000	190.00	82.00	272.00
4-0 x 7-0	EA	1.333	200.00	110.00	310.00
5-0 x 7-0	EA	1.333	210.00	110.00	320.00
6-0 x 7-0	EA	1.333	220.00	110.00	330.00
Mullions, vertical					
5-1/4" x 1-3/4"	LF	0.100	19.25	8.15	27.40
5-1/4" x 2"	LF	0.100	24.00	8.15	32.15

© 2020 BNi Publications, Inc.

	Unit	Man-Hrs	Material	Labor	Total
08111.34 METAL DOOR FRAMES (Cont.)					
Mullions					
Horizontal					
5-1/4" x 1-3/4"	LF	0.100	19.25	8.15	27.40
5-1/4" x 2"	LF	0.100	24.00	8.15	32.15
08111.61 ALUMINUM DOORS					
ALUMINUM DOORS					
Aluminum doors, commercial					
Narrow stile					
2-6 x 7-0	EA	4.000	940.00	360.00	1,300.00
3-0 x 7-0	EA	4.000	990.00	360.00	1,350.00
3-6 x 7-0	EA	4.000	1,010.00	360.00	1,370.00
Pair					
5-0 x 7-0	EA	8.000	1,570.00	720.00	2,290.00
6-0 x 7-0	EA	8.000	1,590.00	720.00	2,310.00
7-0 x 7-0	EA	8.000	1,660.00	720.00	2,380.00
Wide stile					
2-6 x 7-0	EA	4.000	1,320.00	360.00	1,680.00
3-0 x 7-0	EA	4.000	1,360.00	360.00	1,720.00
3-6 x 7-0	EA	4.000	1,400.00	360.00	1,760.00
Pair					
5-0 x 7-0	EA	8.000	2,410.00	720.00	3,130.00
6-0 x 7-0	EA	8.000	2,520.00	720.00	3,240.00
7-0 x 7-0	EA	8.000	2,570.00	720.00	3,290.00
08140.01 WOOD DOORS					
WOOD DOORS					
Solid core, 1-3/8" thick					
Birch faced					
2-4 x 7-0	EA	1.000	180.00	82.00	262.00
2-8 x 7-0	EA	1.000	180.00	82.00	262.00
3-0 x 7-0	EA	1.000	180.00	82.00	262.00
3-4 x 7-0	EA	1.000	370.00	82.00	452.00
2-4 x 6-8	EA	1.000	180.00	82.00	262.00
2-6 x 6-8	EA	1.000	180.00	82.00	262.00
2-8 x 6-8	EA	1.000	180.00	82.00	262.00
3-0 x 6-8	EA	1.000	180.00	82.00	262.00
Lauan faced					
2-4 x 6-8	EA	1.000	160.00	82.00	242.00
2-8 x 6-8	EA	1.000	170.00	82.00	252.00
3-0 x 6-8	EA	1.000	180.00	82.00	262.00
3-4 x 6-8	EA	1.000	190.00	82.00	272.00
Tempered hardboard faced					
2-4 x 7-0	EA	1.000	200.00	82.00	282.00
2-8 x 7-0	EA	1.000	210.00	82.00	292.00
3-0 x 7-0	EA	1.000	240.00	82.00	322.00
3-4 x 7-0	EA	1.000	250.00	82.00	332.00
Hollow core, 1-3/8" thick					
Birch faced					
2-4 x 7-0	EA	1.000	160.00	82.00	242.00
2-8 x 7-0	EA	1.000	160.00	82.00	242.00
3-0 x 7-0	EA	1.000	170.00	82.00	252.00
3-4 x 7-0	EA	1.000	180.00	82.00	262.00
Lauan faced					
2-4 x 6-8	EA	1.000	69.00	82.00	151.00
2-6 x 6-8	EA	1.000	74.00	82.00	156.00
2-8 x 6-8	EA	1.000	93.00	82.00	175.00
3-0 x 6-8	EA	1.000	97.00	82.00	179.00
3-4 x 6-8	EA	1.000	110.00	82.00	192.00
Tempered hardboard faced					
2-4 x 7-0	EA	1.000	84.00	82.00	166.00
2-6 x 7-0	EA	1.000	90.00	82.00	172.00
2-8 x 7-0	EA	1.000	100.00	82.00	182.00
3-0 x 7-0	EA	1.000	110.00	82.00	192.00
3-4 x 7-0	EA	1.000	120.00	82.00	202.00

DIVISION 08 DOORS AND WINDOWS

	Unit	Man-Hrs	Material	Labor	Total
08140.01 WOOD DOORS (Cont.)					
Solid core, 1-3/4" thick					
Birch faced					
2-4 x 7-0	EA	1.000	280.00	82.00	362.00
2-6 x 7-0	EA	1.000	280.00	82.00	362.00
2-8 x 7-0	EA	1.000	290.00	82.00	372.00
3-0 x 7-0	EA	1.000	270.00	82.00	352.00
3-4 x 7-0	EA	1.000	280.00	82.00	362.00
Lauan faced					
2-4 x 7-0	EA	1.000	190.00	82.00	272.00
2-6 x 7-0	EA	1.000	220.00	82.00	302.00
2-8 x 7-0	EA	1.000	230.00	82.00	312.00
3-4 x 7-0	EA	1.000	240.00	82.00	322.00
3-0 x 7-0	EA	1.000	260.00	82.00	342.00
Tempered hardboard faced					
2-4 x 7-0	EA	1.000	250.00	82.00	332.00
2-6 x 7-0	EA	1.000	280.00	82.00	362.00
2-8 x 7-0	EA	1.000	300.00	82.00	382.00
3-0 x 7-0	EA	1.000	320.00	82.00	402.00
3-4 x 7-0	EA	1.000	340.00	82.00	422.00
Hollow core, 1-3/4" thick					
Birch faced					
2-4 x 7-0	EA	1.000	190.00	82.00	272.00
2-6 x 7-0	EA	1.000	190.00	82.00	272.00
2-8 x 7-0	EA	1.000	200.00	82.00	282.00
3-0 x 7-0	EA	1.000	200.00	82.00	282.00
3-4 x 7-0	EA	1.000	220.00	82.00	302.00
Lauan faced					
2-4 x 6-8	EA	1.000	110.00	82.00	192.00
2-6 x 6-8	EA	1.000	130.00	82.00	212.00
2-8 x 6-8	EA	1.000	110.00	82.00	192.00
3-0 x 6-8	EA	1.000	120.00	82.00	202.00
3-4 x 6-8	EA	1.000	120.00	82.00	202.00
Tempered hardboard					
2-4 x 7-0	EA	1.000	100.00	82.00	182.00
2-6 x 7-0	EA	1.000	110.00	82.00	192.00
2-8 x 7-0	EA	1.000	110.00	82.00	192.00
3-0 x 7-0	EA	1.000	120.00	82.00	202.00
3-4 x 7-0	EA	1.000	130.00	82.00	212.00
Add-on, louver	EA	0.800	35.00	65.00	100.00
Glass	EA	0.800	110.00	65.00	175.00
Exterior doors, 3-0 x 7-0 x 2-1/2", solid core					
Carved					
One face	EA	2.000	1,460.00	160.00	1,620.00
Two faces	EA	2.000	2,020.00	160.00	2,180.00
Closet doors, 1-3/4" thick					
Bi-fold or bi-passing, includes frame and trim					
Paneled					
4-0 x 6-8	EA	1.333	510.00	110.00	620.00
6-0 x 6-8	EA	1.333	580.00	110.00	690.00
Louvered					
4-0 x 6-8	EA	1.333	350.00	110.00	460.00
6-0 x 6-8	EA	1.333	420.00	110.00	530.00
Flush					
4-0 x 6-8	EA	1.333	260.00	110.00	370.00
6-0 x 6-8	EA	1.333	330.00	110.00	440.00
Primed					
4-0 x 6-8	EA	1.333	280.00	110.00	390.00
6-0 x 6-8	EA	1.333	310.00	110.00	420.00
08140.09 WOOD FRAMES					
WOOD FRAMES					
Frame, interior, pine					
2-6 x 6-8	EA	1.143	100.00	93.00	193.00
2-8 x 6-8	EA	1.143	110.00	93.00	203.00
3-0 x 6-8	EA	1.143	120.00	93.00	213.00

© 2020 BNi Publications, Inc.

	Unit	Man-Hrs	Material	Labor	Total
08140.09 WOOD FRAMES (Cont.)					
Frame, interior, pine					
5-0 x 6-8	EA	1.143	120.00	93.00	213.00
6-0 x 6-8	EA	1.143	130.00	93.00	223.00
2-6 x 7-0	EA	1.143	120.00	93.00	213.00
2-8 x 7-0	EA	1.143	140.00	93.00	233.00
3-0 x 7-0	EA	1.143	140.00	93.00	233.00
5-0 x 7-0	EA	1.600	150.00	130.00	280.00
6-0 x 7-0	EA	1.600	160.00	130.00	290.00
Exterior, custom, with threshold, including trim					
Walnut					
3-0 x 7-0	EA	2.000	420.00	160.00	580.00
6-0 x 7-0	EA	2.000	480.00	160.00	640.00
Oak					
3-0 x 7-0	EA	2.000	380.00	160.00	540.00
6-0 x 7-0	EA	2.000	430.00	160.00	590.00
Pine					
2-4 x 7-0	EA	1.600	160.00	130.00	290.00
2-6 x 7-0	EA	1.600	160.00	130.00	290.00
2-8 x 7-0	EA	1.600	170.00	130.00	300.00
3-0 x 7-0	EA	1.600	180.00	130.00	310.00
3-4 x 7-0	EA	1.600	200.00	130.00	330.00
6-0 x 7-0	EA	2.667	210.00	220.00	430.00
08311.31 CONTROL					
CONTROL					
Access control, 7' high, indoor or outdoor impenetrability					
Remote or card control, type B	EA	10.667	1,880.00	890.00	2,770.00
Free passage, type B	EA	10.667	1,530.00	890.00	2,420.00
Remote or card control, type AA	EA	10.667	3,000.00	890.00	3,890.00
Free passage, type AA	EA	10.667	2,720.00	890.00	3,610.00
08340.01 SPECIAL DOORS					
SPECIAL DOORS					
Vault door and frame, class 5, steel	EA	8.000	7,940.00	650.00	8,590.00
Overhead door, coiling insulated					
Chain gear, no frame, 12' x 12'	EA	10.000	3,410.00	820.00	4,230.00
Aluminum, bronze glass panels, 12-9 x 13-0	EA	8.000	3,850.00	650.00	4,500.00
Garage, flush, ins. metal, primed, 9-0 x 7-0	EA	2.667	1,100.00	220.00	1,320.00
Sliding fire doors, motorized, fusible link, 3 hr.					
3-0 x 6-8	EA	16.000	5,620.00	1,300.00	6,920.00
3-8 x 6-8	EA	16.000	5,690.00	1,300.00	6,990.00
4-0 x 8-0	EA	16.000	5,790.00	1,300.00	7,090.00
5-0 x 8-0	EA	16.000	5,900.00	1,300.00	7,200.00
Metal clad doors, including electric motor					
Light duty					
Minimum	SF	0.133	45.00	10.75	55.75
Maximum	SF	0.320	73.00	26.00	99.00
Heavy duty					
Minimum	SF	0.400	70.00	32.50	102.50
Maximum	SF	0.500	110.00	40.75	150.75
Hangar doors, based on 150' openings					
To 20' high	SF	0.096	61.00	10.25	71.25
20' to 40' high	SF	0.060	67.00	6.45	73.45
40' to 60' high	SF	0.040	70.00	4.30	74.30
60' to 80' high	SF	0.024	73.00	2.58	75.58
Over 80' high	SF	0.019	100.00	2.06	102.06
Counter doors (roll-up shutters), std, manual					
Opening, 4' high					
4' wide	EA	6.667	1,300.00	540.00	1,840.00
6' wide	EA	6.667	1,760.00	540.00	2,300.00
8' wide	EA	7.273	1,980.00	590.00	2,570.00
10' wide	EA	10.000	2,200.00	820.00	3,020.00
14' wide	EA	10.000	2,750.00	820.00	3,570.00
6' high					
4' wide	EA	6.667	1,540.00	540.00	2,080.00
6' wide	EA	7.273	2,010.00	590.00	2,600.00

	Unit	Man-Hrs	Material	Labor	Total

08340.01 SPECIAL DOORS (Cont.)

6' high

	Unit	Man-Hrs	Material	Labor	Total
8' wide	EA	8.000	2,200.00	650.00	2,850.00
10' wide	EA	10.000	2,480.00	820.00	3,300.00
14' wide	EA	11.429	2,810.00	930.00	3,740.00
For stainless steel, add to material, 40%					
For motor operator, add	EA				1,520.00

Service doors (roll-up shutters), std, manual

Opening

	Unit	Man-Hrs	Material	Labor	Total
8' high x 8' wide	EA	4.444	1,650.00	360.00	2,010.00
10' high x 10' wide	EA	6.667	2,060.00	540.00	2,600.00
12' high x 12' wide	EA	10.000	2,310.00	820.00	3,130.00
14' high x 14' wide	EA	13.333	3,030.00	1,090.00	4,120.00
16' high x 14' wide	EA	13.333	4,240.00	1,090.00	5,330.00
20' high x 14' wide	EA	20.000	4,790.00	1,630.00	6,420.00
24' high x 16' wide	EA	17.778	7,810.00	1,450.00	9,260.00

For motor operator

	Unit	Man-Hrs	Material	Labor	Total
Up to 12-0 x 12-0, add	EA				1,550.00
Over 12-0 x 12-0, add	EA				1,980.00

Roll-up doors

	Unit	Man-Hrs	Material	Labor	Total
13-0 high x 14-0 wide	EA	11.429	1,560.00	930.00	2,490.00
12-0 high x 14-0 wide	EA	11.429	1,980.00	930.00	2,910.00

Top coiling grilles, manual, steel or aluminum

Opening, 4' high x

	Unit	Man-Hrs	Material	Labor	Total
4' wide	EA	3.200	1,830.00	260.00	2,090.00
6' wide	EA	3.200	1,890.00	260.00	2,150.00
8' wide	EA	4.444	2,190.00	360.00	2,550.00
12' wide	EA	4.444	2,530.00	360.00	2,890.00
16' wide	EA	6.667	2,900.00	540.00	3,440.00

6' high x

	Unit	Man-Hrs	Material	Labor	Total
4' wide	EA	6.667	1,920.00	540.00	2,460.00
6' wide	EA	7.273	2,140.00	590.00	2,730.00
8' wide	EA	8.000	2,220.00	650.00	2,870.00
12' wide	EA	8.889	2,690.00	720.00	3,410.00
16' wide	EA	11.429	3,420.00	930.00	4,350.00

Side coiling grilles, manual, aluminum

Opening, 8' high x

	Unit	Man-Hrs	Material	Labor	Total
18' wide	EA	60.000	4,370.00	6,460.00	10,830.00
24' wide	EA	68.571	5,640.00	7,380.00	13,020.00

12' high x

	Unit	Man-Hrs	Material	Labor	Total
12' wide	EA	60.000	4,430.00	6,460.00	10,890.00
18' wide	EA	68.571	5,640.00	7,380.00	13,020.00
24' wide	EA	80.000	8,060.00	8,610.00	16,670.00

Accordion folding, tracks and fittings included

	Unit	Man-Hrs	Material	Labor	Total
Vinyl covered, 2 layers	SF	0.320	14.50	26.00	40.50
Woven mahogany and vinyl	SF	0.320	18.25	26.00	44.25
Economy vinyl	SF	0.320	12.25	26.00	38.25
Rigid polyvinyl chloride	SF	0.320	20.00	26.00	46.00

Sectional wood overhead, frames not incl.

Commercial grade, HD, 1-3/4" thick, manual

	Unit	Man-Hrs	Material	Labor	Total
8' x 8'	EA	6.667	1,080.00	540.00	1,620.00
10' x 10'	EA	7.273	1,560.00	590.00	2,150.00
12' x 12'	EA	8.000	2,030.00	650.00	2,680.00

Chain hoist

	Unit	Man-Hrs	Material	Labor	Total
12' x 16' high	EA	13.333	3,000.00	1,090.00	4,090.00
14' x 14' high	EA	10.000	3,290.00	820.00	4,110.00
20' x 8' high	EA	16.000	2,830.00	1,300.00	4,130.00
16' high	EA	20.000	6,350.00	1,630.00	7,980.00

Sectional metal overhead doors, complete

Residential grade, manual

	Unit	Man-Hrs	Material	Labor	Total
9' x 7'	EA	3.200	740.00	260.00	1,000.00
16' x 7'	EA	4.000	1,330.00	330.00	1,660.00

Commercial grade

	Unit	Man-Hrs	Material	Labor	Total
8' x 8'	EA	6.667	860.00	540.00	1,400.00
10' x 10'	EA	7.273	1,150.00	590.00	1,740.00

© 2020 BNi Publications, Inc.

	Unit	Man-Hrs	Material	Labor	Total

08340.01 SPECIAL DOORS (Cont.)

	Unit	Man-Hrs	Material	Labor	Total
Commercial grade					
12' x 12'	EA	8.000	1,910.00	650.00	2,560.00
20' x 14', with chain hoist	EA	16.000	4,560.00	1,300.00	5,860.00
Sliding glass doors					
Tempered plate glass, 1/4" thick					
6' wide					
Economy grade	EA	2.667	1,180.00	220.00	1,400.00
Premium grade	EA	2.667	1,350.00	220.00	1,570.00
12' wide					
Economy grade	EA	4.000	1,650.00	330.00	1,980.00
Premium grade	EA	4.000	2,480.00	330.00	2,810.00
Insulating glass, 5/8" thick					
6' wide					
Economy grade	EA	2.667	1,450.00	220.00	1,670.00
Premium grade	EA	2.667	1,860.00	220.00	2,080.00
12' wide					
Economy grade	EA	4.000	1,800.00	330.00	2,130.00
Premium grade	EA	4.000	2,890.00	330.00	3,220.00
1" thick					
6' wide					
Economy grade	EA	2.667	1,820.00	220.00	2,040.00
Premium grade	EA	2.667	2,100.00	220.00	2,320.00
12' wide					
Economy grade	EA	4.000	2,830.00	330.00	3,160.00
Premium grade	EA	4.000	4,140.00	330.00	4,470.00
Added costs					
Custom quality, add to material, 30%					
Tempered glass, 6' wide, add	SF				5.08
Vertical lift doors, channel frame construction					
20' high x					
10' wide	EA	9.600	41,820.00	1,140.00	42,960.00
15' wide	EA	9.600	52,280.00	1,140.00	53,420.00
20' wide	EA	17.143	57,500.00	2,040.00	59,540.00
25' wide	EA	17.143	62,730.00	2,040.00	64,770.00
25' high x					
20' wide	EA	17.143	65,340.00	2,040.00	67,380.00
25' wide	EA	20.000	73,190.00	2,380.00	75,570.00
30' high x					
25' wide	EA	20.000	78,420.00	2,380.00	80,800.00
30' wide	EA	20.000	86,260.00	2,380.00	88,640.00
35' wide	EA	20.000	101,940.00	2,380.00	104,320.00
Residential storm door					
Minimum	EA	1.333	180.00	110.00	290.00
Average	EA	1.333	240.00	110.00	350.00
Maximum	EA	2.000	530.00	160.00	690.00

08410.01 STOREFRONTS

	Unit	Man-Hrs	Material	Labor	Total
STOREFRONTS					
Storefront, aluminum and glass					
Minimum	SF	0.100	29.25	9.00	38.25
Average	SF	0.114	43.75	10.25	54.00
Maximum	SF	0.133	87.00	12.00	99.00
Entrance doors, premium, closers, panic dev.,etc.					
1/2" thick glass					
3' x 7'	EA	6.667	3,890.00	600.00	4,490.00
6' x 7'	EA	10.000	6,650.00	900.00	7,550.00
3/4" thick glass					
3' x 7'	EA	6.667	4,030.00	600.00	4,630.00
6' x 7'	EA	10.000	6,720.00	900.00	7,620.00
1" thick glass					
3' x 7'	EA	6.667	4,370.00	600.00	4,970.00
6' x 7'	EA	10.000	7,720.00	900.00	8,620.00

	Unit	Man-Hrs	Material	Labor	Total

08410.01 STOREFRONTS (Cont.)

Revolving doors
7' diameter, 7' high

	Unit	Man-Hrs	Material	Labor	Total
Minimum	EA	60.000	27,660.00	7,130.00	34,790.00
Average	EA	96.000	34,800.00	11,400.00	46,200.00
Maximum	EA	120.000	44,910.00	14,250.00	59,160.00

08440.01 GLAZED CURTAIN WALLS

GLAZED CURTAIN WALLS

Curtain wall, aluminum system, framing sections

2" x 3"

	Unit	Man-Hrs	Material	Labor	Total
Jamb	LF	0.067	19.50	6.00	25.50
Horizontal	LF	0.067	19.75	6.00	25.75
Mullion	LF	0.067	26.50	6.00	32.50

2" x 4"

	Unit	Man-Hrs	Material	Labor	Total
Jamb	LF	0.100	26.50	9.00	35.50
Horizontal	LF	0.100	27.25	9.00	36.25
Mullion	LF	0.100	26.50	9.00	35.50

3" x 5-1/2"

	Unit	Man-Hrs	Material	Labor	Total
Jamb	LF	0.100	35.00	9.00	44.00
Horizontal	LF	0.100	38.75	9.00	47.75
Mullion	LF	0.100	35.25	9.00	44.25
4" corner mullion	LF	0.133	46.75	12.00	58.75

Coping sections

	Unit	Man-Hrs	Material	Labor	Total
1/8" x 8"	LF	0.133	44.25	12.00	56.25
1/8" x 9"	LF	0.133	44.50	12.00	56.50
1/8" x 12-1/2"	LF	0.160	45.75	14.50	60.25

Sill section

	Unit	Man-Hrs	Material	Labor	Total
1/8" x 6"	LF	0.080	43.75	7.20	50.95
1/8" x 7"	LF	0.080	44.25	7.20	51.45
1/8" x 8-1/2"	LF	0.080	45.00	7.20	52.20

Column covers, aluminum

	Unit	Man-Hrs	Material	Labor	Total
1/8" x 26"	LF	0.200	43.75	18.00	61.75
1/8" x 34"	LF	0.211	48.50	19.00	67.50
1/8" x 38"	LF	0.211	49.00	19.00	68.00

Doors
Aluminum framed, standard hardware
Narrow stile

	Unit	Man-Hrs	Material	Labor	Total
2-6 x 7-0	EA	4.000	810.00	360.00	1,170.00
3-0 x 7-0	EA	4.000	810.00	360.00	1,170.00
3-6 x 7-0	EA	4.000	840.00	360.00	1,200.00

Wide stile

	Unit	Man-Hrs	Material	Labor	Total
2-6 x 7-0	EA	4.000	1,380.00	360.00	1,740.00
3-0 x 7-0	EA	4.000	1,490.00	360.00	1,850.00
3-6 x 7-0	EA	4.000	1,600.00	360.00	1,960.00

Flush panel doors, to match adjacent wall panels

	Unit	Man-Hrs	Material	Labor	Total
2-6 x 7-0	EA	5.000	1,170.00	450.00	1,620.00
3-0 x 7-0	EA	5.000	1,230.00	450.00	1,680.00
3-6 x 7-0	EA	5.000	1,270.00	450.00	1,720.00

Wall panel, insulated

	Unit	Man-Hrs	Material	Labor	Total
U=.08	SF	0.067	14.75	6.00	20.75
U=.10	SF	0.067	14.00	6.00	20.00
U=.15	SF	0.067	12.50	6.00	18.50

Window wall system, complete

	Unit	Man-Hrs	Material	Labor	Total
Minimum	SF	0.080	42.75	7.20	49.95
Average	SF	0.089	68.00	8.00	76.00
Maximum	SF	0.114	160.00	10.25	170.25

Added costs
For bronze, add 20% to material
For stainless steel, add 50% to material

08511.31 ALUMINUM WINDOWS

ALUMINUM WINDOWS

Jalousie

	Unit	Man-Hrs	Material	Labor	Total
3-0 x 4-0	EA	1.000	390.00	90.00	480.00
3-0 x 5-0	EA	1.000	450.00	90.00	540.00

© 2020 BNi Publications, Inc.

	Unit	Man-Hrs	Material	Labor	Total

08511.31 ALUMINUM WINDOWS (Cont.)

Fixed window

6 sf to 8 sf	SF	0.114	19.25	10.25	29.50
12 sf to 16 sf	SF	0.089	17.00	8.00	25.00

Projecting window

6 sf to 8 sf	SF	0.200	42.50	18.00	60.50
12 sf to 16 sf	SF	0.133	38.25	12.00	50.25

Horizontal sliding

6 sf to 8 sf	SF	0.100	27.75	9.00	36.75
12 sf to 16 sf	SF	0.080	25.50	7.20	32.70

Double hung

6 sf to 8 sf	SF	0.160	38.25	14.50	52.75
10 sf to 12 sf	SF	0.133	34.00	12.00	46.00

Storm window, 0.5 cfm, up to

60 u.i. (united inches)	EA	0.400	89.00	36.00	125.00
70 u.i.	EA	0.400	92.00	36.00	128.00
80 u.i.	EA	0.400	100.00	36.00	136.00
90 u.i.	EA	0.444	100.00	40.00	140.00
100 u.i.	EA	0.444	110.00	40.00	150.00

2.0 cfm, up to

60 u.i.	EA	0.400	110.00	36.00	146.00
70 u.i.	EA	0.400	120.00	36.00	156.00
80 u.i.	EA	0.400	120.00	36.00	156.00
90 u.i.	EA	0.444	130.00	40.00	170.00
100 u.i.	EA	0.444	130.00	40.00	170.00

08512.31 STEEL WINDOWS

STEEL WINDOWS

Steel windows, primed

Casements

Operable

Minimum	SF	0.047	54.00	4.23	58.23
Maximum	SF	0.053	81.00	4.80	85.80
Fixed sash	SF	0.040	43.25	3.60	46.85
Double hung	SF	0.044	81.00	4.00	85.00

Industrial windows

Horizontally pivoted sash	SF	0.053	69.00	4.80	73.80
Fixed sash	SF	0.044	54.00	4.00	58.00

Security sash

Operable	SF	0.053	86.00	4.80	90.80
Fixed	SF	0.044	76.00	4.00	80.00
Picture window	SF	0.044	37.00	4.00	41.00

Projecting sash

Minimum	SF	0.050	64.00	4.50	68.50
Maximum	SF	0.050	79.00	4.50	83.50
Mullions	LF	0.040	16.75	3.60	20.35

08520.01 WOOD WINDOWS

WOOD WINDOWS

Double hung

24" x 36"

Minimum	EA	0.800	240.00	65.00	305.00
Average	EA	1.000	350.00	82.00	432.00
Maximum	EA	1.333	470.00	110.00	580.00

24" x 48"

Minimum	EA	0.800	280.00	65.00	345.00
Average	EA	1.000	410.00	82.00	492.00
Maximum	EA	1.333	570.00	110.00	680.00

30" x 48"

Minimum	EA	0.889	290.00	72.00	362.00
Average	EA	1.143	410.00	93.00	503.00
Maximum	EA	1.600	590.00	130.00	720.00

30" x 60"

Minimum	EA	0.889	320.00	72.00	392.00
Average	EA	1.143	510.00	93.00	603.00
Maximum	EA	1.600	630.00	130.00	760.00

DIVISION 08 DOORS AND WINDOWS

08520.01 WOOD WINDOWS (Cont.)

	Unit	Man-Hrs	Material	Labor	Total
Casement					
1 leaf, 22" x 38" high					
Minimum	EA	0.800	350.00	65.00	415.00
Average	EA	1.000	430.00	82.00	512.00
Maximum	EA	1.333	500.00	110.00	610.00
2 leaf, 50" x 50" high					
Minimum	EA	1.000	940.00	82.00	1,022.00
Average	EA	1.333	1,230.00	110.00	1,340.00
Maximum	EA	2.000	1,410.00	160.00	1,570.00
3 leaf, 71" x 62" high					
Minimum	EA	1.000	1,550.00	82.00	1,632.00
Average	EA	1.333	1,580.00	110.00	1,690.00
Maximum	EA	2.000	1,890.00	160.00	2,050.00
4 leaf, 95" x 75" high					
Minimum	EA	1.143	2,060.00	93.00	2,153.00
Average	EA	1.600	2,350.00	130.00	2,480.00
Maximum	EA	2.667	3,000.00	220.00	3,220.00
5 leaf, 119" x 75" high					
Minimum	EA	1.143	2,670.00	93.00	2,763.00
Average	EA	1.600	2,880.00	130.00	3,010.00
Maximum	EA	2.667	3,680.00	220.00	3,900.00
Picture window, fixed glass, 54" x 54" high					
Minimum	EA	1.000	550.00	82.00	632.00
Average	EA	1.143	620.00	93.00	713.00
Maximum	EA	1.333	1,100.00	110.00	1,210.00
68" x 55" high					
Minimum	EA	1.000	990.00	82.00	1,072.00
Average	EA	1.143	1,140.00	93.00	1,233.00
Maximum	EA	1.333	1,490.00	110.00	1,600.00
Sliding, 40" x 31" high					
Minimum	EA	0.800	330.00	65.00	395.00
Average	EA	1.000	500.00	82.00	582.00
Maximum	EA	1.333	600.00	110.00	710.00
52" x 39" high					
Minimum	EA	1.000	410.00	82.00	492.00
Average	EA	1.143	610.00	93.00	703.00
Maximum	EA	1.333	650.00	110.00	760.00
64" x 72" high					
Minimum	EA	1.000	630.00	82.00	712.00
Average	EA	1.333	1,010.00	110.00	1,120.00
Maximum	EA	1.600	1,110.00	130.00	1,240.00
Awning windows					
34" x 21" high					
Minimum	EA	0.800	330.00	65.00	395.00
Average	EA	1.000	380.00	82.00	462.00
Maximum	EA	1.333	440.00	110.00	550.00
40" x 21" high					
Minimum	EA	0.889	390.00	72.00	462.00
Average	EA	1.143	430.00	93.00	523.00
Maximum	EA	1.600	480.00	130.00	610.00
48" x 27" high					
Minimum	EA	0.889	410.00	72.00	482.00
Average	EA	1.143	490.00	93.00	583.00
Maximum	EA	1.600	570.00	130.00	700.00
60" x 36" high					
Minimum	EA	1.000	430.00	82.00	512.00
Average	EA	1.333	760.00	110.00	870.00
Maximum	EA	1.600	860.00	130.00	990.00
Window frame, milled					
Minimum	LF	0.160	6.09	13.00	19.09
Average	LF	0.200	6.80	16.25	23.05
Maximum	LF	0.267	10.25	21.75	32.00

© 2020 BNi Publications, Inc.

DIVISION 08 DOORS AND WINDOWS

	Unit	Man-Hrs	Material	Labor	Total
08620.01 PLASTIC SKYLIGHTS					
PLASTIC SKYLIGHTS					
Single thickness, not including mounting curb					
2' x 4'	EA	1.000	430.00	78.00	508.00
4' x 4'	EA	1.333	580.00	100.00	680.00
5' x 5'	EA	2.000	770.00	160.00	930.00
6' x 8'	EA	2.667	1,630.00	210.00	1,840.00
Double thickness, not including mounting curb					
2' x 4'	EA	1.000	560.00	78.00	638.00
4' x 4'	EA	1.333	710.00	100.00	810.00
5' x 5'	EA	2.000	1,040.00	160.00	1,200.00
6' x 8'	EA	2.667	1,820.00	210.00	2,030.00
Metal framed skylights					
Translucent panels, 2-1/2" thick	SF	0.080	46.00	6.22	52.22
Continuous vaults, 8' wide					
Single glazed	SF	0.100	62.00	7.78	69.78
Double glazed	SF	0.114	100.00	8.89	108.89
08621.01 SOLAR SKYLIGHTS					
SOLAR SKYLIGHTS					
Tubular solar skylight, basic kit					
Minimum	EA	2.667	380.00	220.00	600.00
Average	EA	4.000	430.00	330.00	760.00
Maximum	EA	8.000	480.00	650.00	1,130.00
Tubular solar skylight dome, 10" Diameter					
Minimum	EA	0.800	79.00	65.00	144.00
Average	EA	1.000	85.00	82.00	167.00
Maximum	EA	1.333	91.00	110.00	201.00
14" Diameter					
Minimum	EA	0.800	91.00	65.00	156.00
Average	EA	1.000	97.00	82.00	179.00
Maximum	EA	1.333	100.00	110.00	210.00
Straight extension tube, 10" Diameter x 12" long					
Minimum	EA	0.667	52.00	54.00	106.00
Average	EA	0.800	61.00	65.00	126.00
Maximum	EA	1.000	67.00	82.00	149.00
24" long					
Minimum	EA	0.667	61.00	54.00	115.00
Average	EA	0.800	67.00	65.00	132.00
Maximum	EA	1.000	73.00	82.00	155.00
36" long					
Minimum	EA	0.667	90.00	54.00	144.00
Average	EA	0.800	97.00	65.00	162.00
Maximum	EA	1.000	100.00	82.00	182.00
48" long					
Minimum	EA	0.800	110.00	65.00	175.00
Average	EA	1.000	110.00	82.00	192.00
Maximum	EA	1.333	120.00	110.00	230.00
14" Diameter x 12" long					
Minimum	EA	0.667	67.00	54.00	121.00
Average	EA	0.800	73.00	65.00	138.00
Maximum	EA	1.000	79.00	82.00	161.00
24" long					
Minimum	EA	0.667	85.00	54.00	139.00
Average	EA	0.800	97.00	65.00	162.00
Maximum	EA	1.000	110.00	82.00	192.00
36" long					
Minimum	EA	0.667	110.00	54.00	164.00
Average	EA	0.800	120.00	65.00	185.00
Maximum	EA	1.000	130.00	82.00	212.00
90 Degree extension tubes, 10" Diameter					
Minimum	EA	0.444	61.00	36.25	97.25
Average	EA	0.500	70.00	40.75	110.75
Maximum	EA	0.571	79.00	46.50	125.50

	Unit	Man-Hrs	Material	Labor	Total

08621.01 SOLAR SKYLIGHTS (Cont.)

90 Degree extension tubes
14" Diameter

Minimum	EA	0.444	75.00	36.25	111.25
Average	EA	0.500	83.00	40.75	123.75
Maximum	EA	0.571	91.00	46.50	137.50

Bottom tube adaptor, 10" Diameter

Minimum	EA	0.444	64.00	36.25	100.25
Average	EA	0.500	70.00	40.75	110.75
Maximum	EA	0.571	75.00	46.50	121.50

14" Diameter

Minimum	EA	0.444	79.00	36.25	115.25
Average	EA	0.500	85.00	40.75	125.75
Maximum	EA	0.571	91.00	46.50	137.50

Top tube adaptor, 10" Diameter

Minimum	EA	0.444	64.00	36.25	100.25
Average	EA	0.500	70.00	40.75	110.75
Maximum	EA	0.571	75.00	46.50	121.50

14" Diameter

Minimum	EA	0.444	79.00	36.25	115.25
Average	EA	0.500	85.00	40.75	125.75
Maximum	EA	0.571	91.00	46.50	137.50

Tube flashing

Minimum	EA	0.667	85.00	54.00	139.00
Average	EA	0.800	97.00	65.00	162.00
Maximum	EA	1.000	110.00	82.00	192.00

Daylight dimmer switch

Minimum	EA	0.444	63.00	36.25	99.25
Average	EA	0.500	68.00	40.75	108.75
Maximum	EA	0.571	73.00	46.50	119.50

Dimmer

Minimum	EA	0.444	250.00	36.25	286.25
Average	EA	0.500	280.00	40.75	320.75
Maximum	EA	0.571	300.00	46.50	346.50

08630.11 METAL-FRAMED SKYLIGHTS

METAL-FRAMED SKYLIGHTS

Metal Framed, 2-1/4" Thick, Translucent, <5,000 SF	SF	0.400	30.75	31.25	62.00
>5,000 SF	SF	0.444	27.75	34.50	62.25

Continous Vaulted - Semi-Circular

Skylight, 2-1/4" Thick, to 8', Single Glazed	SF	0.400	36.25	31.25	67.50
Double Glazed	SF	0.400	44.25	31.25	75.50
Skylight, 2-1/4" Thick, to 9', Single Glazed	SF	0.444	62.00	34.50	96.50
Double Glazed	SF	0.444	70.00	34.50	104.50

Pyramid Type, Self Supporting, Clear Opening

Minimum	SF	0.348	49.50	27.00	76.50
Average	SF	0.400	56.00	31.25	87.25
Maximum	SF	0.533	72.00	41.50	113.50

Grid Type, 4' x 10' Modlule

Minimum	SF	0.320	30.25	25.00	55.25
Maximum	SF	0.533	56.00	41.50	97.50

Preformed Acrylic Skylight

Minimum	SF	0.320	24.25	25.00	49.25
Maximum	SF	0.533	40.25	41.50	81.75

08710.01 HINGES

HINGES
Hinges, material only

3 x 3 butts, steel, interior, plain bearing	PAIR				20.75
4 x 4 butts, steel, standard	PAIR				30.50
5 x 4-1/2 butts, bronze/s. steel, heavy duty	PAIR				79.00

Pivot hinges

Top pivot	EA				88.00
Intermediate pivot	EA				94.00
Bottom pivot	EA				180.00

© 2020 BNi Publications, Inc.

	Unit	Man-Hrs	Material	Labor	Total

08710.01 HINGES (Cont.)

Hinges, material only
  BHMA specifications
    3-1/2 x 3-1/2, full mortise butts

	Unit	Man-Hrs	Material	Labor	Total
Plain bearing	PAIR				24.75
Ball bearing	PAIR				29.75
Half surface butts	PAIR				42.25

4 x 4

	Unit	Man-Hrs	Material	Labor	Total
Full mortise butts, plain bearing, standard duty	PAIR				27.00
Full mortise butts, ball bearing	PAIR				32.50

Half surface butts

	Unit	Man-Hrs	Material	Labor	Total
Standard duty	PAIR				42.50
Ball bearing	PAIR				42.50

4-1/2 x 4-1/2

	Unit	Man-Hrs	Material	Labor	Total
Full mortise butts, plain bearing	PAIR				35.75
Ball bearing, heavy duty	PAIR				73.00

Half mortise and half surface butts

	Unit	Man-Hrs	Material	Labor	Total
Plain bearing	PAIR				42.25

Full surface and half surface butts

	Unit	Man-Hrs	Material	Labor	Total
Standard duty	PAIR				72.00
Heavy duty	PAIR				130.00
Full mortise and full slide-in butts, ball bearing	PAIR				33.00

Half mortise butts, ball bearing

	Unit	Man-Hrs	Material	Labor	Total
Standard duty	PAIR				150.00
Heavy duty	PAIR				170.00

5 x 5, ball bearing

	Unit	Man-Hrs	Material	Labor	Total
Full mortise butts	PAIR				69.00
Half mortise, full & half surface butts	PAIR				150.00
Full mortise, full surface and half surface butts	PAIR				200.00

4 x 4

	Unit	Man-Hrs	Material	Labor	Total
Full mortise butts, plain bearing, standard duty	PAIR				16.50

5 x 4-1/2

	Unit	Man-Hrs	Material	Labor	Total
Full mortise butts, ball bearing, heavy duty	PAIR				77.00

08710.02 LOCKSETS

LOCKSETS
  Latchset, heavy duty

	Unit	Man-Hrs	Material	Labor	Total
Cylindrical	EA	0.500	190.00	40.75	230.75
Mortise	EA	0.800	200.00	65.00	265.00

Lockset, heavy duty

	Unit	Man-Hrs	Material	Labor	Total
Cylindrical	EA	0.500	310.00	40.75	350.75
Mortise	EA	0.800	350.00	65.00	415.00

Mortise locks and latchsets, chrome

	Unit	Man-Hrs	Material	Labor	Total
Latchset passage or closet latch	EA	0.667	240.00	54.00	294.00
Privacy (bath or bedroom)	EA	0.667	250.00	54.00	304.00
Entry lockset	EA	0.667	310.00	54.00	364.00
Classroom lockset (outside key operated)	EA	0.667	310.00	54.00	364.00
Storeroom lock	EA	0.667	310.00	54.00	364.00
Front door lock	EA	0.667	310.00	54.00	364.00
Dormitory or exit lock	EA	0.667	310.00	54.00	364.00

Preassembled locks and latches, brass

	Unit	Man-Hrs	Material	Labor	Total
Latchset, passage or closet latch	EA	0.667	280.00	54.00	334.00

Lockset

	Unit	Man-Hrs	Material	Labor	Total
Privacy (bath or bathroom)	EA	0.667	340.00	54.00	394.00
Entry lock	EA	0.667	490.00	54.00	544.00
Classroom lock (outside key operated)	EA	0.667	490.00	54.00	544.00
Storeroom lock	EA	0.667	540.00	54.00	594.00

Bored locks and latches, satin chrome plated

	Unit	Man-Hrs	Material	Labor	Total
Latchset passage or closet latch	EA	0.667	160.00	54.00	214.00

Lockset

	Unit	Man-Hrs	Material	Labor	Total
Privacy (bath or bedroom)	EA	0.667	220.00	54.00	274.00
Entry lock	EA	0.667	240.00	54.00	294.00
Classroom lock	EA	0.667	240.00	54.00	294.00
Corridor lock	EA	0.667	240.00	54.00	294.00

Miscellaneous locks

	Unit	Man-Hrs	Material	Labor	Total
Exit lock with alarm, single door	EA	3.200	780.00	260.00	1,040.00

	Unit	Man-Hrs	Material	Labor	Total
08710.02 LOCKSETS (Cont.)					
Miscellaneous locks					
Electric strike					
Rim mounted wrought steel	EA	2.000	580.00	160.00	740.00
Mortised, wrought steel with bronze plating	EA	3.200	230.00	260.00	490.00
Dead bolt					
Bored, wrought brass, keyed both sides	EA	1.333	120.00	110.00	230.00
Mortised, cast brass	EA	1.333	330.00	110.00	440.00
Lockset, cipher, mechanical	EA	0.800	2,020.00	65.00	2,085.00
08710.03 CLOSERS					
CLOSERS					
Door closers					
Surface mounted, traditional type, parallel arm					
Standard	EA	1.000	240.00	82.00	322.00
Heavy duty	EA	1.000	280.00	82.00	362.00
Modern type, parallel arm, standard duty	EA	1.000	290.00	82.00	372.00
Overhead, concealed, pivot hung, single acting					
Interior	EA	1.000	450.00	82.00	532.00
Exterior	EA	1.000	670.00	82.00	752.00
Floor concealed, single acting, offset, pivoted					
Interior	EA	2.667	730.00	220.00	950.00
Exterior	EA	2.667	930.00	220.00	1,150.00
08710.04 DOOR TRIM					
DOOR TRIM					
Door bumper, bronze, wall type	EA	0.160	6.35	13.00	19.35
Wall type, 4" dia. with convex rubber pad, aluminum	EA	0.160	11.75	13.00	24.75
Floor type					
Aluminum	EA	0.160	5.37	13.00	18.37
Brass	EA	0.160	6.46	13.00	19.46
Door holders					
Wall type, bronze	EA	0.160	32.00	13.00	45.00
Overhead	EA	0.400	26.75	32.50	59.25
Floor type	EA	0.400	26.75	32.50	59.25
Plunger type	EA	0.400	26.00	32.50	58.50
Wall type, aluminum	EA	0.400	25.25	32.50	57.75
Surface bolt	EA	0.160	22.50	13.00	35.50
Panic device					
Rim type with thumb piece	EA	2.000	650.00	160.00	810.00
Mortise	EA	2.000	810.00	160.00	970.00
Vertical rod	EA	2.000	1,230.00	160.00	1,390.00
Labeled, rim type	EA	2.000	850.00	160.00	1,010.00
Mortise	EA	2.000	1,110.00	160.00	1,270.00
Vertical rod	EA	2.000	1,180.00	160.00	1,340.00
Silencers, rubber type	EA	0.016	3.06	1.30	4.36
Dust proof strike with plate, brass	EA	0.267	18.75	21.75	40.50
Flush bolt, lever extension, brass, rated	EA	0.160	34.25	13.00	47.25
Surface bolt with strike, brass, 6" long	EA	0.160	26.00	13.00	39.00
Door coordinator, labeled, brass, satin chrome	EA	0.571	120.00	46.50	166.50
Door plates					
Kick plate, aluminum, 3 beveled edges					
10" x 28"	EA	0.400	30.50	32.50	63.00
10" x 30"	EA	0.400	33.50	32.50	66.00
10" x 34"	EA	0.400	36.50	32.50	69.00
10" x 38"	EA	0.400	39.75	32.50	72.25
Push plate, 4" x 16"					
Aluminum	EA	0.160	27.75	13.00	40.75
Bronze	EA	0.160	88.00	13.00	101.00
Stainless steel	EA	0.160	70.00	13.00	83.00
Armor plate, 40" x 34"	EA	0.320	81.00	26.00	107.00
Pull handle, 4" x 16"					
Aluminum	EA	0.160	98.00	13.00	111.00
Bronze	EA	0.160	190.00	13.00	203.00
Stainless steel	EA	0.160	140.00	13.00	153.00

© 2020 BNi Publications, Inc.

	Unit	Man-Hrs	Material	Labor	Total
08710.04 DOOR TRIM (Cont.)					
Hasp assembly					
3"	EA	0.133	4.62	10.75	15.37
4-1/2"	EA	0.178	5.77	14.50	20.27
6"	EA	0.229	9.18	18.75	27.93
Electro-magnetic door holder					
Wall mounted	EA	2.667	200.00	220.00	420.00
Floor mounted	EA	2.667	350.00	220.00	570.00
Smoke detector door holder					
Photoelectric type	EA	2.667	300.00	220.00	520.00
Ionization type	EA	2.667	300.00	220.00	520.00
Pneumatic operators, activated by rubber mats					
Swing					
Single	EA	6.667	4,330.00	540.00	4,870.00
Double	EA	10.000	7,160.00	820.00	7,980.00
Sliding					
Single	EA	6.667	4,790.00	540.00	5,330.00
Double	EA	10.000	8,320.00	820.00	9,140.00
08710.06 WEATHERSTRIPPING					
WEATHERSTRIPPING					
Weatherstrip, head and jamb, metal strip, neoprene bulb					
Standard duty	LF	0.044	5.19	3.62	8.81
Heavy duty	LF	0.050	5.77	4.07	9.84
Spring type					
Metal doors	EA	2.000	57.00	160.00	217.00
Wood doors	EA	2.667	57.00	220.00	277.00
Sponge type with adhesive backing	EA	0.800	54.00	65.00	119.00
Astragal					
1-3/4" x 13 ga., aluminum	LF	0.067	7.10	5.43	12.53
1-3/8" x 5/8", oak	LF	0.053	5.77	4.34	10.11
Thresholds					
Bronze	LF	0.200	56.00	16.25	72.25
Aluminum					
Plain	LF	0.200	40.25	16.25	56.50
Vinyl insert	LF	0.200	41.25	16.25	57.50
Aluminum with grit	LF	0.200	39.25	16.25	55.50
Steel					
Plain	LF	0.200	31.00	16.25	47.25
Interlocking	LF	0.667	41.50	54.00	95.50
08810.01 GLASS GLAZING					
GLASS GLAZING					
Sheet glass, 1/8" thick	SF	0.044	8.91	4.00	12.91
Plate glass, bronze or grey, 1/4" thick	SF	0.073	13.00	6.54	19.54
Clear	SF	0.073	10.25	6.54	16.79
Polished	SF	0.073	12.00	6.54	18.54
Plexiglass					
1/8" thick	SF	0.073	5.73	6.54	12.27
1/4" thick	SF	0.044	10.25	4.00	14.25
Float glass, clear					
3/16" thick	SF	0.067	6.93	6.00	12.93
1/4" thick	SF	0.073	7.07	6.54	13.61
5/16" thick	SF	0.080	13.25	7.20	20.45
3/8" thick	SF	0.100	14.25	9.00	23.25
1/2" thick	SF	0.133	24.00	12.00	36.00
5/8" thick	SF	0.160	31.75	14.50	46.25
3/4" thick	SF	0.200	34.50	18.00	52.50
1" thick	SF	0.267	61.00	24.00	85.00
Tinted glass, polished plate, twin ground					
3/16" thick	SF	0.067	9.55	6.00	15.55
1/4" thick	SF	0.073	9.55	6.54	16.09
3/8" thick	SF	0.100	15.25	9.00	24.25
1/2" thick	SF	0.133	24.75	12.00	36.75

08810.01 GLASS GLAZING (Cont.)

	Unit	Man-Hrs	Material	Labor	Total
Total, full vision, all glass window system					
To 10' high					
Minimum	SF	0.200	64.00	18.00	82.00
Average	SF	0.200	84.00	18.00	102.00
Maximum	SF	0.200	100.00	18.00	118.00
10' to 20' high					
Minimum	SF	0.200	77.00	18.00	95.00
Average	SF	0.200	94.00	18.00	112.00
Maximum	SF	0.200	120.00	18.00	138.00
Insulated glass, bronze or gray					
1/2" thick	SF	0.133	19.50	12.00	31.50
1" thick	SF	0.200	23.25	18.00	41.25
Spandrel, polished, 1 side, 1/4" thick	SF	0.073	15.50	6.54	22.04
Tempered glass (safety)					
Clear sheet glass					
1/8" thick	SF	0.044	10.75	4.00	14.75
3/16" thick	SF	0.062	13.00	5.53	18.53
Clear float glass					
1/4" thick	SF	0.067	11.25	6.00	17.25
5/16" thick	SF	0.080	20.00	7.20	27.20
3/8" thick	SF	0.100	24.50	9.00	33.50
1/2" thick	SF	0.133	33.50	12.00	45.50
5/8" thick	SF	0.160	38.00	14.50	52.50
3/4" thick	SF	0.267	47.00	24.00	71.00
Tinted float glass					
3/16" thick	SF	0.062	13.50	5.53	19.03
1/4" thick	SF	0.067	14.75	6.00	20.75
3/8" thick	SF	0.100	26.75	9.00	35.75
1/2" thick	SF	0.133	35.75	12.00	47.75
Laminated glass					
Float safety glass with polyvinyl plastic layer					
1/4", sheet or float					
Two lites, 1/8" thick, clear glass	SF	0.067	14.25	6.00	20.25
1/2" thick, float glass					
Two lites, 1/4" thick, clear glass	SF	0.133	21.75	12.00	33.75
Tinted glass	SF	0.133	25.50	12.00	37.50
Insulating glass, two lites, clear float glass					
1/2" thick	SF	0.133	13.75	12.00	25.75
5/8" thick	SF	0.160	16.00	14.50	30.50
3/4" thick	SF	0.200	17.50	18.00	35.50
7/8" thick	SF	0.229	18.50	20.50	39.00
1" thick	SF	0.267	24.75	24.00	48.75
Glass seal edge					
3/8" thick	SF	0.133	11.75	12.00	23.75
Tinted glass					
1/2" thick	SF	0.133	23.75	12.00	35.75
1" thick	SF	0.267	25.50	24.00	49.50
Tempered, clear					
1" thick	SF	0.267	46.50	24.00	70.50
Wire reinforced	SF	0.267	59.00	24.00	83.00
Plate mirror glass					
1/4" thick					
15 sf	SF	0.080	11.75	7.20	18.95
Over 15 sf	SF	0.073	10.75	6.54	17.29
Door type, 1/4" thick	SF	0.080	12.00	7.20	19.20
Transparent, one-way vision, 1/4" thick	SF	0.080	25.75	7.20	32.95
Sheet mirror glass					
3/16" thick	SF	0.080	10.75	7.20	17.95
1/4" thick	SF	0.067	11.25	6.00	17.25
Wall tiles, 12" x 12"					
Clear glass	SF	0.044	3.64	4.00	7.64
Veined glass	SF	0.044	4.62	4.00	8.62
Wire glass, 1/4" thick					
Clear	SF	0.267	21.75	24.00	45.75
Hammered	SF	0.267	21.75	24.00	45.75

© 2020 BNi Publications, Inc.

	Unit	Man-Hrs	Material	Labor	Total
08810.01 GLASS GLAZING (Cont.)					
Wire glass, 1/4" thick					
Obscure	SF	0.267	25.25	24.00	49.25
Bullet resistant, plate, with inter-leaved vinyl					
1-3/16" thick					
To 15 sf	SF	0.400	110.00	36.00	146.00
Over 15 sf	SF	0.400	120.00	36.00	156.00
2" thick					
To 15 sf	SF	0.667	150.00	60.00	210.00
Over 15 sf	SF	0.667	160.00	60.00	220.00
Glazing accessories					
Neoprene glazing gaskets					
1/4" glass	LF	0.032	2.28	2.88	5.16
3/8" glass	LF	0.033	2.54	3.00	5.54
1/2" glass	LF	0.035	2.67	3.13	5.80
3/4" glass	LF	0.036	3.81	3.27	7.08
1" glass	LF	0.040	4.44	3.60	8.04
Mullion section					
1/4" glass	LF	0.016	0.70	1.44	2.14
3/8" glass	LF	0.020	0.89	1.80	2.69
1/2" glass	LF	0.023	1.27	2.05	3.32
3/4" glass	LF	0.027	1.90	2.40	4.30
1" glass	LF	0.032	2.54	2.88	5.42
Molded corners	EA	0.533	2.72	48.00	50.72
08910.01 VENTS AND WALL LOUVERS					
VENTS AND WALL LOUVERS					
Block vent, 8"x16"x4" alum., w/screen, mill finish	EA	0.267	180.00	24.00	204.00
Standard	EA	0.250	98.00	22.50	120.50
Vents w/screen, 4" deep, 8" wide, 5" high					
Modular	EA	0.250	110.00	22.50	132.50
Grilles and louvers					
Aluminum gable louvers	SF	0.133	20.75	12.00	32.75
Vent screen aluminum, 4" wide, continuous	LF	0.027	6.02	2.40	8.42
Fixed type louvers					
4 through 10 sf	SF	0.133	35.00	12.00	47.00
Over 10 sf	SF	0.100	41.50	9.00	50.50
Movable type louvers					
4 through 10 sf	SF	0.133	41.50	12.00	53.50
Over 10 sf	SF	0.100	45.75	9.00	54.75
Aluminum louvers					
Louvers, aluminum, anodized, fixed blade					
Horizontal line	SF	0.200	61.00	18.00	79.00
Vertical line	SF	0.200	61.00	18.00	79.00
Wall louver, aluminum mill finish					
Under, 2 sf	SF	0.100	46.25	9.00	55.25
2 to 4 sf	SF	0.089	40.50	8.00	48.50
5 to 10 sf	SF	0.089	38.00	8.00	46.00
Galvanized steel					
Under 2 sf	SF	0.100	41.75	9.00	50.75
2 to 4 sf	SF	0.089	28.75	8.00	36.75
5 to 10 sf	SF	0.089	27.00	8.00	35.00
Residential use, fixed type, with screen					
8" x 8"	EA	0.400	21.25	36.00	57.25
12" x 12"	EA	0.400	23.25	36.00	59.25
12" x 18"	EA	0.400	28.00	36.00	64.00
14" x 24"	EA	0.400	40.25	36.00	76.25
18" x 24"	EA	0.400	45.25	36.00	81.25
30" x 24"	EA	0.444	62.00	40.00	102.00
08912.61 DOOR LOUVERS					
DOOR LOUVERS					
Fixed, 1" thick, enameled steel					
8"x8"	EA	0.100	64.00	8.15	72.15
12"x8"	EA	0.100	73.00	8.15	81.15
12"x12"	EA	0.114	82.00	9.32	91.32
16"x12"	EA	0.123	120.00	10.00	130.00

08912.61 DOOR LOUVERS (Cont.)

Fixed, 1" thick, enameled steel

	Unit	Man-Hrs	Material	Labor	Total
18"x12"	EA	0.200	120.00	16.25	136.25
20"x8"	EA	0.114	130.00	9.32	139.32
20"x12"	EA	0.229	150.00	18.75	168.75
20"x16"	EA	0.267	150.00	21.75	171.75
20"x20"	EA	0.320	160.00	26.00	186.00
24"x12"	EA	0.267	130.00	21.75	151.75
24"x16"	EA	0.286	140.00	23.25	163.25
24"x18"	EA	0.308	160.00	25.00	185.00
24"x20"	EA	0.333	170.00	27.25	197.25
24"x24"	EA	0.364	170.00	29.75	199.75
26"x26"	EA	0.500	200.00	40.75	240.75

© 2020 BNi Publications, Inc.

	Unit	Man-Hrs	Material	Labor	Total

09211.61 METAL STUDS

METAL STUDS
  Studs, non load bearing, galvanized
    2-1/2", 20 ga.

	Unit	Man-Hrs	Material	Labor	Total
12" o.c.	SF	0.017	0.68	1.35	2.03
16" o.c.	SF	0.013	0.52	1.08	1.60

    25 ga.

	Unit	Man-Hrs	Material	Labor	Total
12" o.c.	SF	0.017	0.46	1.35	1.81
16" o.c.	SF	0.013	0.36	1.08	1.44
24" o.c.	SF	0.011	0.28	0.90	1.18

    3-5/8", 20 ga.

	Unit	Man-Hrs	Material	Labor	Total
12" o.c.	SF	0.020	0.81	1.63	2.44
16" o.c.	SF	0.016	0.62	1.30	1.92
24" o.c.	SF	0.013	0.47	1.08	1.55

    25 ga.

	Unit	Man-Hrs	Material	Labor	Total
12" o.c.	SF	0.020	0.53	1.63	2.16
16" o.c.	SF	0.016	0.44	1.30	1.74
24" o.c.	SF	0.013	0.33	1.08	1.41

    4", 20 ga.

	Unit	Man-Hrs	Material	Labor	Total
12" o.c.	SF	0.020	0.89	1.63	2.52
16" o.c.	SF	0.016	0.68	1.30	1.98
24" o.c.	SF	0.013	0.52	1.08	1.60

    25 ga.

	Unit	Man-Hrs	Material	Labor	Total
12" o.c.	SF	0.020	0.60	1.63	2.23
16" o.c.	SF	0.016	0.47	1.30	1.77
24" o.c.	SF	0.013	0.35	1.08	1.43

    6", 20 ga.

	Unit	Man-Hrs	Material	Labor	Total
12" o.c.	SF	0.025	1.14	2.03	3.17
16" o.c.	SF	0.020	0.83	1.63	2.46
24" o.c.	SF	0.017	0.68	1.35	2.03

    25 ga.

	Unit	Man-Hrs	Material	Labor	Total
12" o.c.	SF	0.025	0.73	2.03	2.76
16" o.c.	SF	0.020	0.58	1.63	2.21
24" o.c.	SF	0.017	0.44	1.35	1.79

  Load bearing studs, galvanized
    3-5/8", 16 ga.

	Unit	Man-Hrs	Material	Labor	Total
12" o.c.	SF	0.020	1.47	1.63	3.10
16" o.c.	SF	0.016	1.36	1.30	2.66

    18 ga.

	Unit	Man-Hrs	Material	Labor	Total
12" o.c.	SF	0.013	1.15	1.08	2.23
16" o.c.	SF	0.016	1.05	1.30	2.35

    4", 16 ga.

	Unit	Man-Hrs	Material	Labor	Total
12" o.c.	SF	0.020	1.55	1.63	3.18
16" o.c.	SF	0.016	1.40	1.30	2.70

    6", 16 ga.

	Unit	Man-Hrs	Material	Labor	Total
12" o.c.	SF	0.025	1.98	2.03	4.01
16" o.c.	SF	0.020	1.78	1.63	3.41

  Furring
    On beams and columns

	Unit	Man-Hrs	Material	Labor	Total
7/8" channel	LF	0.053	0.52	4.34	4.86
1-1/2" channel	LF	0.062	0.62	5.01	5.63

    On ceilings
      3/4" furring channels

	Unit	Man-Hrs	Material	Labor	Total
12" o.c.	SF	0.033	0.37	2.71	3.08
16" o.c.	SF	0.032	0.29	2.60	2.89
24" o.c.	SF	0.029	0.20	2.33	2.53

      1-1/2" furring channels

	Unit	Man-Hrs	Material	Labor	Total
12" o.c.	SF	0.036	0.62	2.96	3.58
16" o.c.	SF	0.033	0.47	2.71	3.18
24" o.c.	SF	0.031	0.31	2.50	2.81

    On walls
      3/4" furring channels

	Unit	Man-Hrs	Material	Labor	Total
12" o.c.	SF	0.027	0.37	2.17	2.54
16" o.c.	SF	0.025	0.29	2.03	2.32
24" o.c.	SF	0.024	0.20	1.91	2.11

	Unit	Man-Hrs	Material	Labor	Total
09211.61 METAL STUDS (Cont.)					
On walls					
1-1/2" furring channels					
12" o.c.	SF	0.029	0.62	2.33	2.95
16" o.c.	SF	0.027	0.47	2.17	2.64
24" o.c.	SF	0.025	0.31	2.03	2.34
09223.61 GYPSUM LATH					
GYPSUM LATH					
Gypsum lath, 1/2" thick					
Clipped	SY	0.044	4.92	3.62	8.54
Nailed	SY	0.050	4.92	4.07	8.99
09223.62 METAL LATH					
METAL LATH					
Diamond expanded, galvanized					
2.5 lb., on walls					
Nailed	SY	0.100	4.22	8.15	12.37
Wired	SY	0.114	4.22	9.32	13.54
On ceilings					
Nailed	SY	0.114	4.22	9.32	13.54
Wired	SY	0.133	4.22	10.75	14.97
3.4 lb., on walls					
Nailed	SY	0.100	5.73	8.15	13.88
Wired	SY	0.114	5.73	9.32	15.05
On ceilings					
Nailed	SY	0.114	5.73	9.32	15.05
Wired	SY	0.133	5.73	10.75	16.48
Flat rib					
2.75 lb., on walls					
Nailed	SY	0.100	3.99	8.15	12.14
Wired	SY	0.114	3.99	9.32	13.31
On ceilings					
Nailed	SY	0.114	3.99	9.32	13.31
Wired	SY	0.133	3.99	10.75	14.74
3.4 lb., on walls					
Nailed	SY	0.100	4.80	8.15	12.95
Wired	SY	0.114	4.80	9.32	14.12
On ceilings					
Nailed	SY	0.114	4.80	9.32	14.12
Wired	SY	0.133	4.80	10.75	15.55
Stucco lath					
1.8 lb.	SY	0.100	4.96	8.15	13.11
3.6 lb.	SY	0.100	5.56	8.15	13.71
Paper backed					
Minimum	SY	0.080	3.85	6.52	10.37
Maximum	SY	0.114	6.21	9.32	15.53
09223.66 PLASTER ACCESSORIES					
PLASTER ACCESSORIES					
Expansion joint, 3/4", 26 ga., galv.	LF	0.020	1.63	1.63	3.26
Plaster corner beads, 3/4", galvanized	LF	0.023	0.45	1.86	2.31
Casing bead, expanded flange, galvanized	LF	0.020	0.56	1.63	2.19
Expanded wing, 1-1/4" wide, galvanized	LF	0.020	0.72	1.63	2.35
Joint clips for lath	EA	0.004	0.19	0.32	0.51
Metal base, galvanized, 2-1/2" high	LF	0.027	0.83	2.17	3.00
Stud clips for gypsum lath	EA	0.004	0.19	0.32	0.51
Tie wire galvanized, 18 ga., 25 lb. hank	EA				52.00
Sound deadening board, 1/4"	SF	0.013	0.35	1.08	1.43
09230.01 PLASTER					
PLASTER					
Gypsum plaster, trowel finish, 2 coats					
Ceilings	SY	0.250	4.30	19.00	23.30
Walls	SY	0.235	4.30	17.75	22.05
3 coats					
Ceilings	SY	0.348	5.96	26.50	32.46
Walls	SY	0.308	5.96	23.25	29.21

© 2020 BNi Publications, Inc.

	Unit	Man-Hrs	Material	Labor	Total
09230.01 PLASTER (Cont.)					
Vermiculite plaster					
2 coats					
Ceilings	SY	0.381	4.89	29.00	33.89
Walls	SY	0.348	4.89	26.50	31.39
3 coats					
Ceilings	SY	0.471	7.68	35.75	43.43
Walls	SY	0.421	7.68	32.00	39.68
Keenes cement plaster					
2 coats					
Ceilings	SY	0.308	2.09	23.25	25.34
Walls	SY	0.267	2.09	20.25	22.34
3 coats					
Ceilings	SY	0.348	2.14	26.50	28.64
Walls	SY	0.308	2.14	23.25	25.39
On columns, add to installation, 50%	SY				
Chases, fascia, and soffits, add to installation, 50%	SY				
Beams, add to installation, 50%	SY				
09240.01 PORTLAND CEMENT PLASTER					
PORTLAND CEMENT PLASTER					
Stucco, portland, gray, 3 coat, 1" thick					
Sand finish	SY	0.348	8.43	26.50	34.93
Trowel finish	SY	0.364	8.43	27.50	35.93
White cement					
Sand finish	SY	0.364	9.63	27.50	37.13
Trowel finish	SY	0.400	9.63	30.50	40.13
Scratch coat					
For ceramic tile	SY	0.080	3.05	6.07	9.12
For quarry tile	SY	0.080	3.05	6.07	9.12
Portland cement plaster					
2 coats, 1/2"	SY	0.160	6.07	12.25	18.32
3 coats, 7/8"	SY	0.200	7.25	15.25	22.50
09290.01 GYPSUM BOARD					
GYPSUM BOARD					
Drywall, plasterboard, 3/8" clipped to					
Metal furred ceiling	SF	0.009	0.41	0.72	1.13
Columns and beams	SF	0.020	0.41	1.63	2.04
Walls	SF	0.008	0.41	0.65	1.06
Nailed or screwed to					
Wood or metal framed ceiling	SF	0.008	0.41	0.65	1.06
Columns and beams	SF	0.018	0.41	1.44	1.85
Walls	SF	0.007	0.41	0.59	1.00
1/2", clipped to					
Metal furred ceiling	SF	0.009	0.42	0.72	1.14
Columns and beams	SF	0.020	0.38	1.63	2.01
Walls	SF	0.008	0.38	0.65	1.03
Nailed or screwed to					
Wood or metal framed ceiling	SF	0.008	0.38	0.65	1.03
Columns and beams	SF	0.018	0.38	1.44	1.82
Walls	SF	0.007	0.38	0.59	0.97
5/8", clipped to					
Metal furred ceiling	SF	0.010	0.42	0.81	1.23
Columns and beams	SF	0.022	0.42	1.81	2.23
Walls	SF	0.009	0.42	0.72	1.14
Nailed or screwed to					
Wood or metal framed ceiling	SF	0.010	0.42	0.81	1.23
Columns and beams	SF	0.022	0.42	1.81	2.23
Walls	SF	0.009	0.42	0.72	1.14
Vinyl faced, clipped to metal studs					
1/2"	SF	0.010	1.19	0.81	2.00
5/8"	SF	0.010	1.13	0.81	1.94
Add for					
Fire resistant	SF				0.12
Water resistant	SF				0.19
Water and fire resistant	SF				0.24

	Unit	Man-Hrs	Material	Labor	Total

09290.01 GYPSUM BOARD (Cont.)

Add for

Taping and finishing joints

	Unit	Man-Hrs	Material	Labor	Total
Minimum	SF	0.005	0.04	0.43	0.47
Average	SF	0.007	0.07	0.54	0.61
Maximum	SF	0.008	0.10	0.65	0.75

Casing bead

	Unit	Man-Hrs	Material	Labor	Total
Minimum	LF	0.023	0.16	1.86	2.02
Average	LF	0.027	0.18	2.17	2.35
Maximum	LF	0.040	0.22	3.26	3.48

Corner bead

	Unit	Man-Hrs	Material	Labor	Total
Minimum	LF	0.023	0.18	1.86	2.04
Average	LF	0.027	0.22	2.17	2.39
Maximum	LF	0.040	0.27	3.26	3.53

09301.31 CERAMIC TILE

CERAMIC TILE

Glazed wall tile, 4-1/4" x 4-1/4"

	Unit	Man-Hrs	Material	Labor	Total
Minimum	SF	0.057	2.32	4.44	6.76
Average	SF	0.067	3.68	5.18	8.86
Maximum	SF	0.080	13.25	6.22	19.47

6" x 6"

	Unit	Man-Hrs	Material	Labor	Total
Minimum	SF	0.050	1.65	3.88	5.53
Average	SF	0.057	2.22	4.44	6.66
Maximum	SF	0.067	2.77	5.18	7.95

Base, 4-1/4" high

	Unit	Man-Hrs	Material	Labor	Total
Minimum	LF	0.100	4.47	7.77	12.24
Average	LF	0.100	5.20	7.77	12.97
Maximum	LF	0.100	6.87	7.77	14.64

Glazed moldings and trim, 12" x 12"

	Unit	Man-Hrs	Material	Labor	Total
Minimum	LF	0.080	2.46	6.22	8.68
Average	LF	0.080	3.75	6.22	9.97
Maximum	LF	0.080	5.04	6.22	11.26

Unglazed floor tile

Portland cem., cushion edge, face mtd

	Unit	Man-Hrs	Material	Labor	Total
1" x 1"	SF	0.073	8.87	5.65	14.52
2" x 2"	SF	0.067	9.38	5.18	14.56
4" x 4"	SF	0.067	8.73	5.18	13.91
6" x 6"	SF	0.057	3.12	4.44	7.56
12" x 12"	SF	0.050	2.75	3.88	6.63
16" x 16"	SF	0.044	2.38	3.45	5.83
18" x 18"	SF	0.040	2.31	3.11	5.42

Adhesive bed, with white grout

	Unit	Man-Hrs	Material	Labor	Total
1" x 1"	SF	0.073	7.38	5.65	13.03
2" x 2"	SF	0.067	7.81	5.18	12.99
4" x 4"	SF	0.067	7.81	5.18	12.99
6" x 6"	SF	0.057	2.60	4.44	7.04
12" x 12"	SF	0.050	2.28	3.88	6.16
16" x 16"	SF	0.044	1.98	3.45	5.43
18" x 18"	SF	0.040	1.92	3.11	5.03

Organic adhesive bed, thin set, back mounted

	Unit	Man-Hrs	Material	Labor	Total
1" x 1"	SF	0.073	7.38	5.65	13.03
2" x 2"	SF	0.067	8.59	5.18	13.77

For group 2 colors, add to material, 10%
For group 3 colors, add to material, 20%
For abrasive surface, add to material, 25%

Porcelain floor tile

	Unit	Man-Hrs	Material	Labor	Total
1" x 1"	SF	0.073	9.90	5.65	15.55
2" x 2"	SF	0.070	9.05	5.40	14.45
4" x 4"	SF	0.067	8.41	5.18	13.59
6" x 6"	SF	0.057	3.02	4.44	7.46
12" x 12"	SF	0.050	2.72	3.88	6.60
16" x 16"	SF	0.044	2.16	3.45	5.61
18" x 18"	SF	0.040	2.04	3.11	5.15

© 2020 BNi Publications, Inc.

	Unit	Man-Hrs	Material	Labor	Total
09301.31 CERAMIC TILE (Cont.)					
Unglazed wall tile					
Organic adhesive, face mounted cushion edge					
1" x 1"					
Minimum	SF	0.067	4.65	5.18	9.83
Average	SF	0.073	6.09	5.65	11.74
Maximum	SF	0.080	9.09	6.22	15.31
2" x 2"					
Minimum	SF	0.062	5.37	4.78	10.15
Average	SF	0.067	6.09	5.18	11.27
Maximum	SF	0.073	9.96	5.65	15.61
Back mounted					
1" x 1"					
Minimum	SF	0.067	4.65	5.18	9.83
Average	SF	0.073	6.09	5.65	11.74
Maximum	SF	0.080	9.09	6.22	15.31
2" x 2"					
Minimum	SF	0.062	5.37	4.78	10.15
Average	SF	0.067	6.09	5.18	11.27
Maximum	SF	0.073	9.96	5.65	15.61
For glazed finish, add to material, 25%					
For glazed mosaic, add to material, 100%					
For metallic colors, add to material, 125%					
For exterior wall use, add to total, 25%					
For exterior soffit, add to total, 25%					
For portland cement bed, add to total, 25%					
For dry set portland cement bed, add to total, 10%					
Conductive floor tile, unglazed square edged					
Portland cement bed					
1 x 1	SF	0.100	6.93	7.77	14.70
1-9/16 x 1-9/16	SF	0.100	6.38	7.77	14.15
Dry set					
1 x 1	SF	0.100	6.93	7.77	14.70
1-9/16 x 1-9/16	SF	0.100	6.38	7.77	14.15
Epoxy bed with epoxy joints					
1 x 1	SF	0.100	6.93	7.77	14.70
1-9/16 x 1-9/16	SF	0.100	6.38	7.77	14.15
For WWF in bed add to total, 15%					
For abrasive surface, add to material, 40%					
Ceramic accessories					
Towel bar, 24" long					
Minimum	EA	0.320	18.00	24.75	42.75
Average	EA	0.400	22.25	31.00	53.25
Maximum	EA	0.533	59.00	41.50	100.50
Soap dish					
Minimum	EA	0.533	8.47	41.50	49.97
Average	EA	0.667	11.50	52.00	63.50
Maximum	EA	0.800	30.25	62.00	92.25
09301.61 QUARRY TILE					
QUARRY TILE					
Floor					
4 x 4 x 1/2"	SF	0.107	6.57	8.29	14.86
6 x 6 x 1/2"	SF	0.100	6.44	7.77	14.21
6 x 6 x 3/4"	SF	0.100	7.99	7.77	15.76
12 x 12 x 3/4"	SF	0.089	11.25	6.91	18.16
16 x 1 6 x 3/4"	SF	0.080	7.83	6.22	14.05
18 x 18 x 3/4"	SF	0.067	5.52	5.18	10.70
Medallion					
36" dia.	EA	2.000	350.00	160.00	510.00
48" dia.	EA	2.000	410.00	160.00	570.00
Wall, applied to 3/4" portland cement bed					
4 x 4 x 1/2"	SF	0.160	5.84	12.50	18.34
6 x 6 x 3/4"	SF	0.133	6.53	10.25	16.78

	Unit	Man-Hrs	Material	Labor	Total

09301.61 QUARRY TILE (Cont.)

Cove base
5 x 6 x 1/2" straight top	LF	0.133	6.66	10.25	16.91
6 x 6 x 3/4" round top	LF	0.133	6.18	10.25	16.43

Moldings
2 x 12	LF	0.080	10.50	6.22	16.72
4 x 12	LF	0.080	16.50	6.22	22.72
Stair treads 6 x 6 x 3/4"	LF	0.200	9.13	15.50	24.63
Window sill 6 x 8 x 3/4"	LF	0.160	8.33	12.50	20.83

For abrasive surface, add to material, 25%

09510.01 CEILINGS AND WALLS

CEILINGS AND WALLS
Acoustical panels, suspension system not included
Fiberglass panels
5/8" thick
2' x 2'	SF	0.011	1.61	0.93	2.54
2' x 4'	SF	0.009	1.34	0.72	2.06

3/4" thick
2' x 2'	SF	0.011	2.14	0.93	3.07
2' x 4'	SF	0.009	2.07	0.72	2.79

Glass cloth faced fiberglass panels
3/4" thick	SF	0.013	3.05	1.08	4.13
1" thick	SF	0.013	3.41	1.08	4.49

Mineral fiber panels
5/8" thick
2' x 2'	SF	0.011	1.37	0.93	2.30
2' x 4'	SF	0.009	1.37	0.72	2.09

3/4" thick
2' x 2'	SF	0.011	2.14	0.93	3.07
2' x 4'	SF	0.009	2.07	0.72	2.79

For aluminum faced panels, add to material, 80%
For vinyl faced panels, add to total, 125%
For fire rated panels, add to material, 75%
Wood fiber panels
1/2" thick
2' x 2'	SF	0.011	1.77	0.93	2.70
2' x 4'	SF	0.009	1.77	0.72	2.49

5/8" thick
2' x 2'	SF	0.011	2.03	0.93	2.96
2' x 4'	SF	0.009	2.03	0.72	2.75

3/4" thick
2' x 2'	SF	0.011	2.49	0.93	3.42
2' x 4'	SF	0.009	2.49	0.72	3.21

2" thick
2' x 2'	SF	0.013	2.91	1.08	3.99
2' x 4'	SF	0.010	2.91	0.81	3.72

For flameproofing, add to material, 10%
For sculptured finish, add to material, 15%
Air distributing panels
3/4" thick	SF	0.020	2.64	1.63	4.27
5/8" thick	SF	0.016	2.26	1.30	3.56

Acoustical tiles, suspension system not included
Fiberglass tile, 12" x 12"
5/8" thick	SF	0.015	2.00	1.18	3.18
3/4" thick	SF	0.018	2.32	1.44	3.76

Glass cloth faced fiberglass tile
3/4" thick	SF	0.018	3.73	1.44	5.17
3" thick	SF	0.020	4.17	1.63	5.80

Mineral fiber tile, 12" x 12"
5/8" thick
Standard	SF	0.016	1.05	1.30	2.35
Vinyl faced	SF	0.016	2.08	1.30	3.38

3/4" thick
Standard	SF	0.016	1.53	1.30	2.83
Vinyl faced	SF	0.016	2.66	1.30	3.96

© 2020 BNi Publications, Inc.

	Unit	Man-Hrs	Material	Labor	Total

09510.01 CEILINGS AND WALLS (Cont.)

Mineral fiber tile, 12" x 12"

	Unit	Man-Hrs	Material	Labor	Total
Fire rated	SF	0.016	3.39	1.30	4.69
Aluminum or mylar faced	SF	0.016	6.47	1.30	7.77

Wood fiber tile, 12" x 12"

	Unit	Man-Hrs	Material	Labor	Total
1/2" thick	SF	0.016	1.68	1.30	2.98
3/4" thick	SF	0.016	2.44	1.30	3.74

For flameproofing, add to material, 10%

For sculptured 3 dimensional, add to material, 50%

Metal pan units, 24 ga. steel

	Unit	Man-Hrs	Material	Labor	Total
12" x 12"	SF	0.032	6.00	2.60	8.60
12" x 24"	SF	0.027	6.83	2.17	9.00

Aluminum, .025" thick

	Unit	Man-Hrs	Material	Labor	Total
12" x 12"	SF	0.032	7.03	2.60	9.63
12" x 24"	SF	0.027	7.24	2.17	9.41

Anodized aluminum, 0.25" thick

	Unit	Man-Hrs	Material	Labor	Total
12" x 12"	SF	0.032	7.72	2.60	10.32
12" x 24"	SF	0.027	9.17	2.17	11.34

Stainless steel, 24 ga.

	Unit	Man-Hrs	Material	Labor	Total
12" x 12"	SF	0.032	17.75	2.60	20.35
12" x 24"	SF	0.027	15.25	2.17	17.42
For flameproof sound absorbing pads, add to material	SF				2.28

Metal ceiling systems

.020" thick panels

	Unit	Man-Hrs	Material	Labor	Total
10', 12', and 16' lengths	SF	0.023	5.49	1.86	7.35
Custom lengths, 3' to 20'	SF	0.023	5.55	1.86	7.41

.025" thick panels

	Unit	Man-Hrs	Material	Labor	Total
32 sf, 38 sf, and 52 sf pieces	SF	0.027	5.51	2.17	7.68
Custom lengths, 10 sf to 65 sf	SF	0.027	6.43	2.17	8.60
Carriers, black, add	SF				3.31
Recess filler strip, add	SF				1.11
Custom lengths, add	SF				1.65

Sound absorption walls, with fabric cover

	Unit	Man-Hrs	Material	Labor	Total
2-6" x 9' x 3/4"	SF	0.027	10.25	2.17	12.42
2' x 9' x 1"	SF	0.027	11.25	2.17	13.42
Starter spline	LF	0.020	1.65	1.63	3.28
Internal spline	LF	0.020	1.44	1.63	3.07

Acoustical treatment

Barriers for plenums

Leaded vinyl

	Unit	Man-Hrs	Material	Labor	Total
0.48 lb per sf	SF	0.038	4.23	3.10	7.33
0.87 lb per sf	SF	0.040	5.11	3.26	8.37

Aluminum foil, fiberglass reinforcement

	Unit	Man-Hrs	Material	Labor	Total
Minimum	SF	0.027	1.16	2.17	3.33
Maximum	SF	0.040	1.32	3.26	4.58
Aluminum mesh, paper backed	SF	0.027	1.09	2.17	3.26
Fibered cement sheet, 3/16" thick	SF	0.029	2.25	2.33	4.58
Sheet lead, 1/64" thick	SF	0.020	3.83	1.63	5.46

Sound attenuation blanket

	Unit	Man-Hrs	Material	Labor	Total
1" thick	SF	0.080	0.43	6.52	6.95
1-1/2" thick	SF	0.080	0.60	6.52	7.12
2" thick	SF	0.080	0.75	6.52	7.27
3" thick	SF	0.089	0.90	7.24	8.14

Ceiling suspension systems

T-bar system

	Unit	Man-Hrs	Material	Labor	Total
2' x 4'	SF	0.008	1.27	0.65	1.92
2' x 2'	SF	0.009	1.37	0.72	2.09
Concealed Z-bar suspension system, 12" module	SF	0.013	1.30	1.08	2.38
For 1-1/2" carrier channels, 4' o.c., add	SF				0.41
Carrier channel for recessed light fixtures	SF				0.75

09630.01 FLOOR LEVELING

FLOOR LEVELING

Repair and level floors to receive new flooring

	Unit	Man-Hrs	Material	Labor	Total
Minimum	SY	0.027	1.65	2.17	3.82
Average	SY	0.067	3.92	5.43	9.35

	Unit	Man-Hrs	Material	Labor	Total

09630.01 FLOOR LEVELING (Cont.)

Repair and level floors to receive new flooring

	Unit	Man-Hrs	Material	Labor	Total
Maximum	SY	0.080	5.81	6.52	12.33

09631.61 UNIT MASONRY FLOORING

UNIT MASONRY FLOORING

Clay brick

9 x 4-1/2 x 3" thick

	Unit	Man-Hrs	Material	Labor	Total
Glazed	SF	0.067	8.43	5.43	13.86
Unglazed	SF	0.067	8.08	5.43	13.51

8 x 4 x 3/4" thick

	Unit	Man-Hrs	Material	Labor	Total
Glazed	SF	0.070	7.62	5.67	13.29
Unglazed	SF	0.070	7.27	5.67	12.94

For herringbone pattern, add to labor, 15%

09640.01 WOOD FLOORING

WOOD FLOORING

Wood strip flooring, unfinished

Fir floor

C and better

	Unit	Man-Hrs	Material	Labor	Total
Vertical grain	SF	0.027	3.52	2.17	5.69
Flat grain	SF	0.027	4.40	2.17	6.57

Oak floor

	Unit	Man-Hrs	Material	Labor	Total
Minimum	SF	0.038	3.72	3.10	6.82
Average	SF	0.038	5.13	3.10	8.23
Maximum	SF	0.038	7.42	3.10	10.52

Maple floor

25/32" x 2-1/4"

	Unit	Man-Hrs	Material	Labor	Total
Minimum	SF	0.038	5.32	3.10	8.42
Maximum	SF	0.038	7.54	3.10	10.64

33/32" x 3-1/4"

	Unit	Man-Hrs	Material	Labor	Total
Minimum	SF	0.038	7.42	3.10	10.52
Maximum	SF	0.038	8.38	3.10	11.48

Added costs

For factory finish, add to material, 10%

For random width floor, add to total, 20%

For simulated pegs, add to total, 10%

Wood block industrial flooring

Creosoted

	Unit	Man-Hrs	Material	Labor	Total
2" thick	SF	0.021	4.18	1.71	5.89
2-1/2" thick	SF	0.025	4.34	2.03	6.37
3" thick	SF	0.027	4.51	2.17	6.68

Parquet, 5/16", white oak

	Unit	Man-Hrs	Material	Labor	Total
Finished	SF	0.040	10.00	3.26	13.26
Unfinished	SF	0.040	4.84	3.26	8.10
Gym floor, 2 ply felt, 25/32" maple, finished, in mastic	SF	0.044	8.54	3.62	12.16
Over wood sleepers	SF	0.050	8.69	4.07	12.76
Finishing, sand, fill, finish, and wax	SF	0.020	0.66	1.63	2.29
Refinish sand, seal, and 2 coats of polyurethane	SF	0.027	1.16	2.17	3.33
Clean and wax floors	SF	0.004	0.24	0.32	0.56

09651.31 RESILIENT BASE AND ACCESSORIES

RESILIENT BASE AND ACCESSORIES

Wall base, vinyl

Group 1

	Unit	Man-Hrs	Material	Labor	Total
4" high	LF	0.027	1.41	2.17	3.58
6" high	LF	0.027	1.92	2.17	4.09

Group 2

	Unit	Man-Hrs	Material	Labor	Total
4" high	LF	0.027	1.24	2.17	3.41
6" high	LF	0.027	1.97	2.17	4.14

Group 3

	Unit	Man-Hrs	Material	Labor	Total
4" high	LF	0.027	2.80	2.17	4.97
6" high	LF	0.027	3.15	2.17	5.32

Stair accessories

Treads, 1/4" x 12", rubber diamond surface

	Unit	Man-Hrs	Material	Labor	Total
Marbled	LF	0.067	17.00	5.43	22.43
Plain	LF	0.067	17.50	5.43	22.93

© 2020 BNi Publications, Inc.

	Unit	Man-Hrs	Material	Labor	Total
09651.31 RESILIENT BASE AND ACCESSORIES (Cont.)					
Treads					
Grit strip safety tread, 12" wide, colors					
3/16" thick	LF	0.067	17.50	5.43	22.93
5/16" thick	LF	0.067	23.50	5.43	28.93
Risers, 7" high, 1/8" thick, colors					
Flat	LF	0.040	6.57	3.26	9.83
Coved	LF	0.040	4.53	3.26	7.79
Nosing, rubber					
3/16" thick, 3" wide					
Black	LF	0.040	5.69	3.26	8.95
Colors	LF	0.040	6.41	3.26	9.67
6" wide					
Black	LF	0.067	6.99	5.43	12.42
Colors	LF	0.067	7.29	5.43	12.72
09651.61 RESILIENT SHEET FLOORING					
RESILIENT SHEET FLOORING					
Vinyl sheet flooring					
Minimum	SF	0.008	4.22	0.65	4.87
Average	SF	0.010	6.81	0.77	7.58
Maximum	SF	0.013	11.50	1.08	12.58
Cove, to 6"	LF	0.016	2.51	1.30	3.81
Fluid applied resilient flooring					
Polyurethane, poured in place, 3/8" thick	SF	0.067	10.50	5.43	15.93
Vinyl sheet goods, backed					
0.070" thick	SF	0.010	4.10	0.81	4.91
0.093" thick	SF	0.010	6.35	0.81	7.16
0.125" thick	SF	0.010	7.33	0.81	8.14
0.250" thick	SF	0.010	8.43	0.81	9.24
09651.91 RESILIENT TILE FLOORING					
RESILIENT TILE FLOORING					
Solid vinyl tile, 1/8" thick, 12" x 12"					
Marble patterns	SF	0.020	5.13	1.63	6.76
Solid colors	SF	0.020	6.65	1.63	8.28
Travertine patterns	SF	0.020	7.47	1.63	9.10
Conductive resilient flooring, vinyl tile					
1/8" thick, 12" x 12"	SF	0.023	8.11	1.86	9.97
09661.31 TERRAZZO					
TERRAZZO					
Floors on concrete, 1-3/4" thick, 5/8" topping					
Gray cement	SF	0.114	5.67	8.68	14.35
White cement	SF	0.114	5.92	8.68	14.60
Sand cushion, 3" thick, 5/8" top, 1/4"					
Gray cement	SF	0.133	6.69	10.00	16.69
White cement	SF	0.133	6.96	10.00	16.96
Monolithic terrazzo, 3-1/2" base slab, 5/8" topping	SF	0.100	4.75	7.59	12.34
Terrazzo wainscot, cast-in-place, 1/2" thick	SF	0.200	5.77	15.25	21.02
Base, cast-in-place, terrazzo cove type, 6" high	LF	0.114	7.26	8.68	15.94
Curb, cast-in-place, 6" wide x 6" high, polished top	LF	0.400	6.60	30.50	37.10
For venetian type terrazzo, add to material, 10%					
For abrasive heavy duty terrazzo, add to material, 15%					
Divider strips					
Zinc	LF				1.43
Brass	LF				2.66
Stairs, cast-in-place, topping on concrete or metal					
1-1/2" thick treads, 12" wide	LF	0.400	5.61	30.50	36.11
Combined tread and riser	LF	1.000	8.42	76.00	84.42
Precast terrazzo, thin set					
Terrazzo tiles, non-slip surface					
9" x 9" x 1" thick	SF	0.114	16.00	8.68	24.68
12" x 12"					
1" thick	SF	0.107	17.25	8.10	25.35
1-1/2" thick	SF	0.114	18.00	8.68	26.68
18" x 18" x 1-1/2" thick	SF	0.114	23.50	8.68	32.18

	Unit	Man-Hrs	Material	Labor	Total

09661.31 TERRAZZO (Cont.)

Terrazzo tiles, non-slip surface

	Unit	Man-Hrs	Material	Labor	Total
24" x 24" x 1-1/2" thick	SF	0.094	30.25	7.14	37.39

For white cement, add to material, 10%
For venetian type terrazzo, add to material, 25%

Terrazzo wainscot

	Unit	Man-Hrs	Material	Labor	Total
12" x 12" x 1" thick	SF	0.200	8.83	15.25	24.08
18" x 18" x 1-1/2" thick	SF	0.229	14.50	17.25	31.75

Base
6" high

	Unit	Man-Hrs	Material	Labor	Total
Straight	LF	0.062	12.75	4.67	17.42
Coved	LF	0.062	15.00	4.67	19.67

8" high

	Unit	Man-Hrs	Material	Labor	Total
Straight	LF	0.067	14.25	5.06	19.31
Coved	LF	0.067	16.75	5.06	21.81

Terrazzo curbs

	Unit	Man-Hrs	Material	Labor	Total
8" wide x 8" high	LF	0.320	33.00	24.25	57.25
6" wide x 6" high	LF	0.267	29.75	20.25	50.00

Precast terrazzo stair treads, 12" wide
1-1/2" thick

	Unit	Man-Hrs	Material	Labor	Total
Diamond pattern	LF	0.145	39.75	11.00	50.75
Non-slip surface	LF	0.145	41.75	11.00	52.75

2" thick

	Unit	Man-Hrs	Material	Labor	Total
Diamond pattern	LF	0.145	41.75	11.00	52.75
Non-slip surface	LF	0.160	44.00	12.25	56.25

Stair risers, 1" thick to 6" high

	Unit	Man-Hrs	Material	Labor	Total
Straight sections	LF	0.080	13.25	6.07	19.32
Cove sections	LF	0.080	15.75	6.07	21.82

Combined tread and riser
Straight sections

	Unit	Man-Hrs	Material	Labor	Total
1-1/2" tread, 3/4" riser	LF	0.229	57.00	17.25	74.25
3" tread, 1" riser	LF	0.229	69.00	17.25	86.25

Curved sections

	Unit	Man-Hrs	Material	Labor	Total
2" tread, 1" riser	LF	0.267	73.00	20.25	93.25
3" tread, 1" riser	LF	0.267	76.00	20.25	96.25

Stair stringers, notched for treads and risers

	Unit	Man-Hrs	Material	Labor	Total
1" thick	LF	0.200	34.50	15.25	49.75
2" thick	LF	0.267	36.00	20.25	56.25

Landings, structural, nonslip

	Unit	Man-Hrs	Material	Labor	Total
1-1/2" thick	SF	0.133	32.75	10.00	42.75
3" thick	SF	0.160	45.75	12.25	58.00

Conductive terrazzo, spark proof industrial floor
Epoxy terrazzo

	Unit	Man-Hrs	Material	Labor	Total
Floor	SF	0.050	6.89	3.79	10.68
Base	SF	0.067	7.70	5.06	12.76

Polyacrylate

	Unit	Man-Hrs	Material	Labor	Total
Floor	SF	0.050	8.85	3.79	12.64
Base	SF	0.067	10.00	5.06	15.06

Polyester

	Unit	Man-Hrs	Material	Labor	Total
Floor	SF	0.032	4.12	2.43	6.55
Base	SF	0.040	4.40	3.03	7.43

Synthetic latex mastic

	Unit	Man-Hrs	Material	Labor	Total
Floor	SF	0.050	7.15	3.79	10.94
Base	SF	0.067	7.15	5.06	12.21

09670.01 SPECIAL FLOORING

SPECIAL FLOORING
Epoxy flooring, marble chips

	Unit	Man-Hrs	Material	Labor	Total
Epoxy with colored quartz chips in 1/4" base	SF	0.044	4.48	3.62	8.10
Heavy duty epoxy topping, 3/16" thick	SF	0.044	3.62	3.62	7.24

Epoxy terrazzo

	Unit	Man-Hrs	Material	Labor	Total
1/4" thick chemical resistant	SF	0.050	6.58	4.07	10.65

09680.01 CARPET PADDING

CARPET PADDING
Carpet padding

	Unit	Man-Hrs	Material	Labor	Total
Foam rubber, waffle type, 0.3" thick	SY	0.040	6.74	3.26	10.00

© 2020 BNi Publications, Inc.

	Unit	Man-Hrs	Material	Labor	Total
09680.01 CARPET PADDING (Cont.)					
Carpet padding					
Jute padding					
Minimum	SY	0.036	4.57	2.96	7.53
Average	SY	0.040	5.95	3.26	9.21
Maximum	SY	0.044	8.98	3.62	12.60
Sponge rubber cushion					
Minimum	SY	0.036	5.42	2.96	8.38
Average	SY	0.040	7.22	3.26	10.48
Maximum	SY	0.044	10.25	3.62	13.87
Urethane cushion, 3/8" thick					
Minimum	SY	0.036	5.42	2.96	8.38
Average	SY	0.040	6.32	3.26	9.58
Maximum	SY	0.044	8.24	3.62	11.86
09680.02 CARPET					
CARPET					
Carpet, acrylic					
24 oz., light traffic	SY	0.089	17.75	7.24	24.99
28 oz., medium traffic	SY	0.089	21.25	7.24	28.49
Residential					
Nylon					
15 oz., light traffic	SY	0.089	24.50	7.24	31.74
28 oz., medium traffic	SY	0.089	32.00	7.24	39.24
Commercial					
Nylon					
28 oz., medium traffic	SY	0.089	30.50	7.24	37.74
35 oz., heavy traffic	SY	0.089	37.25	7.24	44.49
Wool					
30 oz., medium traffic	SY	0.089	51.00	7.24	58.24
36 oz., medium traffic	SY	0.089	53.00	7.24	60.24
42 oz., heavy traffic	SY	0.089	71.00	7.24	78.24
Carpet tile					
Foam backed					
Minimum	SF	0.016	4.07	1.30	5.37
Average	SF	0.018	4.71	1.44	6.15
Maximum	SF	0.020	7.47	1.63	9.10
Tufted loop or shag					
Minimum	SF	0.016	4.41	1.30	5.71
Average	SF	0.018	5.32	1.44	6.76
Maximum	SF	0.020	8.56	1.63	10.19
Clean and vacuum carpet					
Minimum	SY	0.004	0.36	0.25	0.61
Average	SY	0.005	0.56	0.43	0.99
Maximum	SY	0.008	0.77	0.65	1.42
09690.01 ACCESS & PEDESTAL FLOOR					
ACCESS & PEDESTAL FLOOR					
Panels, no covering, 2'x2'					
Plain	SF	0.010	11.75	0.81	12.56
Perforated	SF	0.400	16.25	32.50	48.75
Pedestals					
For 6" to 12" clearance	EA	0.080	9.40	6.52	15.92
Stringers					
2'	LF	0.038	2.59	3.10	5.69
6'	LF	0.027	2.59	2.17	4.76
Accessories					
Ramp assembly	SF	0.032	54.00	2.60	56.60
Elevated floor assembly	SF	0.030	86.00	2.41	88.41
Handrail	LF	0.400	67.00	32.50	99.50
Fascia plate	LF	0.200	32.75	16.25	49.00
For carpet tiles, add	SF				9.08
For vinyl flooring, add	SF				10.25
RF shielding components, floor liner					
Hot rolled steel sheet					
14 ga.	SF	0.020	15.50	1.63	17.13
11 ga.	SF	0.062	21.50	5.01	26.51

	Unit	Man-Hrs	Material	Labor	Total
09720.01 WALL COVERING					
Vinyl wall covering					
Medium duty	SF	0.011	1.10	0.77	1.87
Heavy duty	SF	0.013	2.26	0.90	3.16
Over pipes and irregular shapes					
Lightweight, 13 oz.	SF	0.016	1.89	1.08	2.97
Medium weight, 25 oz.	SF	0.018	2.26	1.20	3.46
Heavyweight, 34 oz.	SF	0.020	2.77	1.36	4.13
Cork wall covering					
1' x 1' squares					
1/4" thick	SF	0.020	5.66	1.36	7.02
1/2" thick	SF	0.020	7.19	1.36	8.55
3/4" thick	SF	0.020	8.10	1.36	9.46
Wall fabrics					
Natural fabrics, grass cloths					
Minimum	SF	0.012	1.65	0.83	2.48
Average	SF	0.013	1.83	0.90	2.73
Maximum	SF	0.016	6.16	1.08	7.24
Flexible gypsum coated wall fabric, fire resistant	SF	0.008	1.85	0.54	2.39
Vinyl corner guards					
3/4" x 3/4" x 8'	EA	0.100	8.70	6.80	15.50
2-3/4" x 2-3/4" x 4'	EA	0.100	5.14	6.80	11.94
09910.01 PAINTING PREPARATION					
PAINTING PREPARATION					
Dropcloths					
Minimum	SF	0.001	0.16	0.03	0.19
Average	SF	0.001	0.18	0.04	0.22
Maximum	SF	0.001	0.37	0.06	0.43
Masking					
Paper and tape					
Minimum	LF	0.008	0.04	0.54	0.58
Average	LF	0.010	0.06	0.68	0.74
Maximum	LF	0.013	0.07	0.90	0.97
Doors					
Minimum	EA	0.100	0.05	6.80	6.85
Average	EA	0.133	0.06	9.07	9.13
Maximum	EA	0.178	0.07	12.00	12.07
Windows					
Minimum	EA	0.100	0.05	6.80	6.85
Average	EA	0.133	0.06	9.07	9.13
Maximum	EA	0.178	0.07	12.00	12.07
Sanding					
Walls and flat surfaces					
Minimum	SF	0.005		0.36	0.36
Average	SF	0.007		0.45	0.45
Maximum	SF	0.008		0.54	0.54
Doors and windows					
Minimum	EA	0.133		9.07	9.07
Average	EA	0.200		13.50	13.50
Maximum	EA	0.267		18.25	18.25
Trim					
Minimum	LF	0.010		0.68	0.68
Average	LF	0.013		0.90	0.90
Maximum	LF	0.018		1.20	1.20
Puttying					
Minimum	SF	0.012	0.01	0.83	0.84
Average	SF	0.016	0.02	1.08	1.10
Maximum	SF	0.020	0.03	1.36	1.39
09910.09 PAINT					
PAINT					
Paint, enamel					
600 sf per gal.	GAL				54.00
550 sf per gal.	GAL				50.00
500 sf per gal.	GAL				36.00
450 sf per gal.	GAL				33.75

© 2020 BNi Publications, Inc.

	Unit	Man-Hrs	Material	Labor	Total

09910.09 PAINT (Cont.)

Paint, enamel
350 sf per gal.	GAL				32.50
Filler, 60 sf per gal.	GAL				38.50
Latex, 400 sf per gal.	GAL				36.00

Aluminum
400 sf per gal.	GAL				48.00
500 sf per gal.	GAL				77.00
Red lead, 350 sf per gal.	GAL				67.00

Primer
400 sf per gal.	GAL				32.50
300 sf per gal.	GAL				32.50
Latex base, interior, white	GAL				36.00

Sealer and varnish
400 sf per gal.	GAL				33.75
425 sf per gal.	GAL				48.00
600 sf per gal.	GAL				62.00

09911.30 EXT. PAINTING, SITEWORK

EXT. PAINTING, SITEWORK

Benches, Brush, First Coat
	Unit	Man-Hrs	Material	Labor	Total
Minimum	SF	0.008	0.19	0.54	0.73
Average	SF	0.010	0.21	0.68	0.89
Maximum	SF	0.013	0.22	0.90	1.12

Second Coat
Minimum	SF	0.005	0.18	0.34	0.52
Average	SF	0.006	0.19	0.38	0.57
Maximum	SF	0.007	0.21	0.45	0.66

Roller, First Coat
Minimum	SF	0.004	0.19	0.27	0.46
Average	SF	0.004	0.21	0.30	0.51
Maximum	SF	0.005	0.22	0.34	0.56

Second Coat
Minimum	SF	0.003	0.18	0.19	0.37
Average	SF	0.003	0.19	0.22	0.41
Maximum	SF	0.004	0.21	0.24	0.45

Brickwork, Brush, First Coat
Minimum	SF	0.005	0.19	0.34	0.53
Average	SF	0.007	0.21	0.45	0.66
Maximum	SF	0.010	0.22	0.68	0.90

Second Coat
Minimum	SF	0.004	0.19	0.30	0.49
Average	SF	0.005	0.21	0.36	0.57
Maximum	SF	0.007	0.22	0.45	0.67

Spray, First Coat
Minimum	SF	0.002	0.15	0.15	0.30
Average	SF	0.003	0.17	0.19	0.36
Maximum	SF	0.004	0.18	0.24	0.42

Second Coat
Minimum	SF	0.002	0.15	0.14	0.29
Average	SF	0.003	0.17	0.17	0.34
Maximum	SF	0.003	0.18	0.22	0.40

Concrete Block, Roller, First Coat
Minimum	SF	0.004	0.19	0.27	0.46
Average	SF	0.005	0.21	0.36	0.57
Maximum	SF	0.008	0.22	0.54	0.76

	Unit	Man-Hrs	Material	Labor	Total

09911.30 EXT. PAINTING, SITEWORK (Cont.)

Roller

Second Coat

	Unit	Man-Hrs	Material	Labor	Total
Minimum	SF	0.003	0.19	0.22	0.41
Average	SF	0.004	0.21	0.30	0.51
Maximum	SF	0.007	0.22	0.45	0.67

Spray

First Coat

	Unit	Man-Hrs	Material	Labor	Total
Minimum	SF	0.002	0.15	0.15	0.30
Average	SF	0.003	0.17	0.18	0.35
Maximum	SF	0.003	0.18	0.20	0.38

Second Coat

	Unit	Man-Hrs	Material	Labor	Total
Minimum	SF	0.001	0.15	0.09	0.24
Average	SF	0.002	0.17	0.12	0.29
Maximum	SF	0.003	0.18	0.17	0.35

Fences, Chain Link

Brush

First Coat

	Unit	Man-Hrs	Material	Labor	Total
Minimum	SF	0.008	0.13	0.54	0.67
Average	SF	0.009	0.14	0.60	0.74
Maximum	SF	0.010	0.15	0.68	0.83

Second Coat

	Unit	Man-Hrs	Material	Labor	Total
Minimum	SF	0.005	0.13	0.36	0.49
Average	SF	0.006	0.14	0.41	0.55
Maximum	SF	0.007	0.15	0.49	0.64

Roller

First Coat

	Unit	Man-Hrs	Material	Labor	Total
Minimum	SF	0.006	0.13	0.38	0.51
Average	SF	0.007	0.14	0.45	0.59
Maximum	SF	0.008	0.15	0.51	0.66

Second Coat

	Unit	Man-Hrs	Material	Labor	Total
Minimum	SF	0.003	0.13	0.22	0.35
Average	SF	0.004	0.14	0.27	0.41
Maximum	SF	0.005	0.15	0.34	0.49

Spray

First Coat

	Unit	Man-Hrs	Material	Labor	Total
Minimum	SF	0.003	0.10	0.17	0.27
Average	SF	0.003	0.11	0.19	0.30
Maximum	SF	0.003	0.13	0.22	0.35

Second Coat

	Unit	Man-Hrs	Material	Labor	Total
Minimum	SF	0.002	0.10	0.12	0.22
Average	SF	0.002	0.11	0.15	0.26
Maximum	SF	0.003	0.13	0.17	0.30

Fences, Wood or Masonry

Brush

First Coat

	Unit	Man-Hrs	Material	Labor	Total
Minimum	SF	0.008	0.19	0.57	0.76
Average	SF	0.010	0.21	0.68	0.89
Maximum	SF	0.013	0.22	0.90	1.12

Second Coat

	Unit	Man-Hrs	Material	Labor	Total
Minimum	SF	0.005	0.19	0.34	0.53
Average	SF	0.006	0.21	0.41	0.62
Maximum	SF	0.008	0.22	0.54	0.76

Roller

First Coat

	Unit	Man-Hrs	Material	Labor	Total
Minimum	SF	0.004	0.19	0.30	0.49
Average	SF	0.005	0.21	0.36	0.57
Maximum	SF	0.006	0.22	0.41	0.63

Second Coat

	Unit	Man-Hrs	Material	Labor	Total
Minimum	SF	0.003	0.19	0.20	0.39
Average	SF	0.004	0.21	0.25	0.46
Maximum	SF	0.005	0.22	0.34	0.56

Spray

First Coat

	Unit	Man-Hrs	Material	Labor	Total
Minimum	SF	0.003	0.15	0.19	0.34
Average	SF	0.004	0.17	0.24	0.41

© 2020 BNi Publications, Inc.

	Unit	Man-Hrs	Material	Labor	Total

09911.30 EXT. PAINTING, SITEWORK (Cont.)

First Coat

Maximum	SF	0.005	0.18	0.34	0.52

Second Coat

Minimum	SF	0.002	0.15	0.13	0.28
Average	SF	0.003	0.17	0.17	0.34
Maximum	SF	0.003	0.18	0.22	0.40

Storage Tanks

Roller

First Coat

Minimum	SF	0.003	0.15	0.22	0.37
Average	SF	0.004	0.17	0.27	0.44
Maximum	SF	0.005	0.18	0.34	0.52

Second Coat

Minimum	SF	0.003	0.15	0.18	0.33
Average	SF	0.003	0.17	0.21	0.38
Maximum	SF	0.004	0.18	0.27	0.45

Spray

First Coat

Minimum	SF	0.002	0.13	0.13	0.26
Average	SF	0.002	0.14	0.16	0.30
Maximum	SF	0.003	0.15	0.19	0.34

Second Coat

Minimum	SF	0.002	0.13	0.10	0.23
Average	SF	0.002	0.14	0.12	0.26
Maximum	SF	0.002	0.15	0.13	0.28

09911.31 EXT. PAINTING, BUILDINGS

EXT. PAINTING, BUILDINGS

Decks, Metal

Spray

First Coat

Minimum	SF	0.004	0.13	0.24	0.37
Average	SF	0.004	0.14	0.27	0.41
Maximum	SF	0.004	0.15	0.30	0.45

Second Coat

Minimum	SF	0.003	0.11	0.17	0.28
Average	SF	0.003	0.13	0.19	0.32
Maximum	SF	0.003	0.14	0.22	0.36

Decks, Wood, Stained

Brush

First Coat

Minimum	SF	0.004	0.15	0.27	0.42
Average	SF	0.004	0.17	0.30	0.47
Maximum	SF	0.005	0.18	0.34	0.52

Second Coat

Minimum	SF	0.003	0.15	0.19	0.34
Average	SF	0.003	0.17	0.20	0.37
Maximum	SF	0.003	0.18	0.22	0.40

Roller

First Coat

Minimum	SF	0.003	0.15	0.19	0.34
Average	SF	0.003	0.17	0.20	0.37
Maximum	SF	0.003	0.18	0.22	0.40

Second Coat

Minimum	SF	0.003	0.15	0.17	0.32
Average	SF	0.003	0.17	0.18	0.35
Maximum	SF	0.003	0.18	0.20	0.38

Spray

First Coat

Minimum	SF	0.003	0.13	0.17	0.30
Average	SF	0.003	0.14	0.18	0.32
Maximum	SF	0.003	0.15	0.20	0.35

Second Coat

Minimum	SF	0.002	0.13	0.15	0.28
Average	SF	0.002	0.14	0.16	0.30

	Unit	Man-Hrs	Material	Labor	Total
09911.31 EXT. PAINTING, BUILDINGS (Cont.)					
Second Coat					
Maximum	SF	0.003	0.15	0.18	0.33
Doors, Metal					
Roller					
First Coat					
Minimum	SF	0.006	0.15	0.38	0.53
Average	SF	0.007	0.17	0.45	0.62
Maximum	SF	0.008	0.18	0.54	0.72
Second Coat					
Minimum	SF	0.004	0.15	0.27	0.42
Average	SF	0.004	0.17	0.30	0.47
Maximum	SF	0.005	0.18	0.34	0.52
Spray					
First Coat					
Minimum	SF	0.005	0.13	0.34	0.47
Average	SF	0.006	0.14	0.38	0.52
Maximum	SF	0.007	0.15	0.45	0.60
Second Coat					
Minimum	SF	0.004	0.13	0.24	0.37
Average	SF	0.004	0.14	0.27	0.41
Maximum	SF	0.004	0.15	0.30	0.45
Door Frames, Metal					
Brush					
First Coat					
Minimum	LF	0.010	0.19	0.68	0.87
Average	LF	0.013	0.21	0.85	1.06
Maximum	LF	0.015	0.22	0.98	1.20
Second Coat					
Minimum	LF	0.006	0.19	0.38	0.57
Average	LF	0.007	0.21	0.45	0.66
Maximum	LF	0.008	0.22	0.54	0.76
Spray					
First Coat					
Minimum	LF	0.004	0.13	0.30	0.43
Average	LF	0.006	0.14	0.38	0.52
Maximum	LF	0.008	0.15	0.54	0.69
Second Coat					
Minimum	LF	0.004	0.13	0.24	0.37
Average	LF	0.004	0.14	0.27	0.41
Maximum	LF	0.004	0.15	0.30	0.45
Doors, Wood					
Brush					
First Coat					
Minimum	SF	0.012	0.15	0.83	0.98
Average	SF	0.016	0.17	1.08	1.25
Maximum	SF	0.020	0.18	1.36	1.54
Second Coat					
Minimum	SF	0.010	0.15	0.68	0.83
Average	SF	0.011	0.17	0.77	0.94
Maximum	SF	0.013	0.18	0.90	1.08
Roller					
First Coat					
Minimum	SF	0.005	0.15	0.36	0.51
Average	SF	0.007	0.17	0.45	0.62
Maximum	SF	0.010	0.18	0.68	0.86
Second Coat					
Minimum	SF	0.004	0.15	0.27	0.42
Average	SF	0.004	0.17	0.30	0.47
Maximum	SF	0.007	0.18	0.45	0.63
Spray					
First Coat					
Minimum	SF	0.003	0.13	0.17	0.30
Average	SF	0.003	0.14	0.20	0.34
Maximum	SF	0.004	0.15	0.27	0.42

© 2020 BNi Publications, Inc.

	Unit	Man-Hrs	Material	Labor	Total

09911.31 EXT. PAINTING, BUILDINGS (Cont.)

Spray
  Second Coat

	Unit	Man-Hrs	Material	Labor	Total
Minimum	SF	0.002	0.13	0.13	0.26
Average	SF	0.002	0.14	0.15	0.29
Maximum	SF	0.003	0.15	0.18	0.33

Gutters and Downspouts
  Brush
    First Coat

	Unit	Man-Hrs	Material	Labor	Total
Minimum	LF	0.010	0.19	0.68	0.87
Average	LF	0.011	0.21	0.77	0.98
Maximum	LF	0.013	0.22	0.90	1.12

    Second Coat

	Unit	Man-Hrs	Material	Labor	Total
Minimum	LF	0.007	0.19	0.45	0.64
Average	LF	0.008	0.21	0.54	0.75
Maximum	LF	0.010	0.22	0.68	0.90

Siding, Metal
  Roller
    First Coat

	Unit	Man-Hrs	Material	Labor	Total
Minimum	SF	0.003	0.15	0.22	0.37
Average	SF	0.004	0.17	0.24	0.41
Maximum	SF	0.004	0.18	0.27	0.45

    Second Coat

	Unit	Man-Hrs	Material	Labor	Total
Minimum	SF	0.003	0.15	0.20	0.35
Average	SF	0.003	0.17	0.22	0.39
Maximum	SF	0.004	0.18	0.24	0.42

  Spray
    First Coat

	Unit	Man-Hrs	Material	Labor	Total
Minimum	SF	0.003	0.13	0.17	0.30
Average	SF	0.003	0.14	0.19	0.33
Maximum	SF	0.003	0.15	0.22	0.37

    Second Coat

	Unit	Man-Hrs	Material	Labor	Total
Minimum	SF	0.002	0.13	0.10	0.23
Average	SF	0.002	0.14	0.13	0.27
Maximum	SF	0.003	0.15	0.18	0.33

Siding, Wood
  Roller
    First Coat

	Unit	Man-Hrs	Material	Labor	Total
Minimum	SF	0.003	0.13	0.19	0.32
Average	SF	0.003	0.14	0.22	0.36
Maximum	SF	0.004	0.15	0.24	0.39

    Second Coat

	Unit	Man-Hrs	Material	Labor	Total
Minimum	SF	0.003	0.13	0.22	0.35
Average	SF	0.004	0.14	0.24	0.38
Maximum	SF	0.004	0.15	0.27	0.42

  Spray
    First Coat

	Unit	Man-Hrs	Material	Labor	Total
Minimum	SF	0.003	0.13	0.18	0.31
Average	SF	0.003	0.14	0.19	0.33
Maximum	SF	0.003	0.15	0.20	0.35

    Second Coat

	Unit	Man-Hrs	Material	Labor	Total
Minimum	SF	0.002	0.13	0.13	0.26
Average	SF	0.003	0.14	0.18	0.32
Maximum	SF	0.004	0.15	0.27	0.42

Stucco
  Roller
    First Coat

	Unit	Man-Hrs	Material	Labor	Total
Minimum	SF	0.004	0.19	0.24	0.43
Average	SF	0.004	0.21	0.28	0.49
Maximum	SF	0.005	0.22	0.34	0.56

    Second Coat

	Unit	Man-Hrs	Material	Labor	Total
Minimum	SF	0.003	0.19	0.20	0.39
Average	SF	0.003	0.21	0.23	0.44
Maximum	SF	0.004	0.22	0.27	0.49

	Unit	Man-Hrs	Material	Labor	Total

09911.31 EXT. PAINTING, BUILDINGS (Cont.)

Stucco
  Spray
    First Coat

	Unit	Man-Hrs	Material	Labor	Total
Minimum	SF	0.003	0.15	0.17	0.32
Average	SF	0.003	0.17	0.19	0.36
Maximum	SF	0.003	0.18	0.22	0.40

    Second Coat

	Unit	Man-Hrs	Material	Labor	Total
Minimum	SF	0.002	0.15	0.13	0.28
Average	SF	0.002	0.17	0.15	0.32
Maximum	SF	0.003	0.18	0.18	0.36

Trim
  Brush
    First Coat

	Unit	Man-Hrs	Material	Labor	Total
Minimum	LF	0.003	0.19	0.22	0.41
Average	LF	0.004	0.21	0.27	0.48
Maximum	LF	0.005	0.22	0.34	0.56

    Second Coat

	Unit	Man-Hrs	Material	Labor	Total
Minimum	LF	0.003	0.19	0.17	0.36
Average	LF	0.003	0.21	0.22	0.43
Maximum	LF	0.005	0.22	0.34	0.56

Walls
  Roller
    First Coat

	Unit	Man-Hrs	Material	Labor	Total
Minimum	SF	0.003	0.15	0.19	0.34
Average	SF	0.003	0.17	0.20	0.37
Maximum	SF	0.003	0.18	0.21	0.39

    Second Coat

	Unit	Man-Hrs	Material	Labor	Total
Minimum	SF	0.003	0.15	0.17	0.32
Average	SF	0.003	0.17	0.18	0.35
Maximum	SF	0.003	0.18	0.20	0.38

  Spray
    First Coat

	Unit	Man-Hrs	Material	Labor	Total
Minimum	SF	0.001	0.11	0.08	0.19
Average	SF	0.002	0.13	0.10	0.23
Maximum	SF	0.002	0.14	0.13	0.27

    Second Coat

	Unit	Man-Hrs	Material	Labor	Total
Minimum	SF	0.001	0.11	0.07	0.18
Average	SF	0.001	0.13	0.09	0.22
Maximum	SF	0.002	0.14	0.12	0.26

Windows
  Brush
    First Coat

	Unit	Man-Hrs	Material	Labor	Total
Minimum	SF	0.013	0.13	0.90	1.03
Average	SF	0.016	0.14	1.08	1.22
Maximum	SF	0.020	0.15	1.36	1.51

    Second Coat

	Unit	Man-Hrs	Material	Labor	Total
Minimum	SF	0.011	0.13	0.77	0.90
Average	SF	0.013	0.14	0.90	1.04
Maximum	SF	0.016	0.15	1.08	1.23

09911.32 EXT. PAINTING, MISC.

EXT. PAINTING, MISC.
  Gratings, Metal
    Roller
      First Coat

	Unit	Man-Hrs	Material	Labor	Total
Minimum	SF	0.023	0.15	1.55	1.70
Average	SF	0.027	0.17	1.81	1.98
Maximum	SF	0.032	0.18	2.17	2.35

      Second Coat

	Unit	Man-Hrs	Material	Labor	Total
Minimum	SF	0.016	0.15	1.08	1.23
Average	SF	0.020	0.17	1.36	1.53
Maximum	SF	0.027	0.18	1.81	1.99

© 2020 BNi Publications, Inc.

	Unit	Man-Hrs	Material	Labor	Total

09911.32 EXT. PAINTING, MISC. (Cont.)

Gratings, Metal
  Spray
    First Coat

	Unit	Man-Hrs	Material	Labor	Total
Minimum	SF	0.011	0.13	0.77	0.90
Average	SF	0.013	0.14	0.90	1.04
Maximum	SF	0.016	0.15	1.08	1.23

    Second Coat

	Unit	Man-Hrs	Material	Labor	Total
Minimum	SF	0.009	0.13	0.60	0.73
Average	SF	0.010	0.14	0.68	0.82
Maximum	SF	0.011	0.15	0.77	0.92

Ladders
  Brush
    First Coat

	Unit	Man-Hrs	Material	Labor	Total
Minimum	LF	0.020	0.19	1.36	1.55
Average	LF	0.023	0.21	1.55	1.76
Maximum	LF	0.027	0.22	1.81	2.03

    Second Coat

	Unit	Man-Hrs	Material	Labor	Total
Minimum	LF	0.016	0.19	1.08	1.27
Average	LF	0.018	0.21	1.20	1.41
Maximum	LF	0.020	0.22	1.36	1.58

  Spray
    First Coat

	Unit	Man-Hrs	Material	Labor	Total
Minimum	LF	0.013	0.13	0.90	1.03
Average	LF	0.015	0.14	0.98	1.12
Maximum	LF	0.016	0.15	1.08	1.23

    Second Coat

	Unit	Man-Hrs	Material	Labor	Total
Minimum	LF	0.011	0.13	0.77	0.90
Average	LF	0.012	0.14	0.83	0.97
Maximum	LF	0.013	0.15	0.90	1.05

Shakes
  Spray
    First Coat

	Unit	Man-Hrs	Material	Labor	Total
Minimum	SF	0.003	0.14	0.22	0.36
Average	SF	0.004	0.15	0.24	0.39
Maximum	SF	0.004	0.17	0.27	0.44

    Second Coat

	Unit	Man-Hrs	Material	Labor	Total
Minimum	SF	0.003	0.14	0.20	0.34
Average	SF	0.003	0.15	0.22	0.37
Maximum	SF	0.004	0.17	0.24	0.41

Shingles, Wood
  Roller
    First Coat

	Unit	Man-Hrs	Material	Labor	Total
Minimum	SF	0.004	0.15	0.30	0.45
Average	SF	0.005	0.17	0.34	0.51
Maximum	SF	0.006	0.18	0.38	0.56

    Second Coat

	Unit	Man-Hrs	Material	Labor	Total
Minimum	SF	0.003	0.15	0.20	0.35
Average	SF	0.003	0.17	0.22	0.39
Maximum	SF	0.004	0.18	0.24	0.42

  Spray
    First Coat

	Unit	Man-Hrs	Material	Labor	Total
Minimum	LF	0.003	0.13	0.20	0.33
Average	LF	0.003	0.14	0.22	0.36
Maximum	LF	0.004	0.15	0.24	0.39

    Second Coat

	Unit	Man-Hrs	Material	Labor	Total
Minimum	LF	0.002	0.13	0.16	0.29
Average	LF	0.003	0.14	0.17	0.31
Maximum	LF	0.003	0.15	0.18	0.33

Shutters and Louvers
  Brush
    First Coat

	Unit	Man-Hrs	Material	Labor	Total
Minimum	EA	0.160	0.19	11.00	11.19
Average	EA	0.200	0.21	13.50	13.71
Maximum	EA	0.267	0.22	18.25	18.47

	Unit	Man-Hrs	Material	Labor	Total

09911.32 EXT. PAINTING, MISC. (Cont.)

Brush
  Second Coat

	Unit	Man-Hrs	Material	Labor	Total
Minimum	EA	0.100	0.19	6.80	6.99
Average	EA	0.123	0.21	8.37	8.58
Maximum	EA	0.160	0.22	11.00	11.22

Spray
  First Coat

	Unit	Man-Hrs	Material	Labor	Total
Minimum	EA	0.053	0.14	3.62	3.76
Average	EA	0.064	0.15	4.35	4.50
Maximum	EA	0.080	0.17	5.44	5.61

  Second Coat

	Unit	Man-Hrs	Material	Labor	Total
Minimum	EA	0.040	0.14	2.72	2.86
Average	EA	0.053	0.15	3.62	3.77
Maximum	EA	0.064	0.17	4.35	4.52

Stairs, metal
Brush
  First Coat

	Unit	Man-Hrs	Material	Labor	Total
Minimum	SF	0.009	0.19	0.60	0.79
Average	SF	0.010	0.21	0.68	0.89
Maximum	SF	0.011	0.22	0.77	0.99

  Second Coat

	Unit	Man-Hrs	Material	Labor	Total
Minimum	SF	0.005	0.19	0.34	0.53
Average	SF	0.006	0.21	0.38	0.59
Maximum	SF	0.007	0.22	0.45	0.67

Spray
  First Coat

	Unit	Man-Hrs	Material	Labor	Total
Minimum	SF	0.004	0.14	0.30	0.44
Average	SF	0.006	0.15	0.38	0.53
Maximum	SF	0.006	0.17	0.41	0.58

  Second Coat

	Unit	Man-Hrs	Material	Labor	Total
Minimum	SF	0.003	0.14	0.22	0.36
Average	SF	0.004	0.15	0.27	0.42
Maximum	SF	0.005	0.17	0.34	0.51

Steel, Structural, Light
Brush
  First Coat

	Unit	Man-Hrs	Material	Labor	Total
Minimum	SF	0.016	0.15	1.08	1.23
Average	SF	0.020	0.17	1.36	1.53
Maximum	SF	0.027	0.18	1.81	1.99

  Second Coat

	Unit	Man-Hrs	Material	Labor	Total
Minimum	SF	0.011	0.14	0.77	0.91
Average	SF	0.013	0.15	0.90	1.05
Maximum	SF	0.016	0.17	1.08	1.25

Roller
  First Coat

	Unit	Man-Hrs	Material	Labor	Total
Minimum	SF	0.011	0.15	0.77	0.92
Average	SF	0.013	0.17	0.90	1.07
Maximum	SF	0.016	0.18	1.08	1.26

  Second Coat

	Unit	Man-Hrs	Material	Labor	Total
Minimum	SF	0.007	0.14	0.45	0.59
Average	SF	0.008	0.15	0.54	0.69
Maximum	SF	0.010	0.17	0.68	0.85

Spray
  First Coat

	Unit	Man-Hrs	Material	Labor	Total
Minimum	SF	0.007	0.14	0.45	0.59
Average	SF	0.008	0.15	0.54	0.69
Maximum	SF	0.010	0.17	0.68	0.85

  Second Coat

	Unit	Man-Hrs	Material	Labor	Total
Minimum	SF	0.006	0.10	0.38	0.48
Average	SF	0.007	0.11	0.45	0.56
Maximum	SF	0.008	0.13	0.54	0.67

© 2020 BNi Publications, Inc.

	Unit	Man-Hrs	Material	Labor	Total
09911.32 EXT. PAINTING, MISC. (Cont.)					
Steel, Medium to Heavy					
Brush					
First Coat					
Minimum	SF	0.008	0.15	0.54	0.69
Average	SF	0.009	0.17	0.60	0.77
Maximum	SF	0.010	0.18	0.68	0.86
Second Coat					
Minimum	SF	0.007	0.14	0.45	0.59
Average	SF	0.008	0.15	0.54	0.69
Maximum	SF	0.009	0.17	0.64	0.81
Roller					
First Coat					
Minimum	SF	0.007	0.15	0.45	0.60
Average	SF	0.008	0.17	0.54	0.71
Maximum	SF	0.009	0.18	0.64	0.82
Second Coat					
Minimum	SF	0.005	0.14	0.34	0.48
Average	SF	0.006	0.15	0.38	0.53
Maximum	SF	0.007	0.17	0.45	0.62
Spray					
First Coat					
Minimum	SF	0.004	0.14	0.30	0.44
Average	SF	0.005	0.15	0.34	0.49
Maximum	SF	0.006	0.17	0.38	0.55
Second Coat					
Minimum	SF	0.004	0.10	0.24	0.34
Average	SF	0.004	0.11	0.27	0.38
Maximum	SF	0.004	0.13	0.30	0.43
09912.33 INT. PAINTING, BUILDINGS					
INT. PAINTING, BUILDINGS					
Acoustical Ceiling					
Roller					
First Coat					
Minimum	SF	0.005	0.19	0.34	0.53
Average	SF	0.007	0.21	0.45	0.66
Maximum	SF	0.010	0.22	0.68	0.90
Second Coat					
Minimum	SF	0.004	0.19	0.27	0.46
Average	SF	0.005	0.21	0.34	0.55
Maximum	SF	0.007	0.22	0.45	0.67
Spray					
First Coat					
Minimum	SF	0.002	0.15	0.15	0.30
Average	SF	0.003	0.17	0.18	0.35
Maximum	SF	0.003	0.18	0.22	0.40
Second Coat					
Minimum	SF	0.002	0.15	0.12	0.27
Average	SF	0.002	0.17	0.13	0.30
Maximum	SF	0.002	0.18	0.15	0.33
Cabinets and Casework					
Brush					
First Coat					
Minimum	SF	0.008	0.19	0.54	0.73
Average	SF	0.009	0.21	0.60	0.81
Maximum	SF	0.010	0.22	0.68	0.90
Second Coat					
Minimum	SF	0.007	0.19	0.45	0.64
Average	SF	0.007	0.21	0.49	0.70
Maximum	SF	0.008	0.22	0.54	0.76
Spray					
First Coat					
Minimum	SF	0.004	0.15	0.27	0.42
Average	SF	0.005	0.17	0.32	0.49
Maximum	SF	0.006	0.18	0.38	0.56

	Unit	Man-Hrs	Material	Labor	Total

09912.33 INT. PAINTING, BUILDINGS (Cont.)

Spray
Second Coat

	Unit	Man-Hrs	Material	Labor	Total
Minimum	SF	0.003	0.15	0.21	0.36
Average	SF	0.003	0.17	0.23	0.40
Maximum	SF	0.004	0.18	0.30	0.48

Ceilings
Roller
First Coat

	Unit	Man-Hrs	Material	Labor	Total
Minimum	SF	0.003	0.15	0.22	0.37
Average	SF	0.004	0.17	0.24	0.41
Maximum	SF	0.004	0.18	0.27	0.45

Second Coat

	Unit	Man-Hrs	Material	Labor	Total
Minimum	SF	0.003	0.15	0.18	0.33
Average	SF	0.003	0.17	0.20	0.37
Maximum	SF	0.003	0.18	0.22	0.40

Spray
First Coat

	Unit	Man-Hrs	Material	Labor	Total
Minimum	SF	0.002	0.13	0.13	0.26
Average	SF	0.002	0.14	0.15	0.29
Maximum	SF	0.003	0.15	0.17	0.32

Second Coat

	Unit	Man-Hrs	Material	Labor	Total
Minimum	SF	0.002	0.13	0.10	0.23
Average	SF	0.002	0.14	0.11	0.25
Maximum	SF	0.002	0.15	0.13	0.28

Doors, Metal
Roller
First Coat

	Unit	Man-Hrs	Material	Labor	Total
Minimum	SF	0.005	0.19	0.36	0.55
Average	SF	0.006	0.21	0.41	0.62
Maximum	SF	0.007	0.22	0.49	0.71

Second Coat

	Unit	Man-Hrs	Material	Labor	Total
Minimum	SF	0.004	0.19	0.25	0.44
Average	SF	0.004	0.21	0.28	0.49
Maximum	SF	0.005	0.22	0.32	0.54

Spray
First Coat

	Unit	Man-Hrs	Material	Labor	Total
Minimum	SF	0.004	0.13	0.30	0.43
Average	SF	0.005	0.14	0.34	0.48
Maximum	SF	0.006	0.15	0.38	0.53

Second Coat

	Unit	Man-Hrs	Material	Labor	Total
Minimum	SF	0.003	0.19	0.22	0.41
Average	SF	0.004	0.21	0.24	0.45
Maximum	SF	0.004	0.22	0.27	0.49

Doors, Wood
Brush
First Coat

	Unit	Man-Hrs	Material	Labor	Total
Minimum	SF	0.011	0.19	0.77	0.96
Average	SF	0.015	0.21	0.98	1.19
Maximum	SF	0.018	0.22	1.20	1.42

Second Coat

	Unit	Man-Hrs	Material	Labor	Total
Minimum	SF	0.009	0.14	0.60	0.74
Average	SF	0.010	0.15	0.68	0.83
Maximum	SF	0.011	0.17	0.77	0.94

Spray
First Coat

	Unit	Man-Hrs	Material	Labor	Total
Minimum	SF	0.002	0.14	0.16	0.30
Average	SF	0.003	0.15	0.19	0.34
Maximum	SF	0.004	0.17	0.24	0.41

Second Coat

	Unit	Man-Hrs	Material	Labor	Total
Minimum	SF	0.002	0.14	0.12	0.26
Average	SF	0.002	0.15	0.14	0.29
Maximum	SF	0.003	0.17	0.17	0.34

© 2020 BNi Publications, Inc.

	Unit	Man-Hrs	Material	Labor	Total
09912.33 INT. PAINTING, BUILDINGS (Cont.)					
Ductwork					
Brush					
Minimum	LF	0.010	0.15	0.68	0.83
Average	LF	0.011	0.17	0.77	0.94
Maximum	LF	0.013	0.18	0.90	1.08
Roller					
Minimum	SF	0.007	0.15	0.45	0.60
Average	SF	0.007	0.17	0.49	0.66
Maximum	SF	0.008	0.18	0.54	0.72
Spray					
Minimum	SF	0.003	0.15	0.19	0.34
Average	SF	0.003	0.17	0.20	0.37
Maximum	SF	0.003	0.18	0.22	0.40
Floors					
Roller					
First Coat					
Minimum	SF	0.003	0.15	0.17	0.32
Average	SF	0.003	0.17	0.20	0.37
Maximum	SF	0.003	0.18	0.22	0.40
Second Coat					
Minimum	SF	0.002	0.15	0.13	0.28
Average	SF	0.002	0.17	0.15	0.32
Maximum	SF	0.002	0.18	0.16	0.34
Spray					
First Coat					
Minimum	SF	0.002	0.14	0.12	0.26
Average	SF	0.002	0.15	0.12	0.27
Maximum	SF	0.002	0.17	0.14	0.31
Second Coat					
Minimum	SF	0.002	0.14	0.10	0.24
Average	SF	0.002	0.15	0.11	0.26
Maximum	SF	0.002	0.17	0.12	0.29
Pipes to 6" diameter					
Brush					
Minimum	LF	0.010	0.19	0.68	0.87
Average	LF	0.011	0.21	0.77	0.98
Maximum	LF	0.013	0.22	0.90	1.12
Spray					
Minimum	LF	0.003	0.15	0.22	0.37
Average	LF	0.004	0.17	0.27	0.44
Maximum	LF	0.005	0.18	0.36	0.54
Pipes to 12" diameter					
Brush					
Minimum	LF	0.020	0.35	1.36	1.71
Average	LF	0.023	0.36	1.55	1.91
Maximum	LF	0.027	0.38	1.81	2.19
Spray					
Minimum	LF	0.007	0.31	0.45	0.76
Average	LF	0.008	0.33	0.54	0.87
Maximum	LF	0.010	0.34	0.68	1.02
Trim					
Brush					
First Coat					
Minimum	LF	0.003	0.19	0.21	0.40
Average	LF	0.004	0.21	0.24	0.45
Maximum	LF	0.004	0.22	0.30	0.52
Second Coat					
Minimum	LF	0.002	0.19	0.16	0.35
Average	LF	0.003	0.21	0.20	0.41
Maximum	LF	0.004	0.22	0.30	0.52
Walls					
Roller					
First Coat					
Minimum	SF	0.003	0.15	0.19	0.34
Average	SF	0.003	0.17	0.20	0.37

	Unit	Man-Hrs	Material	Labor	Total
09912.33 INT. PAINTING, BUILDINGS (Cont.)					
First Coat					
Maximum	SF	0.003	0.18	0.22	0.40
Second Coat					
Minimum	SF	0.003	0.15	0.17	0.32
Average	SF	0.003	0.17	0.18	0.35
Maximum	SF	0.003	0.18	0.20	0.38
Spray					
First Coat					
Minimum	SF	0.001	0.13	0.08	0.21
Average	SF	0.002	0.14	0.10	0.24
Maximum	SF	0.002	0.15	0.13	0.28
Second Coat					
Minimum	SF	0.001	0.13	0.07	0.20
Average	SF	0.001	0.14	0.09	0.23
Maximum	SF	0.002	0.15	0.12	0.27

© 2020 BNi Publications, Inc.

	Unit	Man-Hrs	Material	Labor	Total

10111.30 CHALKBOARDS

CHALKBOARDS

Chalkboard, metal frame, 1/4" thick

	Unit	Man-Hrs	Material	Labor	Total
48"x60"	EA	0.800	490.00	65.00	555.00
48"x96"	EA	0.889	670.00	72.00	742.00
48"x144"	EA	1.000	890.00	82.00	972.00
48"x192"	EA	1.143	1,210.00	93.00	1,303.00

Liquid chalkboard

	Unit	Man-Hrs	Material	Labor	Total
48"x60"	EA	0.800	650.00	65.00	715.00
48"x96"	EA	0.889	830.00	72.00	902.00
48"x144"	EA	1.000	1,240.00	82.00	1,322.00
48"x192"	EA	1.143	1,420.00	93.00	1,513.00
Map rail, deluxe	LF	0.040	8.11	3.26	11.37

10130.01 IDENTIFYING DEVICES

IDENTIFYING DEVICES

Directory and bulletin boards

Open face boards

	Unit	Man-Hrs	Material	Labor	Total
Chrome plated steel frame	SF	0.400	38.25	32.50	70.75
Aluminum framed	SF	0.400	66.00	32.50	98.50
Bronze framed	SF	0.400	86.00	32.50	118.50
Stainless steel framed	SF	0.400	120.00	32.50	152.50
Tack board, aluminum framed	SF	0.400	27.00	32.50	59.50
Visual aid board, aluminum framed	SF	0.400	27.00	32.50	59.50

Glass encased boards, hinged and keyed

	Unit	Man-Hrs	Material	Labor	Total
Aluminum framed	SF	1.000	150.00	82.00	232.00
Bronze framed	SF	1.000	170.00	82.00	252.00
Stainless steel framed	SF	1.000	210.00	82.00	292.00
Chrome plated steel framed	SF	1.000	230.00	82.00	312.00

10140.04 SIGNAGE

SIGNAGE

Metal plaque

	Unit	Man-Hrs	Material	Labor	Total
Cast bronze	SF	0.667	660.00	54.00	714.00
Aluminum	SF	0.667	380.00	54.00	434.00

Metal engraved plaque

	Unit	Man-Hrs	Material	Labor	Total
Porcelain steel	SF	0.667	790.00	54.00	844.00
Stainless steel	SF	0.667	630.00	54.00	684.00
Brass	SF	0.667	940.00	54.00	994.00
Aluminum	SF	0.667	580.00	54.00	634.00

Metal built-up plaque

	Unit	Man-Hrs	Material	Labor	Total
Bronze	SF	0.800	710.00	65.00	775.00
Copper and bronze	SF	0.800	630.00	65.00	695.00
Copper and aluminum	SF	0.800	700.00	65.00	765.00

Metal nameplate plaques

	Unit	Man-Hrs	Material	Labor	Total
Cast bronze	SF	0.500	710.00	40.75	750.75
Cast aluminum	SF	0.500	520.00	40.75	560.75

Engraved, 1-1/2" x 6"

	Unit	Man-Hrs	Material	Labor	Total
Bronze	EA	0.500	300.00	40.75	340.75
Aluminum	EA	0.500	230.00	40.75	270.75

Letters, on masonry, aluminum, satin finish

1/2" thick

	Unit	Man-Hrs	Material	Labor	Total
2" high	EA	0.320	27.50	26.00	53.50
4" high	EA	0.400	41.25	32.50	73.75
6" high	EA	0.444	55.00	36.25	91.25

3/4" thick

	Unit	Man-Hrs	Material	Labor	Total
8" high	EA	0.500	82.00	40.75	122.75
10" high	EA	0.571	95.00	46.50	141.50

1" thick

	Unit	Man-Hrs	Material	Labor	Total
12" high	EA	0.667	110.00	54.00	164.00
14" high	EA	0.800	120.00	65.00	185.00
16" high	EA	1.000	150.00	82.00	232.00

	Unit	Man-Hrs	Material	Labor	Total
10140.04 SIGNAGE (Cont.)					
Letters, on masonry, aluminum, satin finish					
For polished aluminum add, 15%					
For clear anodized aluminum add, 15%					
For colored anodic aluminum add, 30%					
For profiled and color enameled letters add, 50%					
Cast bronze, satin finish letters					
3/8" thick					
2" high	EA	0.320	33.25	26.00	59.25
4" high	EA	0.400	50.00	32.50	82.50
1/2" thick, 6" high	EA	0.444	68.00	36.25	104.25
5/8" thick, 8" high	EA	0.500	100.00	40.75	140.75
1" thick					
10" high	EA	0.571	120.00	46.50	166.50
12" high	EA	0.667	160.00	54.00	214.00
14" high	EA	0.800	190.00	65.00	255.00
16" high	EA	1.000	280.00	82.00	362.00
Interior door signs, adhesive, flexible					
2" x 8"	EA	0.200	25.75	12.75	38.50
4" x 4"	EA	0.200	27.00	12.75	39.75
6" x 7"	EA	0.200	34.25	12.75	47.00
6" x 9"	EA	0.200	43.75	12.75	56.50
10" x 9"	EA	0.200	57.00	12.75	69.75
10" x 12"	EA	0.200	74.00	12.75	86.75
Hard plastic type, no frame					
3" x 8"	EA	0.200	57.00	12.75	69.75
4" x 4"	EA	0.200	57.00	12.75	69.75
4" x 12"	EA	0.200	62.00	12.75	74.75
Hard plastic type, with frame					
3" x 8"	EA	0.200	170.00	12.75	182.75
4" x 4"	EA	0.200	140.00	12.75	152.75
4" x 12"	EA	0.200	210.00	12.75	222.75
10145.30 SIGNAGE					
SIGNAGE					
Traffic signs					
Reflectorized per OSHA stds., incl. post					
Stop, 24"x24"	EA	0.533	89.00	34.00	123.00
Yield, 30" triangle	EA	0.533	48.50	34.00	82.50
Speed limit, 12"x18"	EA	0.533	55.00	34.00	89.00
Directional, 12"x18"	EA	0.533	67.00	34.00	101.00
Exit, 12"x18"	EA	0.533	67.00	34.00	101.00
Entry, 12"x18"	EA	0.533	67.00	34.00	101.00
Warning, 24"x24"	EA	0.533	88.00	34.00	122.00
Informational, 12"x18"	EA	0.533	44.75	34.00	78.75
Handicap parking, 12"x18"	EA	0.533	46.00	34.00	80.00
10170.01 TELEPHONE ENCLOSURES					
TELEPHONE ENCLOSURES					
Enclosure, wall mounted, shelf, 28" x 30" x 15"	EA	2.000	2,030.00	160.00	2,190.00
Directory shelf, stainless steel, 3 binders	EA	1.333	1,740.00	110.00	1,850.00
10211.30 TOILET PARTITIONS					
TOILET PARTITIONS					
Toilet partition, plastic laminate					
Ceiling mounted	EA	2.667	1,200.00	220.00	1,420.00
Floor mounted	EA	2.000	790.00	160.00	950.00
Metal					
Ceiling mounted	EA	2.667	820.00	220.00	1,040.00
Floor mounted	EA	2.000	780.00	160.00	940.00
Wheelchair partition, plastic laminate					
Ceiling mounted	EA	2.667	1,800.00	220.00	2,020.00
Floor mounted	EA	2.000	1,580.00	160.00	1,740.00
Painted metal					
Ceiling mounted	EA	2.667	1,280.00	220.00	1,500.00
Floor mounted	EA	2.000	1,170.00	160.00	1,330.00

© 2020 BNi Publications, Inc.

	Unit	Man-Hrs	Material	Labor	Total

10211.30 TOILET PARTITIONS (Cont.)

Urinal screen, plastic laminate

	Unit	Man-Hrs	Material	Labor	Total
Wall hung	EA	1.000	550.00	82.00	632.00
Floor mounted	EA	1.000	500.00	82.00	582.00
Porcelain enameled steel, floor mounted	EA	1.000	640.00	82.00	722.00
Painted metal, floor mounted	EA	1.000	420.00	82.00	502.00
Stainless steel, floor mounted	EA	1.000	810.00	82.00	892.00

Metal toilet partitions
Front door and side divider, floor mounted

	Unit	Man-Hrs	Material	Labor	Total
Porcelain enameled steel	EA	2.000	1,320.00	160.00	1,480.00
Painted steel	EA	2.000	780.00	160.00	940.00
Stainless steel	EA	2.000	1,930.00	160.00	2,090.00

10211.60 SHOWER STALLS

SHOWER STALLS
Shower receptors
Precast, terrazzo

	Unit	Man-Hrs	Material	Labor	Total
32" x 32"	EA	0.667	700.00	60.00	760.00
32" x 48"	EA	0.800	740.00	72.00	812.00

Concrete

	Unit	Man-Hrs	Material	Labor	Total
32" x 32"	EA	0.667	290.00	60.00	350.00
48" x 48"	EA	0.889	320.00	79.00	399.00

Shower door, trim and hardware

	Unit	Man-Hrs	Material	Labor	Total
Economy, 24" wide, chrome, tempered glass	EA	0.800	310.00	72.00	382.00
Porcelain enameled steel, flush	EA	0.800	570.00	72.00	642.00
Baked enameled steel, flush	EA	0.800	340.00	72.00	412.00
Aluminum, tempered glass, 48" wide, sliding	EA	1.000	700.00	89.00	789.00
Folding	EA	1.000	680.00	89.00	769.00

Aluminum and tempered glass, molded plastic
Complete with receptor and door

	Unit	Man-Hrs	Material	Labor	Total
32" x 32"	EA	2.000	860.00	180.00	1,040.00
36" x 36"	EA	2.000	970.00	180.00	1,150.00
40" x 40"	EA	2.286	1,000.00	200.00	1,200.00

Shower compartment, precast concrete receptor
Single entry type

	Unit	Man-Hrs	Material	Labor	Total
Porcelain enameled steel	EA	8.000	2,420.00	720.00	3,140.00
Baked enameled steel	EA	8.000	2,320.00	720.00	3,040.00
Stainless steel	EA	8.000	2,230.00	720.00	2,950.00

Double entry type

	Unit	Man-Hrs	Material	Labor	Total
Porcelain enameled steel	EA	10.000	4,320.00	890.00	5,210.00
Baked enameled steel	EA	10.000	2,950.00	890.00	3,840.00
Stainless steel	EA	10.000	4,770.00	890.00	5,660.00

10212.30 CUBICLES

CUBICLES
Hospital track

	Unit	Man-Hrs	Material	Labor	Total
Ceiling hung	LF	0.089	7.73	7.24	14.97
Suspended	LF	0.114	8.38	9.32	17.70

Hospital metal dividers, galvanized steel
Baked enamel finish
54" high

	Unit	Man-Hrs	Material	Labor	Total
10" glass light	LF	0.400	130.00	32.50	162.50
14" glass light	LF	0.400	130.00	32.50	162.50
24" glass light	LF	0.400	120.00	32.50	152.50

60" high

	Unit	Man-Hrs	Material	Labor	Total
10" glass light	LF	0.444	140.00	36.25	176.25
14" glass light	LF	0.444	140.00	36.25	176.25
24" glass light	LF	0.444	130.00	36.25	166.25

Stainless steel
54" high

	Unit	Man-Hrs	Material	Labor	Total
10" glass light	LF	0.444	220.00	36.25	256.25
14" glass light	LF	0.444	240.00	36.25	276.25
24" glass light	LF	0.444	290.00	36.25	326.25

60" high

	Unit	Man-Hrs	Material	Labor	Total
10" glass light	LF	0.500	250.00	40.75	290.75
14" glass light	LF	0.500	250.00	40.75	290.75

	Unit	Man-Hrs	Material	Labor	Total
10212.30 CUBICLES (Cont.)					
60" high					
24" glass light	LF	0.500	310.00	40.75	350.75
10221.90 MOVABLE PARTITIONS					
MOVABLE PARTITIONS					
Partition, movable, 2-1/2" thick, vinyl-gypsum	SF	0.040	24.50	3.26	27.76
Enameled steel frame, with 1/4" thick clear glass	SF	0.040	30.00	3.26	33.26
Door frame and hardware for movable partitions	EA	2.667	830.00	220.00	1,050.00
Add for acoustic movable partition	SF				1.82
Accordion partition, 12' high					
Vinyl	SF	0.133	13.25	10.75	24.00
Acoustical	SF	0.133	15.75	10.75	26.50
Standard office cubicles, 8' high, steel framed					
Baked enamel finish					
100% flush	LF	0.200	200.00	16.25	216.25
75% flush and 25% glass	LF	0.222	250.00	18.00	268.00
50% flush and 50% glass	LF	0.222	350.00	18.00	368.00
100% glass	LF	0.267	410.00	21.75	431.75
Natural hardwood panels					
100% flush	LF	0.267	220.00	21.75	241.75
50% flush and 50% glass	LF	0.286	290.00	23.25	313.25
Plastic laminated panels					
100% flush	LF	0.267	250.00	21.75	271.75
75% flush and 25% glass	LF	0.286	330.00	23.25	353.25
50% flush and 50% glass	LF	0.286	360.00	23.25	383.25
Vinyl covered panels					
100% flush	LF	0.276	220.00	22.50	242.50
75% flush and 25% glass	LF	0.296	290.00	24.25	314.25
50% and 50% glass	LF	0.296	350.00	24.25	374.25
Aluminum framed					
Enameled or anodized aluminum panels					
100% flush	LF	0.200	180.00	16.25	196.25
75% flush and 25% glass	LF	0.222	170.00	18.00	188.00
50% flush and 50% glass	LF	0.222	150.00	18.00	168.00
Vinyl covered panels					
100% flush	LF	0.276	180.00	22.50	202.50
75% flush and 25% glass	LF	0.296	200.00	24.25	224.25
50% flush and 50% glass	LF	0.296	230.00	24.25	254.25
60" high partitions, steel framed					
Enameled panels	LF	0.178	89.00	14.50	103.50
Natural hardwood panels, two sides	LF	0.186	350.00	15.25	365.25
Plastic laminated panels	LF	0.186	190.00	15.25	205.25
Vinyl covered panels	LF	0.178	240.00	14.50	254.50
Aluminum framed					
Anodized or baked enamel panels	LF	0.178	130.00	14.50	144.50
Natural hardwood panels	LF	0.186	380.00	15.25	395.25
Plastic laminated panels	LF	0.186	190.00	15.25	205.25
Vinyl covered panels	LF	0.178	240.00	14.50	254.50
Wire mesh partitions					
Wall panels					
4' x 7'	EA	0.500	180.00	40.75	220.75
4' x 8'	EA	0.533	200.00	43.50	243.50
4' x 10'	EA	0.615	220.00	50.00	270.00
Wall filler panels					
1' x 7'	EA	0.500	98.00	40.75	138.75
1' x 8'	EA	0.533	110.00	43.50	153.50
1' x 10'	EA	0.571	130.00	46.50	176.50
2' x 7'	EA	0.500	110.00	40.75	150.75
2' x 8'	EA	0.533	120.00	43.50	163.50
2' x 10'	EA	0.571	140.00	46.50	186.50
3' x 7'	EA	0.500	140.00	40.75	180.75
3' x 8'	EA	0.533	190.00	43.50	233.50
3' x 10'	EA	0.571	210.00	46.50	256.50

© 2020 BNi Publications, Inc.

	Unit	Man-Hrs	Material	Labor	Total
10221.90 MOVABLE PARTITIONS (Cont.)					
Ceiling panels					
10' x 2'	EA	1.143	140.00	93.00	233.00
10' x 4'	EA	1.600	210.00	130.00	340.00
Wall panel with service window					
5' wide					
7' high	EA	0.500	570.00	40.75	610.75
8' high	EA	0.533	590.00	43.50	633.50
10' high	EA	0.571	570.00	46.50	616.50
Doors					
Sliding					
3' x 7'	EA	2.000	380.00	160.00	540.00
3' x 8'	EA	2.286	510.00	190.00	700.00
3' x 10'	EA	3.200	540.00	260.00	800.00
4' x 7'	EA	2.286	480.00	190.00	670.00
4' x 8'	EA	3.200	540.00	260.00	800.00
4' x 10'	EA	4.000	570.00	330.00	900.00
5' x 7'	EA	3.200	530.00	260.00	790.00
5' x 8'	EA	4.000	570.00	330.00	900.00
5' x 10'	EA	4.000	650.00	330.00	980.00
Swing door					
3' x 7'	EA	2.000	320.00	160.00	480.00
4' x 7'	EA	2.286	350.00	190.00	540.00
Swing door, with 1' transom					
3' x 7'	EA	2.286	470.00	190.00	660.00
4' x 7'	EA	3.200	520.00	260.00	780.00
Swing door, with 3' transom					
3' x 7'	EA	3.200	570.00	260.00	830.00
4' x 7'	EA	4.000	610.00	330.00	940.00
10281.60 BATH ACCESSORIES					
BATH ACCESSORIES					
Ash receiver, wall mounted, aluminum	EA	0.400	170.00	32.50	202.50
Grab bar, 1-1/2" dia., stainless steel, wall mounted					
24" long	EA	0.400	57.00	32.50	89.50
36" long	EA	0.421	64.00	34.25	98.25
42" long	EA	0.444	71.00	36.25	107.25
48" long	EA	0.471	78.00	38.25	116.25
52" long	EA	0.500	85.00	40.75	125.75
1" dia., stainless steel					
12" long	EA	0.348	35.50	28.25	63.75
18" long	EA	0.364	42.50	29.75	72.25
24" long	EA	0.400	48.25	32.50	80.75
30" long	EA	0.421	57.00	34.25	91.25
36" long	EA	0.444	64.00	36.25	100.25
48" long	EA	0.471	71.00	38.25	109.25
Hand dryer, surface mounted, 110 volt	EA	1.000	810.00	82.00	892.00
Medicine cabinet, 16 x 22, baked enamel, lighted	EA	0.320	160.00	26.00	186.00
With mirror, lighted	EA	0.533	230.00	43.50	273.50
Mirror, 1/4" plate glass, up to 10 sf	SF	0.080	12.50	6.52	19.02
Mirror, stainless steel frame					
18"x24"	EA	0.267	95.00	21.75	116.75
18"x32"	EA	0.320	110.00	26.00	136.00
18"x36"	EA	0.400	110.00	32.50	142.50
24"x30"	EA	0.400	120.00	32.50	152.50
24"x36"	EA	0.444	120.00	36.25	156.25
24"x48"	EA	0.667	170.00	54.00	224.00
24"x60"	EA	0.800	430.00	65.00	495.00
30"x30"	EA	0.800	380.00	65.00	445.00
30"x72"	EA	1.000	680.00	82.00	762.00
48"x72"	EA	1.333	740.00	110.00	850.00
With shelf, 18"x24"	EA	0.320	290.00	26.00	316.00
Sanitary napkin dispenser, stainless steel	EA	0.533	700.00	43.50	743.50
Shower rod, 1" diameter					
Chrome finish over brass	EA	0.400	250.00	32.50	282.50

	Unit	Man-Hrs	Material	Labor	Total
10281.60 BATH ACCESSORIES (Cont.)					
Shower rod, 1" diameter					
Stainless steel	EA	0.400	180.00	32.50	212.50
Soap dish, stainless steel, wall mounted	EA	0.533	160.00	43.50	203.50
Toilet tissue dispenser, stainless, wall mounted					
Single roll	EA	0.200	79.00	16.25	95.25
Double roll	EA	0.229	150.00	18.75	168.75
Towel dispenser, stainless steel					
Flush mounted	EA	0.444	300.00	36.25	336.25
Surface mounted	EA	0.400	430.00	32.50	462.50
Combination towel and waste receptacle	EA	0.533	660.00	43.50	703.50
Towel bar, stainless steel					
18" long	EA	0.320	98.00	26.00	124.00
24" long	EA	0.364	130.00	29.75	159.75
30" long	EA	0.400	140.00	32.50	172.50
36" long	EA	0.444	150.00	36.25	186.25
Toothbrush and tumbler holder	EA	0.267	62.00	21.75	83.75
Waste receptacle, stainless steel, wall mounted	EA	0.667	500.00	54.00	554.00
10440.01 FIRE PROTECTION					
FIRE PROTECTION					
Portable fire extinguishers					
Water pump tank type					
2.5 gal.					
Red enameled galvanized	EA	0.533	150.00	34.00	184.00
Red enameled copper	EA	0.533	220.00	34.00	254.00
Polished copper	EA	0.533	290.00	34.00	324.00
Carbon dioxide type, red enamel steel					
Squeeze grip with hose and horn					
2.5 lb	EA	0.533	230.00	34.00	264.00
5 lb	EA	0.615	330.00	39.25	369.25
10 lb	EA	0.800	340.00	51.00	391.00
15 lb	EA	1.000	380.00	64.00	444.00
20 lb	EA	1.000	460.00	64.00	524.00
Wheeled type					
125 lb	EA	1.600	4,120.00	100.00	4,220.00
250 lb	EA	1.600	5,210.00	100.00	5,310.00
500 lb	EA	1.600	6,730.00	100.00	6,830.00
Dry chemical, pressurized type					
Red enameled steel					
2.5 lb	EA	0.533	72.00	34.00	106.00
5 lb	EA	0.615	98.00	39.25	137.25
10 lb	EA	0.800	200.00	51.00	251.00
20 lb	EA	1.000	260.00	64.00	324.00
30 lb	EA	1.000	330.00	64.00	394.00
Chrome plated steel, 2.5 lb	EA	0.533	310.00	34.00	344.00
Other type extinguishers					
2.5 gal, stainless steel, pressurized water tanks	EA	0.533	230.00	34.00	264.00
Soda and acid type	EA	0.533	190.00	34.00	224.00
Cartridge operated, water type	EA	0.533	170.00	34.00	204.00
Loaded stream, water type	EA	0.533	210.00	34.00	244.00
Foam type	EA	0.533	270.00	34.00	304.00
40 gal, wheeled foam type	EA	1.600	6,160.00	100.00	6,260.00
Fire extinguisher cabinets					
Enameled steel					
8" x 12" x 27"	EA	1.600	160.00	100.00	260.00
8" x 16" x 38"	EA	1.600	190.00	100.00	290.00
Aluminum					
8" x 12" x 27"	EA	1.600	240.00	100.00	340.00
8" x 16" x 38"	EA	1.600	290.00	100.00	390.00
Stainless steel					
8" x 16" x 38"	EA	1.600	270.00	100.00	370.00

© 2020 BNi Publications, Inc.

	Unit	Man-Hrs	Material	Labor	Total
10510.01 LOCKERS					
LOCKERS					
Locker bench, floor mounted, laminated maple					
4'	EA	0.667	390.00	54.00	444.00
6'	EA	0.667	550.00	54.00	604.00
Wardrobe locker, 12" x 60" x 15", baked on enamel					
1-tier	EA	0.400	420.00	32.50	452.50
2-tier	EA	0.400	450.00	32.50	482.50
3-tier	EA	0.421	500.00	34.25	534.25
4-tier	EA	0.421	540.00	34.25	574.25
12" x 72" x 15", baked on enamel					
1-tier	EA	0.400	360.00	32.50	392.50
2-tier	EA	0.400	430.00	32.50	462.50
4-tier	EA	0.421	530.00	34.25	564.25
5-tier	EA	0.421	530.00	34.25	564.25
15" x 60" x 15", baked on enamel					
1-tier	EA	0.400	470.00	32.50	502.50
4-tier	EA	0.421	510.00	34.25	544.25
Wardrobe locker, single tier type					
12" x 15" x 72"	EA	0.800	320.00	65.00	385.00
18" x 15" x 72"	EA	0.842	390.00	69.00	459.00
12" x 18" x 72"	EA	0.889	350.00	72.00	422.00
18" x 18" x 72"	EA	0.941	450.00	77.00	527.00
Double tier type					
12" x 15" x 36"	EA	0.400	250.00	32.50	282.50
18" x 15" x 36"	EA	0.400	240.00	32.50	272.50
12" x 18" x 36"	EA	0.400	260.00	32.50	292.50
18" x 18" x 36"	EA	0.400	280.00	32.50	312.50
Two person unit					
18" x 15" x 72"	EA	1.333	670.00	110.00	780.00
18" x 18" x 72"	EA	1.600	750.00	130.00	880.00
Duplex unit					
15" x 15" x 72"	EA	0.800	680.00	65.00	745.00
15" x 21" x 72"	EA	0.800	720.00	65.00	785.00
Basket lockers, basket sets with baskets					
24 basket set	SET	4.000	1,680.00	330.00	2,010.00
30 basket set	SET	5.000	2,010.00	410.00	2,420.00
36 basket set	SET	6.667	2,280.00	540.00	2,820.00
42 basket set	SET	8.000	2,550.00	650.00	3,200.00
10550.01 POSTAL SPECIALTIES					
POSTAL SPECIALTIES					
Mail chutes					
Single mail chute					
Finished aluminum	LF	2.000	880.00	160.00	1,040.00
Bronze	LF	2.000	1,220.00	160.00	1,380.00
Single mail chute receiving box					
Finished aluminum	EA	4.000	1,300.00	330.00	1,630.00
Bronze	EA	4.000	1,560.00	330.00	1,890.00
Twin mail chute, double parallel					
Finished aluminum	FLR	4.000	1,920.00	330.00	2,250.00
Bronze	FLR	4.000	2,510.00	330.00	2,840.00
Receiving box, 36" x 20" x 12"					
Finished aluminum	EA	6.667	3,000.00	540.00	3,540.00
Bronze	EA	6.667	4,040.00	540.00	4,580.00
Locked receiving mail box					
Finished aluminum	EA	4.000	1,320.00	330.00	1,650.00
Bronze	EA	4.000	2,570.00	330.00	2,900.00
Commercial postal accessories for mail chutes					
Letter slot, brass	EA	1.333	120.00	110.00	230.00
Bulk mail slot, brass	EA	1.333	260.00	110.00	370.00
Mail boxes					
Residential postal accessories					
Letter slot	EA	0.400	99.00	32.50	131.50
Rural letter box	EA	1.000	190.00	82.00	272.00
Apartment house, keyed, 3.5" x 4.5" x 16"	EA	0.267	180.00	21.75	201.75

	Unit	Man-Hrs	Material	Labor	Total
10550.01 POSTAL SPECIALTIES (Cont.)					
Residential postal accessories					
Ranch style	EA	0.400	190.00	32.50	222.50
Commercial postal accessories					
Letter box, with combination lock	EA	0.286	140.00	23.25	163.25
Key lock	EA	0.286	150.00	23.25	173.25
Mail box, aluminum w/glass front, 4x5					
Horizontal rear load	EA	0.229	230.00	18.75	248.75
Vertical front load	EA	0.229	130.00	18.75	148.75
10570.01 WARDROBE SPECIALTIES					
WARDROBE SPECIALTIES					
Hospital wardrobe units, 24" x 24" x 76", with door					
Baked enameled steel	EA	4.444	3,250.00	360.00	3,610.00
Hardwood	EA	4.444	1,740.00	360.00	2,100.00
Stainless steel	EA	4.444	5,430.00	360.00	5,790.00
Plastic laminated	EA	4.444	1,960.00	360.00	2,320.00
Dormitory wardrobe units, 24" x 76", with door					
Hardwood	EA	4.444	1,810.00	360.00	2,170.00
Plastic laminated	EA	4.444	1,640.00	360.00	2,000.00
Hat and coat rack					
Single tier					
Baked enameled steel	LF	0.200	210.00	16.25	226.25
Stainless steel	LF	0.200	230.00	16.25	246.25
Aluminum	LF	0.200	220.00	16.25	236.25
Double tier					
Baked enameled steel	LF	0.229	390.00	18.75	408.75
Stainless steel	LF	0.229	530.00	18.75	548.75
Aluminum	LF	0.229	450.00	18.75	468.75
10572.30 SHELVING					
SHELVING					
Shelving, enamel, closed side and back, 12" x 36"					
5 shelves	EA	1.333	320.00	110.00	430.00
8 shelves	EA	1.778	350.00	140.00	490.00
Open					
5 shelves	EA	1.333	160.00	110.00	270.00
8 shelves	EA	1.778	180.00	140.00	320.00
Metal storage shelving, baked enamel					
7 shelf unit, 72" or 84" high					
10" shelf	LF	0.800	46.00	65.00	111.00
12" shelf	LF	0.842	51.00	69.00	120.00
15" shelf	LF	0.889	88.00	72.00	160.00
18" shelf	LF	0.941	88.00	77.00	165.00
24" shelf	LF	1.000	110.00	82.00	192.00
30" shelf	LF	1.067	100.00	87.00	187.00
36" shelf	LF	1.143	120.00	93.00	213.00
4 shelf unit, 40" high					
10" shelf	LF	0.667	63.00	54.00	117.00
12" shelf	LF	0.727	68.00	59.00	127.00
15" shelf	LF	0.800	82.00	65.00	147.00
18" shelf	LF	0.842	93.00	69.00	162.00
24" shelf	LF	0.889	140.00	72.00	212.00
3 shelf unit, 32" high					
10" shelf	LF	0.400	54.00	32.50	86.50
12" shelf	LF	0.421	54.00	34.25	88.25
15" shelf	LF	0.444	59.00	36.25	95.25
18" shelf	LF	0.471	62.00	38.25	100.25
24" shelf	LF	0.500	68.00	40.75	108.75
Single shelf unit, attached to masonry					
10" shelf	LF	0.133	19.00	10.75	29.75
12" shelf	LF	0.145	21.00	11.75	32.75
15" shelf	LF	0.154	21.75	12.50	34.25
18" shelf	LF	0.163	24.50	13.25	37.75
24" shelf	LF	0.174	29.75	14.25	44.00

© 2020 BNi Publications, Inc.

	Unit	Man-Hrs	Material	Labor	Total
10572.30 SHELVING (Cont.)					
Metal storage shelving, baked enamel					
For stainless steel, add to material, 120%					
For attachment to gypsum board, add to labor, 50%					
Built-in wood shelves					
Posts and trimmed plywood	LF	0.114	4.94	9.32	14.26
Solid clear pine	LF	0.123	7.79	10.00	17.79
Closet shelf, pine with rod	LF	0.123	5.28	10.00	15.28
For lumber edge band, add to material	LF				2.70
For prefinished shelves, add to material, 225%					
10750.01 FLAGPOLES					
FLAGPOLES					
Installed in concrete base					
Fiberglass					
25' high	EA	5.333	1,670.00	430.00	2,100.00
50' high	EA	13.333	4,410.00	1,090.00	5,500.00
Aluminum					
25' high	EA	5.333	1,620.00	430.00	2,050.00
50' high	EA	13.333	3,200.00	1,090.00	4,290.00
Bonderized steel					
25' high	EA	6.154	1,810.00	500.00	2,310.00
50' high	EA	16.000	3,620.00	1,300.00	4,920.00
Freestanding tapered, fiberglass					
30' high	EA	5.714	1,990.00	470.00	2,460.00
40' high	EA	7.273	2,580.00	590.00	3,170.00
50' high	EA	8.000	6,580.00	650.00	7,230.00
60' high	EA	9.412	7,030.00	770.00	7,800.00
Wall mounted, with collar, brushed aluminum finish					
15' long	EA	4.000	1,540.00	330.00	1,870.00
18' long	EA	4.000	1,740.00	330.00	2,070.00
20' long	EA	4.211	1,900.00	340.00	2,240.00
24' long	EA	4.706	2,040.00	380.00	2,420.00
Outrigger, wall, including base					
10' long	EA	5.333	1,560.00	430.00	1,990.00
20' long	EA	6.667	2,060.00	540.00	2,600.00
10810.01 PEST CONTROL					
PEST CONTROL					
Termite control					
Under slab spraying					
Minimum	SF	0.002	1.24	0.12	1.36
Average	SF	0.004	1.24	0.25	1.49
Maximum	SF	0.008	1.76	0.51	2.27

	Unit	Man-Hrs	Material	Labor	Total
11110.01 SPECIAL SYSTEMS					
SPECIAL SYSTEMS					
Air compressor, air cooled, two stage					
5.0 cfm, 175 psi	EA	16.000	2,840.00	1,430.00	4,270.00
10 cfm, 175 psi	EA	17.778	3,470.00	1,590.00	5,060.00
20 cfm, 175 psi	EA	19.048	4,780.00	1,700.00	6,480.00
50 cfm, 125 psi	EA	21.053	6,970.00	1,880.00	8,850.00
80 cfm, 125 psi	EA	22.857	9,980.00	2,040.00	12,020.00
Single stage, 125 psi					
1.0 cfm	EA	11.429	2,740.00	1,020.00	3,760.00
1.5 cfm	EA	11.429	2,790.00	1,020.00	3,810.00
2.0 cfm	EA	11.429	2,860.00	1,020.00	3,880.00
Automotive, hose reel, air and water, 50' hose	EA	6.667	1,280.00	600.00	1,880.00
Lube equipment, 3 reel, with pumps	EA	32.000	6,680.00	2,860.00	9,540.00
Tire changer					
Truck	EA	11.429	15,150.00	1,020.00	16,170.00
Passenger car	EA	6.154	3,580.00	550.00	4,130.00
Air hose reel, includes 50' hose	EA	6.154	950.00	550.00	1,500.00
Hose reel, 5 reel, motor oil, gear oil, lube, air & water	EA	32.000	8,840.00	2,860.00	11,700.00
Water hose reel, 50' hose	EA	6.154	950.00	550.00	1,500.00
Pump, for motor or gear oil, fits 55 gal drum	EA	0.800	1,240.00	72.00	1,312.00
For chassis lube	EA	0.800	2,020.00	72.00	2,092.00
Fuel dispensing pump, lighted dial, one product					
One hose	EA	6.667	4,410.00	600.00	5,010.00
Two hose	EA	6.667	7,780.00	600.00	8,380.00
Two products, two hose	EA	6.667	8,200.00	600.00	8,800.00
11130.01 LOADING DOCK EQUIPMENT					
LOADING DOCK EQUIPMENT					
Dock leveler, 10 ton capacity					
6' x 8'	EA	8.000	5,860.00	650.00	6,510.00
7' x 8'	EA	8.000	6,730.00	650.00	7,380.00
Bumpers, laminated rubber					
4-1/2" thick					
6" x 14"	EA	0.160	72.00	13.00	85.00
6" x 36"	EA	0.178	140.00	14.50	154.50
10" x 14"	EA	0.200	96.00	16.25	112.25
10" x 24"	EA	0.229	140.00	18.75	158.75
10" x 36"	EA	0.267	200.00	21.75	221.75
12" x 14"	EA	0.211	120.00	17.25	137.25
12" x 24"	EA	0.250	170.00	20.50	190.50
12" x 36"	EA	0.296	250.00	24.25	274.25
6" thick					
10" x 14"	EA	0.229	110.00	18.75	128.75
10" x 24"	EA	0.276	120.00	22.50	142.50
10" x 36"	EA	0.400	260.00	32.50	292.50
Extruded rubber bumpers					
T-section, 22" x 22" x 3"	EA	0.160	170.00	13.00	183.00
Molded rubber bumpers					
24" x 12" x 3" thick	EA	0.400	95.00	32.50	127.50
Door seal, 12" x 12", vinyl covered	LF	0.200	58.00	16.25	74.25
Dock boards, heavy duty, 5' x 5'					
5000 lb					
Minimum	EA	6.667	1,380.00	540.00	1,920.00
Maximum	EA	6.667	1,520.00	540.00	2,060.00
9000 lb					
Minimum	EA	6.667	1,590.00	540.00	2,130.00
Maximum	EA	7.273	1,910.00	590.00	2,500.00
15,000 lb	EA	7.273	2,160.00	590.00	2,750.00
Truck shelters					
Minimum	EA	6.154	1,220.00	500.00	1,720.00
Maximum	EA	11.429	2,030.00	930.00	2,960.00

© 2020 BNi Publications, Inc.

	Unit	Man-Hrs	Material	Labor	Total
11150.01 SECURITY EQUIPMENT					
SECURITY EQUIPMENT					
Bulletproof teller window					
4' x 4'	EA	13.333	2,660.00	1,090.00	3,750.00
5' x 4'	EA	16.000	3,430.00	1,300.00	4,730.00
Bulletproof partitions					
Up to 12' high, 2.5" thick	SF	0.053	230.00	4.34	234.34
Counter for banks					
Minimum	LF	1.600	940.00	130.00	1,070.00
Maximum	LF	2.667	4,200.00	220.00	4,420.00
Drive-up window					
Minimum	EA	11.429	5,850.00	930.00	6,780.00
Maximum	EA	26.667	6,330.00	2,170.00	8,500.00
Night depository					
Minimum	EA	11.429	10,960.00	930.00	11,890.00
Maximum	EA	26.667	15,580.00	2,170.00	17,750.00
Office safes, 30" x 20" x 20", 1 hr rating	EA	2.000	4,260.00	160.00	4,420.00
30" x 16" x 15", 2 hr rating	EA	1.600	2,180.00	130.00	2,310.00
30" x 28" x 20", H&G rating	EA	1.000	5,050.00	82.00	5,132.00
Service windows, pass through painted steel					
24" x 36"	EA	8.000	3,670.00	650.00	4,320.00
48" x 40"	EA	10.000	5,720.00	820.00	6,540.00
72" x 40"	EA	16.000	7,190.00	1,300.00	8,490.00
Special doors and windows					
3' x 7' bulletproof door with frame	EA	11.429	7,310.00	930.00	8,240.00
12" x 12" vision panel	EA	5.714	4,240.00	470.00	4,710.00
Surveillance system					
Minimum	EA	16.000	7,240.00	1,300.00	8,540.00
Maximum	EA	80.000	13,090.00	6,520.00	19,610.00
Vault door, 3' wide, 6'6" high					
3-1/2" thick	EA	100.000	4,710.00	8,150.00	12,860.00
7" thick	EA	133.333	7,550.00	10,870.00	18,420.00
10" thick	EA	160.000	9,430.00	13,050.00	22,480.00
Insulated vault door					
2 hr rating					
32" wide	EA	8.000	4,710.00	650.00	5,360.00
40" wide	EA	8.421	5,240.00	690.00	5,930.00
4 hr rating					
32" wide	EA	8.889	5,210.00	720.00	5,930.00
40" wide	EA	10.000	6,070.00	820.00	6,890.00
6 hr rating					
32" wide	EA	8.889	6,000.00	720.00	6,720.00
40" wide	EA	10.000	7,010.00	820.00	7,830.00
Insulated file room door					
1 hr rating					
32" wide	EA	8.000	4,640.00	650.00	5,290.00
40" wide	EA	8.889	5,160.00	720.00	5,880.00
11160.01 VAULTS					
VAULTS					
Floor safes					
Class C					
1.0 cf	EA	0.667	930.00	54.00	984.00
1.3 cf	EA	1.000	1,030.00	82.00	1,112.00
1.9 cf	EA	1.333	1,350.00	110.00	1,460.00
5.2 cf	EA	1.333	2,760.00	110.00	2,870.00
11213.30 CHECKROOM EQUIPMENT					
CHECKROOM EQUIPMENT					
Motorized checkroom equipment					
No shelf system, 6'4" height					
7'6" length	EA	8.000	5,510.00	650.00	6,160.00
14'6" length	EA	8.000	5,580.00	650.00	6,230.00
28' length	EA	8.000	6,720.00	650.00	7,370.00
One shelf, 6'8" height					
7'6" length	EA	8.000	6,760.00	650.00	7,410.00
14'6" length	EA	8.000	6,940.00	650.00	7,590.00

	Unit	Man-Hrs	Material	Labor	Total
11213.30 CHECKROOM EQUIPMENT (Cont.)					
One shelf, 6'8" height					
28' length	EA	8.000	8,340.00	650.00	8,990.00
Two shelves, 7'5" height					
7'6" length	EA	8.000	8,300.00	650.00	8,950.00
14'6" length	EA	8.000	10,490.00	650.00	11,140.00
28' length	EA	8.000	10,700.00	650.00	11,350.00
Three shelves, 8' height					
7'6" length	EA	16.000	8,490.00	1,300.00	9,790.00
14'6" length	EA	16.000	10,690.00	1,300.00	11,990.00
28' length	EA	16.000	10,790.00	1,300.00	12,090.00
Four shelves, 8'7" height					
7'6" length	EA	16.000	8,580.00	1,300.00	9,880.00
14'6" length	EA	16.000	10,950.00	1,300.00	12,250.00
28' length	EA	16.000	11,200.00	1,300.00	12,500.00
11230.01 LAUNDRY EQUIPMENT					
LAUNDRY EQUIPMENT					
High capacity, heavy duty					
Washer extractors					
135 lb					
Standard	EA	6.667	37,840.00	540.00	38,380.00
Pass through	EA	6.667	43,480.00	540.00	44,020.00
200 lb					
Standard	EA	6.667	46,470.00	540.00	47,010.00
Pass through	EA	6.667	56,430.00	540.00	56,970.00
110 lb dryer	EA	6.667	14,230.00	540.00	14,770.00
Hand operated presser	EA	8.889	10,210.00	720.00	10,930.00
Mushroom press	EA	8.889	6,380.00	720.00	7,100.00
Spreader feeders					
2 station	EA	8.889	72,660.00	720.00	73,380.00
4 station	EA	16.000	85,870.00	1,300.00	87,170.00
Delivery carts					
12 bushel	EA	0.100	370.00	8.15	378.15
16 bushel	EA	0.107	460.00	8.69	468.69
18 bushel	EA	0.114	570.00	9.32	579.32
30 bushel	EA	0.133	830.00	10.75	840.75
40 bushel	EA	0.160	1,000.00	13.00	1,013.00
Low capacity					
Pressers					
Air operated	EA	3.200	7,930.00	260.00	8,190.00
Hand operated	EA	3.200	6,280.00	260.00	6,540.00
Extractor, low capacity	EA	3.200	5,720.00	260.00	5,980.00
Ironer, 48"	EA	1.600	4,320.00	130.00	4,450.00
Coin washers					
10 lb capacity	EA	1.600	2,100.00	130.00	2,230.00
20 lb capacity	EA	1.600	4,950.00	130.00	5,080.00
Coin dryer	EA	1.000	1,000.00	82.00	1,082.00
Coin dry cleaner, 20 lb	EA	3.200	4,320.00	260.00	4,580.00
11240.01 MAINTENANCE EQUIPMENT					
MAINTENANCE EQUIPMENT					
Vacuum cleaning system					
3 valves					
1.5 hp	EA	8.889	1,010.00	720.00	1,730.00
2.5 hp	EA	11.429	1,220.00	930.00	2,150.00
5 valves	EA	16.000	1,900.00	1,300.00	3,200.00
7 valves	EA	20.000	2,530.00	1,630.00	4,160.00
11260.01 FOOD SERVICE EQUIPMENT					
FOOD SERVICE EQUIPMENT					
Unit kitchens					
30" compact kitchen					
Refrigerator, with range, sink	EA	4.000	1,620.00	330.00	1,950.00
Sink only	EA	2.667	2,070.00	220.00	2,290.00
Range only	EA	2.000	1,680.00	170.00	1,850.00

© 2020 BNi Publications, Inc.

11260.01 FOOD SERVICE EQUIPMENT (Cont.)

	Unit	Man-Hrs	Material	Labor	Total
30" compact kitchen					
Cabinet for upper wall section	EA	1.143	420.00	95.00	515.00
Stainless shield, for rear wall	EA	0.320	170.00	26.50	196.50
Side wall	EA	0.320	120.00	26.50	146.50
42" compact kitchen					
Refrigerator with range, sink	EA	4.444	1,980.00	370.00	2,350.00
Sink only	EA	4.000	1,080.00	330.00	1,410.00
Cabinet for upper wall section	EA	1.333	840.00	110.00	950.00
Stainless shield, for rear wall	EA	0.333	670.00	27.75	697.75
Side wall	EA	0.333	190.00	27.75	217.75
54" compact kitchen					
Refrigerator, oven, range, sink	EA	5.714	2,650.00	470.00	3,120.00
Cabinet for upper wall section	EA	1.600	1,080.00	130.00	1,210.00
Stainless shield, for					
Rear wall	EA	0.364	670.00	30.25	700.25
Side wall	EA	0.364	190.00	30.25	220.25
60" compact kitchen					
Refrigerator, oven, range, sink	EA	5.714	3,600.00	470.00	4,070.00
Cabinet for upper wall section	EA	1.600	250.00	130.00	380.00
Stainless shield, for					
Rear wall	EA	0.364	800.00	30.25	830.25
Side wall	EA	0.364	200.00	30.25	230.25
72" compact kitchen					
Refrigerator, oven, range, sink	EA	6.667	3,810.00	550.00	4,360.00
Cabinet for upper wall section	EA	1.600	260.00	130.00	390.00
Stainless shield for					
Rear wall	EA	0.400	870.00	33.25	903.25
Side wall	EA	0.400	200.00	33.25	233.25
Bake oven					
Single deck					
Minimum	EA	1.000	3,830.00	83.00	3,913.00
Maximum	EA	2.000	7,330.00	170.00	7,500.00
Double deck					
Minimum	EA	1.333	6,830.00	110.00	6,940.00
Maximum	EA	2.000	21,340.00	170.00	21,510.00
Triple deck					
Minimum	EA	1.333	24,220.00	110.00	24,330.00
Maximum	EA	2.667	43,210.00	220.00	43,430.00
Convection type oven, electric, 40" x 45" x 57"					
Minimum	EA	1.000	3,780.00	83.00	3,863.00
Maximum	EA	2.000	6,650.00	170.00	6,820.00
Broiler, without oven, 69" x 26" x 39"					
Minimum	EA	1.000	6,020.00	83.00	6,103.00
Maximum	EA	1.333	9,470.00	110.00	9,580.00
Coffee urns, 10 gallons					
Minimum	EA	2.667	4,580.00	220.00	4,800.00
Maximum	EA	4.000	5,180.00	330.00	5,510.00
Fryer, with submerger					
Single					
Minimum	EA	1.600	1,880.00	130.00	2,010.00
Maximum	EA	2.667	5,160.00	220.00	5,380.00
Double					
Minimum	EA	2.000	3,110.00	170.00	3,280.00
Maximum	EA	2.667	16,700.00	220.00	16,920.00
Griddle, counter					
3' long					
Minimum	EA	1.333	2,570.00	110.00	2,680.00
Maximum	EA	1.600	5,300.00	130.00	5,430.00
5' long					
Minimum	EA	2.000	5,580.00	170.00	5,750.00
Maximum	EA	2.667	12,850.00	220.00	13,070.00
Kettles, steam, jacketed					
20 gallons					
Minimum	EA	2.000	12,270.00	170.00	12,440.00
Maximum	EA	4.000	13,410.00	330.00	13,740.00

DIVISION 11 EQUIPMENT

	Unit	Man-Hrs	Material	Labor	Total
11260.01 FOOD SERVICE EQUIPMENT (Cont.)					
Kettles, steam, jacketed					
40 gallons					
Minimum	EA	2.000	18,820.00	170.00	18,990.00
Maximum	EA	4.000	27,180.00	330.00	27,510.00
60 gallons					
Minimum	EA	2.000	20,690.00	170.00	20,860.00
Maximum	EA	4.000	29,270.00	330.00	29,600.00
Range					
Heavy duty, single oven, open top					
Minimum	EA	1.000	7,910.00	83.00	7,993.00
Maximum	EA	2.667	16,650.00	220.00	16,870.00
Fry top					
Minimum	EA	1.000	8,080.00	83.00	8,163.00
Maximum	EA	2.667	11,320.00	220.00	11,540.00
Steamers, electric					
27 kw					
Minimum	EA	2.000	14,360.00	170.00	14,530.00
Maximum	EA	2.667	26,240.00	220.00	26,460.00
18 kw					
Minimum	EA	2.000	7,900.00	170.00	8,070.00
Maximum	EA	2.667	18,540.00	220.00	18,760.00
Dishwasher, rack type					
Single tank, 190 racks/hr	EA	4.000	21,050.00	330.00	21,380.00
Double tank					
234 racks/hr	EA	4.444	43,460.00	370.00	43,830.00
265 racks/hr	EA	5.333	51,950.00	440.00	52,390.00
Dishwasher, automatic 100 meals/hr	EA	2.667	16,900.00	220.00	17,120.00
Disposals					
100 gal/hr	EA	2.667	1,410.00	220.00	1,630.00
120 gal/hr	EA	2.759	1,640.00	230.00	1,870.00
250 gal/hr	EA	2.857	1,930.00	240.00	2,170.00
Exhaust hood for dishwasher, gutter 4 sides					
4'x4'x2'	EA	2.963	3,420.00	250.00	3,670.00
4'x7'x2'	EA	3.200	4,630.00	270.00	4,900.00
Food preparation machines					
Vertical cutter mixers					
25 quart	EA	2.667	13,940.00	220.00	14,160.00
40 quart	EA	2.667	18,000.00	220.00	18,220.00
80 quart	EA	4.000	23,000.00	330.00	23,330.00
130 quart	EA	6.667	30,660.00	550.00	31,210.00
Choppers					
5 lb	EA	2.000	3,890.00	170.00	4,060.00
16 lb	EA	2.667	6,130.00	220.00	6,350.00
40 lb	EA	4.000	7,710.00	330.00	8,040.00
Mixers, floor models					
20 quart	EA	1.000	4,290.00	83.00	4,373.00
60 quart	EA	1.000	21,320.00	83.00	21,403.00
80 quart	EA	1.143	34,840.00	95.00	34,935.00
140 quart	EA	1.600	41,570.00	130.00	41,700.00
Ice cube maker					
50 lb per day					
Minimum	EA	8.000	2,640.00	660.00	3,300.00
Maximum	EA	8.000	3,900.00	660.00	4,560.00
500 lb per day					
Minimum	EA	13.333	6,270.00	1,110.00	7,380.00
Maximum	EA	13.333	7,410.00	1,110.00	8,520.00
Ice flakers					
300 lb per day	EA	8.000	4,600.00	660.00	5,260.00
600 lb per day	EA	13.333	7,540.00	1,110.00	8,650.00
1000 lb per day	EA	17.778	8,600.00	1,480.00	10,080.00
2000 lb per day	EA	20.000	16,590.00	1,660.00	18,250.00
Refrigerated cases					
Dairy products					
Multi-deck type	LF	0.533	1,490.00	44.25	1,534.25
For rear sliding doors, add	LF				280.00

© 2020 BNi Publications, Inc.

	Unit	Man-Hrs	Material	Labor	Total
11260.01 FOOD SERVICE EQUIPMENT (Cont.)					
Refrigerated cases					
Delicatessen case, service deli					
Single deck	LF	4.000	1,060.00	330.00	1,390.00
Multi-deck	LF	5.000	1,210.00	420.00	1,630.00
Meat case					
Single deck	LF	4.706	910.00	390.00	1,300.00
Multi-deck	LF	5.000	1,070.00	420.00	1,490.00
Produce case					
Single deck	LF	4.706	1,060.00	390.00	1,450.00
Multi-deck	LF	5.000	1,130.00	420.00	1,550.00
Bottle coolers					
6' long					
Minimum	EA	16.000	3,010.00	1,330.00	4,340.00
Maximum	EA	16.000	4,460.00	1,330.00	5,790.00
10' long					
Minimum	EA	26.667	3,900.00	2,210.00	6,110.00
Maximum	EA	26.667	7,670.00	2,210.00	9,880.00
Frozen food cases					
Chest type	LF	4.706	810.00	390.00	1,200.00
Reach-in, glass door	LF	5.000	1,120.00	420.00	1,540.00
Island case, single	LF	4.706	1,000.00	390.00	1,390.00
Multi-deck	LF	5.000	1,590.00	420.00	2,010.00
Ice storage bins					
500 lb capacity	EA	11.429	1,680.00	950.00	2,630.00
1000 lb capacity	EA	22.857	2,510.00	1,900.00	4,410.00
11270.01 DARKROOM EQUIPMENT					
DARKROOM EQUIPMENT					
Dryers					
36" x 25" x 68"	EA	4.000	11,680.00	360.00	12,040.00
48" x 25" x 68"	EA	4.000	12,070.00	360.00	12,430.00
Processors, film					
Black and white	EA	4.000	18,620.00	360.00	18,980.00
Color negatives	EA	4.000	21,090.00	360.00	21,450.00
Prints	EA	4.000	24,180.00	360.00	24,540.00
Transparencies	EA	4.000	26,530.00	360.00	26,890.00
Sinks with cabinet and/or stand					
5" sink with stand					
24" x 48"	EA	2.000	1,040.00	180.00	1,220.00
32" x 64"	EA	2.667	1,600.00	240.00	1,840.00
38" x 52"	EA	2.667	2,250.00	240.00	2,490.00
42" x 132"	EA	4.000	3,360.00	360.00	3,720.00
48" x 52"	EA	4.000	2,580.00	360.00	2,940.00
5" sink with cabinet					
24" x 48"	EA	2.000	2,150.00	180.00	2,330.00
32" x 64"	EA	2.667	2,690.00	240.00	2,930.00
38" x 52"	EA	2.667	2,760.00	240.00	3,000.00
42" x 132"	EA	4.000	4,490.00	360.00	4,850.00
48" x 52"	EA	4.000	3,760.00	360.00	4,120.00
10" sink with stand					
24" x 48"	EA	2.000	1,780.00	180.00	1,960.00
32" x 64"	EA	2.667	1,880.00	240.00	2,120.00
38" x 52"	EA	2.667	2,550.00	240.00	2,790.00
10" sink with cabinet					
24" x 48"	EA	2.000	1,950.00	180.00	2,130.00
38" x 52"	EA	2.667	3,610.00	240.00	3,850.00
11310.01 RESIDENTIAL EQUIPMENT					
RESIDENTIAL EQUIPMENT					
Compactor, 4 to 1 compaction	EA	2.000	1,680.00	170.00	1,850.00
Dishwasher, built-in					
2 cycles	EA	4.000	830.00	330.00	1,160.00
4 or more cycles	EA	4.000	2,230.00	330.00	2,560.00
Disposal					
Garbage disposer	EA	2.667	230.00	220.00	450.00

11310.01 RESIDENTIAL EQUIPMENT (Cont.)

	Unit	Man-Hrs	Material	Labor	Total
Heaters, electric, built-in					
Ceiling type	EA	2.667	470.00	220.00	690.00
Wall type					
Minimum	EA	2.000	240.00	170.00	410.00
Maximum	EA	2.667	820.00	220.00	1,040.00
Hood for range, 2-speed, vented					
30" wide	EA	2.667	650.00	220.00	870.00
42" wide	EA	2.667	1,200.00	220.00	1,420.00
Ice maker, automatic					
30 lb per day	EA	1.143	2,200.00	95.00	2,295.00
50 lb per day	EA	4.000	2,790.00	330.00	3,120.00
Folding access stairs, disappearing metal stair					
8' long	EA	1.143	1,150.00	95.00	1,245.00
11' long	EA	1.143	1,200.00	95.00	1,295.00
12' long	EA	1.143	1,280.00	95.00	1,375.00
Wood frame, wood stair					
22" x 54" x 8'9" long	EA	0.800	220.00	66.00	286.00
25" x 54" x 10' long	EA	0.800	270.00	66.00	336.00
Ranges, electric					
Built-in, 30", 1 oven	EA	2.667	2,410.00	220.00	2,630.00
2 oven	EA	2.667	2,790.00	220.00	3,010.00
Countertop, 4 burner, standard	EA	2.000	1,390.00	170.00	1,560.00
With grill	EA	2.000	3,480.00	170.00	3,650.00
Freestanding, 21", 1 oven	EA	2.667	1,250.00	220.00	1,470.00
30", 1 oven	EA	1.600	2,440.00	130.00	2,570.00
2 oven	EA	1.600	3,970.00	130.00	4,100.00
Water softener					
30 grains per gallon	EA	2.667	1,360.00	220.00	1,580.00
70 grains per gallon	EA	4.000	1,720.00	330.00	2,050.00

11530.01 LABORATORY EQUIPMENT

	Unit	Man-Hrs	Material	Labor	Total
LABORATORY EQUIPMENT					
Cabinets, base					
Minimum	LF	0.667	510.00	54.00	564.00
Maximum	LF	0.667	930.00	54.00	984.00
Full storage, 7' high					
Minimum	LF	0.667	490.00	54.00	544.00
Maximum	LF	0.667	930.00	54.00	984.00
Wall					
Minimum	LF	0.800	180.00	65.00	245.00
Maximum	LF	0.800	310.00	65.00	375.00
Countertops					
Minimum	SF	0.100	76.00	8.15	84.15
Average	SF	0.114	89.00	9.32	98.32
Maximum	SF	0.133	100.00	10.75	110.75
Tables					
Open underneath	SF	0.400	160.00	32.50	192.50
Doors underneath	SF	0.500	550.00	40.75	590.75
Medical laboratory equipment					
Analyzer					
Chloride	EA	0.400	6,100.00	33.25	6,133.25
Blood	EA	0.667	33,540.00	55.00	33,595.00
Bath, water, utility, countertop unit	EA	0.800	1,260.00	66.00	1,326.00
Hot plate, lab, countertop	EA	0.727	480.00	60.00	540.00
Stirrer	EA	0.727	580.00	60.00	640.00
Incubator, anaerobic, 23x23x36"	EA	4.000	10,340.00	330.00	10,670.00
Dry heat bath	EA	1.333	1,120.00	110.00	1,230.00
Incinerator, for sterilizing	EA	0.080	770.00	6.64	776.64
Meter, serum protein	EA	0.100	1,190.00	8.30	1,198.30
pH analog, general purpose	EA	0.114	1,280.00	9.48	1,289.48
Refrigerator, blood bank	EA	1.333	9,780.00	110.00	9,890.00
5.4 cf, undercounter type	EA	1.333	6,640.00	110.00	6,750.00
Refrigerator/freezer, 4.4 cf, undercounter type	EA	1.333	1,260.00	110.00	1,370.00
Sealer, impulse, free standing, 20x12x4"	EA	0.267	700.00	22.25	722.25

© 2020 BNi Publications, Inc.

	Unit	Man-Hrs	Material	Labor	Total
11530.01 LABORATORY EQUIPMENT (Cont.)					
Medical laboratory equipment					
Timer, electric, 1-60 minutes, bench or wall mounted	EA	0.444	270.00	37.00	307.00
Glassware washer-dryer, undercounter	EA	10.000	11,580.00	830.00	12,410.00
Balance, torsion suspension, tabletop, 4.5 lb capacity	EA	0.444	1,520.00	37.00	1,557.00
Binocular microscope, with in-base illuminator	EA	0.308	4,650.00	25.50	4,675.50
Centrifuge, table model, 19x16x13"	EA	0.320	1,780.00	26.50	1,806.50
Clinical model, with four place head	EA	0.178	1,930.00	14.75	1,944.75
11570.01 INDUSTRIAL EQUIPMENT					
INDUSTRIAL EQUIPMENT					
Vehicular paint spray booth, solid back, 14'4" x 9'6"					
24' deep	EA	8.000	9,610.00	650.00	10,260.00
26'6" deep	EA	8.000	10,980.00	650.00	11,630.00
28'6" deep	EA	8.000	12,680.00	650.00	13,330.00
Drive through, 14'9" x 9'6"					
24' deep	EA	8.000	10,230.00	650.00	10,880.00
26'6" deep	EA	8.000	12,330.00	650.00	12,980.00
28'6" deep	EA	8.000	14,070.00	650.00	14,720.00
Water wash, paint spray booth					
5' x 11'2" x 10'8"	EA	8.000	6,940.00	650.00	7,590.00
6' x 11'2" x 10'8"	EA	8.000	7,260.00	650.00	7,910.00
8' x 11'2" x 10'8"	EA	8.000	7,850.00	650.00	8,500.00
10' x 11'2" x 11'2"	EA	8.000	8,900.00	650.00	9,550.00
12' x 12'2" x 11'2"	EA	8.000	10,340.00	650.00	10,990.00
14' x 12'2" x 11'2"	EA	8.000	11,700.00	650.00	12,350.00
16' x 12'2" x 11'2"	EA	8.000	14,250.00	650.00	14,900.00
20' x 12'2" x 11'2"	EA	8.000	17,290.00	650.00	17,940.00
Dry type spray booth, with paint arrestors					
5'4" x 7'2" x 6'8"	EA	8.000	4,190.00	650.00	4,840.00
6'4" x 7'2" x 6'8"	EA	8.000	5,450.00	650.00	6,100.00
8'4" x 7'2" x 9'2"	EA	8.000	6,180.00	650.00	6,830.00
10'4" x 7'2" x 9'2"	EA	8.000	7,270.00	650.00	7,920.00
12'4" x 7'6" x 9'2"	EA	8.000	7,230.00	650.00	7,880.00
14'4" x 7'6" x 9'8"	EA	8.000	9,780.00	650.00	10,430.00
16'4" x 7'7" x 9'8"	EA	8.000	11,180.00	650.00	11,830.00
20'4" x 7'7" x 10'8"	EA	8.000	12,720.00	650.00	13,370.00
Air compressor, electric					
1 hp					
115 volt	EA	5.333	1,600.00	430.00	2,030.00
7.5 hp					
115 volt	EA	8.000	4,750.00	650.00	5,400.00
230 volt	EA	8.000	5,940.00	650.00	6,590.00
Hydraulic lifts					
8,000 lb capacity	EA	20.000	3,280.00	1,630.00	4,910.00
11,000 lb capacity	EA	32.000	5,870.00	2,610.00	8,480.00
24,000 lb capacity	EA	53.333	10,340.00	4,350.00	14,690.00
Power tools					
Band saws					
10"	EA	0.667	1,400.00	54.00	1,454.00
14"	EA	0.800	2,100.00	65.00	2,165.00
Motorized shaper	EA	0.615	1,120.00	50.00	1,170.00
Motorized lathe	EA	0.667	1,330.00	54.00	1,384.00
Bench saws					
9" saw	EA	0.533	3,490.00	43.50	3,533.50
10" saw	EA	0.571	4,190.00	46.50	4,236.50
12" saw	EA	0.667	5,160.00	54.00	5,214.00
Electric grinders					
1/3 hp	EA	0.320	540.00	26.00	566.00
1/2 hp	EA	0.348	560.00	28.25	588.25
3/4 hp	EA	0.348	940.00	28.25	968.25
11610.01 THEATER EQUIPMENT					
THEATER EQUIPMENT					
Roll out stage, steel frame, wood floor					
Manual	SF	0.050	59.00	4.07	63.07
Electric	SF	0.080	56.00	6.52	62.52

	Unit	Man-Hrs	Material	Labor	Total
11610.01 THEATER EQUIPMENT (Cont.)					
Portable stages					
8" high	SF	0.040	23.00	3.26	26.26
18" high	SF	0.044	26.75	3.62	30.37
36" high	SF	0.047	31.25	3.83	35.08
48" high	SF	0.050	35.00	4.07	39.07
Band risers					
Minimum	SF	0.040	60.00	3.26	63.26
Maximum	SF	0.040	120.00	3.26	123.26
Chairs for risers					
Minimum	EA	0.036	780.00	2.32	782.32
Maximum	EA	0.036	1,250.00	2.32	1,252.32
11660.01 ATHLETIC EQUIPMENT					
ATHLETIC EQUIPMENT					
Basketball backboard					
Fixed	EA	10.000	2,570.00	820.00	3,390.00
Swing-up	EA	16.000	4,100.00	1,300.00	5,400.00
Portable, hydraulic	EA	4.000	20,150.00	330.00	20,480.00
Suspended type, standard	EA	16.000	5,840.00	1,300.00	7,140.00
For glass backboard, add	EA				1,700.00
For electrically operated, add	EA				1,980.00
Bleacher, telescoping, manual					
15 tier, minimum	SEAT	0.160	160.00	13.00	173.00
Maximum	SEAT	0.160	380.00	13.00	393.00
20 tier, minimum	SEAT	0.178	110.00	14.50	124.50
Maximum	SEAT	0.178	330.00	14.50	344.50
30 tier, minimum	SEAT	0.267	87.00	21.75	108.75
Maximum	SEAT	0.267	260.00	21.75	281.75
Boxing ring, elevated, complete, 22' x 22'	EA	114.286	10,750.00	9,320.00	20,070.00
Gym divider curtain					
Minimum	SF	0.011	3.49	0.86	4.35
Maximum	SF	0.011	5.24	0.86	6.10
Scoreboards, single face					
Minimum	EA	8.000	7,420.00	650.00	8,070.00
Maximum	EA	40.000	40,300.00	3,260.00	43,560.00
Parallel bars					
Minimum	EA	8.000	1,540.00	650.00	2,190.00
Maximum	EA	13.333	8,240.00	1,090.00	9,330.00
11660.02 POLICE EQUIPMENT					
POLICE EQUIPMENT					
Firing range equipment, rifle					
3 position	EA	26.667	19,950.00	2,170.00	22,120.00
4 position	EA	40.000	25,560.00	3,260.00	28,820.00
5 position	EA	44.444	31,170.00	3,620.00	34,790.00
6 position	EA	47.059	37,400.00	3,840.00	41,240.00
11682.30 RECREATIONAL COURTS					
RECREATIONAL COURTS					
Walls, galvanized steel					
8' high	LF	0.160	16.00	10.25	26.25
10' high	LF	0.178	18.75	11.25	30.00
12' high	LF	0.211	21.75	13.50	35.25
Vinyl coated					
8' high	LF	0.160	15.25	10.25	25.50
10' high	LF	0.178	18.75	11.25	30.00
12' high	LF	0.211	20.75	13.50	34.25
Gates, galvanized steel					
Single, 3' transom					
3'x7'	EA	4.000	370.00	260.00	630.00
4'x7'	EA	4.571	390.00	290.00	680.00
5'x7'	EA	5.333	540.00	340.00	880.00
6'x7'	EA	6.400	580.00	410.00	990.00
Double, 3' transom					
10'x7'	EA	16.000	900.00	1,020.00	1,920.00
12'x7'	EA	17.778	1,160.00	1,140.00	2,300.00

© 2020 BNi Publications, Inc.

	Unit	Man-Hrs	Material	Labor	Total
11682.30 RECREATIONAL COURTS (Cont.)					
Double, 3' transom					
14'x7'	EA	20.000	1,390.00	1,280.00	2,670.00
Double, no transom					
10'x10'	EA	13.333	980.00	850.00	1,830.00
12'x10'	EA	16.000	1,170.00	1,020.00	2,190.00
14'x10'	EA	17.778	1,340.00	1,140.00	2,480.00
Vinyl coated					
Single, 3' transom					
3'x7'	EA	4.000	730.00	260.00	990.00
4'x7'	EA	4.571	790.00	290.00	1,080.00
5'x7'	EA	5.333	790.00	340.00	1,130.00
6'x7'	EA	6.400	820.00	410.00	1,230.00
Double, 3'					
10'x7'	EA	16.000	2,150.00	1,020.00	3,170.00
12'x7'	EA	17.778	2,210.00	1,140.00	3,350.00
14'x7'	EA	20.000	2,390.00	1,280.00	3,670.00
Double, no transom					
10'x10'	EA	13.333	2,140.00	850.00	2,990.00
12'x10'	EA	16.000	2,180.00	1,020.00	3,200.00
14'x10'	EA	17.778	2,390.00	1,140.00	3,530.00
Baseball backstop, regulation, including material					
Galvanized	EA				8,210.00
Vinyl coated	EA				11,430.00
Softball backstop, regulation, including material					
14' high					
Galvanized	EA				9,350.00
Vinyl coated	EA				14,850.00
18' high					
Galvanized	EA				10,340.00
Vinyl coated	EA				14,950.00
20' high					
Galvanized	EA				12,250.00
Vinyl coated	EA				17,640.00
22' high					
Galvanized	EA				14,160.00
Vinyl coated	EA				20,680.00
24' high					
Galvanized	EA				14,970.00
Vinyl coated	EA				24,620.00
Wire and miscellaneous metal fences					
Chicken wire, post 4' o.c.					
2" mesh					
4' high	LF	0.040	1.95	2.55	4.50
6' high	LF	0.053	2.20	3.40	5.60
Galvanized steel					
12 gauge, 2" by 4" mesh, posts 5' o.c.					
3' high	LF	0.040	3.12	2.55	5.67
5' high	LF	0.050	4.45	3.19	7.64
14 gauge, 1" by 2" mesh, posts 5' o.c.					
3' high	LF	0.040	2.61	2.55	5.16
5' high	LF	0.050	4.25	3.19	7.44
11683.30 RECREATIONAL FACILITIES					
RECREATIONAL FACILITIES					
Bleachers, outdoor, portable, per seat					
10 tiers					
Minimum	EA	0.150	87.00	17.75	104.75
Maximum	EA	0.200	110.00	23.75	133.75
20 tiers					
Minimum	EA	0.141	92.00	16.75	108.75
Maximum	EA	0.185	120.00	22.00	142.00
Grandstands, fixed, wood seat, steel frame					
Per seat, 15 tiers					
Minimum	EA	0.240	75.00	28.50	103.50
Maximum	EA	0.400	130.00	47.50	177.50

	Unit	Man-Hrs	Material	Labor	Total

11683.30 RECREATIONAL FACILITIES (Cont.)

Per seat

30 tiers

	Unit	Man-Hrs	Material	Labor	Total
Minimum	EA	0.218	78.00	26.00	104.00
Maximum	EA	0.343	170.00	40.75	210.75

Seats

Seat backs only

	Unit	Man-Hrs	Material	Labor	Total
Fiberglass	EA	0.080	43.00	5.10	48.10
Steel and wood seat	EA	0.080	62.00	5.10	67.10

Seat restoration, fiberglass on wood

	Unit	Man-Hrs	Material	Labor	Total
Seats	EA	0.160	31.00	10.25	41.25
Plain bench, no backs	EA	0.067	19.00	4.25	23.25

Benches

Park, precast concrete with backs

	Unit	Man-Hrs	Material	Labor	Total
4' long	EA	2.667	1,190.00	170.00	1,360.00
8' long	EA	4.000	2,620.00	260.00	2,880.00

Fiberglass, with backs

	Unit	Man-Hrs	Material	Labor	Total
4' long	EA	2.000	950.00	130.00	1,080.00
8' long	EA	2.667	1,820.00	170.00	1,990.00

Wood, with backs and fiberglass supports

	Unit	Man-Hrs	Material	Labor	Total
4' long	EA	2.000	530.00	130.00	660.00
8' long	EA	2.667	550.00	170.00	720.00

Steel frame, 6' long

	Unit	Man-Hrs	Material	Labor	Total
All steel	EA	2.000	450.00	130.00	580.00
Hardwood boards	EA	2.000	310.00	130.00	440.00
Players bench, steel frame, fir seat, 10' long	EA	2.667	340.00	170.00	510.00

Backstops

Handball or squash court, outdoor

	Unit	Man-Hrs	Material	Labor	Total
Wood	EA				52,860.00
Masonry	EA				39,450.00
Soccer goal posts	PAIR				3,530.00

Running track

	Unit	Man-Hrs	Material	Labor	Total
Gravel and cinders over stone base	SY	0.060	10.75	7.12	17.87
Rubber-cork base resilient pavement	SY	0.480	15.25	57.00	72.25
For colored surfaces, add	SY	0.048	9.62	5.70	15.32
Colored rubberized asphalt	SY	0.600	20.50	71.00	91.50
Artificial resilient mat over asphalt	SY	1.200	48.25	140.00	188.25

Tennis courts

	Unit	Man-Hrs	Material	Labor	Total
Bituminous pavement, 2-1/2" thick	SY	0.150	33.25	17.75	51.00

Colored sealer, acrylic emulsion

	Unit	Man-Hrs	Material	Labor	Total
3 coats	SY	0.053	8.10	3.40	11.50
For 2 color seal coating, add	SY	0.008	1.48	0.51	1.99
For preparing old courts, add	SY	0.005	3.42	0.34	3.76
Net, nylon, 42' long	EA	1.000	470.00	64.00	534.00
Paint markings on asphalt, 2 coats	EA	8.000	180.00	510.00	690.00

Complete court with fence, etc., bituminous

	Unit	Man-Hrs	Material	Labor	Total
Minimum	EA				33,530.00
Average	EA				57,710.00
Maximum	EA				81,900.00

Clay court

	Unit	Man-Hrs	Material	Labor	Total
Minimum	EA				34,900.00
Average	EA				47,570.00
Maximum	EA				72,140.00

Playground equipment

Basketball backboard

	Unit	Man-Hrs	Material	Labor	Total
Minimum	EA	2.000	1,020.00	130.00	1,150.00
Maximum	EA	2.286	1,930.00	150.00	2,080.00
Bike rack, 10' long	EA	1.600	650.00	100.00	750.00
Golf shelter, fiberglass	EA	2.000	3,240.00	130.00	3,370.00

Ground socket for movable posts

	Unit	Man-Hrs	Material	Labor	Total
Minimum	EA	0.500	150.00	32.00	182.00
Maximum	EA	0.500	300.00	32.00	332.00
Horizontal monkey ladder, 14' long	EA	1.333	990.00	85.00	1,075.00
Posts, tether ball	EA	0.400	480.00	25.50	505.50
Multiple purpose, 10' long	EA	0.800	490.00	51.00	541.00

© 2020 BNi Publications, Inc.

	Unit	Man-Hrs	Material	Labor	Total

11683.30 RECREATIONAL FACILITIES (Cont.)

Playground equipment

See-saw, steel

	Unit	Man-Hrs	Material	Labor	Total
Minimum	EA	3.200	1,170.00	200.00	1,370.00
Average	EA	4.000	2,260.00	260.00	2,520.00
Maximum	EA	5.333	3,320.00	340.00	3,660.00

Slide

	Unit	Man-Hrs	Material	Labor	Total
Minimum	EA	6.400	2,260.00	410.00	2,670.00
Maximum	EA	7.273	5,980.00	460.00	6,440.00

Swings, plain seats

8' high

	Unit	Man-Hrs	Material	Labor	Total
Minimum	EA	5.333	1,080.00	340.00	1,420.00
Maximum	EA	6.154	2,050.00	390.00	2,440.00

12' high

	Unit	Man-Hrs	Material	Labor	Total
Minimum	EA	6.154	1,650.00	390.00	2,040.00
Maximum	EA	8.889	2,980.00	570.00	3,550.00

11720.01 MEDICAL EQUIPMENT

MEDICAL EQUIPMENT

Hospital equipment, lights

	Unit	Man-Hrs	Material	Labor	Total
Examination, portable	EA	0.667	2,130.00	55.00	2,185.00

Meters

	Unit	Man-Hrs	Material	Labor	Total
Air flow meter	EA	0.444	110.00	37.00	147.00
Oxygen flow meters	EA	0.333	140.00	27.75	167.75

Racks

	Unit	Man-Hrs	Material	Labor	Total
40 chart, revolving open frame; mobile caddy	EA	0.667	1,470.00	55.00	1,525.00

Scales

	Unit	Man-Hrs	Material	Labor	Total
Clinical, metric with measure rod, 350 lb	EA	0.727	780.00	60.00	840.00

Physical therapy

	Unit	Man-Hrs	Material	Labor	Total
Chair, hydrotherapy	EA	0.133	820.00	10.75	830.75
Diathermy, shortwave, portable, on casters	EA	0.320	3,540.00	26.00	3,566.00
Exercise bicycle, floor standing, 35" x 15"	EA	0.267	3,440.00	21.75	3,461.75
Hydrocollator, 4 pack, portable, 129 x 90 x 160"	EA	0.114	620.00	9.32	629.32
Lamp, infrared, mobile with variable heat control	EA	0.615	830.00	50.00	880.00
Ultraviolet, base mounted	EA	0.615	770.00	50.00	820.00
Mirror, posture training, 27" wide and 72" high	EA	0.200	850.00	16.25	866.25
Parallel bars, adjustable	EA	1.000	3,670.00	82.00	3,752.00
Platform mat 10'x6', 1" thick	EA	0.200	1,180.00	16.25	1,196.25
Pulley, duplex, wall mounted	EA	2.667	2,010.00	220.00	2,230.00
Rack, crutch, wall mounted, 66 x 16 x 13"	EA	0.800	490.00	65.00	555.00
Stimulator, galvanic-faradic, handheld	EA	0.053	430.00	4.34	434.34
Ultrasound stimulator, portable, 13x13x8"	EA	0.067	3,680.00	5.43	3,685.43
Sandbag set, velcro straps, saddle bag type	EA	0.114	190.00	9.32	199.32
Whirlpool, 85 gallon	EA	4.000	7,070.00	330.00	7,400.00
65 gallon capacity	EA	4.000	6,380.00	330.00	6,710.00

Radiology

	Unit	Man-Hrs	Material	Labor	Total
Radiographic table, motor driven tilting table	EA	80.000	62,350.00	6,520.00	68,870.00
Fluoroscope image/tv system	EA	160.000	103,440.00	13,050.00	116,490.00

Processor for washing and drying radiographs

	Unit	Man-Hrs	Material	Labor	Total
Water filter unit, 30" x 48-1/2" x 37-1/2"	EA	13.333	140.00	1,110.00	1,250.00

Base storage cabinets, sectional design

	Unit	Man-Hrs	Material	Labor	Total
With backsplash, 24" deep and 35" high	LF	0.667	710.00	55.00	765.00
Wall storage cabinets	LF	1.000	280.00	83.00	363.00

Steam sterilizers

	Unit	Man-Hrs	Material	Labor	Total
For heat and moisture stable materials	EA	0.800	6,020.00	66.00	6,086.00
For fast drying after sterilization	EA	1.000	7,790.00	83.00	7,873.00
Compact unit	EA	1.000	2,520.00	83.00	2,603.00
Semi-automatic	EA	4.000	2,980.00	330.00	3,310.00

Floor loading

	Unit	Man-Hrs	Material	Labor	Total
Single door	EA	6.667	88,280.00	550.00	88,830.00
Double door	EA	8.000	96,710.00	660.00	97,370.00
Utensil washer, sanitizer	EA	6.154	19,410.00	510.00	19,920.00
Automatic washer/sterilizer	EA	16.000	21,250.00	1,330.00	22,580.00
16 x 16 x 26", including accessories	EA	26.667	24,430.00	2,210.00	26,640.00
Steam generator, elec., 10 kw to 180 kw	EA	16.000	40,380.00	1,330.00	41,710.00

	Unit	Man-Hrs	Material	Labor	Total

11720.01 MEDICAL EQUIPMENT (Cont.)

Hospital

Surgical scrub

	Unit	Man-Hrs	Material	Labor	Total
Minimum	EA	2.667	2,130.00	220.00	2,350.00
Maximum	EA	2.667	12,330.00	220.00	12,550.00

Gas sterilizers

	Unit	Man-Hrs	Material	Labor	Total
Automatic, freestanding, 21x19x29"	EA	8.000	7,580.00	660.00	8,240.00

Surgical tables

	Unit	Man-Hrs	Material	Labor	Total
Minimum	EA	11.429	26,260.00	950.00	27,210.00
Maximum	EA	16.000	31,950.00	1,330.00	33,280.00

Surgical lights, ceiling mounted

	Unit	Man-Hrs	Material	Labor	Total
Minimum	EA	13.333	10,490.00	1,110.00	11,600.00
Maximum	EA	16.000	21,400.00	1,330.00	22,730.00

Water stills

	Unit	Man-Hrs	Material	Labor	Total
4 liters/hr	EA	2.667	4,750.00	220.00	4,970.00
8 liters/hr	EA	2.667	7,580.00	220.00	7,800.00
19 liters/hr	EA	6.667	15,590.00	550.00	16,140.00

X-ray equipment

Mobile unit

	Unit	Man-Hrs	Material	Labor	Total
Minimum	EA	4.000	13,880.00	330.00	14,210.00
Maximum	EA	8.000	26,880.00	660.00	27,540.00

Film viewers

	Unit	Man-Hrs	Material	Labor	Total
Minimum	EA	1.333	350.00	110.00	460.00
Maximum	EA	2.667	1,200.00	220.00	1,420.00

Autopsy table

	Unit	Man-Hrs	Material	Labor	Total
Minimum	EA	8.000	19,370.00	660.00	20,030.00
Maximum	EA	8.000	27,370.00	660.00	28,030.00

Incubators

	Unit	Man-Hrs	Material	Labor	Total
15 cf	EA	4.000	9,670.00	330.00	10,000.00
29 cf	EA	6.667	13,110.00	550.00	13,660.00
Infant transport, portable	EA	4.211	7,280.00	350.00	7,630.00

Beds

	Unit	Man-Hrs	Material	Labor	Total
Stretcher, with pad, 30" x 78"	EA	2.000	5,410.00	170.00	5,580.00
Transfer, for patient transport	EA	2.000	6,370.00	170.00	6,540.00

Headwall

	Unit	Man-Hrs	Material	Labor	Total
Aluminum, with back frame and console	EA	4.000	5,460.00	330.00	5,790.00

Hospital ground detection system

	Unit	Man-Hrs	Material	Labor	Total
Power ground module	EA	2.286	1,710.00	190.00	1,900.00
Ground slave module	EA	1.739	720.00	140.00	860.00
Master ground module	EA	1.509	640.00	130.00	770.00
Remote indicator	EA	1.600	670.00	130.00	800.00
X-ray indicator	EA	1.739	1,910.00	140.00	2,050.00
Micro ammeter	EA	2.000	2,270.00	170.00	2,440.00
Supervisory module	EA	1.739	1,910.00	140.00	2,050.00
Ground cords	EA	0.296	180.00	24.50	204.50

Hospital isolation monitors, 5 ma

	Unit	Man-Hrs	Material	Labor	Total
120v	EA	3.478	3,620.00	290.00	3,910.00
208v	EA	3.478	3,620.00	290.00	3,910.00
240v	EA	3.478	3,920.00	290.00	4,210.00
Digital clock-timers separate display	EA	1.600	1,590.00	130.00	1,720.00
One display	EA	1.600	1,020.00	130.00	1,150.00
Remote control	EA	1.250	500.00	100.00	600.00
Battery pack	EA	1.250	120.00	100.00	220.00
Surgical chronometer clock and 3 timers	EA	2.500	2,980.00	210.00	3,190.00
Auxiliary control	EA	1.159	810.00	96.00	906.00

11740.01 DENTAL EQUIPMENT

DENTAL EQUIPMENT

Dental care equipment

	Unit	Man-Hrs	Material	Labor	Total
Drill console with accessories	EA	13.333	5,710.00	1,110.00	6,820.00
Amalgamator	EA	0.400	610.00	33.25	643.25
Lathe	EA	0.267	1,410.00	22.25	1,432.25
Finish polisher	EA	0.533	1,850.00	44.25	1,894.25
Model trimmer	EA	0.364	1,140.00	30.25	1,170.25
Motor, wall mounted	EA	0.364	1,280.00	30.25	1,310.25
Cleaner, ultrasonic	EA	0.800	3,430.00	66.00	3,496.00

© 2020 BNi Publications, Inc.

	Unit	Man-Hrs	Material	Labor	Total

11740.01 DENTAL EQUIPMENT (Cont.)

Dental care equipment

	Unit	Man-Hrs	Material	Labor	Total
Curing unit, bench mounted	EA	1.333	5,270.00	110.00	5,380.00
Oral evacuation system, dual pump	EA	1.000	6,420.00	83.00	6,503.00
Sterilizer, table top, self contained	EA	0.444	2,710.00	37.00	2,747.00

Dental lights

	Unit	Man-Hrs	Material	Labor	Total
Light, floor or ceiling mounted	EA	4.000	2,300.00	330.00	2,630.00

X-ray unit

	Unit	Man-Hrs	Material	Labor	Total
Portable	EA	2.000	5,710.00	170.00	5,880.00
Wall mounted with remote control	EA	6.667	7,990.00	550.00	8,540.00
Illuminator, single panel	EA	11.429	820.00	950.00	1,770.00
X-ray film processor	EA	6.667	9,970.00	550.00	10,520.00
Shield, portable x-ray, lead lined	EA	0.533	1,850.00	44.25	1,894.25

11820.01 WASTE HANDLING

WASTE HANDLING

Incinerator, electric

100 lb/hr

	Unit	Man-Hrs	Material	Labor	Total
Minimum	EA	8.000	16,590.00	660.00	17,250.00
Maximum	EA	8.000	28,520.00	660.00	29,180.00

400 lb/hr

	Unit	Man-Hrs	Material	Labor	Total
Minimum	EA	16.000	41,790.00	1,330.00	43,120.00
Maximum	EA	16.000	52,240.00	1,330.00	53,570.00

1000 lb/hr

	Unit	Man-Hrs	Material	Labor	Total
Minimum	EA	24.242	98,330.00	2,010.00	100,340.00
Maximum	EA	24.242	147,500.00	2,010.00	149,510.00

Incinerator, medical-waste

	Unit	Man-Hrs	Material	Labor	Total
25 lb/hr, 2-7 x 4-0	EA	16.000	14,140.00	1,330.00	15,470.00
50 lb/hr, 2-11 x 4-11	EA	16.000	27,410.00	1,330.00	28,740.00
75 lb/hr, 3-8 x 5-0	EA	32.000	36,870.00	2,660.00	39,530.00
100 lb/hr, 3-8 x 6-0	EA	32.000	55,310.00	2,660.00	57,970.00

Industrial compactor

	Unit	Man-Hrs	Material	Labor	Total
1 c.y.	EA	8.889	14,500.00	740.00	15,240.00
3 c.y.	EA	11.429	22,620.00	950.00	23,570.00
5 c.y.	EA	16.000	43,020.00	1,330.00	44,350.00

Trash chutes, steel, including sprinklers

	Unit	Man-Hrs	Material	Labor	Total
18" dia.	LF	4.000	110.00	330.00	440.00
24" dia.	LF	4.211	140.00	340.00	480.00
30" dia.	LF	4.444	170.00	360.00	530.00
36" dia.	LF	4.706	210.00	380.00	590.00
Refuse bottom hopper	EA	4.444	1,840.00	360.00	2,200.00

11822.30 GRAY WATER RECYCLING SYSTEM

GRAY WATER RECYCLING SYSTEM

Residential, small commercial, 150 Gallons

	Unit	Man-Hrs	Material	Labor	Total
Minimum	EA				4,040.00
Average	EA				4,580.00
Maximum	EA				5,110.00

250 Gallons

	Unit	Man-Hrs	Material	Labor	Total
Minimum	EA				4,710.00
Average	EA				5,250.00
Maximum	EA				5,790.00

350 Gallons

	Unit	Man-Hrs	Material	Labor	Total
Minimum	EA				5,110.00
Average	EA				5,520.00
Maximum	EA				5,920.00

450 Gallons

	Unit	Man-Hrs	Material	Labor	Total
Minimum	EA				5,380.00
Average	EA				5,790.00
Maximum	EA				6,190.00

550 Gallons

	Unit	Man-Hrs	Material	Labor	Total
Minimum	EA				6,600.00
Average	EA				5,450.00
Maximum	EA				7,000.00

	Unit	Man-Hrs	Material	Labor	Total
12210.01 BLINDS					
BLINDS					
Venetian blinds					
2" slats	SF	0.020	40.25	1.63	41.88
1" slats	SF	0.020	43.00	1.63	44.63
12220.01 WINDOW TREATMENT					
WINDOW TREATMENT					
Drapery tracks, wall or ceiling mounted					
Basic traverse rod					
50 to 90"	EA	0.400	56.00	32.50	88.50
84 to 156"	EA	0.444	75.00	36.25	111.25
136 to 250"	EA	0.444	110.00	36.25	146.25
165 to 312"	EA	0.500	170.00	40.75	210.75
Traverse rod with stationary curtain rod					
30 to 50"	EA	0.400	84.00	32.50	116.50
50 to 90"	EA	0.400	97.00	32.50	129.50
84 to 156"	EA	0.444	130.00	36.25	166.25
136 to 250"	EA	0.500	160.00	40.75	200.75
Double traverse rod					
30 to 50"	EA	0.400	99.00	32.50	131.50
50 to 84"	EA	0.400	130.00	32.50	162.50
84 to 156"	EA	0.444	130.00	36.25	166.25
136 to 250"	EA	0.500	170.00	40.75	210.75
12320.01 CASEWORK					
CASEWORK					
Kitchen base cabinet, standard, 24" deep, 35" high					
12" wide	EA	0.800	220.00	65.00	285.00
18" wide	EA	0.800	250.00	65.00	315.00
24" wide	EA	0.889	330.00	72.00	402.00
27" wide	EA	0.889	370.00	72.00	442.00
36" wide	EA	1.000	440.00	82.00	522.00
48" wide	EA	1.000	520.00	82.00	602.00
Drawer base, 24" deep, 35" high					
15" wide	EA	0.800	280.00	65.00	345.00
18" wide	EA	0.800	290.00	65.00	355.00
24" wide	EA	0.889	470.00	72.00	542.00
27" wide	EA	0.889	530.00	72.00	602.00
30" wide	EA	0.889	630.00	72.00	702.00
Sink-ready base cabinet					
30" wide	EA	0.889	290.00	72.00	362.00
36" wide	EA	0.889	310.00	72.00	382.00
42" wide	EA	0.889	340.00	72.00	412.00
60" wide	EA	1.000	400.00	82.00	482.00
Corner cabinet, 36" wide	EA	1.000	550.00	82.00	632.00
Wall cabinet, 12" deep, 12" high					
30" wide	EA	0.800	280.00	65.00	345.00
36" wide	EA	0.800	290.00	65.00	355.00
15" high					
30" wide	EA	0.889	330.00	72.00	402.00
36" wide	EA	0.889	490.00	72.00	562.00
24" high					
30" wide	EA	0.889	360.00	72.00	432.00
36" wide	EA	0.889	370.00	72.00	442.00
30" high					
12" wide	EA	1.000	210.00	82.00	292.00
18" wide	EA	1.000	240.00	82.00	322.00
24" wide	EA	1.000	260.00	82.00	342.00
27" wide	EA	1.000	310.00	82.00	392.00
30" wide	EA	1.143	340.00	93.00	433.00
36" wide	EA	1.143	350.00	93.00	443.00
Corner cabinet, 30" high					
24" wide	EA	1.333	380.00	110.00	490.00
30" wide	EA	1.333	460.00	110.00	570.00
36" wide	EA	1.333	500.00	110.00	610.00

© 2020 BNi Publications, Inc.

	Unit	Man-Hrs	Material	Labor	Total

12320.01 CASEWORK (Cont.)

Casework

Wardrobe	EA	2.000	1,020.00	160.00	1,180.00

Vanity with top, laminated plastic

24" wide	EA	2.000	840.00	160.00	1,000.00
30" wide	EA	2.000	940.00	160.00	1,100.00
36" wide	EA	2.667	1,080.00	220.00	1,300.00
48" wide	EA	3.200	1,210.00	260.00	1,470.00

12360.01 COUNTERTOPS

COUNTERTOPS

Stainless steel, countertop, with backsplash	SF	0.200	250.00	16.25	266.25
Acid-proof, kemrock surface	SF	0.133	100.00	10.75	110.75

12480.01 FLOOR MATS

FLOOR MATS

Recessed entrance mat, 3/8" thick, aluminum link	SF	0.400	59.00	32.50	91.50
Steel, flexible	SF	0.400	21.00	32.50	53.50

	Unit	Man-Hrs	Material	Labor	Total

13110.01 SWIMMING POOL EQUIPMENT

SWIMMING POOL EQUIPMENT

Diving boards

14' long

	Unit	Man-Hrs	Material	Labor	Total
Aluminum	EA	4.444	4,970.00	280.00	5,250.00
Fiberglass	EA	4.444	3,760.00	280.00	4,040.00

Ladders, heavy duty

2 steps

	Unit	Man-Hrs	Material	Labor	Total
Minimum	EA	1.600	1,180.00	100.00	1,280.00
Maximum	EA	1.600	1,840.00	100.00	1,940.00

4 steps

	Unit	Man-Hrs	Material	Labor	Total
Minimum	EA	2.000	1,260.00	130.00	1,390.00
Maximum	EA	2.000	2,020.00	130.00	2,150.00

Lifeguard chair

	Unit	Man-Hrs	Material	Labor	Total
Minimum	EA	8.000	3,340.00	510.00	3,850.00
Maximum	EA	8.000	5,180.00	510.00	5,690.00

Lights, underwater

12 volt, with transformer, 100 watt

	Unit	Man-Hrs	Material	Labor	Total
Incandescent	EA	2.000	250.00	130.00	380.00
Halogen	EA	2.000	210.00	130.00	340.00
LED	EA	2.000	670.00	130.00	800.00

110 volt

	Unit	Man-Hrs	Material	Labor	Total
Minimum	EA	2.000	1,130.00	130.00	1,260.00
Maximum	EA	2.000	2,720.00	130.00	2,850.00
Ground fault interrupter for 110 volt, each light	EA	0.667	240.00	42.50	282.50

Pool cover

	Unit	Man-Hrs	Material	Labor	Total
Reinforced polyethylene	SF	0.062	2.41	3.92	6.33

Vinyl water tube

	Unit	Man-Hrs	Material	Labor	Total
Minimum	SF	0.062	1.48	3.92	5.40
Maximum	SF	0.062	2.20	3.92	6.12

Slides with water tube

	Unit	Man-Hrs	Material	Labor	Total
Minimum	EA	6.667	1,180.00	430.00	1,610.00
Maximum	EA	6.667	25,210.00	430.00	25,640.00

13241.60 SAUNAS

SAUNAS

Prefabricated, cedar siding, insulated panels, prehung door, 240

	Unit	Man-Hrs	Material	Labor	Total
4'x8"x4'-8"x6'-6"	EA				6,500.00
5'-8"x6'-8"x6'-6"	EA				7,870.00
6'-8"x6'-8"x6'-6"	EA				9,160.00
7'-8"x7'-8"x6'-6"	EA				11,060.00
7'-8"x9'-8"x6'-6"	EA				14,570.00

13341.90 PRE-ENGINEERED BUILDINGS

PRE-ENGINEERED BUILDINGS

Pre-engineered metal building, 40'x100'

	Unit	Man-Hrs	Material	Labor	Total
14' eave height	SF	0.032	9.33	5.67	15.00
16' eave height	SF	0.037	10.50	6.54	17.04
20' eave height	SF	0.048	12.00	8.51	20.51

60'x100'

	Unit	Man-Hrs	Material	Labor	Total
14' eave height	SF	0.032	11.75	5.67	17.42
16' eave height	SF	0.037	13.00	6.54	19.54
20' eave height	SF	0.048	14.50	8.51	23.01

80'x100'

	Unit	Man-Hrs	Material	Labor	Total
14' eave height	SF	0.032	9.03	5.67	14.70
16' eave height	SF	0.037	9.33	6.54	15.87
20' eave height	SF	0.048	10.50	8.51	19.01

100'x100'

	Unit	Man-Hrs	Material	Labor	Total
14' eave height	SF	0.032	8.81	5.67	14.48
16' eave height	SF	0.037	9.18	6.54	15.72
20' eave height	SF	0.048	10.00	8.51	18.51

100'x150'

	Unit	Man-Hrs	Material	Labor	Total
14' eave height	SF	0.032	7.85	5.67	13.52
16' eave height	SF	0.037	8.15	6.54	14.69
20' eave height	SF	0.048	8.74	8.51	17.25

© 2020 BNi Publications, Inc.

13341.90 PRE-ENGINEERED BUILDINGS (Cont.)

	Unit	Man-Hrs	Material	Labor	Total
Pre-engineered metal building					
120'x150'					
14' eave height	SF	0.032	8.30	5.67	13.97
16' eave height	SF	0.037	8.44	6.54	14.98
20' eave height	SF	0.048	8.81	8.51	17.32
140'x150'					
14' eave height	SF	0.032	7.85	5.67	13.52
16' eave height	SF	0.037	8.05	6.54	14.59
20' eave height	SF	0.048	8.74	8.51	17.25
160'x200'					
14' eave height	SF	0.032	6.05	5.67	11.72
16' eave height	SF	0.037	6.24	6.54	12.78
20' eave height	SF	0.048	6.60	8.51	15.11
200'x200'					
14' eave height	SF	0.032	5.21	5.67	10.88
16' eave height	SF	0.037	5.73	6.54	12.27
20' eave height	SF	0.048	6.10	8.51	14.61
Hollow metal door and frame, 6' x 7'	EA				1,390.00
Sectional steel overhead door, manually operated					
8' x 8'	EA				2,280.00
12' x 12'	EA				3,040.00
Roll-up steel door, manually operated					
10' x 10'	EA				1,770.00
12' x 12'	EA				3,180.00
For gravity ridge ventilator with birdscreen	EA				760.00
9" throat x 10'	EA				830.00
12" throat x 10'	EA				1,010.00
For 20" rotary vent with damper	EA				380.00
For 4' x 3' fixed louver	EA				270.00
For 4' x 3' aluminum sliding window	EA				240.00
For 3' x 9' fiberglass panels	EA				180.00
Liner panel, 26 ga, painted steel	SF	0.020	3.34	1.80	5.14
Wall panel insulated, 26 ga. steel, foam core	SF	0.020	10.50	1.80	12.30
Roof panel, 26 ga. painted steel	SF	0.011	3.16	1.02	4.18
Plastic (skylight)	SF	0.011	7.12	1.02	8.14
Insulation, 3-1/2" thick blanket, R11	SF	0.005	2.13	0.48	2.61

	Unit	Man-Hrs	Material	Labor	Total

14110.01 DUMBWAITERS

DUMBWAITERS

	Unit	Man-Hrs	Material	Labor	Total
28' travel, extruded alum., 4 stops, 100 lbs. capacity	EA				6,760.00
150 lbs. capacity	EA				9,510.00
200 lbs. capacity	EA				13,650.00

14210.01 ELEVATORS

ELEVATORS

Passenger elevators, electric, geared

Based on a shaft of 6 stops and 6 openings

	Unit	Man-Hrs	Material	Labor	Total
50 fpm, 2000 lb	EA	24.000	145,640.00	2,850.00	148,490.00
100 fpm, 2000 lb	EA	26.667	151,020.00	3,170.00	154,190.00
150 fpm					
2000 lb	EA	30.000	166,620.00	3,560.00	170,180.00
3000 lb	EA	34.286	209,870.00	4,070.00	213,940.00
4000 lb	EA	40.000	218,380.00	4,750.00	223,130.00
200 fpm					
2500 lb	EA	34.286	201,370.00	4,070.00	205,440.00
3000 lb	EA	36.923	207,040.00	4,390.00	211,430.00
4000 lb	EA	40.000	218,380.00	4,750.00	223,130.00
250 fpm					
2500 lb	EA	34.286	208,460.00	4,070.00	212,530.00
3000 lb	EA	36.923	220,010.00	4,390.00	224,400.00
4000 lb	EA	40.000	225,120.00	4,750.00	229,870.00
300 fpm					
2500 lb	EA	34.286	206,470.00	4,070.00	210,540.00
3000 lb	EA	36.923	218,380.00	4,390.00	222,770.00
4000 lb	EA	24.000	222,210.00	2,850.00	225,060.00

For each additional; 50 fpm, add per stop, $3000

500 lb, add per stop, $4000

Opening, add per stop, $4500

Stop, add per stop, $4000

Bonderized steel door, add per opening, $150

Colored aluminum door, add per opening, $850

Stainless steel door, add per opening, $600

Cast bronze door, add per opening, $1100

Two speed door, add per opening, $360

Bi-parting door, add per opening, $850

Custom cab interior add, $4800

Based on a shaft of 8 stops and 8 openings

	Unit	Man-Hrs	Material	Labor	Total
300 fpm					
3000 lb	EA	48.000	270,190.00	5,700.00	275,890.00
3500 lb	EA	48.000	274,450.00	5,700.00	280,150.00
4000 lb	EA	53.333	287,960.00	6,330.00	294,290.00
5000 lb	EA	57.143	319,960.00	6,790.00	326,750.00
400 fpm					
3000 lb	EA	48.000	283,060.00	5,700.00	288,760.00
3500 lb	EA	48.000	287,960.00	5,700.00	293,660.00
4000 lb	EA	53.333	307,870.00	6,330.00	314,200.00
5000 lb	EA	57.143	350,530.00	6,790.00	357,320.00
600 fpm					
3000 lb	EA	53.333	398,670.00	6,330.00	405,000.00
3500 lb	EA	57.143	408,130.00	6,790.00	414,920.00
4000 lb	EA	58.537	412,390.00	6,950.00	419,340.00
5000 lb	EA	60.000	423,770.00	7,130.00	430,900.00
800 fpm					
3000 lb	EA	53.333	472,830.00	6,330.00	479,160.00
3500 lb	EA	57.143	477,810.00	6,790.00	484,600.00
4000 lb	EA	58.537	483,490.00	6,950.00	490,440.00
5000 lb	EA	60.000	486,690.00	7,130.00	493,820.00

For each additional; 100 fpm add per stop, $13,000

500 lb, add per stop, $6500

Opening add per stop, $12,000

Stop add per stop, $4800

Bypass floor, add per each, $2000

Bonderized steel door, add per opening, $150

© 2020 BNi Publications, Inc.

	Unit	Man-Hrs	Material	Labor	Total

14210.01 ELEVATORS (Cont.)

For each additional; 100 fpm add per stop, $13,000
  Colored aluminum door, add per opening, $900
  Stainless steel door, add per opening, $600
  Cast bronze door, add per opening, $600
  Two speed bi-parting door, add per opening, $1000
  Custom cab interior, add $5000
Hydraulic, based on a shaft of 3 stops, 3 openings

	Unit	Man-Hrs	Material	Labor	Total
50 fpm					
2000 lb	EA	20.000	101,250.00	2,380.00	103,630.00
2500 lb	EA	20.000	108,270.00	2,380.00	110,650.00
3000 lb	EA	20.870	114,260.00	2,480.00	116,740.00
100 fpm					
2000 lb	EA	20.000	110,920.00	2,380.00	113,300.00
2500 lb	EA	20.870	116,960.00	2,480.00	119,440.00
3000 lb	EA	21.818	125,140.00	2,590.00	127,730.00
150 fpm					
2000 lb	EA	20.000	120,160.00	2,380.00	122,540.00
2500 lb	EA	20.870	131,540.00	2,480.00	134,020.00
3000 lb	EA	22.857	140,780.00	2,710.00	143,490.00

For each additional; 50 fpm add per stop, $3500
  500 lb, add per stop, $3500
  Opening, add, $4200
  Stop, add per stop, $5300
  Bonderized steel door, add per opening, $400
  Colored aluminum door, add per opening, $1500
  Stainless steel door, add per opening, $650
  Cast bronze door, add per opening, $1200
  Two speed door, add per opening, $400
  Bi-parting door, add per opening, $900
  Custom cab interior, add per cab, $5000
Small elevators, 4 to 6 passenger capacity

	Unit	Man-Hrs	Material	Labor	Total
Electric, push					
2 stops	EA	20.000	34,510.00	2,380.00	36,890.00
3 stops	EA	21.818	43,140.00	2,590.00	45,730.00
4 stops	EA	24.000	49,110.00	2,850.00	51,960.00

Freight elevators, electric
Based on a shaft of 6 stops and 6 openings

	Unit	Man-Hrs	Material	Labor	Total
50 fpm					
3500 lb	EA	26.667	260,160.00	3,170.00	263,330.00
4000 lb	EA	26.667	260,820.00	3,170.00	263,990.00
5000 lb	EA	30.000	265,470.00	3,560.00	269,030.00
100 fpm					
3500 lb	EA	30.000	272,100.00	3,560.00	275,660.00
4000 lb	EA	30.000	276,080.00	3,560.00	279,640.00
5000 lb	EA	34.286	280,930.00	4,070.00	285,000.00
200 fpm					
3500 lb	EA	34.286	270,770.00	4,070.00	274,840.00
4000 lb	EA	34.286	272,100.00	4,070.00	276,170.00
5000 lb	EA	40.000	274,760.00	4,750.00	279,510.00

For elevator with manual door, deduct 15%
For variable voltage control, add 20%
Based on shaft of 8 stops and 8 openings

	Unit	Man-Hrs	Material	Labor	Total
100 fpm					
4000 lb	EA	30.000	261,950.00	3,560.00	265,510.00
6000 lb	EA	30.769	264,140.00	3,650.00	267,790.00
8000 lb	EA	32.432	268,780.00	3,850.00	272,630.00
150 fpm					
4000 lb	EA	34.286	265,470.00	4,070.00	269,540.00
6000 lb	EA	35.294	265,470.00	4,190.00	269,660.00
8000 lb	EA	37.500	273,430.00	4,450.00	277,880.00
200 fpm					
4000 lb	EA	40.000	266,790.00	4,750.00	271,540.00
6000 lb	EA	41.379	273,430.00	4,910.00	278,340.00
8000 lb	EA	43.636	285,370.00	5,180.00	290,550.00

	Unit	Man-Hrs	Material	Labor	Total

14210.01 ELEVATORS (Cont.)

Based on shaft of 8 stops and 8 openings
  For each additional; 50 fpm, add per stop, $2000
    500 lb, add per stop, $600
    Opening, add per stop, $7000
    Stop, add per stop, $5500
  For variable voltage, add 20%
  Hydraulic, based on 3 stops and 3 openings
    50 fpm

	Unit	Man-Hrs	Material	Labor	Total
3000 lb	EA	17.143	111,500.00	2,040.00	113,540.00
4000 lb	EA	17.778	122,110.00	2,110.00	124,220.00
6000 lb	EA	18.462	142,020.00	2,190.00	144,210.00

    100 fpm

	Unit	Man-Hrs	Material	Labor	Total
3000 lb	EA	17.143	126,100.00	2,040.00	128,140.00
4000 lb	EA	17.778	132,730.00	2,110.00	134,840.00
6000 lb	EA	18.462	156,620.00	2,190.00	158,810.00

    150 fpm

	Unit	Man-Hrs	Material	Labor	Total
3000 lb	EA	17.143	138,040.00	2,040.00	140,080.00
4000 lb	EA	17.778	148,660.00	2,110.00	150,770.00
6000 lb	EA	18.462	169,900.00	2,190.00	172,090.00

  For each additional; 50 fpm, add per stop, $2000
    500 lb, add per stop, $600
    Opening, add per stop, $5500
    Stop, add per stop, $5500
  For elevator with manual door deduct from total, 15%

14310.01 ESCALATORS

ESCALATORS
  Escalators
    32" wide, floor to floor

	Unit	Man-Hrs	Material	Labor	Total
12' high	EA	40.000	180,150.00	4,750.00	184,900.00
15' high	EA	48.000	196,830.00	5,700.00	202,530.00
18' high	EA	60.000	211,990.00	7,130.00	219,120.00
22' high	EA	80.000	209,770.00	9,500.00	219,270.00
25' high	EA	96.000	238,380.00	11,400.00	249,780.00

    48" wide

	Unit	Man-Hrs	Material	Labor	Total
12' high	EA	41.379	200,710.00	4,910.00	205,620.00
15' high	EA	50.000	219,050.00	5,940.00	224,990.00
18' high	EA	63.158	235,310.00	7,500.00	242,810.00
22' high	EA	85.714	263,410.00	10,180.00	273,590.00
25' high	EA	96.000	281,260.00	11,400.00	292,660.00

14410.01 PERSONNEL LIFTS

PERSONNEL LIFTS
  Electrically operated, 1 or 2 person lift
  With attached foot platforms

	Unit	Man-Hrs	Material	Labor	Total
3 stops	EA				12,390.00
5 stops	EA				19,320.00
7 stops	EA				22,520.00

  For each additional stop, add $1250

	Unit	Man-Hrs	Material	Labor	Total
Residential stair climber, per story	EA	6.667	5,750.00	550.00	6,300.00
curved	EA	8.000	12,150.00	660.00	12,810.00

14420.01 WHEELCHAIR LIFTS

WHEELCHAIR LIFTS

	Unit	Man-Hrs	Material	Labor	Total
600 lb, Residential	EA	8.000	6,830.00	660.00	7,490.00
Commercial	EA	8.000	16,150.00	660.00	16,810.00

14450.01 VEHICLE LIFTS

VEHICLE LIFTS

	Unit	Man-Hrs	Material	Labor	Total
Automotive hoist, one post, semi-hydraulic, 8,000 lb	EA	24.000	4,140.00	2,850.00	6,990.00
Full hydraulic, 8,000 lb	EA	24.000	4,270.00	2,850.00	7,120.00
2 post, semi-hydraulic, 10,000 lb	EA	34.286	4,460.00	4,070.00	8,530.00

  Full hydraulic

	Unit	Man-Hrs	Material	Labor	Total
10,000 lb	EA	34.286	5,250.00	4,070.00	9,320.00
13,000 lb	EA	60.000	6,570.00	7,130.00	13,700.00
18,500 lb	EA	60.000	10,500.00	7,130.00	17,630.00
24,000 lb	EA	60.000	14,770.00	7,130.00	21,900.00

© 2020 BNi Publications, Inc.

	Unit	Man-Hrs	Material	Labor	Total

14450.01 VEHICLE LIFTS (Cont.)

Full hydraulic

26,000 lb	EA	60.000	14,380.00	7,130.00	21,510.00

Pneumatic hoist, fully hydraulic

11,000 lb	EA	80.000	7,090.00	9,500.00	16,590.00
24,000 lb	EA	80.000	12,800.00	9,500.00	22,300.00

14910.01 CHUTES

CHUTES

Linen chutes, stainless steel, with supports

18" dia.	LF	0.057	170.00	5.14	175.14
24" dia.	LF	0.062	210.00	5.53	215.53
30" dia.	LF	0.067	220.00	6.00	226.00
Hopper	EA	0.533	2,680.00	48.00	2,728.00
Skylight	EA	0.800	1,630.00	72.00	1,702.00
Sprinkler unit at top	EA	0.889	610.00	80.00	690.00

For galvanized metal, deduct from material cost, 35%

For aluminum, deduct from material cost, 25%

14920.01 PNEUMATIC SYSTEMS

PNEUMATIC SYSTEMS

Pneumatic message tube system

Average, 20 station job

3" round system	EA	72.727	44,630.00	6,040.00	50,670.00
4" round system	EA	80.000	56,380.00	6,640.00	63,020.00
6" round system	EA	88.889	96,740.00	7,380.00	104,120.00
4" x 7" oval system	EA	160.000	101,900.00	13,280.00	115,180.00

Trash and linen tube system

10 stations	EA	120.000	30,070.00	14,250.00	44,320.00
15 stations	EA	160.000	37,690.00	19,000.00	56,690.00
20 stations	EA	184.615	50,230.00	21,930.00	72,160.00
30 stations	EA	218.182	65,330.00	25,910.00	91,240.00

	Unit	Man-Hrs	Material	Labor	Total

21111.60 HYDRANTS

HYDRANTS

Wall hydrant

	Unit	Man-Hrs	Material	Labor	Total
8" thick	EA	1.333	400.00	120.00	520.00
12" thick	EA	1.600	470.00	140.00	610.00
18" thick	EA	1.778	510.00	160.00	670.00
24" thick	EA	2.000	560.00	180.00	740.00

Ground hydrant

	Unit	Man-Hrs	Material	Labor	Total
2' deep	EA	1.000	740.00	89.00	829.00
4' deep	EA	1.143	860.00	100.00	960.00
6' deep	EA	1.333	970.00	120.00	1,090.00
8' deep	EA	2.000	1,090.00	180.00	1,270.00

21130.01 WET SPRINKLER SYSTEM

WET SPRINKLER SYSTEM

	Unit	Man-Hrs	Material	Labor	Total
Sprinkler head, 212 deg, brass, exposed piping	EA	0.320	16.00	28.50	44.50
Chrome, concealed piping	EA	0.444	19.50	39.75	59.25
Water motor alarm	EA	1.333	370.00	120.00	490.00
Fire department inlet connection	EA	1.600	270.00	140.00	410.00
Wall plate for fire dept connection	EA	0.667	130.00	60.00	190.00
Swing check valve flanged iron body, 4"	EA	2.667	350.00	240.00	590.00
Check valve, 6"	EA	4.000	1,150.00	360.00	1,510.00
Wet pipe valve, flange to groove, 4"	EA	0.889	990.00	79.00	1,069.00
Flange to flange					
6"	EA	1.333	1,340.00	120.00	1,460.00
8"	EA	2.667	2,360.00	240.00	2,600.00
Alarm valve, flange to flange (wet valve)					
4"	EA	0.889	1,530.00	79.00	1,609.00
8"	EA	6.667	2,420.00	600.00	3,020.00
Inspector's test connection	EA	0.667	70.00	60.00	130.00
Wall hydrant, polished brass, 2-1/2" x 2-1/2", single	EA	0.571	470.00	51.00	521.00
2-way	EA	0.571	1,060.00	51.00	1,111.00
3-way	EA	0.571	2,170.00	51.00	2,221.00
Wet valve trim, includes retard chamber & gauges, 4"-6"	EA	0.667	740.00	60.00	800.00
Retard pressure switch for wet systems	EA	1.600	1,300.00	140.00	1,440.00
Air maintenance device	EA	0.667	390.00	60.00	450.00
Wall hydrant non-freeze, 8" thick wall, vacuum breaker	EA	0.400	51.00	35.75	86.75
12" thick wall	EA	0.400	56.00	35.75	91.75

21210.01 CO$_2$ SYSTEM

CO$_2$ SYSTEM

CO$_2$ system, high pressure, 75# cylinder with

	Unit	Man-Hrs	Material	Labor	Total
Valve assemblies	EA	1.600	2,660.00	140.00	2,800.00
Storage rack	EA	1.143	1,420.00	100.00	1,520.00
Manifold	EA	5.714	1,030.00	510.00	1,540.00
Flexible loops	EA	0.100	84.00	8.94	92.94
Beam scale for cylinders	EA	1.333	700.00	120.00	820.00
Mechanically controlled head	EA	0.533	590.00	47.75	637.75
Electrically controlled head	EA	0.533	590.00	47.75	637.75
Stop valves	EA	0.800	1,500.00	72.00	1,572.00
Check valves	EA	1.000	680.00	89.00	769.00
Activation station	EA	0.800	790.00	72.00	862.00
Nozzles	EA	0.667	130.00	60.00	190.00
Hose reel with 75' of 3/4" hose	EA	4.000	4,750.00	360.00	5,110.00
Main/reserve transfer switch	EA	1.333	5,530.00	120.00	5,650.00
Pressure switch	EA	0.800	490.00	72.00	562.00
Heat responsive device	EA	1.333	780.00	120.00	900.00
Battery and charger	EA	4.000	4,430.00	360.00	4,790.00
Low pressure					
Battery and charger	EA	4.000	4,430.00	360.00	4,790.00
Pressure switch	EA	0.889	440.00	79.00	519.00
Nozzles	EA	0.727	130.00	65.00	195.00
Master selector valve	EA	1.333	380.00	120.00	500.00
Selector valve	EA	1.333	5,530.00	120.00	5,650.00
Low pressure hose reel with 75' of 3/4" hose	EA	4.000	6,860.00	360.00	7,220.00
Tank fill lines	EA	1.000	1,550.00	89.00	1,639.00

© 2020 BNi Publications, Inc.

DIVISION 21 FIRE SUPPRESSION

	Unit	Man-Hrs	Material	Labor	Total
21210.01 CO$_2$ SYSTEM (Cont.)					
Low pressure					
Activation stations	EA	0.667	780.00	60.00	840.00
Electro manual pilot panels	EA	1.000	1,550.00	89.00	1,639.00
21240.01 DRY SPRINKLER SYSTEM					
DRY SPRINKLER SYSTEM					
Dry pipe valve, flange to flange					
4"	EA	1.600	2,250.00	140.00	2,390.00
6"	EA	2.000	2,820.00	180.00	3,000.00
Trim, 4" and 6", includes gauges	EA	0.667	870.00	60.00	930.00
Field testing and flushing	EA	6.667		600.00	600.00
Disinfection	EA	6.667		600.00	600.00
Pressure switch double circuit, open/close contacts	EA	2.000	420.00	180.00	600.00
Low air					
Supervisory unit	EA	1.333	1,360.00	120.00	1,480.00
Pressure switch	EA	0.667	430.00	60.00	490.00

22052.36 VALVES

	Unit	Man-Hrs	Material	Labor	Total
VALVES					
Gate valve, 125 lb, bronze, soldered					
1/2"	EA	0.200	37.75	18.00	55.75
3/4"	EA	0.200	45.25	18.00	63.25
1"	EA	0.267	56.00	23.75	79.75
1-1/2"	EA	0.320	97.00	28.50	125.50
2"	EA	0.400	140.00	35.75	175.75
2-1/2"	EA	0.500	310.00	44.75	354.75
Threaded					
1/4", 125 lb	EA	0.320	35.50	28.50	64.00
1/2"					
125 lb	EA	0.320	34.25	28.50	62.75
300 lb	EA	0.320	86.00	28.50	114.50
3/4"					
125 lb	EA	0.320	40.00	28.50	68.50
300 lb	EA	0.320	100.00	28.50	128.50
1"					
125 lb	EA	0.320	52.00	28.50	80.50
300 lb	EA	0.400	150.00	35.75	185.75
1-1/2"					
125 lb	EA	0.400	90.00	35.75	125.75
300 lb	EA	0.444	260.00	39.75	299.75
2"					
125 lb	EA	0.571	120.00	51.00	171.00
300 lb	EA	0.667	330.00	60.00	390.00
Cast iron, flanged					
2", 150 lb	EA	0.667	490.00	60.00	550.00
2-1/2"					
125 lb	EA	0.667	480.00	60.00	540.00
250 lb	EA	0.667	1,310.00	60.00	1,370.00
3"					
125 lb	EA	0.800	570.00	72.00	642.00
250 lb	EA	0.800	1,200.00	72.00	1,272.00
4"					
125 lb	EA	1.143	750.00	100.00	850.00
250 lb	EA	1.143	1,610.00	100.00	1,710.00
6"					
125 lb	EA	1.600	1,380.00	140.00	1,520.00
250 lb	EA	1.600	3,230.00	140.00	3,370.00
8"					
125 lb	EA	2.000	2,200.00	180.00	2,380.00
250 lb	EA	2.000	6,260.00	180.00	6,440.00
OS&Y, flanged					
2"					
125 lb	EA	0.667	450.00	60.00	510.00
250 lb	EA	0.667	1,190.00	60.00	1,250.00
2-1/2"					
125 lb	EA	0.667	470.00	60.00	530.00
250 lb	EA	0.800	1,470.00	72.00	1,542.00
3"					
125 lb	EA	0.800	520.00	72.00	592.00
250 lb	EA	0.800	1,530.00	72.00	1,602.00
4"					
125 lb	EA	1.333	690.00	120.00	810.00
250 lb	EA	1.333	2,340.00	120.00	2,460.00
6"					
125 lb	EA	1.600	1,160.00	140.00	1,300.00
250 lb	EA	1.600	3,700.00	140.00	3,840.00
Ball valve, bronze, 250 lb, threaded					
1/2"	EA	0.320	20.50	28.50	49.00
3/4"	EA	0.320	30.50	28.50	59.00
1"	EA	0.400	38.75	35.75	74.50
1-1/4"	EA	0.444	57.00	39.75	96.75
1-1/2"	EA	0.500	90.00	44.75	134.75

© 2020 BNi Publications, Inc.

	Unit	Man-Hrs	Material	Labor	Total

22052.36 VALVES (Cont.)

Ball valve, bronze, 250 lb, threaded

	Unit	Man-Hrs	Material	Labor	Total
2"	EA	0.571	100.00	51.00	151.00

Angle valve, bronze, 150 lb, threaded

	Unit	Man-Hrs	Material	Labor	Total
1/2"	EA	0.286	100.00	25.50	125.50
3/4"	EA	0.320	140.00	28.50	168.50
1"	EA	0.320	210.00	28.50	238.50
1-1/4"	EA	0.400	270.00	35.75	305.75
1-1/2"	EA	0.444	350.00	39.75	389.75

Balancing valve, meter connections, circuit setter

	Unit	Man-Hrs	Material	Labor	Total
1/2"	EA	0.320	99.00	28.50	127.50
3/4"	EA	0.364	100.00	32.50	132.50
1"	EA	0.400	130.00	35.75	165.75
1-1/4"	EA	0.444	190.00	39.75	229.75
1-1/2"	EA	0.533	230.00	47.75	277.75
2"	EA	0.667	320.00	60.00	380.00
2-1/2"	EA	0.800	630.00	72.00	702.00
3"	EA	1.000	920.00	89.00	1,009.00
4"	EA	1.333	1,290.00	120.00	1,410.00

Pressure reducing valve, bronze, threaded, 250 lb

	Unit	Man-Hrs	Material	Labor	Total
1/2"	EA	0.500	200.00	44.75	244.75
3/4"	EA	0.500	200.00	44.75	244.75
1"	EA	0.500	310.00	44.75	354.75
1-1/4"	EA	0.571	450.00	51.00	501.00
1-1/2"	EA	0.667	520.00	60.00	580.00

Pressure regulating valve, bronze, class 300

	Unit	Man-Hrs	Material	Labor	Total
1"	EA	0.500	750.00	44.75	794.75
1-1/2"	EA	0.615	1,000.00	55.00	1,055.00
2"	EA	0.800	1,130.00	72.00	1,202.00
3"	EA	1.143	1,280.00	100.00	1,380.00
4"	EA	1.600	1,600.00	140.00	1,740.00
5"	EA	2.000	2,420.00	180.00	2,600.00
6"	EA	2.667	2,460.00	240.00	2,700.00

Solar water temperature regulating valve

	Unit	Man-Hrs	Material	Labor	Total
3/4"	EA	0.667	770.00	60.00	830.00
1"	EA	0.800	790.00	72.00	862.00
1-1/4"	EA	0.889	850.00	79.00	929.00
1-1/2"	EA	1.000	950.00	89.00	1,039.00
2"	EA	1.143	1,170.00	100.00	1,270.00
2-1/2"	EA	2.000	2,210.00	180.00	2,390.00

Tempering valve, threaded

	Unit	Man-Hrs	Material	Labor	Total
3/4"	EA	0.267	420.00	23.75	443.75
1"	EA	0.320	530.00	28.50	558.50
1-1/4"	EA	0.400	790.00	35.75	825.75
1-1/2"	EA	0.400	900.00	35.75	935.75
2"	EA	0.500	1,230.00	44.75	1,274.75
2-1/2"	EA	0.667	2,080.00	60.00	2,140.00
3"	EA	0.800	2,750.00	72.00	2,822.00
4"	EA	1.143	5,500.00	100.00	5,600.00

Thermostatic mixing valve, threaded

	Unit	Man-Hrs	Material	Labor	Total
1/2"	EA	0.286	130.00	25.50	155.50
3/4"	EA	0.320	130.00	28.50	158.50
1"	EA	0.348	480.00	31.00	511.00
1-1/2"	EA	0.400	540.00	35.75	575.75
2"	EA	0.500	680.00	44.75	724.75

Sweat connection

	Unit	Man-Hrs	Material	Labor	Total
1/2"	EA	0.286	150.00	25.50	175.50
3/4"	EA	0.320	180.00	28.50	208.50

Mixing valve, sweat connection

	Unit	Man-Hrs	Material	Labor	Total
1/2"	EA	0.286	79.00	25.50	104.50
3/4"	EA	0.320	79.00	28.50	107.50

Liquid level gauge, aluminum body

	Unit	Man-Hrs	Material	Labor	Total
3/4"	EA	0.320	400.00	28.50	428.50

125 psi, PVC body

	Unit	Man-Hrs	Material	Labor	Total
3/4"	EA	0.320	470.00	28.50	498.50

	Unit	Man-Hrs	Material	Labor	Total
22052.36 VALVES (Cont.)					
Liquid level gauge					
150 psi, CRS body					
3/4"	EA	0.320	380.00	28.50	408.50
1"	EA	0.320	410.00	28.50	438.50
175 psi, bronze body, 1/2"	EA	0.286	760.00	25.50	785.50
22052.91 PIPE HANGERS, HEAVY					
PIPE HANGERS, HEAVY					
Hangers					
1/2" pipe, clevis pipe hanger					
Black steel	EA	0.267	1.87	23.75	25.62
Galvanized	EA	0.267	2.81	23.75	26.56
U bolt	EA	0.080	1.74	7.15	8.89
3/4" pipe, clevis pipe hanger					
Black steel	EA	0.267	1.91	23.75	25.66
Galvanized	EA	0.267	2.88	23.75	26.63
1" pipe, clevis pipe hanger					
Black steel	EA	0.267	1.96	23.75	25.71
Galvanized	EA	0.267	3.09	23.75	26.84
2" pipe, clevis pipe hanger					
Black steel	EA	0.267	2.66	23.75	26.41
Galvanized	EA	0.267	4.36	23.75	28.11
3" pipe, clevis pipe hanger					
Black steel	EA	0.267	5.22	23.75	28.97
Galvanized	EA	0.267	9.10	23.75	32.85
4" pipe, clevis pipe hanger					
Black steel	EA	0.267	6.39	23.75	30.14
Galvanized	EA	0.267	11.50	23.75	35.25
6" pipe, clevis pipe hanger					
Black steel	EA	0.320	10.25	28.50	38.75
Galvanized	EA	0.320	20.50	28.50	49.00
12" pipe, clevis pipe hanger					
Black steel	EA	0.320	36.00	28.50	64.50
Galvanized	EA	0.320	53.00	28.50	81.50
Threaded rod, galvanized, material only					
3/8"	LF				0.68
1/2"	LF				1.36
Hex nuts, galvanized					
3/8"	EA				0.23
1/2"	EA				0.48
1"	EA				3.04
C-clamp, steel, with lock nut					
3/8"	EA	0.100	2.71	8.94	11.65
1/2"	EA	0.100	3.04	8.94	11.98
22062.91 PIPE HANGERS, LIGHT					
PIPE HANGERS, LIGHT					
A band, black iron					
1/2"	EA	0.057	1.03	5.10	6.13
1"	EA	0.059	1.11	5.29	6.40
1-1/4"	EA	0.062	1.23	5.50	6.73
1-1/2"	EA	0.067	1.28	5.96	7.24
2"	EA	0.073	1.36	6.50	7.86
2-1/2"	EA	0.080	2.03	7.15	9.18
3"	EA	0.089	2.48	7.94	10.42
4"	EA	0.100	3.26	8.94	12.20
5"	EA	0.107	4.13	9.53	13.66
6"	EA	0.114	7.14	10.25	17.39
8"	EA	0.133	11.50	12.00	23.50
Copper					
1/2"	EA	0.057	1.67	5.10	6.77
3/4"	EA	0.059	1.94	5.29	7.23
1"	EA	0.059	1.94	5.29	7.23
1-1/4"	EA	0.062	2.09	5.50	7.59
1-1/2"	EA	0.067	2.24	5.96	8.20
2"	EA	0.073	2.37	6.50	8.87

© 2020 BNi Publications, Inc.

22062.91 PIPE HANGERS, LIGHT (Cont.)

	Unit	Man-Hrs	Material	Labor	Total
Copper					
2-1/2"	EA	0.080	4.79	7.15	11.94
3"	EA	0.089	4.99	7.94	12.93
4"	EA	0.100	5.51	8.94	14.45
Black riser friction hangers					
3/4"	EA	0.067	4.22	5.96	10.18
1"	EA	0.070	4.27	6.21	10.48
1-1/4"	EA	0.073	5.34	6.50	11.84
1-1/2"	EA	0.076	5.80	6.81	12.61
2"	EA	0.080	5.91	7.15	13.06
2-1/2"	EA	0.089	6.38	7.94	14.32
3"	EA	0.100	6.56	8.94	15.50
4"	EA	0.114	8.37	10.25	18.62
Short pattern black riser clamps					
1-1/2"	EA	0.073	5.55	6.50	12.05
2"	EA	0.076	5.81	6.81	12.62
3"	EA	0.080	6.38	7.15	13.53
4"	EA	0.089	7.32	7.94	15.26
Copper riser friction hanger					
1/2"	EA	0.062	7.19	5.50	12.69
3/4"	EA	0.064	7.40	5.72	13.12
1"	EA	0.067	7.54	5.96	13.50
1-1/4"	EA	0.070	9.39	6.21	15.60
1-1/2"	EA	0.073	10.25	6.50	16.75
2"	EA	0.076	10.50	6.81	17.31
2-1/2"	EA	0.080	11.25	7.15	18.40
3"	EA	0.080	11.50	7.15	18.65
4"	EA	0.089	14.75	7.94	22.69
Auto grip hangers, galvanized					
1/2"	EA	0.057	1.03	5.10	6.13
1"	EA	0.064	1.22	5.72	6.94
2"	EA	0.073	2.03	6.50	8.53
3"	EA	0.080	4.02	7.15	11.17
4"	EA	0.089	4.98	7.94	12.92
Copper					
1/2"	EA	0.057	1.70	5.10	6.80
1"	EA	0.064	1.98	5.72	7.70
2"	EA	0.073	3.28	6.50	9.78
3"	EA	0.080	6.45	7.15	13.60
4"	EA	0.089	7.98	7.94	15.92
Split rings (F&M), galvanized					
1/2"	EA	0.062	3.38	5.50	8.88
1"	EA	0.067	4.67	5.96	10.63
2"	EA	0.076	6.69	6.81	13.50
3"	EA	0.084	16.25	7.52	23.77
4"	EA	0.089	17.00	7.94	24.94
Copper					
1/2"	EA	0.062	5.11	5.50	10.61
1"	EA	0.067	7.06	5.96	13.02
2"	EA	0.076	10.00	6.81	16.81
3"	EA	0.084	24.50	7.52	32.02
4"	EA	0.089	25.50	7.94	33.44
2 hole clips, galvanized					
3/4"	EA	0.053	0.27	4.76	5.03
1"	EA	0.055	0.30	4.93	5.23
1-1/4"	EA	0.057	0.39	5.10	5.49
1-1/2"	EA	0.059	0.48	5.29	5.77
2"	EA	0.062	0.63	5.50	6.13
2-1/2"	EA	0.064	1.14	5.72	6.86
3"	EA	0.067	1.66	5.96	7.62
4"	EA	0.073	3.56	6.50	10.06
Perforated strap					
3/4"					
Galvanized, 20 ga.	LF	0.040	0.44	3.57	4.01
Copper, 22 ga.	LF	0.040	0.69	3.57	4.26

	Unit	Man-Hrs	Material	Labor	Total
22062.91 PIPE HANGERS, LIGHT (Cont.)					
Threaded rod couplings					
1/4"	EA	0.050	1.57	4.47	6.04
3/4"	EA	0.053	1.65	4.76	6.41
1/2"	EA	0.057	1.87	5.10	6.97
5/8"	EA	0.062	2.88	5.50	8.38
Reducing rod coupling, 1/2" x 3/8"	EA	0.057	2.59	5.10	7.69
C-clamps					
3/4"	EA	0.080	2.24	7.15	9.39
Top beam clamp					
3/8"	EA	0.067	3.45	5.96	9.41
1/2"	EA	0.073	4.27	6.50	10.77
Side beam connector					
3/8"	EA	0.067	1.49	5.96	7.45
1/2"	EA	0.073	3.31	6.50	9.81
Hex nuts, heavy, material only					
1"	EA				3.80
Heavy washers					
3/8"	EA				0.11
1/2"	EA				0.26
5/8"	EA				0.53
3/4"	EA				1.06
Lag rod, 3/8" x					
4"	EA				0.49
4-1/2"	EA				0.49
6"	EA				0.51
8"	EA				0.92
10"	EA				1.08
12"	EA				1.34
18"	EA				1.81
J-Hooks					
1/2"	EA	0.036	0.79	3.25	4.04
3/4"	EA	0.036	0.84	3.25	4.09
1"	EA	0.038	0.86	3.40	4.26
1-1/4"	EA	0.039	0.91	3.48	4.39
1-1/2"	EA	0.040	0.93	3.57	4.50
2"	EA	0.040	0.97	3.57	4.54
3"	EA	0.042	1.12	3.76	4.88
4"	EA	0.042	1.21	3.76	4.97
PVC coated hangers, galvanized, 28 ga.					
1-1/2" x 12"	EA	0.053	1.29	4.76	6.05
2" x 12"	EA	0.057	1.41	5.10	6.51
3" x 12"	EA	0.062	1.58	5.50	7.08
4" x 12"	EA	0.067	1.76	5.96	7.72
Copper, 30 ga.					
1-1/2" x 12"	EA	0.053	1.99	4.76	6.75
2" x 12"	EA	0.057	2.36	5.10	7.46
3" x 12"	EA	0.062	2.61	5.50	8.11
4" x 12"	EA	0.067	2.87	5.96	8.83
Wire hook hangers					
Black wire, 1/2" x					
4"	EA	0.040	0.44	3.57	4.01
6"	EA	0.042	0.50	3.76	4.26
8"	EA	0.044	0.55	3.97	4.52
10"	EA	0.044	0.70	3.97	4.67
12"	EA	0.047	0.83	4.20	5.03
3/4" x					
4"	EA	0.042	0.53	3.76	4.29
6"	EA	0.044	0.58	3.97	4.55
8"	EA	0.047	0.59	4.20	4.79
10"	EA	0.050	0.81	4.47	5.28
12"	EA	0.053	0.82	4.76	5.58
1" x					
4"	EA	0.044	0.53	3.97	4.50
6"	EA	0.047	0.55	4.20	4.75

© 2020 BNi Publications, Inc.

	Unit	Man-Hrs	Material	Labor	Total
22062.91 PIPE HANGERS, LIGHT (Cont.)					
1" x					
8"	EA	0.050	0.59	4.47	5.06
10"	EA	0.053	0.80	4.76	5.56
12"	EA	0.057	0.86	5.10	5.96
Copper wire hooks					
1/2" x					
4"	EA	0.040	0.58	3.57	4.15
6"	EA	0.042	0.66	3.76	4.42
8"	EA	0.044	0.74	3.97	4.71
10"	EA	0.047	0.93	4.20	5.13
12"	EA	0.050	1.06	4.47	5.53
3/4" x					
4"	EA	0.042	0.58	3.76	4.34
6"	EA	0.044	0.72	3.97	4.69
8"	EA	0.047	0.83	4.20	5.03
10"	EA	0.050	0.95	4.47	5.42
12"	EA	0.053	1.13	4.76	5.89
22064.81 VIBRATION CONTROL					
VIBRATION CONTROL					
Vibration isolator, in-line, stainless connector					
1/2"	EA	0.444	100.00	39.75	139.75
1"	EA	0.500	120.00	44.75	164.75
2"	EA	0.615	230.00	55.00	285.00
3"	EA	0.727	400.00	65.00	465.00
6"	EA	0.889	860.00	79.00	939.00
22069.31 SPECIALTIES					
SPECIALTIES					
Wall penetration					
Concrete wall, 6" thick					
2" dia.	EA	0.267		17.00	17.00
4" dia.	EA	0.400		25.50	25.50
8" dia.	EA	0.571		36.50	36.50
12" thick					
2" dia.	EA	0.364		23.25	23.25
4" dia.	EA	0.571		36.50	36.50
8" dia.	EA	0.889		57.00	57.00
Non-destructive testing, piping systems					
X-ray of welds					
3" dia. pipe	EA	0.800	25.75	72.00	97.75
4" dia. pipe	EA	0.800	34.25	72.00	106.25
6" dia. pipe	EA	0.800	34.25	72.00	106.25
8" dia. pipe	EA	1.000	34.25	89.00	123.25
10" dia. pipe	EA	1.000	45.00	89.00	134.00
Liquid penetration of welds					
2" dia. pipe	EA	0.500	6.44	44.75	51.19
3" dia. pipe	EA	0.500	6.44	44.75	51.19
4" dia. pipe	EA	0.500	6.44	44.75	51.19
6" dia. pipe	EA	0.500	6.44	44.75	51.19
8" dia. pipe	EA	0.500	9.66	44.75	54.41
10" dia. pipe	EA	0.500	9.66	44.75	54.41
22071.61 EQUIPMENT INSULATION					
EQUIPMENT INSULATION					
Equipment insulation, 2" thick, cellular glass	SF	0.050	3.56	4.47	8.03
Urethane, rigid, jacket, plastered finish	SF	0.100	3.81	8.94	12.75
Fiberglass, rigid, with vapor barrier	SF	0.044	3.56	3.97	7.53
22071.91 FIBERGLASS PIPE INSULATION					
FIBERGLASS PIPE INSULATION					
Fiberglass insulation on 1/2" pipe					
1" thick	LF	0.027	1.25	2.38	3.63
1-1/2" thick	LF	0.033	2.64	2.98	5.62
3/4" pipe					
1" thick	LF	0.027	1.52	2.38	3.90
1-1/2" thick	LF	0.033	2.78	2.98	5.76

	Unit	Man-Hrs	Material	Labor	Total

22071.91 FIBERGLASS PIPE INSULATION (Cont.)

Fiberglass insulation

1" pipe

	Unit	Man-Hrs	Material	Labor	Total
1" thick	LF	0.027	1.52	2.38	3.90
1-1/2" thick	LF	0.033	2.91	2.98	5.89

2" pipe

	Unit	Man-Hrs	Material	Labor	Total
1" thick	LF	0.033	2.07	2.98	5.05
1-1/2" thick	LF	0.036	3.60	3.25	6.85
2" thick	LF	0.040	5.28	3.57	8.85

2-1/2" pipe

	Unit	Man-Hrs	Material	Labor	Total
1" thick	LF	0.033	2.21	2.98	5.19
1-1/2" thick	LF	0.036	3.88	3.25	7.13
2" thick	LF	0.040	5.63	3.57	9.20

3" pipe

	Unit	Man-Hrs	Material	Labor	Total
1" thick	LF	0.038	2.49	3.40	5.89
1-1/2" thick	LF	0.040	4.02	3.57	7.59
2" thick	LF	0.044	6.09	3.97	10.06

4" pipe

	Unit	Man-Hrs	Material	Labor	Total
1" thick	LF	0.038	3.19	3.40	6.59
1-1/2" thick	LF	0.040	4.57	3.57	8.14
2" thick	LF	0.044	7.01	3.97	10.98

5" pipe

	Unit	Man-Hrs	Material	Labor	Total
1" thick	LF	0.038	3.67	3.40	7.07
2" thick	LF	0.040	7.90	3.57	11.47

6" pipe

	Unit	Man-Hrs	Material	Labor	Total
1" thick	LF	0.042	4.15	3.76	7.91
2" thick	LF	0.044	8.61	3.97	12.58

8" pipe

	Unit	Man-Hrs	Material	Labor	Total
2" thick	LF	0.042	10.75	3.76	14.51
3" thick	LF	0.044	17.00	3.97	20.97

10" pipe

	Unit	Man-Hrs	Material	Labor	Total
2" thick	LF	0.042	13.25	3.76	17.01
3" thick	LF	0.044	19.75	3.97	23.72

12" pipe

	Unit	Man-Hrs	Material	Labor	Total
2" thick	LF	0.042	14.75	3.76	18.51
3" thick	LF	0.044	22.25	3.97	26.22

22071.93 EXTERIOR PIPE INSULATION

EXTERIOR PIPE INSULATION

Fiberglass insulation, aluminum jacket

1/2" pipe

	Unit	Man-Hrs	Material	Labor	Total
1" thick	LF	0.062	2.16	5.50	7.66
1-1/2" thick	LF	0.067	4.08	5.96	10.04

3/4" pipe

	Unit	Man-Hrs	Material	Labor	Total
1" thick	LF	0.062	2.55	5.50	8.05
1-1/2" thick	LF	0.067	4.33	5.96	10.29

1" pipe

	Unit	Man-Hrs	Material	Labor	Total
1" thick	LF	0.062	2.64	5.50	8.14
1-1/2" thick	LF	0.067	4.56	5.96	10.52

1-1/4" pipe

	Unit	Man-Hrs	Material	Labor	Total
1" thick	LF	0.073	2.95	6.50	9.45
1-1/2" thick	LF	0.076	4.94	6.81	11.75

1-1/2" pipe

	Unit	Man-Hrs	Material	Labor	Total
1" thick	LF	0.073	3.19	6.50	9.69
1-1/2" thick	LF	0.076	5.13	6.81	11.94

2" pipe

	Unit	Man-Hrs	Material	Labor	Total
1" thick	LF	0.073	3.60	6.50	10.10
1-1/2" thick	LF	0.076	5.36	6.81	12.17

3" pipe

	Unit	Man-Hrs	Material	Labor	Total
1" thick	LF	0.080	4.33	7.15	11.48
1-1/2" thick	LF	0.084	6.40	7.52	13.92

6" pipe

	Unit	Man-Hrs	Material	Labor	Total
1" thick	LF	0.089	7.19	7.94	15.13
2" thick	LF	0.094	12.75	8.41	21.16

© 2020 BNi Publications, Inc.

	Unit	Man-Hrs	Material	Labor	Total

22071.93 EXTERIOR PIPE INSULATION (Cont.)

Fiberglass insulation, aluminum jacket
10" pipe

	Unit	Man-Hrs	Material	Labor	Total
2" thick	LF	0.089	18.25	7.94	26.19
3" thick	LF	0.094	26.25	8.41	34.66

22071.94 PIPE INSULATION FITTINGS

PIPE INSULATION FITTINGS
Insulation protection saddle
1" thick covering

	Unit	Man-Hrs	Material	Labor	Total
1/2" pipe	EA	0.320	7.75	28.50	36.25
3/4" pipe	EA	0.320	7.97	28.50	36.47
1" pipe	EA	0.320	8.17	28.50	36.67
2" pipe	EA	0.320	9.01	28.50	37.51
3" pipe	EA	0.364	10.25	32.50	42.75
6" pipe	EA	0.500	10.25	44.75	55.00

1-1/2" thick covering

	Unit	Man-Hrs	Material	Labor	Total
3/4" pipe	EA	0.320	13.00	28.50	41.50
1" pipe	EA	0.320	13.25	28.50	41.75
2" pipe	EA	0.320	11.50	28.50	40.00
3" pipe	EA	0.320	13.00	28.50	41.50
6" pipe	EA	0.500	15.25	44.75	60.00
10" pipe	EA	0.667	16.00	60.00	76.00

22111.61 COPPER PIPE

COPPER PIPE
Type K copper

	Unit	Man-Hrs	Material	Labor	Total
1/2"	LF	0.025	3.77	2.23	6.00
3/4"	LF	0.027	7.03	2.38	9.41
1"	LF	0.029	9.20	2.55	11.75
1-1/4"	LF	0.031	11.50	2.75	14.25
1-1/2"	LF	0.033	15.00	2.98	17.98
2"	LF	0.036	23.00	3.25	26.25
2-1/2"	LF	0.040	33.75	3.57	37.32
3"	LF	0.042	47.00	3.76	50.76
4"	LF	0.044	78.00	3.97	81.97

DWV, copper

	Unit	Man-Hrs	Material	Labor	Total
1-1/4"	LF	0.033	10.25	2.98	13.23
1-1/2"	LF	0.036	13.00	3.25	16.25
2"	LF	0.040	17.00	3.57	20.57
3"	LF	0.044	29.00	3.97	32.97
4"	LF	0.050	50.00	4.47	54.47
6"	LF	0.057	200.00	5.10	205.10

Refrigeration tubing, copper, sealed

	Unit	Man-Hrs	Material	Labor	Total
1/8"	LF	0.032	0.73	2.86	3.59
3/16"	LF	0.033	0.85	2.98	3.83
1/4"	LF	0.035	1.02	3.10	4.12
5/16"	LF	0.036	1.31	3.25	4.56
3/8"	LF	0.038	1.51	3.40	4.91
1/2"	LF	0.040	1.98	3.57	5.55
7/8"	LF	0.046	4.81	4.08	8.89
1-1/8"	LF	0.053	6.90	4.76	11.66
1-3/8"	LF	0.062	10.50	5.50	16.00

Type L copper

	Unit	Man-Hrs	Material	Labor	Total
1/4"	LF	0.024	1.52	2.10	3.62
3/8"	LF	0.024	2.33	2.10	4.43
1/2"	LF	0.025	2.71	2.23	4.94
3/4"	LF	0.027	4.33	2.38	6.71
1"	LF	0.029	6.50	2.55	9.05
1-1/4"	LF	0.031	9.31	2.75	12.06
1-1/2"	LF	0.033	12.00	2.98	14.98
2"	LF	0.036	18.75	3.25	22.00
2-1/2"	LF	0.040	27.75	3.57	31.32
3"	LF	0.042	37.25	3.76	41.01
3-1/2"	LF	0.043	48.75	3.86	52.61
4"	LF	0.044	62.00	3.97	65.97

	Unit	Man-Hrs	Material	Labor	Total

22111.61 COPPER PIPE (Cont.)

Type M copper

	Unit	Man-Hrs	Material	Labor	Total
1/2"	LF	0.025	1.91	2.23	4.14
3/4"	LF	0.027	3.12	2.38	5.50
1"	LF	0.029	5.06	2.55	7.61
1-1/4"	LF	0.031	7.46	2.75	10.21
2"	LF	0.036	16.25	3.25	19.50
2-1/2"	LF	0.040	23.75	3.57	27.32
3"	LF	0.042	31.50	3.76	35.26
4"	LF	0.044	55.00	3.97	58.97

22111.62 COPPER FITTINGS

COPPER FITTINGS

Coupling, with stop

	Unit	Man-Hrs	Material	Labor	Total
1/4"	EA	0.267	0.95	23.75	24.70
3/8"	EA	0.320	1.24	28.50	29.74
1/2"	EA	0.348	0.99	31.00	31.99
5/8"	EA	0.400	2.87	35.75	38.62
3/4"	EA	0.444	1.97	39.75	41.72
1"	EA	0.471	4.06	42.00	46.06
3"	EA	0.800	49.25	72.00	121.25
4"	EA	1.000	110.00	89.00	199.00

Reducing coupling

	Unit	Man-Hrs	Material	Labor	Total
1/4" x 1/8"	EA	0.320	2.54	28.50	31.04
3/8" x 1/4"	EA	0.348	2.79	31.00	33.79
1/2" x					
3/8"	EA	0.400	2.10	35.75	37.85
1/4"	EA	0.400	2.54	35.75	38.29
1/8"	EA	0.400	2.80	35.75	38.55
3/4" x					
3/8"	EA	0.444	4.50	39.75	44.25
1/2"	EA	0.444	3.56	39.75	43.31
1" x					
3/8"	EA	0.500	8.08	44.75	52.83
1" x 1/2"	EA	0.500	7.82	44.75	52.57
1" x 3/4"	EA	0.500	6.59	44.75	51.34
1-1/4" x					
1/2"	EA	0.533	9.82	47.75	57.57
3/4"	EA	0.533	9.29	47.75	57.04
1"	EA	0.533	9.29	47.75	57.04
1-1/2" x					
1/2"	EA	0.571	16.25	51.00	67.25
3/4"	EA	0.571	15.50	51.00	66.50
1"	EA	0.571	15.50	51.00	66.50
1-1/4"	EA	0.571	15.50	51.00	66.50
2" x					
1/2"	EA	0.667	26.75	60.00	86.75
3/4"	EA	0.667	25.50	60.00	85.50
1"	EA	0.667	25.00	60.00	85.00
1-1/4"	EA	0.667	23.75	60.00	83.75
1-1/2"	EA	0.667	23.75	60.00	83.75
2-1/2" x					
1"	EA	0.800	61.00	72.00	133.00
1-1/4"	EA	0.800	61.00	72.00	133.00
1-1/2"	EA	0.800	54.00	72.00	126.00
2"	EA	0.800	53.00	72.00	125.00
3" x					
1-1/2"	EA	1.000	74.00	89.00	163.00
2"	EA	1.000	66.00	89.00	155.00
2-1/2"	EA	1.000	67.00	89.00	156.00
4" x					
2"	EA	1.143	150.00	100.00	250.00
2-1/2"	EA	1.143	150.00	100.00	250.00
3"	EA	1.143	130.00	100.00	230.00

© 2020 BNi Publications, Inc.

	Unit	Man-Hrs	Material	Labor	Total

22111.62 COPPER FITTINGS (Cont.)

Coupling, with stop
Slip coupling

	Unit	Man-Hrs	Material	Labor	Total
1/4"	EA	0.267	0.78	23.75	24.53
1/2"	EA	0.320	1.31	28.50	29.81
3/4"	EA	0.400	2.74	35.75	38.49
1"	EA	0.444	5.82	39.75	45.57
1-1/4"	EA	0.500	8.76	44.75	53.51
1-1/2"	EA	0.533	11.75	47.75	59.50
2"	EA	0.667	20.00	60.00	80.00
2-1/2"	EA	0.667	26.25	60.00	86.25
3"	EA	0.800	50.00	72.00	122.00
4"	EA	1.000	93.00	89.00	182.00

Coupling with drain

	Unit	Man-Hrs	Material	Labor	Total
1/2"	EA	0.400	10.00	35.75	45.75
3/4"	EA	0.444	14.75	39.75	54.50
1"	EA	0.500	18.25	44.75	63.00

Reducer

	Unit	Man-Hrs	Material	Labor	Total
3/8" x 1/4"	EA	0.320	2.85	28.50	31.35
1/2" x 3/8"	EA	0.320	2.29	28.50	30.79
3/4" x					
1/4"	EA	0.364	4.65	32.50	37.15
3/8"	EA	0.364	4.86	32.50	37.36
1/2"	EA	0.364	5.06	32.50	37.56
1" x					
1/2"	EA	0.400	6.99	35.75	42.74
3/4"	EA	0.400	5.36	35.75	41.11
1-1/4" x					
1/2"	EA	0.444	9.87	39.75	49.62
3/4"	EA	0.444	9.87	39.75	49.62
1"	EA	0.444	9.87	39.75	49.62
1-1/2" x					
1/2"	EA	0.500	12.75	44.75	57.50
3/4"	EA	0.500	12.75	44.75	57.50
1"	EA	0.500	12.75	44.75	57.50
1-1/4"	EA	0.500	12.75	44.75	57.50
2" x					
1/2"	EA	0.571	25.50	51.00	76.50
3/4"	EA	0.571	25.50	51.00	76.50
1"	EA	0.571	25.50	51.00	76.50
1-1/4"	EA	0.571	24.25	51.00	75.25
1-1/2"	EA	0.571	24.25	51.00	75.25
2-1/2" x					
1"	EA	0.667	56.00	60.00	116.00
1-1/4"	EA	0.667	50.00	60.00	110.00
1-1/2"	EA	0.667	49.25	60.00	109.25
2"	EA	0.667	48.25	60.00	108.25
3" x					
1-1/4"	EA	0.800	66.00	72.00	138.00
1-1/2"	EA	0.800	68.00	72.00	140.00
2"	EA	0.800	61.00	72.00	133.00
2-1/2"	EA	0.800	62.00	72.00	134.00
4" x					
2"	EA	1.000	140.00	89.00	229.00
3"	EA	1.000	130.00	89.00	219.00

Female adapters

	Unit	Man-Hrs	Material	Labor	Total
1/4"	EA	0.320	7.40	28.50	35.90
3/8"	EA	0.364	7.58	32.50	40.08
1/2"	EA	0.400	3.60	35.75	39.35
3/4"	EA	0.444	4.94	39.75	44.69
1"	EA	0.444	11.50	39.75	51.25
1-1/4"	EA	0.500	16.75	44.75	61.50
1-1/2"	EA	0.500	26.00	44.75	70.75
2"	EA	0.533	35.75	47.75	83.50
2-1/2"	EA	0.571	130.00	51.00	181.00

	Unit	Man-Hrs	Material	Labor	Total

22111.62 COPPER FITTINGS (Cont.)

Female adapters

	Unit	Man-Hrs	Material	Labor	Total
3"	EA	0.667	200.00	60.00	260.00
4"	EA	0.800	240.00	72.00	312.00

Increasing female adapters

1/8" x

	Unit	Man-Hrs	Material	Labor	Total
3/8"	EA	0.320	7.27	28.50	35.77
1/2"	EA	0.320	6.78	28.50	35.28
1/4" x 1/2"	EA	0.348	7.10	31.00	38.10
3/8" x 1/2"	EA	0.364	7.62	32.50	40.12

1/2" x

	Unit	Man-Hrs	Material	Labor	Total
3/4"	EA	0.400	8.08	35.75	43.83
1"	EA	0.400	16.25	35.75	52.00

3/4" x

	Unit	Man-Hrs	Material	Labor	Total
1"	EA	0.444	17.25	39.75	57.00
1-1/4"	EA	0.444	29.25	39.75	69.00

1" x

	Unit	Man-Hrs	Material	Labor	Total
1-1/4"	EA	0.444	31.00	39.75	70.75
1-1/2"	EA	0.444	34.00	39.75	73.75

1-1/4" x

	Unit	Man-Hrs	Material	Labor	Total
1-1/2"	EA	0.500	37.00	44.75	81.75
2"	EA	0.500	47.25	44.75	92.00
1-1/2" x 2"	EA	0.533	69.00	47.75	116.75

Reducing female adapters

	Unit	Man-Hrs	Material	Labor	Total
3/8" x 1/4"	EA	0.364	6.55	32.50	39.05

1/2" x

	Unit	Man-Hrs	Material	Labor	Total
1/4"	EA	0.400	5.63	35.75	41.38
3/8"	EA	0.400	5.63	35.75	41.38
3/4" x 1/2"	EA	0.444	7.86	39.75	47.61

1" x

	Unit	Man-Hrs	Material	Labor	Total
1/2"	EA	0.444	21.00	39.75	60.75
3/4"	EA	0.444	16.75	39.75	56.50

1-1/4" x

	Unit	Man-Hrs	Material	Labor	Total
1/2"	EA	0.500	28.50	44.75	73.25
3/4"	EA	0.500	35.50	44.75	80.25
1"	EA	0.500	35.50	44.75	80.25

1-1/2" x

	Unit	Man-Hrs	Material	Labor	Total
1"	EA	0.533	33.25	47.75	81.00
1-1/4"	EA	0.533	36.00	47.75	83.75

2" x

	Unit	Man-Hrs	Material	Labor	Total
1"	EA	0.571	45.00	51.00	96.00
1-1/4"	EA	0.571	67.00	51.00	118.00
1-1/2"	EA	0.571	58.00	51.00	109.00

Female fitting adapters

	Unit	Man-Hrs	Material	Labor	Total
1/2"	EA	0.400	10.00	35.75	45.75
3/4"	EA	0.400	13.00	35.75	48.75
3/4" x 1/2"	EA	0.421	15.50	37.75	53.25
1"	EA	0.444	17.25	39.75	57.00
1-1/4"	EA	0.471	27.75	42.00	69.75
1-1/2"	EA	0.500	36.50	44.75	81.25
2"	EA	0.533	48.50	47.75	96.25

Male adapters

	Unit	Man-Hrs	Material	Labor	Total
1/4"	EA	0.364	11.25	32.50	43.75
3/8"	EA	0.364	5.63	32.50	38.13
3"	EA	0.667	140.00	60.00	200.00
4"	EA	0.800	200.00	72.00	272.00

Increasing male adapters

	Unit	Man-Hrs	Material	Labor	Total
3/8" x 1/2"	EA	0.364	7.68	32.50	40.18

1/2" x

	Unit	Man-Hrs	Material	Labor	Total
3/4"	EA	0.400	6.66	35.75	42.41
1"	EA	0.400	15.00	35.75	50.75

3/4" x

	Unit	Man-Hrs	Material	Labor	Total
1"	EA	0.421	14.75	37.75	52.50
1-1/4"	EA	0.421	18.75	37.75	56.50
1" x 1-1/4"	EA	0.444	18.75	39.75	58.50

© 2020 BNi Publications, Inc.

	Unit	Man-Hrs	Material	Labor	Total

22111.62 COPPER FITTINGS (Cont.)

Increasing male adapters

1-1/2" x

	Unit	Man-Hrs	Material	Labor	Total
3/4"	EA	0.471	22.50	42.00	64.50
1"	EA	0.471	33.25	42.00	75.25
1-1/4"	EA	0.471	36.00	42.00	78.00

2" x

	Unit	Man-Hrs	Material	Labor	Total
1"	EA	0.500	85.00	44.75	129.75
1-1/4"	EA	0.500	87.00	44.75	131.75
1-1/2"	EA	0.500	83.00	44.75	127.75
2" x 2-1/2"	EA	0.533	140.00	47.75	187.75

Copper pipe fittings

1/2"

	Unit	Man-Hrs	Material	Labor	Total
90 deg ell	EA	0.178	1.62	16.00	17.62
45 deg ell	EA	0.178	2.04	16.00	18.04
Tee	EA	0.229	2.71	20.50	23.21
Cap	EA	0.089	1.10	7.94	9.04
Coupling	EA	0.178	1.18	16.00	17.18
Union	EA	0.200	8.21	18.00	26.21

3/4"

	Unit	Man-Hrs	Material	Labor	Total
90 deg ell	EA	0.200	3.54	18.00	21.54
45 deg ell	EA	0.200	4.13	18.00	22.13
Tee	EA	0.267	5.92	23.75	29.67
Cap	EA	0.094	2.15	8.41	10.56
Coupling	EA	0.200	2.40	18.00	20.40
Union	EA	0.229	12.00	20.50	32.50

1"

	Unit	Man-Hrs	Material	Labor	Total
90 deg ell	EA	0.267	8.21	23.75	31.96
45 deg ell	EA	0.267	10.75	23.75	34.50
Tee	EA	0.320	13.50	28.50	42.00
Cap	EA	0.133	4.00	12.00	16.00
Coupling	EA	0.267	5.92	23.75	29.67
Union	EA	0.267	15.75	23.75	39.50

1-1/4"

	Unit	Man-Hrs	Material	Labor	Total
90 deg ell	EA	0.229	11.25	20.50	31.75
45 deg ell	EA	0.229	13.75	20.50	34.25
Tee	EA	0.400	18.25	35.75	54.00
Cap	EA	0.133	3.19	12.00	15.19
Union	EA	0.286	26.25	25.50	51.75

1-1/2"

	Unit	Man-Hrs	Material	Labor	Total
90 deg ell	EA	0.286	14.50	25.50	40.00
45 deg ell	EA	0.286	17.25	25.50	42.75
Tee	EA	0.444	24.00	39.75	63.75
Cap	EA	0.133	3.19	12.00	15.19
Coupling	EA	0.267	10.75	23.75	34.50
Union	EA	0.364	39.75	32.50	72.25

2"

	Unit	Man-Hrs	Material	Labor	Total
90 deg ell	EA	0.320	28.50	28.50	57.00
45 deg ell	EA	0.500	26.25	44.75	71.00
Tee	EA	0.500	41.00	44.75	85.75
Cap	EA	0.160	6.61	14.25	20.86
Coupling	EA	0.320	17.25	28.50	45.75
Union	EA	0.400	43.25	35.75	79.00

2-1/2"

	Unit	Man-Hrs	Material	Labor	Total
90 deg ell	EA	0.400	55.00	35.75	90.75
45 deg ell	EA	0.400	47.75	35.75	83.50
Tee	EA	0.571	55.00	51.00	106.00
Cap	EA	0.200	13.50	18.00	31.50
Coupling	EA	0.400	26.25	35.75	62.00
Union	EA	0.444	80.00	39.75	119.75

22111.65 BRASS FITTINGS

BRASS FITTINGS

Compression fittings, union

	Unit	Man-Hrs	Material	Labor	Total
3/8"	EA	0.133	1.90	12.00	13.90
1/2"	EA	0.133	4.11	12.00	16.11

	Unit	Man-Hrs	Material	Labor	Total

22111.65 BRASS FITTINGS (Cont.)

Compression fittings, union

5/8"	EA	0.133	5.23	12.00	17.23

Union elbow

3/8"	EA	0.133	6.09	12.00	18.09
1/2"	EA	0.133	10.25	12.00	22.25
5/8"	EA	0.133	13.50	12.00	25.50

Union tee

3/8"	EA	0.133	5.71	12.00	17.71
1/2"	EA	0.133	8.26	12.00	20.26
5/8"	EA	0.133	11.50	12.00	23.50

Brass flare fittings, union

3/8"	EA	0.129	2.47	11.50	13.97
1/2"	EA	0.129	3.40	11.50	14.90
5/8"	EA	0.129	4.38	11.50	15.88

90 deg elbow union

3/8"	EA	0.129	5.30	11.50	16.80
1/2"	EA	0.129	7.76	11.50	19.26
5/8"	EA	0.129	13.50	11.50	25.00

22111.67 CHROME PLATED FITTINGS

CHROME PLATED FITTINGS

Fittings

90 ell

3/8"	EA	0.200	27.50	18.00	45.50
1/2"	EA	0.200	35.50	18.00	53.50

45 ell

3/8"	EA	0.200	35.50	18.00	53.50
1/2"	EA	0.200	46.75	18.00	64.75

Tee

3/8"	EA	0.267	34.00	23.75	57.75
1/2"	EA	0.267	40.50	23.75	64.25

Coupling

3/8"	EA	0.200	21.50	18.00	39.50
1/2"	EA	0.200	21.50	18.00	39.50

Union

3/8"	EA	0.200	35.50	18.00	53.50
1/2"	EA	0.200	36.75	18.00	54.75

Tee

1/2" x 3/8" x 3/8"	EA	0.267	40.50	23.75	64.25
1/2" x 3/8" x 1/2"	EA	0.267	41.25	23.75	65.00

22111.68 PVC/CPVC PIPE

PVC/CPVC PIPE

PVC schedule 40

1/2" pipe	LF	0.033	0.50	2.98	3.48
3/4" pipe	LF	0.036	0.69	3.25	3.94
1" pipe	LF	0.040	0.88	3.57	4.45
1-1/4" pipe	LF	0.044	1.13	3.97	5.10
1-1/2" pipe	LF	0.050	1.69	4.47	6.16
2" pipe	LF	0.057	2.14	5.10	7.24
2-1/2" pipe	LF	0.067	3.46	5.96	9.42
3" pipe	LF	0.080	4.41	7.15	11.56
4" pipe	LF	0.100	6.30	8.94	15.24
6" pipe	LF	0.200	11.25	18.00	29.25
8" pipe	LF	0.267	16.50	23.75	40.25

PVC schedule 80 pipe

1-1/2" pipe	LF	0.050	2.15	4.47	6.62
2" pipe	LF	0.057	2.91	5.10	8.01
3" pipe	LF	0.080	6.00	7.15	13.15
4" pipe	LF	0.100	7.84	8.94	16.78

Polypropylene, acid resistant, DWV pipe

Schedule 40

1-1/2" pipe	LF	0.057	9.18	5.10	14.28
2" pipe	LF	0.067	12.50	5.96	18.46
3" pipe	LF	0.080	25.25	7.15	32.40
4" pipe	LF	0.100	32.25	8.94	41.19

© 2020 BNi Publications, Inc.

	Unit	Man-Hrs	Material	Labor	Total
22111.68 PVC/CPVC PIPE (Cont.)					
Schedule 40					
6" pipe	LF	0.200	64.00	18.00	82.00
Polyethylene pipe and fittings					
SDR-21					
3" pipe	LF	0.100	4.12	8.94	13.06
4" pipe	LF	0.133	6.51	12.00	18.51
6" pipe	LF	0.200	11.25	18.00	29.25
8" pipe	LF	0.229	16.50	20.50	37.00
10" pipe	LF	0.267	18.50	23.75	42.25
22111.69 STEEL PIPE					
STEEL PIPE					
Black steel, extra heavy pipe, threaded					
1/2" pipe	LF	0.032	2.81	2.86	5.67
3/4" pipe	LF	0.032	3.64	2.86	6.50
1" pipe	LF	0.040	4.68	3.57	8.25
1-1/2" pipe	LF	0.044	7.03	3.97	11.00
2-1/2" pipe	LF	0.100	14.00	8.94	22.94
3" pipe	LF	0.133	18.75	12.00	30.75
4" pipe	LF	0.160	28.25	14.25	42.50
5" pipe	LF	0.200	38.25	18.00	56.25
6" pipe	LF	0.200	47.75	18.00	65.75
8" pipe	LF	0.267	70.00	23.75	93.75
10" pipe	LF	0.320	110.00	28.50	138.50
12" pipe	LF	0.400	140.00	35.75	175.75
Fittings, malleable iron, threaded, 1/2" pipe					
90 deg ell	EA	0.267	3.37	23.75	27.12
45 deg ell	EA	0.267	4.56	23.75	28.31
Tee	EA	0.400	3.66	35.75	39.41
3/4" pipe					
90 deg ell	EA	0.267	3.95	23.75	27.70
45 deg ell	EA	0.400	6.26	35.75	42.01
Tee	EA	0.400	5.31	35.75	41.06
1" pipe					
90 deg ell	EA	0.320	6.12	28.50	34.62
45 deg ell	EA	0.320	8.09	28.50	36.59
Tee	EA	0.444	9.18	39.75	48.93
1-1/2" pipe					
90 deg ell	EA	0.400	12.50	35.75	48.25
45 deg ell	EA	0.400	15.50	35.75	51.25
Tee	EA	0.571	18.25	51.00	69.25
2-1/2" pipe					
90 deg ell	EA	1.000	48.25	89.00	137.25
45 deg ell	EA	1.000	68.00	89.00	157.00
Tee	EA	1.333	67.00	120.00	187.00
3" pipe					
90 deg ell	EA	1.333	71.00	120.00	191.00
45 deg ell	EA	1.333	88.00	120.00	208.00
Tee	EA	2.000	99.00	180.00	279.00
4" pipe					
90 deg ell	EA	1.600	150.00	140.00	290.00
45 deg ell	EA	1.600	170.00	140.00	310.00
Tee	EA	2.667	240.00	240.00	480.00
90 deg ell	EA	1.600	420.00	140.00	560.00
6" pipe					
45 deg ell	EA	1.600	490.00	140.00	630.00
Tee	EA	2.667	750.00	240.00	990.00
8" pipe					
90 deg ell	EA	3.200	840.00	290.00	1,130.00
45 deg ell	EA	3.200	950.00	290.00	1,240.00
Tee	EA	5.000	590.00	450.00	1,040.00
10" pipe					
90 deg ell	EA	4.000	930.00	360.00	1,290.00
45 deg ell	EA	4.000	1,050.00	360.00	1,410.00
Tee	EA	5.000	670.00	450.00	1,120.00

	Unit	Man-Hrs	Material	Labor	Total

22111.69 STEEL PIPE (Cont.)

Fittings, malleable iron, threaded
12" pipe

	Unit	Man-Hrs	Material	Labor	Total
90 deg ell	EA	5.000	1,020.00	450.00	1,470.00
45 deg ell	EA	5.000	1,160.00	450.00	1,610.00
Tee	EA	6.667	780.00	600.00	1,380.00

22111.70 GALVANIZED STEEL PIPE

GALVANIZED STEEL PIPE
Galvanized pipe

	Unit	Man-Hrs	Material	Labor	Total
1/2" pipe	LF	0.080	3.31	7.15	10.46
3/4" pipe	LF	0.100	4.31	8.94	13.25
1" pipe	LF	0.114	6.61	10.25	16.86
1-1/4" pipe	LF	0.133	8.20	12.00	20.20
1-1/2" pipe	LF	0.160	9.00	14.25	23.25
2" pipe	LF	0.200	13.00	18.00	31.00
2-1/2" pipe	LF	0.267	18.75	23.75	42.50
3" pipe	LF	0.286	25.75	25.50	51.25
4" pipe	LF	0.333	35.25	29.75	65.00
6" pipe	LF	0.667	64.00	60.00	124.00

22111.71 STAINLESS STEEL PIPE

STAINLESS STEEL PIPE
Stainless steel, schedule 40, threaded

	Unit	Man-Hrs	Material	Labor	Total
1/2" pipe	LF	0.114	10.50	10.25	20.75
3/4" pipe	LF	0.118	14.75	10.50	25.25
1" pipe	LF	0.123	17.25	11.00	28.25
1-1/2" pipe	LF	0.133	23.50	12.00	35.50
2" pipe	LF	0.145	35.25	13.00	48.25
2-1/2" pipe	LF	0.160	49.50	14.25	63.75
3" pipe	LF	0.178	69.00	16.00	85.00
4" pipe	LF	0.200	89.00	18.00	107.00

22111.91 BACKFLOW PREVENTERS

BACKFLOW PREVENTERS
Backflow preventer, flanged, cast iron, with valves

	Unit	Man-Hrs	Material	Labor	Total
3" pipe	EA	4.000	4,030.00	360.00	4,390.00
4" pipe	EA	4.444	4,700.00	400.00	5,100.00
6" pipe	EA	6.667	8,030.00	600.00	8,630.00
8" pipe	EA	8.000	12,240.00	720.00	12,960.00
Threaded					
3/4" pipe	EA	0.500	750.00	44.75	794.75
2" pipe	EA	0.800	1,320.00	72.00	1,392.00
Reduced pressure assembly, bronze, threaded					
3/4"	EA	0.500	640.00	44.75	684.75
1"	EA	0.571	660.00	51.00	711.00
1-1/4"	EA	0.667	960.00	60.00	1,020.00
1-1/2"	EA	0.800	1,080.00	72.00	1,152.00

22111.96 VACUUM BREAKERS

VACUUM BREAKERS
Vacuum breaker, atmospheric, threaded connection

	Unit	Man-Hrs	Material	Labor	Total
3/4"	EA	0.320	55.00	28.50	83.50
1"	EA	0.320	81.00	28.50	109.50
Anti-siphon, brass					
3/4"	EA	0.320	60.00	28.50	88.50
1"	EA	0.320	93.00	28.50	121.50
1-1/4"	EA	0.400	160.00	35.75	195.75
1-1/2"	EA	0.444	190.00	39.75	229.75
2"	EA	0.500	300.00	44.75	344.75

22112.30 PUMPS

PUMPS
In-line pump, bronze, centrifugal

	Unit	Man-Hrs	Material	Labor	Total
5 gpm, 20' head	EA	0.500	680.00	44.75	724.75
20 gpm, 40' head	EA	0.500	1,220.00	44.75	1,264.75
50 gpm					
50' head	EA	1.000	1,390.00	89.00	1,479.00

	Unit	Man-Hrs	Material	Labor	Total

22112.30 PUMPS (Cont.)

In-line pump
  Cast iron, centrifugal

	Unit	Man-Hrs	Material	Labor	Total
50 gpm, 200' head	EA	1.000	1,320.00	89.00	1,409.00
100 gpm					
100' head	EA	1.333	2,250.00	120.00	2,370.00
Centrifugal, close coupled, C.I., single stage					
50 gpm, 100' head	EA	1.000	1,580.00	89.00	1,669.00
100 gpm, 100' head	EA	1.333	1,920.00	120.00	2,040.00
Base mounted					
50 gpm, 100' head	EA	1.000	3,220.00	89.00	3,309.00
100 gpm, 50' head	EA	1.333	3,660.00	120.00	3,780.00
200 gpm, 100' head	EA	2.000	4,690.00	180.00	4,870.00
300 gpm, 175' head	EA	2.000	6,080.00	180.00	6,260.00
Condensate pump, simplex					
1000 sf EDR, 2 gpm	EA	6.667	1,650.00	600.00	2,250.00
2000 sf EDR, 3 gpm	EA	6.667	1,680.00	600.00	2,280.00
4000 sf EDR, 6 gpm	EA	7.273	1,690.00	650.00	2,340.00
6000 sf EDR, 9 gpm	EA	7.273	1,720.00	650.00	2,370.00
Duplex, bronze					
8000 sf EDR, 12 gpm	EA	7.273	2,360.00	650.00	3,010.00
10,000 sf EDR, 15 gpm	EA	10.000	2,450.00	890.00	3,340.00
15,000 sf EDR, 23 gpm	EA	11.429	2,940.00	1,020.00	3,960.00
20,000 sf EDR, 30 gpm	EA	16.000	3,420.00	1,430.00	4,850.00
25,000 sf EDR, 38 gpm	EA	16.000	3,540.00	1,430.00	4,970.00

22120.04 STORAGE TANKS

STORAGE TANKS
  Hot water storage tank, cement lined

	Unit	Man-Hrs	Material	Labor	Total
10 gallon	EA	2.667	540.00	240.00	780.00
70 gallon	EA	4.000	1,700.00	360.00	2,060.00
200 gallon	EA	5.714	3,220.00	510.00	3,730.00
900 gallon	EA	10.000	13,370.00	890.00	14,260.00
1100 gallon	EA	10.000	17,870.00	890.00	18,760.00
2000 gallon	EA	10.000	25,520.00	890.00	26,410.00

22131.40 EXTRA HEAVY SOIL PIPE

EXTRA HEAVY SOIL PIPE
  Extra heavy soil pipe, single hub

	Unit	Man-Hrs	Material	Labor	Total
2" x 5'	EA	0.160	70.00	14.25	84.25
3" x 5'	EA	0.170	78.00	15.25	93.25
4" x 5'	EA	0.186	90.00	16.75	106.75
6" x 5'	EA	0.200	170.00	18.00	188.00
Double hub					
2" x 5'	EA	0.200	78.00	18.00	96.00
4" x 5'	EA	0.211	99.00	18.75	117.75
5" x 5'	EA	0.222	150.00	19.75	169.75
6" x 5'	EA	0.229	180.00	20.50	200.50
Single hub					
3" x 10'	EA	0.133	160.00	12.00	172.00
4" x 10'	EA	0.138	200.00	12.25	212.25
6" x 10'	EA	0.145	310.00	13.00	323.00

22131.60 C.I. PIPE, ABOVE GROUND

C.I. PIPE, ABOVE GROUND
  No hub pipe

	Unit	Man-Hrs	Material	Labor	Total
1-1/2" pipe	LF	0.057	12.25	5.10	17.35
2" pipe	LF	0.067	10.75	5.96	16.71
3" pipe	LF	0.080	15.00	7.15	22.15
4" pipe	LF	0.133	19.50	12.00	31.50
6" pipe	LF	0.160	34.50	14.25	48.75
8" pipe	LF	0.267	55.00	23.75	78.75
10" pipe	LF	0.320	87.00	28.50	115.50

	Unit	Man-Hrs	Material	Labor	Total
22131.60 C.I. PIPE, ABOVE GROUND (Cont.)					
No hub pipe					
No hub fittings, 1-1/2" pipe					
1/4 bend	EA	0.267	11.25	23.75	35.00
1/8 bend	EA	0.267	9.48	23.75	33.23
Sanitary tee	EA	0.400	15.75	35.75	51.50
Coupling	EA				22.50
Wye	EA	0.400	19.75	35.75	55.50
2" pipe					
1/4 bend	EA	0.320	13.00	28.50	41.50
1/8 bend	EA	0.320	10.50	28.50	39.00
Sanitary tee	EA	0.533	18.00	47.75	65.75
Coupling	EA				19.75
Wye	EA	0.667	16.75	60.00	76.75
3" pipe					
1/4 bend	EA	0.400	18.00	35.75	53.75
1/8 bend	EA	0.400	15.00	35.75	50.75
Sanitary tee	EA	0.500	22.00	44.75	66.75
Coupling	EA				22.50
Wye	EA	0.667	23.75	60.00	83.75
4" pipe					
1/4 bend	EA	0.400	26.00	35.75	61.75
1/8 bend	EA	0.400	19.00	35.75	54.75
Sanitary tee	EA	0.667	34.00	60.00	94.00
Coupling	EA				22.00
Wye	EA	0.667	38.75	60.00	98.75
6" pipe					
1/4 bend	EA	0.667	65.00	60.00	125.00
1/8 bend	EA	0.667	44.00	60.00	104.00
Sanitary tee	EA	0.800	99.00	72.00	171.00
Coupling	EA				56.00
Wye	EA	0.800	100.00	72.00	172.00
8" pipe					
1/4 bend	EA	0.667	110.00	60.00	170.00
1/8 bend	EA	0.667	80.00	60.00	140.00
Sanitary tee	EA	1.000	250.00	89.00	339.00
Coupling	EA				110.00
Wye	EA	0.800	150.00	72.00	222.00
10" pipe					
1/4 bend	EA	0.667	230.00	60.00	290.00
1/8 bend	EA	0.667	150.00	60.00	210.00
Coupling	EA				140.00
Wye	EA	1.333	330.00	120.00	450.00
10x6" wye	EA	1.333	240.00	120.00	360.00
22131.61 C.I. PIPE, BELOW GROUND					
C.I. PIPE, BELOW GROUND					
No hub pipe					
1-1/2" pipe	LF	0.040	9.96	3.57	13.53
2" pipe	LF	0.044	10.25	3.97	14.22
3" pipe	LF	0.050	14.25	4.47	18.72
4" pipe	LF	0.067	18.25	5.96	24.21
6" pipe	LF	0.073	31.50	6.50	38.00
8" pipe	LF	0.089	49.00	7.94	56.94
10" pipe	LF	0.100	82.00	8.94	90.94
Fittings, 1-1/2"					
1/4 bend	EA	0.229	12.00	20.50	32.50
1/8 bend	EA	0.229	9.93	20.50	30.43
Wye	EA	0.320	16.75	28.50	45.25
2"					
1/4 bend	EA	0.267	13.00	23.75	36.75
1/8 bend	EA	0.267	11.00	23.75	34.75
3"					
1/4 bend	EA	0.320	18.00	28.50	46.50
1/8 bend	EA	0.320	15.00	28.50	43.50
Wye	EA	0.500	23.75	44.75	68.50

© 2020 BNi Publications, Inc.

	Unit	Man-Hrs	Material	Labor	Total
22131.61 C.I. PIPE, BELOW GROUND (Cont.)					
Fittings					
4"					
1/4 bend	EA	0.320	26.00	28.50	54.50
1/8 bend	EA	0.320	19.00	28.50	47.50
Wye	EA	0.500	38.75	44.75	83.50
6"					
1/4 bend	EA	0.500	41.25	44.75	86.00
1/8 bend	EA	0.500	27.75	44.75	72.50
8"					
1/4 bend	EA	0.500	110.00	44.75	154.75
1/8 bend	EA	0.500	80.00	44.75	124.75
Wye	EA	0.667	150.00	60.00	210.00
10"					
1/4 bend	EA	0.500	230.00	44.75	274.75
1/8 bend	EA	0.500	150.00	44.75	194.75
Plug	EA				70.00
Wye	EA	1.000	330.00	89.00	419.00
22131.63 ABS DWV PIPE					
ABS DWV PIPE					
Schedule 40 ABS					
1-1/2" pipe	LF	0.040	1.58	3.57	5.15
2" pipe	LF	0.044	2.11	3.97	6.08
3" pipe	LF	0.057	4.32	5.10	9.42
4" pipe	LF	0.080	6.12	7.15	13.27
6" pipe	LF	0.100	12.50	8.94	21.44
22131.65 PLASTIC PIPE					
PLASTIC PIPE					
Fiberglass reinforced pipe					
2" pipe	LF	0.062	4.38	5.50	9.88
3" pipe	LF	0.067	6.23	5.96	12.19
4" pipe	LF	0.073	8.14	6.50	14.64
6" pipe	LF	0.080	15.50	7.15	22.65
8" pipe	LF	0.133	22.75	12.00	34.75
10" pipe	LF	0.160	34.00	14.25	48.25
12" pipe	LF	0.200	44.25	18.00	62.25
22131.67 DRAINS, ROOF & FLOOR					
DRAINS, ROOF & FLOOR					
Floor drain, cast iron, with cast iron top					
2"	EA	0.667	180.00	60.00	240.00
3"	EA	0.667	180.00	60.00	240.00
4"	EA	0.667	390.00	60.00	450.00
6"	EA	0.800	500.00	72.00	572.00
Roof drain, cast iron					
2"	EA	0.667	280.00	60.00	340.00
3"	EA	0.667	290.00	60.00	350.00
4"	EA	0.667	370.00	60.00	430.00
5"	EA	0.800	540.00	72.00	612.00
6"	EA	0.800	550.00	72.00	622.00
22131.68 TRAPS					
TRAPS					
Bucket trap, threaded					
3/4"	EA	0.500	230.00	44.75	274.75
1"	EA	0.533	650.00	47.75	697.75
1-1/4"	EA	0.615	770.00	55.00	825.00
1-1/2"	EA	0.727	1,160.00	65.00	1,225.00
Inverted bucket steam trap, threaded					
3/4"	EA	0.500	280.00	44.75	324.75
1"	EA	0.500	550.00	44.75	594.75
1-1/4"	EA	0.444	830.00	39.75	869.75
1-1/2"	EA	0.667	880.00	60.00	940.00
Float trap, 15 psi					
3/4"	EA	0.500	200.00	44.75	244.75

	Unit	Man-Hrs	Material	Labor	Total
22131.68 TRAPS (Cont.)					
Float trap, 15 psi					
1"	EA	0.533	310.00	47.75	357.75
1-1/4"	EA	0.571	400.00	51.00	451.00
1-1/2"	EA	0.667	510.00	60.00	570.00
2"	EA	0.800	880.00	72.00	952.00
Float and thermostatic trap, 15 psi					
3/4"	EA	0.500	210.00	44.75	254.75
1"	EA	0.533	240.00	47.75	287.75
1-1/4"	EA	0.571	370.00	51.00	421.00
1-1/2"	EA	0.667	480.00	60.00	540.00
2"	EA	0.800	880.00	72.00	952.00
Steam trap, cast iron body, threaded, 125 psi					
3/4"	EA	0.500	250.00	44.75	294.75
1"	EA	0.533	290.00	47.75	337.75
1-1/4"	EA	0.571	430.00	51.00	481.00
1-1/2"	EA	0.667	690.00	60.00	750.00
22131.92 CLEANOUTS					
CLEANOUTS					
Cleanout, wall					
2"	EA	0.533	240.00	47.75	287.75
3"	EA	0.533	340.00	47.75	387.75
4"	EA	0.667	340.00	60.00	400.00
6"	EA	0.800	560.00	72.00	632.00
8"	EA	1.000	780.00	89.00	869.00
Floor					
2"	EA	0.667	220.00	60.00	280.00
3"	EA	0.667	290.00	60.00	350.00
4"	EA	0.800	300.00	72.00	372.00
6"	EA	1.000	410.00	89.00	499.00
8"	EA	1.143	770.00	100.00	870.00
22131.93 GREASE TRAPS					
GREASE TRAPS					
Grease traps, cast iron, 3" pipe					
35 gpm, 70 lb capacity	EA	8.000	5,320.00	720.00	6,040.00
50 gpm, 100 lb capacity	EA	10.000	6,780.00	890.00	7,670.00
22330.01 DOMESTIC WATER HEATERS					
DOMESTIC WATER HEATERS					
Water heater, electric					
6 gal	EA	1.333	450.00	120.00	570.00
10 gal	EA	1.333	460.00	120.00	580.00
15 gal	EA	1.333	450.00	120.00	570.00
20 gal	EA	1.600	630.00	140.00	770.00
30 gal	EA	1.600	650.00	140.00	790.00
40 gal	EA	1.600	710.00	140.00	850.00
52 gal	EA	2.000	800.00	180.00	980.00
66 gal	EA	2.000	970.00	180.00	1,150.00
80 gal	EA	2.000	1,050.00	180.00	1,230.00
100 gal	EA	2.667	1,300.00	240.00	1,540.00
120 gal	EA	2.667	1,670.00	240.00	1,910.00
Oil fired					
20 gal	EA	4.000	1,430.00	360.00	1,790.00
50 gal	EA	5.714	2,230.00	510.00	2,740.00
Tankless water heater, natural gas					
Minimum	EA	5.333	770.00	480.00	1,250.00
Average	EA	8.000	880.00	720.00	1,600.00
Maximum	EA	16.000	990.00	1,430.00	2,420.00
Propane					
Minimum	EA	5.333	660.00	480.00	1,140.00
Average	EA	8.000	770.00	720.00	1,490.00
Maximum	EA	16.000	880.00	1,430.00	2,310.00
For trim and rough-in					
Minimum	EA	2.667	210.00	240.00	450.00
Average	EA	4.000	300.00	360.00	660.00
Maximum	EA	8.000	860.00	720.00	1,580.00

© 2020 BNi Publications, Inc.

	Unit	Man-Hrs	Material	Labor	Total
22330.02 SOLAR WATER HEATERS					
SOLAR WATER HEATERS					
Hydronic system, 100-120 Gallons including material					
Minimum	EA				14,360.00
Average	EA				15,120.00
Maximum	EA				15,880.00
Direct-Solar, 100-120 Gallons					
Minimum	EA				9,530.00
Average	EA				9,970.00
Maximum	EA				10,420.00
Indirect-Solar tank, 50-80 Gallons					
Minimum	EA				1,910.00
Average	EA				2,350.00
Maximum	EA				2,800.00
100-120 Gallons					
Minimum	EA				3,180.00
Average	EA				3,620.00
Maximum	EA				4,070.00
Solar water collector panel, 3 x 8					
Minimum	EA	1.000	1,020.00	89.00	1,109.00
Average	EA	1.143	1,050.00	100.00	1,150.00
Maximum	EA	1.333	1,080.00	120.00	1,200.00
4 x 7					
Minimum	EA	1.000	1,140.00	89.00	1,229.00
Average	EA	1.143	1,180.00	100.00	1,280.00
Maximum	EA	1.333	1,210.00	120.00	1,330.00
4 x 8					
Minimum	EA	1.000	1,210.00	89.00	1,299.00
Average	EA	1.143	1,240.00	100.00	1,340.00
Maximum	EA	1.333	1,270.00	120.00	1,390.00
4 x 10					
Minimum	EA	1.143	1,400.00	100.00	1,500.00
Average	EA	1.333	1,520.00	120.00	1,640.00
Maximum	EA	1.600	1,650.00	140.00	1,790.00
Passive tube tank system, 12 Tube					
Minimum	EA	1.000	760.00	89.00	849.00
Average	EA	1.143	950.00	100.00	1,050.00
Maximum	EA	1.333	1,140.00	120.00	1,260.00
24 Tube					
Minimum	EA	1.000	1,140.00	89.00	1,229.00
Average	EA	1.143	1,330.00	100.00	1,430.00
Maximum	EA	1.333	1,520.00	120.00	1,640.00
27 Tube					
Minimum	EA	1.000	1,270.00	89.00	1,359.00
Average	EA	1.143	1,590.00	100.00	1,690.00
Maximum	EA	1.333	1,910.00	120.00	2,030.00
22420.09 FIXTURE CARRIERS					
FIXTURE CARRIERS					
Water fountain, wall carrier					
Minimum	EA	0.800	70.00	72.00	142.00
Average	EA	1.000	94.00	89.00	183.00
Maximum	EA	1.333	120.00	120.00	240.00
Lavatory, wall carrier					
Minimum	EA	0.800	160.00	72.00	232.00
Average	EA	1.000	230.00	89.00	319.00
Maximum	EA	1.333	290.00	120.00	410.00
Sink, industrial, wall carrier					
Minimum	EA	0.800	210.00	72.00	282.00
Average	EA	1.000	240.00	89.00	329.00
Maximum	EA	1.333	300.00	120.00	420.00
Toilets, water closets, wall carrier					
Minimum	EA	0.800	310.00	72.00	382.00
Average	EA	1.000	360.00	89.00	449.00
Maximum	EA	1.333	470.00	120.00	590.00

	Unit	Man-Hrs	Material	Labor	Total
22420.09 FIXTURE CARRIERS (Cont.)					
Toilets, water closets, wall carrier					
Floor support					
Minimum	EA	0.667	150.00	60.00	210.00
Average	EA	0.800	180.00	72.00	252.00
Maximum	EA	1.000	200.00	89.00	289.00
Urinals, wall carrier					
Minimum	EA	0.800	160.00	72.00	232.00
Average	EA	1.000	210.00	89.00	299.00
Maximum	EA	1.333	250.00	120.00	370.00
Floor support					
Minimum	EA	0.667	130.00	60.00	190.00
Average	EA	0.800	190.00	72.00	262.00
Maximum	EA	1.000	220.00	89.00	309.00
22421.35 URINALS					
URINALS					
Urinal, flush valve, floor mounted					
Minimum	EA	2.000	600.00	180.00	780.00
Average	EA	2.667	710.00	240.00	950.00
Maximum	EA	4.000	830.00	360.00	1,190.00
Wall mounted					
Minimum	EA	2.000	490.00	180.00	670.00
Average	EA	2.667	680.00	240.00	920.00
Maximum	EA	4.000	880.00	360.00	1,240.00
For trim and rough-in					
Minimum	EA	2.000	220.00	180.00	400.00
Average	EA	4.000	320.00	360.00	680.00
Maximum	EA	5.333	430.00	480.00	910.00
22421.36 WATER CLOSETS					
WATER CLOSETS					
Water closet flush tank, floor mounted					
Minimum	EA	2.000	400.00	180.00	580.00
Average	EA	2.667	790.00	240.00	1,030.00
Maximum	EA	4.000	1,240.00	360.00	1,600.00
Handicapped					
Minimum	EA	2.667	540.00	240.00	780.00
Average	EA	4.000	970.00	360.00	1,330.00
Maximum	EA	8.000	1,850.00	720.00	2,570.00
Bowl, with flush valve, floor mounted					
Minimum	EA	2.000	560.00	180.00	740.00
Average	EA	2.667	610.00	240.00	850.00
Maximum	EA	4.000	1,200.00	360.00	1,560.00
Wall mounted					
Minimum	EA	2.000	560.00	180.00	740.00
Average	EA	2.667	650.00	240.00	890.00
Maximum	EA	4.000	1,250.00	360.00	1,610.00
For trim and rough-in					
Minimum	EA	2.000	250.00	180.00	430.00
Average	EA	2.667	300.00	240.00	540.00
Maximum	EA	4.000	400.00	360.00	760.00
22421.62 LAVATORIES					
LAVATORIES					
Lavatory, countertop, porcelain enamel on cast iron					
Minimum	EA	1.600	230.00	140.00	370.00
Average	EA	2.000	350.00	180.00	530.00
Maximum	EA	2.667	630.00	240.00	870.00
Wall hung, china					
Minimum	EA	1.600	320.00	140.00	460.00
Average	EA	2.000	370.00	180.00	550.00
Maximum	EA	2.667	930.00	240.00	1,170.00
Handicapped					
Minimum	EA	2.000	520.00	180.00	700.00
Average	EA	2.667	600.00	240.00	840.00
Maximum	EA	4.000	1,000.00	360.00	1,360.00

© 2020 BNi Publications, Inc.

	Unit	Man-Hrs	Material	Labor	Total
22421.62 LAVATORIES (Cont.)					
Lavatory, countertop, porcelain enamel on cast iron					
For trim and rough-in					
Minimum	EA	2.000	270.00	180.00	450.00
Average	EA	2.667	450.00	240.00	690.00
Maximum	EA	4.000	560.00	360.00	920.00
22421.64 SINKS					
SINKS					
Service sink, 24"x29"					
Minimum	EA	2.000	770.00	180.00	950.00
Average	EA	2.667	960.00	240.00	1,200.00
Maximum	EA	4.000	1,410.00	360.00	1,770.00
Kitchen sink, single, stainless steel, single bowl					
Minimum	EA	1.600	340.00	140.00	480.00
Average	EA	2.000	390.00	180.00	570.00
Maximum	EA	2.667	710.00	240.00	950.00
Double bowl					
Minimum	EA	2.000	390.00	180.00	570.00
Average	EA	2.667	430.00	240.00	670.00
Maximum	EA	4.000	750.00	360.00	1,110.00
Porcelain enamel, cast iron, single bowl					
Minimum	EA	1.600	240.00	140.00	380.00
Average	EA	2.000	320.00	180.00	500.00
Maximum	EA	2.667	490.00	240.00	730.00
Double bowl					
Minimum	EA	2.000	330.00	180.00	510.00
Average	EA	2.667	470.00	240.00	710.00
Maximum	EA	4.000	670.00	360.00	1,030.00
Mop sink, 24"x36"x10"					
Minimum	EA	1.600	590.00	140.00	730.00
Average	EA	2.000	710.00	180.00	890.00
Maximum	EA	2.667	950.00	240.00	1,190.00
Washing machine box					
Minimum	EA	2.000	210.00	180.00	390.00
Average	EA	2.667	310.00	240.00	550.00
Maximum	EA	4.000	370.00	360.00	730.00
For trim and rough-in					
Minimum	EA	2.667	350.00	240.00	590.00
Average	EA	4.000	530.00	360.00	890.00
Maximum	EA	5.333	680.00	480.00	1,160.00
22421.90 BATHS					
BATHS					
Bathtub, 5' long					
Minimum	EA	2.667	640.00	240.00	880.00
Average	EA	4.000	1,400.00	360.00	1,760.00
Maximum	EA	8.000	3,190.00	720.00	3,910.00
6' long					
Minimum	EA	2.667	720.00	240.00	960.00
Average	EA	4.000	1,460.00	360.00	1,820.00
Maximum	EA	8.000	4,140.00	720.00	4,860.00
Square tub, whirlpool, 4'x4'					
Minimum	EA	4.000	2,200.00	360.00	2,560.00
Average	EA	8.000	3,110.00	720.00	3,830.00
Maximum	EA	10.000	9,500.00	890.00	10,390.00
5'x5'					
Minimum	EA	4.000	2,200.00	360.00	2,560.00
Average	EA	8.000	3,110.00	720.00	3,830.00
Maximum	EA	10.000	9,680.00	890.00	10,570.00
6'x6'					
Minimum	EA	4.000	2,680.00	360.00	3,040.00
Average	EA	8.000	3,910.00	720.00	4,630.00
Maximum	EA	10.000	11,220.00	890.00	12,110.00
For trim and rough-in					
Minimum	EA	2.667	230.00	240.00	470.00

	Unit	Man-Hrs	Material	Labor	Total
22421.90 BATHS (Cont.)					
For trim and rough-in					
Average	EA	4.000	330.00	360.00	690.00
Maximum	EA	8.000	950.00	720.00	1,670.00
22422.30 SHOWERS					
SHOWERS					
Shower, fiberglass, 36"x34"x84"					
Minimum	EA	5.714	690.00	510.00	1,200.00
Average	EA	8.000	970.00	720.00	1,690.00
Maximum	EA	8.000	1,400.00	720.00	2,120.00
Steel, 1 piece, 36"x36"					
Minimum	EA	5.714	640.00	510.00	1,150.00
Average	EA	8.000	970.00	720.00	1,690.00
Maximum	EA	8.000	1,140.00	720.00	1,860.00
Receptor, molded stone, 36"x36"					
Minimum	EA	2.667	270.00	240.00	510.00
Average	EA	4.000	450.00	360.00	810.00
Maximum	EA	6.667	690.00	600.00	1,290.00
For trim and rough-in					
Minimum	EA	3.636	270.00	330.00	600.00
Average	EA	4.444	450.00	400.00	850.00
Maximum	EA	8.000	560.00	720.00	1,280.00
22422.60 DISPOSALS & ACCESSORIES					
DISPOSALS & ACCESSORIES					
Disposal, continuous feed					
Minimum	EA	1.600	83.00	140.00	223.00
Maximum	EA	2.667	440.00	240.00	680.00
Batch feed, 1/2 hp					
Minimum	EA	1.600	320.00	140.00	460.00
Maximum	EA	2.667	1,090.00	240.00	1,330.00
Hot water dispenser					
Minimum	EA	1.600	230.00	140.00	370.00
Maximum	EA	2.667	580.00	240.00	820.00
22423.90 FAUCETS					
FAUCETS					
Kitchen					
Minimum	EA	1.333	95.00	120.00	215.00
Average	EA	1.600	270.00	140.00	410.00
Maximum	EA	2.000	330.00	180.00	510.00
Bath					
Minimum	EA	1.333	95.00	120.00	215.00
Average	EA	1.600	280.00	140.00	420.00
Maximum	EA	2.000	430.00	180.00	610.00
Lavatory, domestic					
Minimum	EA	1.333	100.00	120.00	220.00
Average	EA	1.600	320.00	140.00	460.00
Maximum	EA	2.000	530.00	180.00	710.00
Hospital, patient rooms					
Minimum	EA	2.000	140.00	180.00	320.00
Average	EA	2.667	440.00	240.00	680.00
Maximum	EA	4.000	780.00	360.00	1,140.00
Operating room					
Minimum	EA	2.000	290.00	180.00	470.00
Average	EA	2.667	640.00	240.00	880.00
Maximum	EA	4.000	930.00	360.00	1,290.00
Washroom					
Minimum	EA	1.333	130.00	120.00	250.00
Average	EA	1.600	320.00	140.00	460.00
Maximum	EA	2.000	580.00	180.00	760.00
Handicapped					
Minimum	EA	1.600	140.00	140.00	280.00
Average	EA	2.000	420.00	180.00	600.00
Maximum	EA	2.667	650.00	240.00	890.00
Shower					
Minimum	EA	1.333	130.00	120.00	250.00

© 2020 BNi Publications, Inc.

	Unit	Man-Hrs	Material	Labor	Total
22423.90 FAUCETS (Cont.)					
Shower					
Average	EA	1.600	370.00	140.00	510.00
Maximum	EA	2.000	580.00	180.00	760.00
For trim and rough-in					
Minimum	EA	1.600	89.00	140.00	229.00
Average	EA	2.000	140.00	180.00	320.00
Maximum	EA	4.000	230.00	360.00	590.00
22423.98 HOSE BIBBS					
HOSE BIBBS					
Hose bibb					
1/2"	EA	0.267	10.50	23.75	34.25
3/4"	EA	0.267	11.00	23.75	34.75
22470.01 MISCELLANEOUS FIXTURES					
MISCELLANEOUS FIXTURES					
Electric water cooler					
Floor mounted	EA	2.667	1,110.00	240.00	1,350.00
Wall mounted	EA	2.667	1,040.00	240.00	1,280.00
Wash fountain					
Wall mounted	EA	4.000	2,660.00	360.00	3,020.00
Circular, floor supported	EA	8.000	4,660.00	720.00	5,380.00
Deluge shower and eye wash	EA	4.000	1,110.00	360.00	1,470.00
22510.07 SOLAR WATER HEATERS, POOLS					
SOLAR WATER HEATERS, POOLS					
Solar Water Heater, 1000 BTU/SF panel, 4x8	EA	1.000	140.00	89.00	229.00
4 x 10	EA	1.143	160.00	100.00	260.00
4 x 12	EA	1.333	180.00	120.00	300.00
Panel Mounting Kit, 4x8	EA	0.400	38.00	35.75	73.75
4 x 10	EA	0.444	57.00	39.75	96.75
4 x 12	EA	0.500	70.00	44.75	114.75
22660.01 GLASS PIPE					
GLASS PIPE					
Glass pipe					
1-1/2" dia.	LF	0.160	15.50	14.25	29.75
2" dia.	LF	0.178	21.00	16.00	37.00
3" dia.	LF	0.200	28.00	18.00	46.00
4" dia.	LF	0.229	51.00	20.50	71.50
6" dia.	LF	0.267	94.00	23.75	117.75

	Unit	Man-Hrs	Material	Labor	Total
23071.31 DUCTWORK INSULATION					
DUCTWORK INSULATION					
Fiberglass duct insulation, plain blanket					
1-1/2" thick	SF	0.010	0.22	0.89	1.11
2" thick	SF	0.013	0.30	1.19	1.49
With vapor barrier					
1-1/2" thick	SF	0.010	0.26	0.89	1.15
2" thick	SF	0.013	0.33	1.19	1.52
Rigid with vapor barrier					
2" thick	SF	0.027	1.45	2.38	3.83
3" thick	SF	0.032	1.99	2.86	4.85
4" thick	SF	0.040	2.54	3.57	6.11
6" thick	SF	0.053	3.99	4.76	8.75
Weatherproof, poly, 3" thick, w/vapor barrier	SF	0.080	3.08	7.15	10.23
Urethane board with vapor barrier	SF	0.100	4.35	8.94	13.29
23091.31 HVAC CONTROLS					
HVAC CONTROLS					
Pressure gauge, direct reading gauge cock and siphon	EA	0.500	130.00	44.75	174.75
Control valve, 1", modulating					
2-way	EA	0.667	1,010.00	60.00	1,070.00
3-way	EA	1.000	1,140.00	89.00	1,229.00
Self contained control valve w/ sensing elmnt, 3/4"	EA	0.500	190.00	44.75	234.75
Inst air syst 2-1/2 hp comp, rcvr refrg dryer	EA				8,490.00
Thermostat primary control device	EA				190.00
Humidistat primary control device	EA				150.00
Timers primary control device, indoor/outdoor, 24 hour	EA				300.00
Thermometer, dir. reading, 3 dial	EA				150.00
Control dampers, round					
6" dia.	EA	0.320	130.00	28.50	158.50
8" dia	EA	0.320	180.00	28.50	208.50
10" dia	EA	0.320	240.00	28.50	268.50
12" dia	EA	0.320	320.00	28.50	348.50
16" dia	EA	0.400	470.00	35.75	505.75
18" dia	EA	0.400	500.00	35.75	535.75
20" dia	EA	0.400	670.00	35.75	705.75
Rectangular, parallel blade standard leakage					
12" x 12"	EA	0.400	95.00	35.75	130.75
16" x 16"	EA	0.400	140.00	35.75	175.75
20" x 20"	EA	0.400	170.00	35.75	205.75
48" x 48"	EA	1.143	500.00	100.00	600.00
48" x 60"	EA	1.333	640.00	120.00	760.00
48" x 72"	EA	1.333	780.00	120.00	900.00
Low leakage					
12" x 12"	EA	0.400	180.00	35.75	215.75
16" x 16"	EA	0.400	230.00	35.75	265.75
36" x 36"	EA	0.667	590.00	60.00	650.00
48" x 48"	EA	1.143	1,070.00	100.00	1,170.00
48" x 72"	EA	1.333	1,660.00	120.00	1,780.00
Rectangular, opposed horizontal blade					
12" x 12"	EA	0.400	120.00	35.75	155.75
16" x 16"	EA	0.400	170.00	35.75	205.75
24" x 24"	EA	0.400	230.00	35.75	265.75
36" x 36"	EA	0.667	380.00	60.00	440.00
48" x 72"	EA	1.333	1,070.00	120.00	1,190.00
23211.36 EXPANSION TANKS					
EXPANSION TANKS					
Expansion tank, 125 psi, steel					
20 gallon	EA	1.000	820.00	89.00	909.00
80 gallon	EA	2.286	1,250.00	200.00	1,450.00
23211.37 STRAINERS					
STRAINERS					
Strainer, Y pattern, 125 psi, cast iron body, threaded					
3/4"	EA	0.286	13.75	25.50	39.25
1"	EA	0.320	17.75	28.50	46.25
1-1/4"	EA	0.400	22.25	35.75	58.00

© 2020 BNi Publications, Inc.

	Unit	Man-Hrs	Material	Labor	Total
23211.37 STRAINERS (Cont.)					
Strainer, Y pattern, 125 psi, cast iron body, threaded					
1-1/2"	EA	0.400	28.25	35.75	64.00
2"	EA	0.500	42.00	44.75	86.75
250 psi, brass body, threaded					
3/4"	EA	0.320	36.00	28.50	64.50
1"	EA	0.320	50.00	28.50	78.50
1-1/4"	EA	0.400	63.00	35.75	98.75
1-1/2"	EA	0.400	88.00	35.75	123.75
2"	EA	0.500	150.00	44.75	194.75
Cast iron body, threaded					
3/4"	EA	0.320	21.00	28.50	49.50
1"	EA	0.320	26.75	28.50	55.25
1-1/4"	EA	0.400	35.50	35.75	71.25
1-1/2"	EA	0.400	47.00	35.75	82.75
2"	EA	0.500	60.00	44.75	104.75
23311.30 METAL DUCTWORK					
METAL DUCTWORK					
Rectangular duct					
Galvanized steel					
Minimum	LB	0.073	0.92	6.50	7.42
Average	LB	0.089	1.15	7.94	9.09
Maximum	LB	0.133	1.76	12.00	13.76
Aluminum					
Minimum	LB	0.160	2.41	14.25	16.66
Average	LB	0.200	3.21	18.00	21.21
Maximum	LB	0.267	3.98	23.75	27.73
Fittings					
Minimum	EA	0.267	7.62	23.75	31.37
Average	EA	0.400	11.50	35.75	47.25
Maximum	EA	0.800	16.75	72.00	88.75
For work					
10-20' high, add per pound, $.30					
30-50', add per pound, $.50					
23331.30 DAMPERS					
DAMPERS					
Horizontal parallel aluminum backdraft damper					
12" x 12"	EA	0.200	58.00	18.00	76.00
16" x 16"	EA	0.229	60.00	20.50	80.50
24" x 24"	EA	0.400	92.00	35.75	127.75
36" x 36"	EA	0.571	210.00	51.00	261.00
48" x 48"	EA	0.800	380.00	72.00	452.00
"Up", parallel dampers					
12" x 12"	EA	0.200	94.00	18.00	112.00
16" x 16"	EA	0.229	130.00	20.50	150.50
24" x 24"	EA	0.400	160.00	35.75	195.75
36" x 36"	EA	0.571	280.00	51.00	331.00
48" x 48"	EA	0.800	540.00	72.00	612.00
"Down", parallel dampers					
12" x 12"	EA	0.200	94.00	18.00	112.00
16" x 16"	EA	0.229	130.00	20.50	150.50
24" x 24"	EA	0.400	160.00	35.75	195.75
36" x 36"	EA	0.571	280.00	51.00	331.00
48" x 48"	EA	0.800	540.00	72.00	612.00
Fire damper, 1.5 hr rating					
12" x 12"	EA	0.400	38.25	35.75	74.00
16" x 16"	EA	0.400	61.00	35.75	96.75
24" x 24"	EA	0.400	77.00	35.75	112.75
36" x 36"	EA	0.800	130.00	72.00	202.00
48" x 48"	EA	1.143	250.00	100.00	350.00
23334.60 FLEXIBLE DUCTWORK					
FLEXIBLE DUCTWORK					
Flexible duct, 1.25" fiberglass					
5" dia.	LF	0.040	3.47	3.57	7.04

	Unit	Man-Hrs	Material	Labor	Total
23334.60 FLEXIBLE DUCTWORK (Cont.)					
Flexible duct, 1.25" fiberglass					
6" dia.	LF	0.044	3.86	3.97	7.83
7" dia.	LF	0.047	4.77	4.20	8.97
8" dia.	LF	0.050	5.00	4.47	9.47
10" dia.	LF	0.057	6.66	5.10	11.76
12" dia.	LF	0.062	7.27	5.50	12.77
14" dia.	LF	0.067	9.12	5.96	15.08
16" dia.	LF	0.073	13.75	6.50	20.25
Flexible duct connector, 3" wide fabric	LF	0.133	2.42	12.00	14.42
23340.01 EXHAUST FANS					
EXHAUST FANS					
Belt drive roof exhaust fans					
640 cfm, 2618 fpm	EA	1.000	1,140.00	89.00	1,229.00
940 cfm, 2604 fpm	EA	1.000	1,480.00	89.00	1,569.00
1050 cfm, 3325 fpm	EA	1.000	1,320.00	89.00	1,409.00
1170 cfm, 2373 fpm	EA	1.000	1,920.00	89.00	2,009.00
2440 cfm, 4501 fpm	EA	1.000	1,500.00	89.00	1,589.00
2760 cfm, 4950 fpm	EA	1.000	1,660.00	89.00	1,749.00
3890 cfm, 6769 fpm	EA	1.000	1,890.00	89.00	1,979.00
2380 cfm, 3382 fpm	EA	1.000	2,100.00	89.00	2,189.00
2880 cfm, 3859 fpm	EA	1.000	2,200.00	89.00	2,289.00
3200 cfm, 4173 fpm	EA	1.333	2,220.00	120.00	2,340.00
3660 cfm, 3437 fpm	EA	1.333	2,260.00	120.00	2,380.00
Direct drive fans					
60 to 390 cfm	EA	1.000	930.00	89.00	1,019.00
145 to 590 cfm	EA	1.000	1,130.00	89.00	1,219.00
295 to 860 cfm	EA	1.000	1,370.00	89.00	1,459.00
235 to 1300 cfm	EA	1.000	1,470.00	89.00	1,559.00
415 to 1630 cfm	EA	1.000	1,660.00	89.00	1,749.00
590 to 2045 cfm	EA	1.000	1,920.00	89.00	2,009.00
23371.31 DIFFUSERS					
DIFFUSERS					
Ceiling diffusers, round, baked enamel finish					
6" dia.	EA	0.267	40.25	23.75	64.00
12" dia.	EA	0.333	69.00	29.75	98.75
16" dia.	EA	0.364	100.00	32.50	132.50
20" dia.	EA	0.400	140.00	35.75	175.75
Rectangular					
6x6"	EA	0.267	43.00	23.75	66.75
12x12"	EA	0.400	76.00	35.75	111.75
18x18"	EA	0.400	120.00	35.75	155.75
24x24"	EA	0.500	170.00	44.75	214.75
Lay in, flush mounted, perforated face, with grid					
6x6/24x24	EA	0.320	62.00	28.50	90.50
12x12/24x24	EA	0.320	72.00	28.50	100.50
18x18/24x24	EA	0.320	110.00	28.50	138.50
Two-way slot diffuser with balancing damper, 4'	EA	0.800	69.00	72.00	141.00
23371.34 REGISTERS AND GRILLES					
REGISTERS AND GRILLES					
Lay in flush mounted, perforated face, return					
6x6/24x24	EA	0.320	54.00	28.50	82.50
8x8/24x24	EA	0.320	54.00	28.50	82.50
9x9/24x24	EA	0.320	58.00	28.50	86.50
10x10/24x24	EA	0.320	63.00	28.50	91.50
12x12/24x24	EA	0.320	63.00	28.50	91.50
Rectangular, ceiling return, single deflection					
10x10	EA	0.400	32.25	35.75	68.00
12x12	EA	0.400	37.50	35.75	73.25
14x14	EA	0.400	45.75	35.75	81.50
16x8	EA	0.400	37.50	35.75	73.25
16x16	EA	0.400	37.50	35.75	73.25
24x12	EA	0.400	100.00	35.75	135.75
24x18	EA	0.400	130.00	35.75	165.75

© 2020 BNi Publications, Inc.

	Unit	Man-Hrs	Material	Labor	Total
23371.34 REGISTERS AND GRILLES (Cont.)					
Rectangular, ceiling return, single deflection					
36x24	EA	0.444	250.00	39.75	289.75
36x30	EA	0.444	370.00	39.75	409.75
Wall, return air register					
12x12	EA	0.200	53.00	18.00	71.00
16x16	EA	0.200	79.00	18.00	97.00
18x18	EA	0.200	93.00	18.00	111.00
20x20	EA	0.200	110.00	18.00	128.00
24x24	EA	0.200	150.00	18.00	168.00
Ceiling, return air grille					
6x6	EA	0.267	31.00	23.75	54.75
8x8	EA	0.320	38.50	28.50	67.00
10x10	EA	0.320	47.75	28.50	76.25
Ceiling, exhaust grille, aluminum egg crate					
6x6	EA	0.267	21.25	23.75	45.00
8x8	EA	0.320	21.25	28.50	49.75
10x10	EA	0.320	23.50	28.50	52.00
12x12	EA	0.400	29.00	35.75	64.75
14x14	EA	0.400	38.00	35.75	73.75
16x16	EA	0.400	44.75	35.75	80.50
18x18	EA	0.400	54.00	35.75	89.75
23372.32 RELIEF VENTILATORS					
RELIEF VENTILATORS					
Intake ventilator, aluminum, with screen, no curbs					
12" x 12"	EA	0.667	230.00	60.00	290.00
16" x 16"	EA	0.800	310.00	72.00	382.00
36" x 36"	EA	1.333	1,210.00	120.00	1,330.00
48" x 48"	EA	1.600	1,990.00	140.00	2,130.00
23372.38 PENTHOUSE LOUVERS					
PENTHOUSE LOUVERS					
Penthouse louvers					
12" high, extruded aluminum, 4" louver					
6' perimeter	EA	2.000	520.00	180.00	700.00
12' perimeter	EA	2.000	1,270.00	180.00	1,450.00
20' perimeter	EA	5.333	2,620.00	480.00	3,100.00
16" high x 4' perimeter	EA	2.000	430.00	180.00	610.00
6' perimeter	EA	2.000	610.00	180.00	790.00
12' perimeter	EA	2.000	1,420.00	180.00	1,600.00
20' perimeter	EA	5.333	3,060.00	480.00	3,540.00
20" high x 4' perimeter	EA	2.000	610.00	180.00	790.00
6' perimeter	EA	2.000	650.00	180.00	830.00
12' perimeter	EA	2.000	1,600.00	180.00	1,780.00
20' perimeter	EA	5.333	3,280.00	480.00	3,760.00
24" high x 4' perimeter	EA	2.000	610.00	180.00	790.00
6' perimeter	EA	2.000	740.00	180.00	920.00
12' perimeter	EA	2.000	1,780.00	180.00	1,960.00
20' perimeter	EA	5.333	3,700.00	480.00	4,180.00
23522.30 BOILERS					
BOILERS					
Cast iron, gas fired, hot water					
115 mbh	EA	20.000	3,150.00	2,380.00	5,530.00
175 mbh	EA	21.818	3,750.00	2,590.00	6,340.00
235 mbh	EA	24.000	4,800.00	2,850.00	7,650.00
940 mbh	EA	48.000	16,530.00	5,700.00	22,230.00
1600 mbh	EA	60.000	22,860.00	7,130.00	29,990.00
3000 mbh	EA	80.000	36,980.00	9,500.00	46,480.00
6000 mbh	EA	120.000	74,000.00	14,250.00	88,250.00
Steam					
115 mbh	EA	20.000	3,470.00	2,380.00	5,850.00
175 mbh	EA	21.818	4,180.00	2,590.00	6,770.00
235 mbh	EA	24.000	4,950.00	2,850.00	7,800.00
940 mbh	EA	48.000	17,280.00	5,700.00	22,980.00
1600 mbh	EA	60.000	22,360.00	7,130.00	29,490.00

	Unit	Man-Hrs	Material	Labor	Total

23522.30 BOILERS (Cont.)

Steam

	Unit	Man-Hrs	Material	Labor	Total
3000 mbh	EA	80.000	33,300.00	9,500.00	42,800.00
6000 mbh	EA	120.000	70,280.00	14,250.00	84,530.00

Electric, hot water

	Unit	Man-Hrs	Material	Labor	Total
115 mbh	EA	12.000	5,630.00	1,430.00	7,060.00
175 mbh	EA	12.000	6,230.00	1,430.00	7,660.00
235 mbh	EA	12.000	7,110.00	1,430.00	8,540.00
940 mbh	EA	24.000	17,290.00	2,850.00	20,140.00
1600 mbh	EA	48.000	24,490.00	5,700.00	30,190.00
3000 mbh	EA	60.000	36,580.00	7,130.00	43,710.00
6000 mbh	EA	80.000	42,430.00	9,500.00	51,930.00

Steam

	Unit	Man-Hrs	Material	Labor	Total
115 mbh	EA	12.000	7,110.00	1,430.00	8,540.00
175 mbh	EA	12.000	8,700.00	1,430.00	10,130.00
235 mbh	EA	12.000	9,500.00	1,430.00	10,930.00
940 mbh	EA	24.000	18,910.00	2,850.00	21,760.00
1600 mbh	EA	48.000	31,700.00	5,700.00	37,400.00
3000 mbh	EA	60.000	45,040.00	7,130.00	52,170.00
6000 mbh	EA	80.000	46,800.00	9,500.00	56,300.00

Oil fired, hot water

	Unit	Man-Hrs	Material	Labor	Total
115 mbh	EA	16.000	4,150.00	1,900.00	6,050.00
175 mbh	EA	18.462	5,270.00	2,190.00	7,460.00
235 mbh	EA	21.818	7,280.00	2,590.00	9,870.00
940 mbh	EA	40.000	13,820.00	4,750.00	18,570.00
1600 mbh	EA	48.000	21,900.00	5,700.00	27,600.00
3000 mbh	EA	60.000	31,750.00	7,130.00	38,880.00
6000 mbh	EA	120.000	73,440.00	14,250.00	87,690.00

Steam

	Unit	Man-Hrs	Material	Labor	Total
115 mbh	EA	16.000	4,150.00	1,900.00	6,050.00
175 mbh	EA	18.462	5,270.00	2,190.00	7,460.00
235 mbh	EA	21.818	6,720.00	2,590.00	9,310.00
940 mbh	EA	40.000	13,420.00	4,750.00	18,170.00
1600 mbh	EA	48.000	21,900.00	5,700.00	27,600.00
3000 mbh	EA	60.000	29,550.00	7,130.00	36,680.00
6000 mbh	EA	120.000	73,440.00	14,250.00	87,690.00

23541.30 FURNACES

FURNACES

Electric, hot air

	Unit	Man-Hrs	Material	Labor	Total
40 mbh	EA	4.000	850.00	360.00	1,210.00
60 mbh	EA	4.211	920.00	380.00	1,300.00
80 mbh	EA	4.444	1,000.00	400.00	1,400.00
100 mbh	EA	4.706	1,130.00	420.00	1,550.00
125 mbh	EA	4.848	1,380.00	430.00	1,810.00
160 mbh	EA	5.000	1,900.00	450.00	2,350.00
200 mbh	EA	5.161	2,760.00	460.00	3,220.00
400 mbh	EA	5.333	4,890.00	480.00	5,370.00

Gas fired hot air

	Unit	Man-Hrs	Material	Labor	Total
40 mbh	EA	4.000	850.00	360.00	1,210.00
60 mbh	EA	4.211	910.00	380.00	1,290.00
80 mbh	EA	4.444	1,050.00	400.00	1,450.00
100 mbh	EA	4.706	1,090.00	420.00	1,510.00
125 mbh	EA	4.848	1,200.00	430.00	1,630.00
160 mbh	EA	5.000	1,430.00	450.00	1,880.00
200 mbh	EA	5.161	2,540.00	460.00	3,000.00
400 mbh	EA	5.333	4,540.00	480.00	5,020.00

Oil fired hot air

	Unit	Man-Hrs	Material	Labor	Total
40 mbh	EA	4.000	1,140.00	360.00	1,500.00
60 mbh	EA	4.211	1,890.00	380.00	2,270.00
80 mbh	EA	4.444	1,900.00	400.00	2,300.00
100 mbh	EA	4.706	1,930.00	420.00	2,350.00
125 mbh	EA	4.848	2,000.00	430.00	2,430.00
160 mbh	EA	5.000	2,300.00	450.00	2,750.00
200 mbh	EA	5.161	2,700.00	460.00	3,160.00
400 mbh	EA	5.333	4,480.00	480.00	4,960.00

© 2020 BNi Publications, Inc.

	Unit	Man-Hrs	Material	Labor	Total

23630.01 CONDENSING UNITS

CONDENSING UNITS
Air cooled condenser, single circuit

	Unit	Man-Hrs	Material	Labor	Total
3 ton	EA	1.333	1,810.00	120.00	1,930.00
5 ton	EA	1.333	2,720.00	120.00	2,840.00
7.5 ton	EA	3.810	4,450.00	340.00	4,790.00
20 ton	EA	4.000	13,220.00	360.00	13,580.00
25 ton	EA	4.000	19,920.00	360.00	20,280.00
30 ton	EA	4.000	22,710.00	360.00	23,070.00
40 ton	EA	5.714	29,370.00	510.00	29,880.00
50 ton	EA	5.714	35,720.00	510.00	36,230.00
60 ton	EA	5.000	41,120.00	450.00	41,570.00

With low ambient dampers

	Unit	Man-Hrs	Material	Labor	Total
3 ton	EA	2.000	1,980.00	180.00	2,160.00
5 ton	EA	2.000	3,120.00	180.00	3,300.00
7.5 ton	EA	4.000	4,790.00	360.00	5,150.00
20 ton	EA	5.333	13,260.00	480.00	13,740.00
25 ton	EA	5.333	20,190.00	480.00	20,670.00
30 ton	EA	5.333	23,190.00	480.00	23,670.00
40 ton	EA	6.667	30,780.00	600.00	31,380.00
50 ton	EA	7.273	37,120.00	650.00	37,770.00
60 ton	EA	7.273	42,570.00	650.00	43,220.00

Dual circuit

	Unit	Man-Hrs	Material	Labor	Total
10 ton	EA	4.000	4,240.00	360.00	4,600.00
15 ton	EA	5.714	6,200.00	510.00	6,710.00
20 ton	EA	5.714	12,680.00	510.00	13,190.00
25 ton	EA	5.714	20,200.00	510.00	20,710.00
30 ton	EA	5.714	23,500.00	510.00	24,010.00
40 ton	EA	6.667	33,600.00	600.00	34,200.00
50 ton	EA	6.667	37,120.00	600.00	37,720.00
60 ton	EA	6.667	38,530.00	600.00	39,130.00
80 ton	EA	8.889	48,180.00	790.00	48,970.00
100 ton	EA	8.889	56,400.00	790.00	57,190.00
120 ton	EA	8.889	66,970.00	790.00	67,760.00

With low ambient dampers

	Unit	Man-Hrs	Material	Labor	Total
15 ton	EA	5.714	6,910.00	510.00	7,420.00
20 ton	EA	5.714	13,480.00	510.00	13,990.00
25 ton	EA	5.714	21,380.00	510.00	21,890.00
30 ton	EA	5.714	24,110.00	510.00	24,620.00
40 ton	EA	6.667	34,770.00	600.00	35,370.00
50 ton	EA	6.667	38,310.00	600.00	38,910.00
60 ton	EA	6.667	39,710.00	600.00	40,310.00
80 ton	EA	8.889	50,510.00	790.00	51,300.00
100 ton	EA	8.889	58,750.00	790.00	59,540.00
120 ton	EA	8.889	70,030.00	790.00	70,820.00

23640.01 CHILLERS

CHILLERS
Chiller, reciprocal
Air cooled, remote condenser, starter

	Unit	Man-Hrs	Material	Labor	Total
20 ton	EA	8.000	31,460.00	950.00	32,410.00
25 ton	EA	8.000	35,500.00	950.00	36,450.00
30 ton	EA	8.000	37,540.00	950.00	38,490.00
40 ton	EA	12.000	55,510.00	1,430.00	56,940.00
50 ton	EA	13.333	61,620.00	1,580.00	63,200.00
100 ton	EA	24.000	101,140.00	2,850.00	103,990.00
200 ton	EA	40.000	184,300.00	4,750.00	189,050.00

Water cooled, with starter

	Unit	Man-Hrs	Material	Labor	Total
20 ton	EA	8.000	26,970.00	950.00	27,920.00
25 ton	EA	8.000	29,890.00	950.00	30,840.00
30 ton	EA	12.000	35,960.00	1,430.00	37,390.00
40 ton	EA	12.000	49,450.00	1,430.00	50,880.00
50 ton	EA	13.333	53,940.00	1,580.00	55,520.00
100 ton	EA	24.000	78,670.00	2,850.00	81,520.00
200 ton	EA	40.000	125,860.00	4,750.00	130,610.00

	Unit	Man-Hrs	Material	Labor	Total
23640.01 CHILLERS (Cont.)					
Chiller, reciprocal					
Packaged, air cooled, with starter					
20 ton	EA	6.000	30,120.00	710.00	30,830.00
25 ton	EA	6.000	32,590.00	710.00	33,300.00
30 ton	EA	6.000	37,990.00	710.00	38,700.00
40 ton	EA	6.000	43,600.00	710.00	44,310.00
Heat recovery, air cooled, with starter					
50 ton	EA	12.000	58,430.00	1,430.00	59,860.00
100 ton	EA	24.000	83,610.00	2,850.00	86,460.00
Water cooled, with starter					
40 ton	EA	12.000	49,900.00	1,430.00	51,330.00
100 ton	EA	26.667	90,120.00	3,170.00	93,290.00
Centrifugal, single bundle condenser, with starter					
80 ton	EA	34.286	117,990.00	4,070.00	122,060.00
230 ton	EA	53.333	135,930.00	6,330.00	142,260.00
460 ton	EA	80.000	205,960.00	9,500.00	215,460.00
670 ton	EA	96.000	274,660.00	11,400.00	286,060.00
23650.01 COOLING TOWERS					
COOLING TOWERS					
Cooling tower, propeller type					
100 ton	EA	8.000	14,750.00	950.00	15,700.00
400 ton	EA	24.000	49,260.00	2,850.00	52,110.00
1000 ton	EA	60.000	118,280.00	7,130.00	125,410.00
Centrifugal					
100 ton	EA	8.000	20,460.00	950.00	21,410.00
400 ton	EA	24.000	59,000.00	2,850.00	61,850.00
1000 ton	EA	60.000	138,040.00	7,130.00	145,170.00
23740.01 AIR HANDLING UNITS					
AIR HANDLING UNITS					
Air handling unit, medium pressure, single zone					
1500 cfm	EA	5.000	4,840.00	450.00	5,290.00
3000 cfm	EA	8.889	6,360.00	790.00	7,150.00
4000 cfm	EA	10.000	8,150.00	890.00	9,040.00
5000 cfm	EA	10.667	10,270.00	950.00	11,220.00
6000 cfm	EA	11.429	13,200.00	1,020.00	14,220.00
7000 cfm	EA	12.308	15,150.00	1,100.00	16,250.00
8500 cfm	EA	13.333	18,630.00	1,190.00	19,820.00
10,500 cfm	EA	16.000	20,460.00	1,430.00	21,890.00
12,500 cfm	EA	17.778	23,550.00	1,590.00	25,140.00
Rooftop air handling units					
4950 cfm	EA	8.889	13,910.00	790.00	14,700.00
7370 cfm	EA	11.429	17,640.00	1,020.00	18,660.00
9790 cfm	EA	13.333	18,770.00	1,190.00	19,960.00
14,300 cfm	EA	11.429	26,510.00	1,020.00	27,530.00
21,725 cfm	EA	11.429	37,550.00	1,020.00	38,570.00
33,000 cfm	EA	13.333	53,020.00	1,190.00	54,210.00
23740.09 ROOF CURBS					
ROOF CURBS					
8" high, insulated, with liner and raised can					
15" x 15"	EA	0.400	120.00	35.75	155.75
21" x 21"	EA	0.400	150.00	35.75	185.75
36" x 36"	EA	0.571	210.00	51.00	261.00
48" x 48"	EA	0.615	600.00	55.00	655.00
60" x 60"	EA	0.800	1,100.00	72.00	1,172.00
72" x 72"	EA	1.000	1,760.00	89.00	1,849.00
23811.32 ROOFTOP UNITS					
ROOFTOP UNITS					
Packaged, single zone rooftop unit, with roof curb					
2 ton	EA	8.000	4,130.00	720.00	4,850.00
3 ton	EA	8.000	4,340.00	720.00	5,060.00
4 ton	EA	10.000	4,740.00	890.00	5,630.00
5 ton	EA	13.333	5,140.00	1,190.00	6,330.00
7.5 ton	EA	16.000	7,470.00	1,430.00	8,900.00

© 2020 BNi Publications, Inc.

	Unit	Man-Hrs	Material	Labor	Total

23812.30 COMPUTER ROOM A/C

COMPUTER ROOM A/C

Air cooled, alarm, high efficiency filter, elec. heat

	Unit	Man-Hrs	Material	Labor	Total
3 ton	EA	6.154	18,640.00	550.00	19,190.00
5 ton	EA	6.667	19,900.00	600.00	20,500.00
7.5 ton	EA	8.000	36,060.00	720.00	36,780.00
10 ton	EA	10.000	37,680.00	890.00	38,570.00
15 ton	EA	11.429	41,410.00	1,020.00	42,430.00

Steam heat

	Unit	Man-Hrs	Material	Labor	Total
3 ton	EA	6.154	18,130.00	550.00	18,680.00
5 ton	EA	6.667	19,290.00	600.00	19,890.00
7.5 ton	EA	8.000	30,720.00	720.00	31,440.00
10 ton	EA	10.000	31,650.00	890.00	32,540.00
15 ton	EA	11.429	35,000.00	1,020.00	36,020.00

Hot water heat

	Unit	Man-Hrs	Material	Labor	Total
3 ton	EA	6.154	18,130.00	550.00	18,680.00
5 ton	EA	6.667	19,290.00	600.00	19,890.00
7.5 ton	EA	8.000	30,720.00	720.00	31,440.00
10 ton	EA	10.000	31,650.00	890.00	32,540.00
15 ton	EA	11.429	35,110.00	1,020.00	36,130.00

Air cooled condenser, low ambient damper

	Unit	Man-Hrs	Material	Labor	Total
3 ton	EA	1.600	1,810.00	140.00	1,950.00
5 ton	EA	2.000	2,850.00	180.00	3,030.00
7.5 ton	EA	4.000	4,380.00	360.00	4,740.00
10 ton	EA	5.714	6,400.00	510.00	6,910.00
15 ton	EA	4.706	7,070.00	420.00	7,490.00

Water cooled, high efficiency filter, alarm, elec. heat

	Unit	Man-Hrs	Material	Labor	Total
3 ton	EA	5.714	18,800.00	510.00	19,310.00
5 ton	EA	6.667	20,250.00	600.00	20,850.00
7.5 ton	EA	10.000	32,260.00	890.00	33,150.00
10 ton	EA	11.429	33,470.00	1,020.00	34,490.00
15 ton	EA	13.333	39,170.00	1,190.00	40,360.00

Steam heat

	Unit	Man-Hrs	Material	Labor	Total
3 ton	EA	5.714	21,470.00	510.00	21,980.00
5 ton	EA	6.667	24,500.00	600.00	25,100.00
7.5 ton	EA	10.000	34,560.00	890.00	35,450.00
10 ton	EA	11.429	35,780.00	1,020.00	36,800.00
15 ton	EA	13.333	41,600.00	1,190.00	42,790.00

Hot water heat

	Unit	Man-Hrs	Material	Labor	Total
3 ton	EA	5.714	21,470.00	510.00	21,980.00
5 ton	EA	6.667	22,920.00	600.00	23,520.00
7.5 ton	EA	10.000	34,560.00	890.00	35,450.00
10 ton	EA	11.429	35,780.00	1,020.00	36,800.00
15 ton	EA	13.333	41,600.00	1,190.00	42,790.00

23821.90 FAN COIL UNITS

FAN COIL UNITS

Fan coil unit, 2 pipe, complete

	Unit	Man-Hrs	Material	Labor	Total
200 cfm ceiling hung	EA	2.667	1,220.00	240.00	1,460.00
Floor mounted	EA	2.000	1,150.00	180.00	1,330.00
300 cfm, ceiling hung	EA	3.200	1,290.00	290.00	1,580.00
Floor mounted	EA	2.667	1,230.00	240.00	1,470.00
400 cfm, ceiling hung	EA	3.810	1,360.00	340.00	1,700.00
Floor mounted	EA	2.667	1,310.00	240.00	1,550.00
500 cfm, ceiling hung	EA	4.000	1,580.00	360.00	1,940.00
Floor mounted	EA	3.077	1,520.00	280.00	1,800.00
600 cfm, ceiling hung	EA	4.420	2,000.00	400.00	2,400.00
Floor mounted	EA	3.636	1,860.00	330.00	2,190.00

23823.90 UNIT HEATERS

UNIT HEATERS

Steam unit heater, horizontal

	Unit	Man-Hrs	Material	Labor	Total
12,500 btuh, 200 cfm	EA	1.333	560.00	120.00	680.00
17,000 btuh, 300 cfm	EA	1.333	740.00	120.00	860.00
40,000 btuh, 500 cfm	EA	1.333	900.00	120.00	1,020.00
60,000 btuh, 700 cfm	EA	1.333	940.00	120.00	1,060.00
70,000 btuh, 1000 cfm	EA	2.000	980.00	180.00	1,160.00

	Unit	Man-Hrs	Material	Labor	Total

23823.90 UNIT HEATERS (Cont.)

Steam unit heater
Vertical

	Unit	Man-Hrs	Material	Labor	Total
12,500 btuh, 200 cfm	EA	1.333	560.00	120.00	680.00
17,000 btuh, 300 cfm	EA	1.333	930.00	120.00	1,050.00
40,000 btuh, 500 cfm	EA	1.333	900.00	120.00	1,020.00
60,000 btuh, 700 cfm	EA	1.333	940.00	120.00	1,060.00
70,000 btuh, 1000 cfm	EA	1.333	980.00	120.00	1,100.00

Gas unit heater, horizontal

	Unit	Man-Hrs	Material	Labor	Total
27,400 btuh	EA	3.200	860.00	290.00	1,150.00
38,000 btuh	EA	3.200	900.00	290.00	1,190.00
56,000 btuh	EA	3.200	940.00	290.00	1,230.00
82,200 btuh	EA	3.200	980.00	290.00	1,270.00
103,900 btuh	EA	5.000	1,090.00	450.00	1,540.00
125,700 btuh	EA	5.000	1,280.00	450.00	1,730.00
133,200 btuh	EA	5.000	1,380.00	450.00	1,830.00
149,000 btuh	EA	5.000	1,630.00	450.00	2,080.00
172,000 btuh	EA	5.000	1,760.00	450.00	2,210.00
190,000 btuh	EA	5.000	1,850.00	450.00	2,300.00
225,000 btuh	EA	5.000	2,030.00	450.00	2,480.00

Hot water unit heater, horizontal

	Unit	Man-Hrs	Material	Labor	Total
12,500 btuh, 200 cfm	EA	1.333	450.00	120.00	570.00
17,000 btuh, 300 cfm	EA	1.333	500.00	120.00	620.00
25,000 btuh, 500 cfm	EA	1.333	580.00	120.00	700.00
30,000 btuh, 700 cfm	EA	1.333	680.00	120.00	800.00
50,000 btuh, 1000 cfm	EA	2.000	740.00	180.00	920.00
60,000 btuh, 1300 cfm	EA	2.000	780.00	180.00	960.00

Vertical

	Unit	Man-Hrs	Material	Labor	Total
12,500 btuh, 200 cfm	EA	1.333	660.00	120.00	780.00
17,000 btuh, 300 cfm	EA	1.333	660.00	120.00	780.00
25,000 btuh, 500 cfm	EA	1.333	660.00	120.00	780.00
30,000 btuh, 700 cfm	EA	1.333	660.00	120.00	780.00
50,000 btuh, 1000 cfm	EA	1.333	690.00	120.00	810.00
60,000 btuh, 1300 cfm	EA	1.333	850.00	120.00	970.00

Cabinet unit heaters, ceiling, exposed, hot water

	Unit	Man-Hrs	Material	Labor	Total
200 cfm	EA	2.667	1,290.00	240.00	1,530.00
300 cfm	EA	3.200	1,380.00	290.00	1,670.00
400 cfm	EA	3.810	1,440.00	340.00	1,780.00
600 cfm	EA	4.211	1,480.00	380.00	1,860.00
800 cfm	EA	5.000	1,850.00	450.00	2,300.00
1000 cfm	EA	5.714	2,410.00	510.00	2,920.00
1200 cfm	EA	6.667	2,590.00	600.00	3,190.00
2000 cfm	EA	8.889	4,040.00	790.00	4,830.00

23833.30 ELECTRIC HEATING

ELECTRIC HEATING
Baseboard heater

	Unit	Man-Hrs	Material	Labor	Total
2', 375w	EA	1.000	41.75	83.00	124.75
3', 500w	EA	1.000	49.50	83.00	132.50
4', 750w	EA	1.143	55.00	95.00	150.00
5', 935w	EA	1.333	78.00	110.00	188.00
6', 1125w	EA	1.600	92.00	130.00	222.00
7', 1310w	EA	1.818	100.00	150.00	250.00
8', 1500w	EA	2.000	120.00	170.00	290.00
9', 1680w	EA	2.222	130.00	180.00	310.00
10', 1875w	EA	2.286	180.00	190.00	370.00

Unit heater, wall mounted

	Unit	Man-Hrs	Material	Labor	Total
1500w	EA	1.667	220.00	140.00	360.00
2500w	EA	1.818	240.00	150.00	390.00
4000w	EA	2.286	320.00	190.00	510.00

Thermostat

	Unit	Man-Hrs	Material	Labor	Total
Integral	EA	0.500	37.50	41.50	79.00
Line voltage	EA	0.500	38.50	41.50	80.00

© 2020 BNi Publications, Inc.

	Unit	Man-Hrs	Material	Labor	Total
23833.30 ELECTRIC HEATING (Cont.)					
Unit heater, wall mounted					
Electric heater connection	EA	0.250	1.65	20.75	22.40
23841.60 DEHUMIDIFIERS					
DEHUMIDIFIERS					
Desiccant dehumidifier, 1125 cfm	EA				35,230.00

26051.34 COPPER CONDUCTORS

	Unit	Man-Hrs	Material	Labor	Total
COPPER CONDUCTORS					
Copper conductors, type THW, solid					
#14	LF	0.004	0.12	0.33	0.45
#12	LF	0.005	0.18	0.41	0.59
#10	LF	0.006	0.28	0.50	0.78
Stranded					
#14	LF	0.004	0.13	0.33	0.46
#12	LF	0.005	0.16	0.41	0.57
#10	LF	0.006	0.25	0.50	0.75
#8	LF	0.008	0.41	0.66	1.07
#6	LF	0.009	0.67	0.74	1.41
#4	LF	0.010	1.04	0.83	1.87
#3	LF	0.010	1.32	0.83	2.15
#2	LF	0.012	1.66	0.99	2.65
#1	LF	0.014	2.10	1.16	3.26
1/0	LF	0.016	2.50	1.32	3.82
2/0	LF	0.020	3.14	1.66	4.80
3/0	LF	0.025	3.96	2.07	6.03
4/0	LF	0.028	4.95	2.32	7.27
250 MCM	LF	0.030	6.10	2.50	8.60
300 MCM	LF	0.033	7.18	2.76	9.94
350 MCM	LF	0.040	8.40	3.32	11.72
400 MCM	LF	0.044	9.57	3.68	13.25
500 MCM	LF	0.052	11.75	4.28	16.03
600 MCM	LF	0.059	15.75	4.91	20.66
750 MCM	LF	0.067	19.75	5.53	25.28
1000 MCM	LF	0.076	24.75	6.32	31.07
THHN-THWN, solid					
#14	LF	0.004	0.12	0.33	0.45
#12	LF	0.005	0.18	0.41	0.59
#10	LF	0.006	0.28	0.50	0.78
Stranded					
#14	LF	0.004	0.12	0.33	0.45
#12	LF	0.005	0.18	0.41	0.59
#10	LF	0.006	0.28	0.50	0.78
#8	LF	0.008	0.49	0.66	1.15
#6	LF	0.009	0.77	0.74	1.51
#4	LF	0.010	1.22	0.83	2.05
#2	LF	0.012	1.70	0.99	2.69
#1	LF	0.014	2.15	1.16	3.31
1/0	LF	0.016	2.65	1.32	3.97
2/0	LF	0.020	3.27	1.66	4.93
3/0	LF	0.025	4.11	2.07	6.18
4/0	LF	0.028	5.14	2.32	7.46
250 MCM	LF	0.030	6.29	2.50	8.79
350 MCM	LF	0.040	7.50	3.32	10.82

26051.35 SHEATHED CABLE

	Unit	Man-Hrs	Material	Labor	Total
SHEATHED CABLE					
Non-metallic sheathed cable					
Type NM cable with ground					
#14/2	LF	0.015	0.28	1.24	1.52
#12/2	LF	0.016	0.44	1.32	1.76
#10/2	LF	0.018	0.69	1.47	2.16
#8/2	LF	0.020	1.13	1.66	2.79
#6/2	LF	0.025	1.78	2.07	3.85
#14/3	LF	0.026	0.39	2.14	2.53
#12/3	LF	0.027	0.62	2.21	2.83
#10/3	LF	0.027	0.99	2.25	3.24
#8/3	LF	0.028	1.66	2.28	3.94
#6/3	LF	0.028	2.68	2.32	5.00
#4/3	LF	0.032	5.55	2.65	8.20
#2/3	LF	0.035	8.34	2.88	11.22

© 2020 BNi Publications, Inc.

	Unit	Man-Hrs	Material	Labor	Total

26051.35 SHEATHED CABLE (Cont.)

Non-metallic sheathed cable
Type UF cable with ground

	Unit	Man-Hrs	Material	Labor	Total
#14/2	LF	0.016	0.33	1.32	1.65
#12/2	LF	0.019	0.49	1.58	2.07
#10/2	LF	0.020	0.79	1.66	2.45
#8/2	LF	0.023	1.36	1.89	3.25
#6/2	LF	0.027	2.12	2.25	4.37
#14/3	LF	0.020	0.46	1.66	2.12
#12/3	LF	0.022	0.70	1.81	2.51
#10/3	LF	0.025	1.08	2.07	3.15
#8/3	LF	0.028	2.05	2.32	4.37
#6/3	LF	0.032	3.33	2.65	5.98

26052.61 GROUNDING

GROUNDING
Ground rods, copper clad, 1/2" x

	Unit	Man-Hrs	Material	Labor	Total
6'	EA	0.667	17.00	55.00	72.00
8'	EA	0.727	23.50	60.00	83.50
10'	EA	1.000	29.25	83.00	112.25
5/8" x					
5'	EA	0.615	21.00	51.00	72.00
6'	EA	0.727	22.75	60.00	82.75
8'	EA	1.000	29.25	83.00	112.25
10'	EA	1.250	36.25	100.00	136.25
3/4" x					
8'	EA	0.727	52.00	60.00	112.00
10'	EA	0.800	57.00	66.00	123.00
Ground rod clamp					
5/8"	EA	0.123	6.94	10.25	17.19
3/4"	EA	0.123	9.82	10.25	20.07

26052.92 CONDUIT SPECIALTIES

CONDUIT SPECIALTIES

	Unit	Man-Hrs	Material	Labor	Total
Rod beam clamp, 1/2"	EA	0.050	6.94	4.15	11.09
Hanger rod					
3/8"	LF	0.040	1.46	3.32	4.78
1/2"	LF	0.050	3.65	4.15	7.80
All thread rod					
1/4"	LF	0.030	0.47	2.50	2.97
3/8"	LF	0.040	0.53	3.32	3.85
1/2"	LF	0.050	1.00	4.15	5.15
5/8"	LF	0.080	1.76	6.64	8.40
Hanger channel, 1-1/2"					
No holes	EA	0.030	4.62	2.50	7.12
Holes	EA	0.030	5.70	2.50	8.20
Channel strap					
1/2"	EA	0.050	1.44	4.15	5.59
3/4"	EA	0.050	1.93	4.15	6.08
1"	EA	0.050	2.47	4.15	6.62
1-1/4"	EA	0.080	1.99	6.64	8.63
1-1/2"	EA	0.080	2.39	6.64	9.03
2"	EA	0.080	2.59	6.64	9.23
2-1/2"	EA	0.123	4.97	10.25	15.22
3"	EA	0.123	5.41	10.25	15.66
3-1/2"	EA	0.123	6.74	10.25	16.99
4"	EA	0.145	7.62	12.00	19.62
5"	EA	0.145	12.25	12.00	24.25
6"	EA	0.145	14.00	12.00	26.00
Conduit penetrations, roof and wall, 8" thick					
1/2"	EA	0.615		51.00	51.00
3/4"	EA	0.615		51.00	51.00
1"	EA	0.800		66.00	66.00
1-1/4"	EA	0.800		66.00	66.00
1-1/2"	EA	0.800		66.00	66.00
2"	EA	1.600		130.00	130.00
2-1/2"	EA	1.600		130.00	130.00

	Unit	Man-Hrs	Material	Labor	Total

26052.92 CONDUIT SPECIALTIES (Cont.)

Conduit penetrations, roof and wall, 8" thick

	Unit	Man-Hrs	Material	Labor	Total
3"	EA	1.600		130.00	130.00
3-1/2"	EA	2.000		170.00	170.00
4"	EA	2.000		170.00	170.00

Fireproofing, for conduit penetrations

	Unit	Man-Hrs	Material	Labor	Total
1/2"	EA	0.500	3.57	41.50	45.07
3/4"	EA	0.500	3.70	41.50	45.20
1"	EA	0.500	3.78	41.50	45.28
1-1/4"	EA	0.727	8.89	65.00	73.89
1-1/2"	EA	0.727	5.25	60.00	65.25
2"	EA	0.727	5.39	60.00	65.39
2-1/2"	EA	0.899	10.25	75.00	85.25
3"	EA	0.899	10.75	80.00	90.75
3-1/2"	EA	1.250	12.50	100.00	112.50
4"	EA	1.509	15.00	130.00	145.00

26053.34 SURFACE MOUNTED RACEWAY

SURFACE MOUNTED RACEWAY

Single Raceway

	Unit	Man-Hrs	Material	Labor	Total
3/4" x 17/32" Conduit	LF	0.040	1.93	3.32	5.25
Mounting Strap	EA	0.053	0.52	4.42	4.94
Connector	EA	0.053	0.69	4.42	5.11
Elbow					
45 degree	EA	0.050	8.80	4.15	12.95
90 degree	EA	0.050	2.80	4.15	6.95
internal	EA	0.050	3.53	4.15	7.68
external	EA	0.050	3.26	4.15	7.41
Switch	EA	0.400	22.75	33.25	56.00
Utility Box	EA	0.400	15.25	33.25	48.50
Receptacle	EA	0.400	27.00	33.25	60.25
3/4" x 21/32" Conduit	LF	0.040	2.19	3.32	5.51
Mounting Strap	EA	0.053	0.81	4.42	5.23
Connector	EA	0.053	0.83	4.42	5.25
Elbow					
45 degree	EA	0.050	10.75	4.15	14.90
90 degree	EA	0.050	2.99	4.15	7.14
internal	EA	0.050	4.06	4.15	8.21
external	EA	0.050	4.06	4.15	8.21
Switch	EA	0.400	22.75	33.25	56.00
Utility Box	EA	0.400	15.25	33.25	48.50
Receptacle	EA	0.400	27.00	33.25	60.25

26053.35 PULL BOXES AND CABINETS

PULL BOXES AND CABINETS

Galvanized pull boxes, screw cover

	Unit	Man-Hrs	Material	Labor	Total
4x4x4	EA	0.190	7.83	15.75	23.58
4x6x4	EA	0.190	9.33	15.75	25.08
6x6x4	EA	0.190	11.75	15.75	27.50
6x8x4	EA	0.190	14.00	15.75	29.75
8x8x4	EA	0.250	17.50	20.75	38.25
8x10x4	EA	0.242	20.25	20.00	40.25
8x12x4	EA	0.250	22.25	20.75	43.00

Screw cover

	Unit	Man-Hrs	Material	Labor	Total
10x10x4	EA	0.308	22.25	25.50	47.75
12x12x6	EA	0.444	32.75	37.00	69.75
12x15x6	EA	0.444	39.00	37.00	76.00
12x18x6	EA	0.500	43.25	41.50	84.75
15x18x6	EA	0.571	48.25	47.50	95.75
18x24x6	EA	0.615	90.00	51.00	141.00
18x30x6	EA	0.727	100.00	60.00	160.00
24x36x6	EA	0.727	150.00	60.00	210.00

© 2020 BNi Publications, Inc.

	Unit	Man-Hrs	Material	Labor	Total
26053.37 WIREWAYS					
WIREWAYS					
Wireway, hinge cover type					
2-1/2" x 2-1/2"					
1' section	EA	0.154	17.50	12.75	30.25
2'	EA	0.190	25.00	15.75	40.75
3'	EA	0.250	33.75	20.75	54.50
5'	EA	0.381	57.00	31.50	88.50
10'	EA	0.667	120.00	55.00	175.00
4" x 4"					
1'	EA	0.250	19.25	20.75	40.00
2'	EA	0.250	28.00	20.75	48.75
3'	EA	0.308	41.50	25.50	67.00
4'	EA	0.308	57.00	25.50	82.50
10'	EA	0.800	170.00	66.00	236.00
26053.39 PULL AND JUNCTION BOXES					
PULL AND JUNCTION BOXES					
4"					
Octagon box	EA	0.114	3.96	9.48	13.44
Box extension	EA	0.059	6.67	4.91	11.58
Plaster ring	EA	0.059	3.66	4.91	8.57
Cover blank	EA	0.059	1.61	4.91	6.52
Square box	EA	0.114	5.70	9.48	15.18
Box extension	EA	0.059	5.59	4.91	10.50
Plaster ring	EA	0.059	3.06	4.91	7.97
Cover blank	EA	0.059	1.57	4.91	6.48
4-11/16"					
Square box	EA	0.114	11.50	9.48	20.98
Box extension	EA	0.059	12.50	4.91	17.41
Plaster ring	EA	0.059	7.61	4.91	12.52
Cover blank	EA	0.059	2.82	4.91	7.73
Switch and device boxes					
2 gang	EA	0.114	17.25	9.48	26.73
3 gang	EA	0.114	30.25	9.48	39.73
4 gang	EA	0.160	40.50	13.25	53.75
Device covers					
2 gang	EA	0.059	13.75	4.91	18.66
3 gang	EA	0.059	14.25	4.91	19.16
4 gang	EA	0.059	19.25	4.91	24.16
Handy box	EA	0.114	4.25	9.48	13.73
Extension	EA	0.059	4.00	4.91	8.91
Switch cover	EA	0.059	2.12	4.91	7.03
Switch box with knockout	EA	0.145	6.38	12.00	18.38
Weatherproof cover, spring type	EA	0.080	11.75	6.64	18.39
Cover plate, dryer receptacle 1 gang plastic	EA	0.100	1.81	8.30	10.11
For 4" receptacle, 2 gang	EA	0.100	3.23	8.30	11.53
Duplex receptacle cover plate, plastic	EA	0.059	0.79	4.91	5.70
4", vertical bracket box, 1-1/2" with					
RMX clamps	EA	0.145	8.22	12.00	20.22
BX clamps	EA	0.145	8.82	12.00	20.82
4", octagon device cover					
1 switch	EA	0.059	4.82	4.91	9.73
1 duplex recept	EA	0.059	4.82	4.91	9.73
4", square face bracket boxes, 1-1/2"					
RMX	EA	0.145	9.81	12.00	21.81
BX	EA	0.145	10.75	12.00	22.75
26053.41 ALUMINUM CONDUIT					
ALUMINUM CONDUIT					
Aluminum conduit					
1/2"	LF	0.030	2.21	2.50	4.71
3/4"	LF	0.040	2.84	3.32	6.16
1"	LF	0.050	3.99	4.15	8.14
1-1/4"	LF	0.059	5.33	4.91	10.24
1-1/2"	LF	0.080	6.62	6.64	13.26

	Unit	Man-Hrs	Material	Labor	Total
26053.41 ALUMINUM CONDUIT (Cont.)					
Aluminum conduit					
2"	LF	0.089	8.83	7.37	16.20
2-1/2"	LF	0.100	14.00	8.30	22.30
3"	LF	0.107	18.25	8.85	27.10
3-1/2"	LF	0.123	22.00	10.25	32.25
4"	LF	0.145	26.00	12.00	38.00
5"	LF	0.182	37.25	15.00	52.25
6"	LF	0.200	49.25	16.50	65.75
26053.42 EMT CONDUIT					
EMT conduit					
1/2"	LF	0.030	0.60	2.50	3.10
3/4"	LF	0.040	1.09	3.32	4.41
1"	LF	0.050	1.82	4.15	5.97
1-1/4"	LF	0.059	2.92	4.91	7.83
1-1/2"	LF	0.080	3.69	6.64	10.33
2"	LF	0.089	4.62	7.37	11.99
2-1/2"	LF	0.100	9.21	8.30	17.51
3"	LF	0.123	10.25	10.25	20.50
3-1/2"	LF	0.145	14.50	12.00	26.50
4"	LF	0.182	14.00	15.00	29.00
26053.43 FLEXIBLE CONDUIT					
Flexible conduit, steel					
3/8"	LF	0.030	0.75	2.50	3.25
1/2	LF	0.030	0.85	2.50	3.35
3/4"	LF	0.040	1.17	3.32	4.49
1"	LF	0.040	2.23	3.32	5.55
1-1/4"	LF	0.050	2.79	4.15	6.94
1-1/2"	LF	0.059	4.63	4.91	9.54
2"	LF	0.080	5.69	6.64	12.33
2-1/2"	LF	0.089	6.93	7.37	14.30
3"	LF	0.107	12.00	8.85	20.85
26053.44 GALVANIZED CONDUIT					
Galvanized rigid steel conduit					
1/2"	LF	0.040	2.97	3.32	6.29
3/4"	LF	0.050	3.28	4.15	7.43
1"	LF	0.059	4.74	4.91	9.65
1-1/4"	LF	0.080	6.55	6.64	13.19
1-1/2"	LF	0.089	7.71	7.37	15.08
2"	LF	0.100	9.81	8.30	18.11
2-1/2"	LF	0.145	18.00	12.00	30.00
3"	LF	0.182	18.75	15.00	33.75
3-1/2"	LF	0.190	27.00	15.75	42.75
4"	LF	0.211	30.75	17.50	48.25
5"	LF	0.286	57.00	23.75	80.75
6"	LF	0.381	82.00	31.50	113.50
26053.45 PLASTIC COATED CONDUIT					
Rigid steel conduit, plastic coated					
1/2"	LF	0.050	7.06	4.15	11.21
3/4"	LF	0.059	8.20	4.91	13.11
1"	LF	0.080	10.50	6.64	17.14
1-1/4"	LF	0.100	13.50	8.30	21.80
1-1/2"	LF	0.123	16.25	10.25	26.50
2"	LF	0.145	21.25	12.00	33.25
2-1/2"	LF	0.190	32.25	15.75	48.00
3"	LF	0.222	40.75	18.50	59.25
3-1/2"	LF	0.250	49.75	20.75	70.50
4"	LF	0.308	60.00	25.50	85.50
5"	LF	0.381	100.00	31.50	131.50

© 2020 BNi Publications, Inc.

	Unit	Man-Hrs	Material	Labor	Total

26053.47 STEEL CONDUIT

STEEL CONDUIT
Intermediate metal conduit (IMC)

	Unit	Man-Hrs	Material	Labor	Total
1/2"	LF	0.030	2.02	2.50	4.52
3/4"	LF	0.040	2.48	3.32	5.80
1"	LF	0.050	3.76	4.15	7.91
1-1/4"	LF	0.059	4.81	4.91	9.72
1-1/2"	LF	0.080	6.02	6.64	12.66
2"	LF	0.089	7.86	7.37	15.23
2-1/2"	LF	0.119	15.50	9.91	25.41
3"	LF	0.145	20.00	12.00	32.00
3-1/2"	LF	0.182	23.50	15.00	38.50
4"	LF	0.190	26.00	15.75	41.75

26053.61 CABLE TRAY

CABLE TRAY

	Unit	Man-Hrs	Material	Labor	Total
Cable tray, 6"	LF	0.059	22.00	4.91	26.91
Ventilated cover	LF	0.030	8.89	2.50	11.39
Solid cover	LF	0.030	6.93	2.50	9.43

26120.01 MEDIUM-VOLTAGE TRANSFORMERS

MEDIUM-VOLTAGE TRANSFORMERS
Floor mtd, one phase, int. dry, 480v-120/240v

	Unit	Man-Hrs	Material	Labor	Total
3 kva	EA	1.818	690.00	150.00	840.00
5 kva	EA	3.077	920.00	260.00	1,180.00
7.5 kva	EA	3.478	1,240.00	290.00	1,530.00
10 kva	EA	3.810	1,550.00	320.00	1,870.00
15 kva	EA	4.301	2,070.00	360.00	2,430.00
100 kva	EA	11.594	8,340.00	960.00	9,300.00

Three phase, 480v-120/208v

	Unit	Man-Hrs	Material	Labor	Total
15 kva	EA	6.015	2,270.00	500.00	2,770.00
30 kva	EA	9.412	2,720.00	780.00	3,500.00
45 kva	EA	10.811	3,620.00	900.00	4,520.00
225 kva	EA	15.385	13,010.00	1,280.00	14,290.00

26241.30 SWITCHBOARDS

SWITCHBOARDS
Switchboard, 90" high, no main disconnect, 208/120v

	Unit	Man-Hrs	Material	Labor	Total
400a	EA	7.921	3,040.00	660.00	3,700.00
600a	EA	8.000	4,710.00	660.00	5,370.00
1000a	EA	8.000	5,930.00	660.00	6,590.00
1200a	EA	10.000	6,280.00	830.00	7,110.00
1600a	EA	11.940	6,900.00	990.00	7,890.00
2000a	EA	14.035	7,410.00	1,160.00	8,570.00
2500a	EA	16.000	7,500.00	1,330.00	8,830.00

277/480v

	Unit	Man-Hrs	Material	Labor	Total
600a	EA	8.163	5,410.00	680.00	6,090.00
800a	EA	8.163	5,930.00	680.00	6,610.00
1600a	EA	11.940	7,470.00	990.00	8,460.00
2000a	EA	14.035	7,990.00	1,160.00	9,150.00
2500a	EA	16.000	8,510.00	1,330.00	9,840.00
3000a	EA	27.586	9,800.00	2,290.00	12,090.00
4000a	EA	29.630	11,870.00	2,460.00	14,330.00

26241.60 PANELBOARDS

PANELBOARDS

	Unit	Man-Hrs	Material	Labor	Total
3 phase, 480/277v, main lugs only, 120a, 30 circuits	EA	3.478	1,670.00	290.00	1,960.00

277/480v, 4 wire, flush surface

	Unit	Man-Hrs	Material	Labor	Total
225a, 30 circuits	EA	4.000	2,720.00	330.00	3,050.00
400a, 30 circuits	EA	5.000	3,690.00	420.00	4,110.00
600a, 42 circuits	EA	6.015	7,120.00	500.00	7,620.00

208/120v, main circuit breaker, 3 phase, 4 wire
100a

	Unit	Man-Hrs	Material	Labor	Total
12 circuits	EA	5.096	1,440.00	420.00	1,860.00
20 circuits	EA	6.299	1,790.00	520.00	2,310.00
30 circuits	EA	7.018	2,640.00	580.00	3,220.00

	Unit	Man-Hrs	Material	Labor	Total
26241.60 PANELBOARDS (Cont.)					
208/120v, main circuit breaker, 3 phase, 4 wire					
400a					
30 circuits	EA	14.815	5,550.00	1,230.00	6,780.00
42 circuits	EA	16.000	6,660.00	1,330.00	7,990.00
600a, 42 circuits	EA	18.182	12,950.00	1,510.00	14,460.00
120/208v, flush, 3 ph., 4 wire, main only					
100a					
12 circuits	EA	5.096	1,020.00	420.00	1,440.00
20 circuits	EA	6.299	1,410.00	520.00	1,930.00
30 circuits	EA	7.018	2,090.00	580.00	2,670.00
400a					
30 circuits	EA	14.815	4,080.00	1,230.00	5,310.00
42 circuits	EA	16.000	5,940.00	1,330.00	7,270.00
600a, 42 circuits	EA	18.182	9,260.00	1,510.00	10,770.00
26241.90 MOTOR CONTROLS					
MOTOR CONTROLS					
Motor generator set, 3 phase, 480/277v, w/controls					
10kw	EA	27.586	13,490.00	2,290.00	15,780.00
15kw	EA	30.769	17,600.00	2,550.00	20,150.00
20kw	EA	32.000	19,530.00	2,660.00	22,190.00
40kw	EA	38.095	27,490.00	3,160.00	30,650.00
100kw	EA	61.538	40,960.00	5,110.00	46,070.00
200kw	EA	72.727	93,620.00	6,040.00	99,660.00
300kw	EA	80.000	117,020.00	6,640.00	123,660.00
2 pole, 230 volt starter, w/NEMA-1					
1 hp, 9a, size 00	EA	1.000	150.00	83.00	233.00
2 hp, 18a, size 0	EA	1.000	170.00	83.00	253.00
3 hp, 27a, size 1	EA	1.000	240.00	83.00	323.00
5 hp, 45a, size 1p	EA	1.000	240.00	83.00	323.00
7-1/2 hp, 45a, size 2	EA	1.000	580.00	83.00	663.00
15 hp, 90a, size 3	EA	1.000	880.00	83.00	963.00
26272.68 RECEPTACLES					
RECEPTACLES					
Contractor grade duplex receptacles, 15a 120v					
Duplex	EA	0.200	1.60	16.50	18.10
125 volt, 20a, duplex, standard grade	EA	0.200	12.00	16.50	28.50
Ground fault interrupter type	EA	0.296	38.75	24.50	63.25
250 volt, 20a, 2 pole, single, grounding type	EA	0.200	20.00	16.50	36.50
120/208v, 4 pole, single receptacle, twist lock					
20a	EA	0.348	23.75	28.75	52.50
50a	EA	0.348	45.25	28.75	74.00
125/250v, 3 pole, flush receptacle					
30a	EA	0.296	24.00	24.50	48.50
50a	EA	0.296	29.75	24.50	54.25
60a	EA	0.348	77.00	28.75	105.75
277v, 20a, 2 pole, grounding type, twist lock	EA	0.200	13.00	16.50	29.50
Dryer receptacle, 250v, 30a/50a, 3 wire	EA	0.296	18.00	24.50	42.50
Clock receptacle, 2 pole, grounding type	EA	0.200	12.00	16.50	28.50
125v, 20a single recept. grounding type					
Standard grade	EA	0.200	13.00	16.50	29.50
Specification	EA	0.200	15.50	16.50	32.00
Hospital	EA	0.200	16.25	16.50	32.75
Isolated ground orange	EA	0.250	55.00	20.75	75.75
Duplex					
Specification grade	EA	0.200	13.00	16.50	29.50
Hospital	EA	0.200	26.50	16.50	43.00
Isolated ground orange	EA	0.250	55.00	20.75	75.75
GFI hospital grade recepts, 20a, 125v, duplex	EA	0.296	58.00	24.50	82.50
26281.30 FUSES					
FUSES					
Fuse, one-time, 250v					
30a	EA	0.050	2.77	4.15	6.92
60a	EA	0.050	4.68	4.15	8.83

© 2020 BNi Publications, Inc.

	Unit	Man-Hrs	Material	Labor	Total
26281.30 FUSES (Cont.)					
Fuse, one-time, 250v					
100a	EA	0.050	19.50	4.15	23.65
200a	EA	0.050	47.25	4.15	51.40
400a	EA	0.050	110.00	4.15	114.15
600a	EA	0.050	180.00	4.15	184.15
600v					
30a	EA	0.050	14.00	4.15	18.15
60a	EA	0.050	22.25	4.15	26.40
100a	EA	0.050	42.00	4.15	46.15
200a	EA	0.050	110.00	4.15	114.15
400a	EA	0.050	230.00	4.15	234.15
26281.61 CIRCUIT BREAKERS					
CIRCUIT BREAKERS					
Molded case, 240v, 15-60a, bolt-on					
1 pole	EA	0.250	20.00	20.75	40.75
2 pole	EA	0.348	42.50	28.75	71.25
70-100a, 2 pole	EA	0.533	120.00	44.25	164.25
15-60a, 3 pole	EA	0.400	150.00	33.25	183.25
70-100a, 3 pole	EA	0.615	240.00	51.00	291.00
480v, 2 pole					
15-60a	EA	0.296	310.00	24.50	334.50
70-100a	EA	0.400	390.00	33.25	423.25
3 pole					
15-60a	EA	0.400	390.00	33.25	423.25
70-100a	EA	0.444	470.00	37.00	507.00
70-225a	EA	0.615	960.00	51.00	1,011.00
Load center circuit breakers, 240v					
1 pole, 10-60a	EA	0.250	21.25	20.75	42.00
2 pole					
10-60a	EA	0.400	43.25	33.25	76.50
70-100a	EA	0.667	130.00	55.00	185.00
110-150a	EA	0.727	280.00	60.00	340.00
3 pole					
10-60a	EA	0.500	120.00	41.50	161.50
70-100a	EA	0.727	180.00	60.00	240.00
Load center, GFI breakers, 240v					
1 pole, 15-30a	EA	0.296	160.00	24.50	184.50
2 pole, 15-30a	EA	0.400	280.00	33.25	313.25
Key operated breakers, 240v, 1 pole, 10-30a	EA	0.296	100.00	24.50	124.50
Tandem breakers, 240v					
1 pole, 15-30a	EA	0.400	35.00	33.25	68.25
2 pole, 15-30a	EA	0.533	64.00	44.25	108.25
Bolt-on, GFI breakers, 240v, 1 pole, 15-30a	EA	0.348	150.00	28.75	178.75
26281.64 SWITCHES					
SWITCHES					
Fused interrupter load, 35kv, 20a					
1 pole	EA	16.000	26,000.00	1,330.00	27,330.00
2 pole	EA	17.021	28,170.00	1,410.00	29,580.00
Weatherproof switch, including box & cover, 20a					
1 pole	EA	16.000	28,160.00	1,330.00	29,490.00
2 pole	EA	17.021	30,330.00	1,410.00	31,740.00
Specification grade toggle switches, 20a, 120-277v					
Single pole	EA	0.200	3.93	16.50	20.43
Double pole	EA	0.296	9.43	24.50	33.93
3 way	EA	0.250	10.25	20.75	31.00
4 way	EA	0.296	31.00	24.50	55.50
Switch plates, plastic ivory					
1 gang	EA	0.080	0.43	6.64	7.07
2 gang	EA	0.100	1.01	8.30	9.31
3 gang	EA	0.119	1.58	9.91	11.49
4 gang	EA	0.145	4.04	12.00	16.04
5 gang	EA	0.160	4.23	13.25	17.48
6 gang	EA	0.182	4.99	15.00	19.99

	Unit	Man-Hrs	Material	Labor	Total

26281.64 SWITCHES (Cont.)

Switch plates
Stainless steel

	Unit	Man-Hrs	Material	Labor	Total
1 gang	EA	0.080	3.64	6.64	10.28
2 gang	EA	0.100	5.06	8.30	13.36
3 gang	EA	0.123	7.76	10.25	18.01
4 gang	EA	0.145	13.25	12.00	25.25
5 gang	EA	0.160	15.50	13.25	28.75
6 gang	EA	0.182	19.50	15.00	34.50

Brass

	Unit	Man-Hrs	Material	Labor	Total
1 gang	EA	0.080	6.79	6.64	13.43
2 gang	EA	0.100	14.50	8.30	22.80
3 gang	EA	0.123	22.50	10.25	32.75
4 gang	EA	0.145	26.00	12.00	38.00
5 gang	EA	0.160	32.25	13.25	45.50
6 gang	EA	0.182	38.75	15.00	53.75

26281.66 SAFETY SWITCHES

SAFETY SWITCHES
Fused, 3 phase, 30 amp, 600v, heavy duty

	Unit	Man-Hrs	Material	Labor	Total
NEMA 1	EA	1.143	240.00	95.00	335.00
NEMA 3r	EA	1.143	540.00	95.00	635.00
NEMA 4	EA	1.600	1,510.00	130.00	1,640.00
NEMA 12	EA	1.739	480.00	140.00	620.00

60a

	Unit	Man-Hrs	Material	Labor	Total
NEMA 1	EA	1.143	330.00	95.00	425.00
NEMA 3r	EA	1.143	640.00	95.00	735.00
NEMA 4	EA	1.600	1,670.00	130.00	1,800.00
NEMA 12	EA	1.739	570.00	140.00	710.00

100a

	Unit	Man-Hrs	Material	Labor	Total
NEMA 1	EA	1.739	570.00	140.00	710.00
NEMA 3r	EA	1.739	990.00	140.00	1,130.00
NEMA 4	EA	2.000	3,550.00	170.00	3,720.00
NEMA 12	EA	2.500	860.00	210.00	1,070.00

200a

	Unit	Man-Hrs	Material	Labor	Total
NEMA 1	EA	2.500	840.00	210.00	1,050.00
NEMA 3r	EA	2.500	1,370.00	210.00	1,580.00
NEMA 4	EA	2.759	4,660.00	230.00	4,890.00
NEMA 12	EA	3.478	1,270.00	290.00	1,560.00

Non-fused, 240-600v, heavy duty, 3 phase, 30 amp

	Unit	Man-Hrs	Material	Labor	Total
NEMA 1	EA	1.143	170.00	95.00	265.00
NEMA 3r	EA	1.143	270.00	95.00	365.00
NEMA 4	EA	1.739	1,070.00	140.00	1,210.00
NEMA 12	EA	1.739	320.00	140.00	460.00

60a

	Unit	Man-Hrs	Material	Labor	Total
NEMA1	EA	1.143	220.00	95.00	315.00
NEMA 3r	EA	1.143	410.00	95.00	505.00
NEMA 4	EA	1.739	1,160.00	140.00	1,300.00
NEMA 12	EA	1.739	390.00	140.00	530.00

100a

	Unit	Man-Hrs	Material	Labor	Total
NEMA 1	EA	1.739	360.00	140.00	500.00
NEMA 3r	EA	1.739	570.00	140.00	710.00
NEMA 4	EA	2.500	2,340.00	210.00	2,550.00
NEMA 12	EA	2.500	550.00	210.00	760.00
200a, NEMA 1	EA	2.500	550.00	210.00	760.00
600a, NEMA 12	EA	12.308	3,080.00	1,020.00	4,100.00

26281.68 SAFETY SWITCHES, HEAVY DUTY

SAFETY SWITCHES, HEAVY DUTY
Safety switch, 600v, 3 pole, heavy duty, NEMA-1

	Unit	Man-Hrs	Material	Labor	Total
30a	EA	1.000	210.00	83.00	293.00
60a	EA	1.143	280.00	95.00	375.00
100a	EA	1.600	530.00	130.00	660.00
200a	EA	2.500	830.00	210.00	1,040.00
400a	EA	5.517	2,140.00	460.00	2,600.00
600a	EA	8.000	3,800.00	660.00	4,460.00
800a	EA	10.526	8,600.00	870.00	9,470.00

© 2020 BNi Publications, Inc.

	Unit	Man-Hrs	Material	Labor	Total

26281.68 SAFETY SWITCHES, HEAVY DUTY (Cont.)

Safety switch, 600v, 3 pole, heavy duty, NEMA-1

	Unit	Man-Hrs	Material	Labor	Total
1200a	EA	14.286	10,680.00	1,190.00	11,870.00

26281.69 TRANSFER SWITCHES

TRANSFER SWITCHES

Automatic transfer switch 600v, 3 pole

	Unit	Man-Hrs	Material	Labor	Total
30a	EA	3.478	2,680.00	290.00	2,970.00
100a	EA	4.762	3,550.00	400.00	3,950.00
400a	EA	10.000	8,010.00	830.00	8,840.00
800a	EA	18.182	14,740.00	1,510.00	16,250.00
1200a	EA	22.857	24,300.00	1,900.00	26,200.00
2600a	EA	42.105	63,670.00	3,490.00	67,160.00

26320.01 GENERATORS

GENERATORS

Diesel generator, with auto transfer switch

	Unit	Man-Hrs	Material	Labor	Total
50kw	EA	30.769	32,530.00	2,550.00	35,080.00
125kw	EA	50.000	48,980.00	4,150.00	53,130.00
300kw	EA	100.000	80,230.00	8,300.00	88,530.00
750kw	EA	200.000	233,920.00	16,600.00	250,520.00

26335.30 UNINTERRUPTIBLE POWER

UNINTERRUPTIBLE POWER

	Unit	Man-Hrs	Material	Labor	Total
Uninterruptible power systems, (UPS), 3 kva	EA	8.000	7,750.00	660.00	8,410.00
5 kva	EA	11.004	8,690.00	910.00	9,600.00
7.5 kva	EA	16.000	10,430.00	1,330.00	11,760.00
10 kva	EA	21.978	13,040.00	1,820.00	14,860.00
15 kva	EA	22.857	15,650.00	1,900.00	17,550.00
20 kva	EA	24.024	21,730.00	1,990.00	23,720.00
25 kva	EA	25.000	27,820.00	2,080.00	29,900.00
30 kva	EA	25.974	28,680.00	2,160.00	30,840.00
35 kva	EA	27.027	30,420.00	2,240.00	32,660.00
40 kva	EA	27.972	33,030.00	2,320.00	35,350.00
45 kva	EA	28.986	34,770.00	2,410.00	37,180.00
50 kva	EA	29.963	37,380.00	2,490.00	39,870.00
62.5 kva	EA	32.000	44,330.00	2,660.00	46,990.00
75 kva	EA	34.934	51,280.00	2,900.00	54,180.00
100 kva	EA	36.036	68,670.00	2,990.00	71,660.00
150 kva	EA	50.000	104,310.00	4,150.00	108,460.00
200 kva	EA	55.172	139,080.00	4,580.00	143,660.00
300 kva	EA	74.766	208,620.00	6,210.00	214,830.00
400 kva	EA	89.888	312,100.00	7,460.00	319,560.00
500 kva	EA	109.589	390,120.00	9,100.00	399,220.00

26411.30 LIGHTNING PROTECTION

LIGHTNING PROTECTION

Lightning protection

Copper point, nickel plated, 12'

	Unit	Man-Hrs	Material	Labor	Total
1/2" dia.	EA	1.000	46.25	83.00	129.25
5/8" dia.	EA	1.000	52.00	83.00	135.00

26514.01 INDUSTRIAL LIGHTING

INDUSTRIAL LIGHTING

Surface mounted fluorescent, wrap around lens

	Unit	Man-Hrs	Material	Labor	Total
1 lamp	EA	0.800	90.00	66.00	156.00
2 lamps	EA	0.889	130.00	74.00	204.00
4 lamps	EA	1.000	140.00	83.00	223.00

Wall mounted fluorescent

	Unit	Man-Hrs	Material	Labor	Total
2-20w lamps	EA	0.500	93.00	41.50	134.50
2-30w lamps	EA	0.500	110.00	41.50	151.50
2-40w lamps	EA	0.667	110.00	55.00	165.00

Indirect, with wood shielding, 2049w lamps

	Unit	Man-Hrs	Material	Labor	Total
4'	EA	1.000	110.00	83.00	193.00
8'	EA	1.600	140.00	130.00	270.00

Industrial fluorescent, 2 lamp

	Unit	Man-Hrs	Material	Labor	Total
4'	EA	0.727	72.00	60.00	132.00
8'	EA	1.333	110.00	110.00	220.00

26514.01 INDUSTRIAL LIGHTING (Cont.)

	Unit	Man-Hrs	Material	Labor	Total
Surface mounted fluorescent, wrap around lens					
Strip fluorescent					
4'					
1 lamp	EA	0.667	45.50	55.00	100.50
2 lamps	EA	0.667	55.00	55.00	110.00
8'					
1 lamp	EA	0.727	66.00	60.00	126.00
2 lamps	EA	0.889	99.00	74.00	173.00
Wire guard for strip fixture, 4' long	EA	0.348	10.25	28.75	39.00
Strip fluorescent, 8' long, two 4' lamps	EA	1.333	140.00	110.00	250.00
With four 4' lamps	EA	1.600	170.00	130.00	300.00
Wet location fluorescent, plastic housing					
4' long					
1 lamp	EA	1.000	110.00	83.00	193.00
2 lamps	EA	1.333	160.00	110.00	270.00
8' long					
2 lamps	EA	1.600	280.00	130.00	410.00
4 lamps	EA	1.739	370.00	140.00	510.00
Parabolic troffer, 2'x2'					
With 2 U lamps	EA	1.000	130.00	83.00	213.00
With 3 U lamps	EA	1.143	150.00	95.00	245.00
2'x4'					
With 2 40w lamps	EA	1.143	150.00	95.00	245.00
With 3 40w lamps	EA	1.333	150.00	110.00	260.00
With 4 40w lamps	EA	1.333	160.00	110.00	270.00
1'x4'					
With 1 T-12 lamp, 9 cell	EA	0.727	78.00	60.00	138.00
With 2 T-12 lamps	EA	0.889	88.00	74.00	162.00
With 1 T-12 lamp, 20 cell	EA	0.727	88.00	60.00	148.00
With 2 T-12 lamps	EA	0.889	98.00	74.00	172.00
Steel sided surface fluorescent, 2'x4'					
3 lamps	EA	1.333	150.00	110.00	260.00
4 lamps	EA	1.333	170.00	110.00	280.00
Outdoor sign fluor., 1 lamp, remote ballast					
4' long	EA	6.015	3,160.00	500.00	3,660.00
6' long	EA	8.000	3,800.00	660.00	4,460.00
Recess mounted, commercial, 2'x2', 13" high					
100w	EA	4.000	1,050.00	330.00	1,380.00
250w	EA	4.494	1,160.00	370.00	1,530.00
High pressure sodium, hi-bay open					
400w	EA	1.739	460.00	140.00	600.00
1000w	EA	2.424	790.00	200.00	990.00
Enclosed					
400w	EA	2.424	740.00	200.00	940.00
1000w	EA	2.963	1,030.00	250.00	1,280.00
Metal halide hi-bay, open					
400w	EA	1.739	280.00	140.00	420.00
1000w	EA	2.424	580.00	200.00	780.00
Enclosed					
400w	EA	2.424	640.00	200.00	840.00
1000w	EA	2.963	610.00	250.00	860.00
High pressure sodium, low-bay surface mounted					
100w	EA	1.000	230.00	83.00	313.00
150w	EA	1.143	260.00	95.00	355.00
250w	EA	1.333	290.00	110.00	400.00
400w	EA	1.600	360.00	130.00	490.00
Metal halide, low-bay, pendant mounted					
175w	EA	1.333	370.00	110.00	480.00
250w	EA	1.600	510.00	130.00	640.00
400w	EA	2.222	550.00	180.00	730.00
Indirect luminaire, square, metal halide, freestanding					
175w	EA	1.000	460.00	83.00	543.00
250w	EA	1.000	500.00	83.00	583.00
400w	EA	1.000	510.00	83.00	593.00

© 2020 BNi Publications, Inc.

26514.01 INDUSTRIAL LIGHTING (Cont.)

	Unit	Man-Hrs	Material	Labor	Total
Indirect luminaire, square, metal halide, freestanding					
High pressure sodium					
150w	EA	1.000	830.00	83.00	913.00
250w	EA	1.000	890.00	83.00	973.00
400w	EA	1.000	980.00	83.00	1,063.00
Round, metal halide					
175w	EA	1.000	960.00	83.00	1,043.00
250w	EA	1.000	990.00	83.00	1,073.00
400w	EA	1.000	1,040.00	83.00	1,123.00
High pressure sodium					
150w	EA	1.000	910.00	83.00	993.00
250w	EA	1.000	1,060.00	83.00	1,143.00
400w	EA	1.000	1,110.00	83.00	1,193.00
Wall mounted, metal halide					
175w	EA	2.500	420.00	210.00	630.00
250w	EA	2.500	410.00	210.00	620.00
400w	EA	3.200	450.00	270.00	720.00
High pressure sodium					
150w	EA	2.500	390.00	210.00	600.00
250w	EA	2.500	410.00	210.00	620.00
400w	EA	3.200	420.00	270.00	690.00
Wall pack lithonia, high pressure sodium					
35w	EA	0.889	60.00	74.00	134.00
55w	EA	1.000	76.00	83.00	159.00
150w	EA	1.600	190.00	130.00	320.00
250w	EA	1.739	200.00	140.00	340.00
Low pressure sodium					
35w	EA	1.739	320.00	140.00	460.00
55w	EA	2.000	440.00	170.00	610.00
Wall pack hubbell, high pressure sodium					
35w	EA	0.889	270.00	74.00	344.00
150w	EA	1.600	330.00	130.00	460.00
250w	EA	1.739	430.00	140.00	570.00
Compact fluorescent					
2-7w	EA	1.000	160.00	83.00	243.00
2-13w	EA	1.333	180.00	110.00	290.00
1-18w	EA	1.333	220.00	110.00	330.00
Handball & racquet ball court, 2'x2', metal halide					
250w	EA	2.500	580.00	210.00	790.00
400w	EA	2.759	690.00	230.00	920.00
High pressure sodium					
250w	EA	2.500	640.00	210.00	850.00
400w	EA	2.759	690.00	230.00	920.00
Bollard light, 42" w/found., high pressure sodium					
70w	EA	2.581	970.00	210.00	1,180.00
100w	EA	2.581	990.00	210.00	1,200.00
150w	EA	2.581	1,000.00	210.00	1,210.00
Light fixture lamps					
Lamp					
20w med. bi-pin base, cool white, 24"	EA	0.145	7.78	12.00	19.78
30w cool white, rapid start, 36"	EA	0.145	9.86	12.00	21.86
40w cool white U, 3"	EA	0.145	21.50	12.00	33.50
40w cool white, rapid start, 48"	EA	0.145	9.18	12.00	21.18
70w high pressure sodium, mogul base	EA	0.200	71.00	16.50	87.50
75w slimline, 96"	EA	0.200	21.25	16.50	37.75
100w					
Incandescent, 100a, inside frost	EA	0.100	3.69	8.30	11.99
Mercury vapor, clear, mogul base	EA	0.200	64.00	16.50	80.50
High pressure sodium, mogul base	EA	0.200	98.00	16.50	114.50
150w					
Par 38 flood or spot, incandescent	EA	0.100	21.75	8.30	30.05
High pressure sodium, 1/2 mogul base	EA	0.200	87.00	16.50	103.50
175w					
Mercury vapor, clear, mogul base	EA	0.200	39.00	16.50	55.50
Metal halide, clear, mogul base	EA	0.200	78.00	16.50	94.50

	Unit	Man-Hrs	Material	Labor	Total
26514.01 INDUSTRIAL LIGHTING (Cont.)					
Lamp					
High pressure sodium, mogul base	EA	0.200	87.00	16.50	103.50
250w					
Mercury vapor, clear, mogul base	EA	0.200	54.00	16.50	70.50
Metal halide, clear, mogul base	EA	0.200	78.00	16.50	94.50
High pressure sodium, mogul base	EA	0.200	92.00	16.50	108.50
400w					
Mercury vapor, clear, mogul base	EA	0.200	59.00	16.50	75.50
Metal halide, clear, mogul base	EA	0.200	78.00	16.50	94.50
High pressure sodium, mogul base	EA	0.200	95.00	16.50	111.50
1000w					
Mercury vapor, clear, mogul base	EA	0.250	140.00	20.75	160.75
High pressure sodium, mogul base	EA	0.250	250.00	20.75	270.75
26560.03 EXTERIOR LIGHTING					
EXTERIOR LIGHTING					
Exterior light fixtures					
Rectangle, high pressure sodium					
70w	EA	2.500	330.00	210.00	540.00
100w	EA	2.581	340.00	210.00	550.00
150w	EA	2.581	360.00	210.00	570.00
250w	EA	2.759	490.00	230.00	720.00
400w	EA	3.478	550.00	290.00	840.00
Flood, rectangular, high pressure sodium					
70w	EA	2.500	240.00	210.00	450.00
100w	EA	2.581	280.00	210.00	490.00
150w	EA	2.581	260.00	210.00	470.00
400w	EA	3.478	320.00	290.00	610.00
1000w	EA	4.494	540.00	370.00	910.00
Round					
400w	EA	3.478	600.00	290.00	890.00
1000w	EA	4.494	940.00	370.00	1,310.00
Round, metal halide					
400w	EA	3.478	670.00	290.00	960.00
1000w	EA	4.494	990.00	370.00	1,360.00
Light fixture arms, cobra head, 6', high press. sodium					
100w	EA	2.000	360.00	170.00	530.00
150w	EA	2.500	570.00	210.00	780.00
250w	EA	2.500	600.00	210.00	810.00
400w	EA	2.963	620.00	250.00	870.00
Flood, metal halide					
400w	EA	3.478	600.00	290.00	890.00
1000w	EA	4.494	820.00	370.00	1,190.00
1500w	EA	6.015	1,030.00	500.00	1,530.00
Mercury vapor					
250w	EA	2.759	390.00	230.00	620.00
400w	EA	3.478	440.00	290.00	730.00
Incandescent					
300w	EA	1.739	91.00	140.00	231.00
500w	EA	2.000	160.00	170.00	330.00
1000w	EA	3.200	180.00	270.00	450.00
26560.04 ENERGY EFFICIENT EXTERIOR LIGHTING					
ENERGY EFFICIENT EXTERIOR LIGHTING					
Solar Powered, LED area light, 100 Watt, Zone 4					
Minimum	EA	1.333	1,190.00	110.00	1,300.00
Average	EA	1.600	1,330.00	130.00	1,460.00
Maximum	EA	2.000	1,450.00	170.00	1,620.00
Zone 2					
Minimum	EA	1.333	1,570.00	110.00	1,680.00
Average	EA	1.600	1,630.00	130.00	1,760.00
Maximum	EA	2.000	1,690.00	170.00	1,860.00
Zone 4DD					
Minimum	EA	1.333	1,800.00	110.00	1,910.00
Average	EA	1.600	1,930.00	130.00	2,060.00
Maximum	EA	2.000	2,060.00	170.00	2,230.00

© 2020 BNi Publications, Inc.

26560.04 ENERGY EFFICIENT EXTERIOR LIGHTING (Cont.)

Solar Powered, LED area light, 100 Watt
Zone 2DD

	Unit	Man-Hrs	Material	Labor	Total
Minimum	EA	1.333	1,990.00	110.00	2,100.00
Average	EA	1.600	2,150.00	130.00	2,280.00
Maximum	EA	2.000	2,300.00	170.00	2,470.00

	Unit	Man-Hrs	Material	Labor	Total
27320.01 TELEPHONE SYSTEMS					
TELEPHONE SYSTEMS					
Communication cable					
25 pair	LF	0.026	0.98	2.14	3.12
100 pair	LF	0.029	4.67	2.37	7.04
400 pair	LF	0.044	16.50	3.68	20.18
Cable tap in manhole or junction box					
25 pair cable	EA	3.810	6.81	320.00	326.81
100 pair cable	EA	15.094	27.50	1,250.00	1,277.50
400 pair cable	EA	61.538	110.00	5,110.00	5,220.00
Cable terminations, manhole or junction box					
25 pair cable	EA	3.756	6.81	310.00	316.81
100 pair cable	EA	15.094	27.50	1,250.00	1,277.50
400 pair cable	EA	61.538	85.00	5,110.00	5,195.00
27410.05 TELEVISION SYSTEMS					
TELEVISION SYSTEMS					
TV outlet, self terminating, w/cover plate	EA	0.308	5.95	25.50	31.45
Thru splitter	EA	1.600	13.00	130.00	143.00
End of line	EA	1.333	10.75	110.00	120.75
In line splitter multitap					
4 way	EA	1.818	21.75	150.00	171.75
2 way	EA	1.702	16.25	140.00	156.25
Equipment cabinet	EA	1.600	54.00	130.00	184.00
Antenna					
Broad band UHF	EA	3.478	110.00	290.00	400.00
Lightning arrester	EA	0.727	33.00	60.00	93.00
TV cable	LF	0.005	0.49	0.41	0.90

© 2020 BNi Publications, Inc.

28160.05 SECURITY SYSTEMS

	Unit	Man-Hrs	Material	Labor	Total
SECURITY SYSTEMS					
Sensors					
Balanced magnetic door switch, surface mounted	EA	0.500	180.00	41.50	221.50
With remote test	EA	1.000	230.00	83.00	313.00
Flush mounted	EA	1.860	170.00	150.00	320.00
Mounted bracket	EA	0.348	12.75	28.75	41.50
Mounted bracket spacer	EA	0.348	11.25	28.75	40.00
Photoelectric sensor, for fence					
6 beam	EA	2.759	18,550.00	230.00	18,780.00
9 beam	EA	4.255	22,680.00	350.00	23,030.00
Photoelectric sensor, 12 volt dc					
500' range	EA	1.600	550.00	130.00	680.00
800' range	EA	2.000	610.00	170.00	780.00
Capacitance wire grid kit					
Surface	EA	1.000	150.00	83.00	233.00
Duct	EA	1.600	110.00	130.00	240.00
Tube grid kit	EA	0.500	190.00	41.50	231.50
Vibration sensor, 30 max per zone	EA	0.500	230.00	41.50	271.50
Audio sensor, 30 max per zone	EA	0.500	240.00	41.50	281.50
Inertia sensor					
Outdoor	EA	0.727	180.00	60.00	240.00
Indoor	EA	0.500	110.00	41.50	151.50
Ultrasonic transmitter, 20 max per zone					
Omni-directional	EA	1.600	130.00	130.00	260.00
Directional	EA	1.333	140.00	110.00	250.00
Transceiver					
Omni-directional	EA	1.000	140.00	83.00	223.00
Directional	EA	1.000	150.00	83.00	233.00
Passive infrared sensor, 20 max per zone	EA	1.600	980.00	130.00	1,110.00
Access/secure unit, balanced magnetic switch	EA	1.600	610.00	130.00	740.00
Photoelectric sensor	EA	1.600	1,000.00	130.00	1,130.00
Photoelectric fence sensor	EA	1.600	1,030.00	130.00	1,160.00
Capacitance sensor	EA	1.739	1,190.00	140.00	1,330.00
Audio and vibration sensor	EA	1.600	1,050.00	130.00	1,180.00
Inertia sensor	EA	1.600	1,410.00	130.00	1,540.00
Ultrasonic sensor	EA	1.739	1,610.00	140.00	1,750.00
infrared sensor	EA	2.000	1,000.00	170.00	1,170.00
Monitor panel, with access/secure tone, standard	EA	1.739	690.00	140.00	830.00
High security	EA	2.000	1,000.00	170.00	1,170.00
Emergency power indicator	EA	0.500	410.00	41.50	451.50
Monitor rack with 115v power supply					
1 zone	EA	1.000	570.00	83.00	653.00
10 zone	EA	2.500	2,910.00	210.00	3,120.00
Monitor cabinet, wall mounted					
1 zone	EA	1.000	880.00	83.00	963.00
5 zone	EA	1.600	1,450.00	130.00	1,580.00
10 zone	EA	1.739	3,160.00	140.00	3,300.00
20 zone	EA	2.000	4,410.00	170.00	4,580.00
Floor mounted, 50 zone	EA	4.000	4,590.00	330.00	4,920.00
Security system accessories					
Tamper assembly for monitor cabinet	EA	0.444	110.00	37.00	147.00
Monitor panel blank	EA	0.348	15.25	28.75	44.00
Audible alarm	EA	0.500	130.00	41.50	171.50
Audible alarm control	EA	0.348	530.00	28.75	558.75
Termination screw, terminal cabinet					
25 pair	EA	1.600	380.00	130.00	510.00
50 pair	EA	2.500	610.00	210.00	820.00
150 pair	EA	5.000	990.00	420.00	1,410.00
Universal termination, cabinets & panel					
Remote test	EA	1.739	89.00	140.00	229.00
No remote test	EA	0.727	63.00	60.00	123.00
High security line supervision termination	EA	1.000	440.00	83.00	523.00
Door cord for capacitance sensor, 12"	EA	0.500	15.25	41.50	56.75
Insulation block kit for capacitance sensor	EA	0.348	71.00	28.75	99.75
Termination block for capacitance sensor	EA	0.348	15.50	28.75	44.25

	Unit	Man-Hrs	Material	Labor	Total

28160.05 SECURITY SYSTEMS (Cont.)

Sensors

	Unit	Man-Hrs	Material	Labor	Total
Guard alert display	EA	0.615	1,610.00	51.00	1,661.00
Uninterrupted power supply	EA	8.000	1,640.00	660.00	2,300.00
Plug-in 40kva transformer					
12 volt	EA	0.348	65.00	28.75	93.75
18 volt	EA	0.348	43.00	28.75	71.75
24 volt	EA	0.348	30.50	28.75	59.25
Test relay	EA	0.348	98.00	28.75	126.75
Coaxial cable, 50 ohm	LF	0.006	0.44	0.50	0.94
Door openers	EA	0.500	110.00	41.50	151.50
Push buttons					
Standard	EA	0.348	25.25	28.75	54.00
Weatherproof	EA	0.444	38.00	37.00	75.00
Bells	EA	0.727	97.00	60.00	157.00
Horns					
Standard	EA	1.000	100.00	83.00	183.00
Weatherproof	EA	1.250	190.00	100.00	290.00
Chimes	EA	0.667	150.00	55.00	205.00
Flasher	EA	0.615	110.00	51.00	161.00
Motion detectors	EA	1.509	440.00	130.00	570.00
Intercom units	EA	0.727	100.00	60.00	160.00
Remote annunciator	EA	5.000	4,560.00	420.00	4,980.00

28310.01 FIRE ALARM SYSTEMS

FIRE ALARM SYSTEMS

	Unit	Man-Hrs	Material	Labor	Total
Master fire alarm box, pedestal mounted	EA	16.000	8,210.00	1,330.00	9,540.00
Master fire alarm box	EA	6.015	4,220.00	500.00	4,720.00
Box light	EA	0.500	150.00	41.50	191.50
Ground assembly for box	EA	0.667	120.00	55.00	175.00
Bracket for pole type box	EA	0.727	150.00	60.00	210.00
Pull station					
Waterproof	EA	0.500	75.00	41.50	116.50
Manual	EA	0.400	56.00	33.25	89.25
Horn, waterproof	EA	1.000	110.00	83.00	193.00
Interior alarm	EA	0.727	71.00	60.00	131.00
Coded transmitter, automatic	EA	2.000	1,080.00	170.00	1,250.00
Control panel, 8 zone	EA	8.000	2,480.00	660.00	3,140.00
Battery charger and cabinet	EA	2.000	830.00	170.00	1,000.00
Batteries, nickel cadmium or lead calcium	EA	5.000	620.00	420.00	1,040.00
CO_2 pressure switch connection	EA	0.727	120.00	60.00	180.00
Annunciator panels					
Fire detection annunciator, remote type, 8 zone	EA	1.818	420.00	150.00	570.00
12 zone	EA	2.000	530.00	170.00	700.00
16 zone	EA	2.500	670.00	210.00	880.00
Fire alarm systems					
Bell	EA	0.615	130.00	51.00	181.00
Weatherproof bell	EA	0.667	82.00	55.00	137.00
Horn	EA	0.727	75.00	60.00	135.00
Siren	EA	2.000	760.00	170.00	930.00
Chime	EA	0.615	94.00	51.00	145.00
Audio/visual	EA	0.727	140.00	60.00	200.00
Strobe light	EA	0.727	130.00	60.00	190.00
Smoke detector	EA	0.667	200.00	55.00	255.00
Heat detector	EA	0.500	35.25	41.50	76.75
Thermal detector	EA	0.500	32.75	41.50	74.25
Ionization detector	EA	0.533	170.00	44.25	214.25
Duct detector	EA	2.759	550.00	230.00	780.00
Test switch	EA	0.500	94.00	41.50	135.50
Remote indicator	EA	0.571	58.00	47.50	105.50
Door holder	EA	0.727	200.00	60.00	260.00
Telephone jack	EA	0.296	3.81	24.50	28.31
Fireman phone	EA	1.000	500.00	83.00	583.00
Speaker	EA	0.800	100.00	66.00	166.00

© 2020 BNi Publications, Inc.

28310.01 FIRE ALARM SYSTEMS (Cont.)

	Unit	Man-Hrs	Material	Labor	Total
Fire alarm systems					
Remote fire alarm annunciator panel					
24 zone	EA	6.667	2,580.00	550.00	3,130.00
48 zone	EA	13.008	5,160.00	1,080.00	6,240.00
Control panel					
12 zone	EA	2.963	1,750.00	250.00	2,000.00
16 zone	EA	4.444	2,300.00	370.00	2,670.00
24 zone	EA	6.667	3,520.00	550.00	4,070.00
48 zone	EA	16.000	6,570.00	1,330.00	7,900.00
Power supply	EA	1.509	410.00	130.00	540.00
Status command	EA	5.000	11,130.00	420.00	11,550.00
Printer	EA	1.509	3,550.00	130.00	3,680.00
Transponder	EA	0.899	180.00	75.00	255.00
Transformer	EA	0.667	250.00	55.00	305.00
Transceiver	EA	0.727	360.00	60.00	420.00
Relays	EA	0.500	140.00	41.50	181.50
Flow switch	EA	2.000	460.00	170.00	630.00
Tamper switch	EA	2.963	280.00	250.00	530.00
End of line resistor	EA	0.348	20.00	28.75	48.75
Printed circuit card	EA	0.500	180.00	41.50	221.50
Central processing unit	EA	6.154	12,170.00	510.00	12,680.00
UPS backup to CPU	EA	8.999	22,280.00	750.00	23,030.00
Smoke detector, fixed temp. & rate of rise comb.	EA	1.600	360.00	130.00	490.00

	Unit	Man-Hrs	Material	Labor	Total
31110.01 CLEAR WOODED AREAS					
CLEAR WOODED AREAS					
Clear wooded area					
Light density	ACRE	60.000		7,130.00	7,130.00
Medium density	ACRE	80.000		9,500.00	9,500.00
Heavy density	ACRE	96.000		11,400.00	11,400.00
31130.05 TREE CUTTING & CLEARING					
TREE CUTTING & CLEARING					
Cut trees and clear out stumps					
9" to 12" dia.	EA	4.800		570.00	570.00
To 24" dia.	EA	6.000		710.00	710.00
24" dia. and up	EA	8.000		950.00	950.00
Loading and trucking					
For machine load, per load, round trip					
1 mile	EA	0.960		110.00	110.00
3 mile	EA	1.091		130.00	130.00
5 mile	EA	1.200		140.00	140.00
10 mile	EA	1.600		190.00	190.00
20 mile	EA	2.400		290.00	290.00
Hand loaded, round trip					
1 mile	EA	2.000		280.00	280.00
3 mile	EA	2.286		320.00	320.00
5 mile	EA	2.667		370.00	370.00
10 mile	EA	3.200		440.00	440.00
20 mile	EA	4.000		550.00	550.00
Tree trimming for pole line construction					
Light cutting	LF	0.012		1.42	1.42
Medium cutting	LF	0.016		1.90	1.90
Heavy cutting	LF	0.024		2.85	2.85
31221.30 ROUGH GRADING					
ROUGH GRADING					
Site grading, cut & fill, sandy clay, 200' haul, 75 hp dozer	CY	0.032		4.42	4.42
Spread topsoil by equipment on site	CY	0.036		4.91	4.91
Site grading (cut and fill to 6") less than 1 acre					
75 hp dozer	CY	0.053		7.37	7.37
1.5 c.y. backhoe/loader	CY	0.080		11.00	11.00
31231.31 BASE COURSE					
BASE COURSE					
Base course, crushed stone					
3" thick	SY	0.004	3.34	0.77	4.11
4" thick	SY	0.004	4.50	0.84	5.34
6" thick	SY	0.005	6.75	0.91	7.66
8" thick	SY	0.005	9.00	1.03	10.03
10" thick	SY	0.006	11.25	1.11	12.36
12" thick	SY	0.007	13.50	1.29	14.79
Base course, bank run gravel					
4" deep	SY	0.004	3.17	0.81	3.98
6" deep	SY	0.005	4.85	0.88	5.73
8" deep	SY	0.005	6.41	0.97	7.38
10" deep	SY	0.005	8.02	1.03	9.05
12" deep	SY	0.006	9.58	1.19	10.77
Prepare and roll sub-base					
Minimum	SY	0.004		0.77	0.77
Average	SY	0.005		0.97	0.97
Maximum	SY	0.007		1.29	1.29
31231.32 BORROW					
BORROW					
Borrow fill, FOB at pit					
Sand, haul to site, round trip					
10 mile	CY	0.080	23.75	15.50	39.25
20 mile	CY	0.133	23.75	26.00	49.75
30 mile	CY	0.200	23.75	38.75	62.50

© 2020 BNi Publications, Inc.

	Unit	Man-Hrs	Material	Labor	Total
31231.32 BORROW (Cont.)					
Borrow fill, FOB at pit					
Place borrow fill and compact					
Less than 1 in 4 slope	CY	0.040	23.75	7.77	31.52
Greater than 1 in 4 slope	CY	0.053	23.75	10.25	34.00
31231.37 GRAVEL AND STONE					
GRAVEL AND STONE					
FOB at plant, material only					
No. 21 crusher run stone	CY				33.00
No. 26 crusher run stone	CY				33.00
No. 57 stone	CY				33.00
No. 67 gravel	CY				33.00
No. 68 stone	CY				33.00
No. 78 stone	CY				33.00
No. 78 gravel, (pea gravel)	CY				33.00
No. 357 or B-3 stone	CY				33.00
Structural & foundation backfill					
No. 21 crusher run stone	TON				24.50
No. 26 crusher run stone	TON				24.50
No. 57 stone	TON				24.50
No. 67 gravel	TON				24.50
No. 68 stone	TON				24.50
No. 78 stone	TON				24.50
No. 78 gravel (pea gravel)	TON				24.50
No. 357 or B-3 stone	TON				24.50
31231.63 BULK EXCAVATION					
BULK EXCAVATION					
Excavation, by small dozer					
Large areas	CY	0.016		2.21	2.21
Small areas	CY	0.027		3.68	3.68
Trim banks	CY	0.040		5.53	5.53
Drag line					
1-1/2 c.y. bucket					
Sand or gravel	CY	0.040		4.75	4.75
Light clay	CY	0.053		6.33	6.33
Heavy clay	CY	0.060		7.12	7.12
Unclassified	CY	0.064		7.60	7.60
2 c.y. bucket					
Sand or gravel	CY	0.037		4.38	4.38
Light clay	CY	0.048		5.70	5.70
Heavy clay	CY	0.053		6.33	6.33
Unclassified	CY	0.056		6.70	6.70
2-1/2 c.y. bucket					
Sand or gravel	CY	0.034		4.07	4.07
Light clay	CY	0.044		5.18	5.18
Heavy clay	CY	0.048		5.70	5.70
Unclassified	CY	0.051		6.00	6.00
3 c.y. bucket					
Sand or gravel	CY	0.030		3.56	3.56
Light clay	CY	0.040		4.75	4.75
Heavy clay	CY	0.044		5.18	5.18
Unclassified	CY	0.046		5.42	5.42
Hydraulic excavator					
1 c.y. capacity					
Light material	CY	0.040		4.75	4.75
Medium material	CY	0.048		5.70	5.70
Wet material	CY	0.060		7.12	7.12
Blasted rock	CY	0.069		8.14	8.14
1-1/2 c.y. capacity					
Light material	CY	0.010		1.94	1.94
Medium material	CY	0.013		2.59	2.59
Wet material	CY	0.016		3.10	3.10
Blasted rock	CY	0.020		3.88	3.88

	Unit	Man-Hrs	Material	Labor	Total
31231.63 BULK EXCAVATION (Cont.)					
Hydraulic excavator					
2 c.y. capacity					
Light material	CY	0.009		1.72	1.72
Medium material	CY	0.011		2.22	2.22
Wet material	CY	0.013		2.59	2.59
Blasted rock	CY	0.016		3.10	3.10
Wheel mounted front-end loader					
7/8 c.y. capacity					
Light material	CY	0.020		3.88	3.88
Medium material	CY	0.023		4.44	4.44
Wet material	CY	0.027		5.18	5.18
Blasted rock	CY	0.032		6.21	6.21
1-1/2 c.y. capacity					
Light material	CY	0.011		2.22	2.22
Medium material	CY	0.012		2.39	2.39
Wet material	CY	0.013		2.59	2.59
Blasted rock	CY	0.015		2.82	2.82
2-1/2 c.y. capacity					
Light material	CY	0.009		1.82	1.82
Medium material	CY	0.010		1.94	1.94
Wet material	CY	0.011		2.07	2.07
Blasted rock	CY	0.011		2.22	2.22
3-1/2 c.y. capacity					
Light material	CY	0.009		1.72	1.72
Medium material	CY	0.009		1.82	1.82
Wet material	CY	0.010		1.94	1.94
Blasted rock	CY	0.011		2.07	2.07
6 c.y. capacity					
Light material	CY	0.005		1.03	1.03
Medium material	CY	0.006		1.11	1.11
Wet material	CY	0.006		1.19	1.19
Blasted rock	CY	0.007		1.29	1.29
Track mounted front-end loader					
1-1/2 c.y. capacity					
Light material	CY	0.013		2.59	2.59
Medium material	CY	0.015		2.82	2.82
Wet material	CY	0.016		3.10	3.10
Blasted rock	CY	0.018		3.45	3.45
2-3/4 c.y. capacity					
Light material	CY	0.008		1.55	1.55
Medium material	CY	0.009		1.72	1.72
Wet material	CY	0.010		1.94	1.94
Blasted rock	CY	0.011		2.22	2.22
31231.64 BUILDING EXCAVATION					
BUILDING EXCAVATION					
Structural excavation, unclassified earth					
3/8 c.y. backhoe	CY	0.107		20.75	20.75
3/4 c.y. backhoe	CY	0.080		15.50	15.50
1 c.y. backhoe	CY	0.067		13.00	13.00
Foundation backfill and compaction by machine	CY	0.160		31.00	31.00
31231.65 HAND EXCAVATION					
HAND EXCAVATION					
Excavation					
To 2' deep					
Normal soil	CY	0.889		57.00	57.00
Sand and gravel	CY	0.800		51.00	51.00
Medium clay	CY	1.000		64.00	64.00
Heavy clay	CY	1.143		73.00	73.00
Loose rock	CY	1.333		85.00	85.00
To 6' deep					
Normal soil	CY	1.143		73.00	73.00
Sand and gravel	CY	1.000		64.00	64.00
Medium clay	CY	1.333		85.00	85.00
Heavy clay	CY	1.600		100.00	100.00

© 2020 BNi Publications, Inc.

	Unit	Man-Hrs	Material	Labor	Total
31231.65 HAND EXCAVATION (Cont.)					
To 6' deep					
Loose rock	CY	2.000		130.00	130.00
Backfilling foundation without compaction, 6" lifts	CY	0.500		32.00	32.00
Compaction of backfill around structures or in trench					
By hand with air tamper	CY	0.571		36.50	36.50
By hand with vibrating plate tamper	CY	0.533		34.00	34.00
1 ton roller	CY	0.400		55.00	55.00
Miscellaneous hand labor					
Trim slopes, sides of excavation	SF	0.001		0.08	0.08
Trim bottom of excavation	SF	0.002		0.10	0.10
Excavation around obstructions and services	CY	2.667		170.00	170.00
31231.67 UTILITY EXCAVATION					
UTILITY EXCAVATION					
Trencher, sandy clay, 8" wide trench					
18" deep	LF	0.018		2.45	2.45
24" deep	LF	0.020		2.76	2.76
36" deep	LF	0.023		3.16	3.16
Trench backfill, 95% compaction					
Tamp by hand	CY	0.500		32.00	32.00
Vibratory compaction	CY	0.400		25.50	25.50
Trench backfilling, with borrow sand, place & compact	CY	0.400	22.75	25.50	48.25
31231.68 ROADWAY EXCAVATION					
ROADWAY EXCAVATION					
Roadway excavation					
1/4 mile haul	CY	0.016		3.10	3.10
2 mile haul	CY	0.027		5.18	5.18
5 mile haul	CY	0.040		7.77	7.77
Excavation of open ditches	CY	0.011		2.22	2.22
Trim banks, swales or ditches	SY	0.013		2.59	2.59
Bulk swale excavation by dragline					
Small jobs	CY	0.060		7.12	7.12
Large jobs	CY	0.034		4.07	4.07
Spread base course	CY	0.020		3.88	3.88
Roll and compact	CY	0.027		5.18	5.18
31231.69 HAULING MATERIAL					
HAULING MATERIAL					
Haul material by 10 c.y. dump truck, round trip distance					
1 mile	CY	0.044		6.14	6.14
2 mile	CY	0.053		7.37	7.37
5 mile	CY	0.073		10.00	10.00
10 mile	CY	0.080		11.00	11.00
20 mile	CY	0.089		12.25	12.25
30 mile	CY	0.107		14.75	14.75
31231.95 WELLPOINT SYSTEMS					
WELLPOINT SYSTEMS					
Pumping, gas driven, 50' hose					
3" header pipe	DAY	8.000		1,110.00	1,110.00
6" header pipe	DAY	10.000		1,380.00	1,380.00
Wellpoint system per job; 150' length of PVC header					
6" header pipe, 2" wellpoints, 5' centers	LF	0.032	60.00	4.42	64.42
8" header pipe	LF	0.040	72.00	5.53	77.53
10" header pipe	LF	0.053	110.00	7.37	117.37
Jetting wellpoint system					
14' long	EA	0.533	82.00	74.00	156.00
18' long	EA	0.667	94.00	92.00	186.00
Sand filter for wellpoints	LF	0.013	3.93	1.84	5.77
Replacement of wellpoint components	EA	0.160		22.25	22.25

	Unit	Man-Hrs	Material	Labor	Total

31233.36 TRENCHING

TRENCHING

Trenching and continuous footing excavation

By gradall

1 c.y. capacity

	Unit	Man-Hrs	Material	Labor	Total
Light soil	CY	0.023		4.44	4.44
Medium soil	CY	0.025		4.78	4.78
Heavy/wet soil	CY	0.027		5.18	5.18
Loose rock	CY	0.029		5.65	5.65
Blasted rock	CY	0.031		5.98	5.98

By hydraulic excavator

1/2 c.y. capacity

	Unit	Man-Hrs	Material	Labor	Total
Light soil	CY	0.027		5.18	5.18
Medium soil	CY	0.029		5.65	5.65
Heavy/wet soil	CY	0.032		6.21	6.21
Loose rock	CY	0.036		6.91	6.91
Blasted rock	CY	0.040		7.77	7.77

1 c.y. capacity

	Unit	Man-Hrs	Material	Labor	Total
Light soil	CY	0.019		3.65	3.65
Medium soil	CY	0.020		3.88	3.88
Heavy/wet soil	CY	0.021		4.14	4.14
Loose rock	CY	0.023		4.44	4.44
Blasted rock	CY	0.025		4.78	4.78

1-1/2 c.y. capacity

	Unit	Man-Hrs	Material	Labor	Total
Light soil	CY	0.017		3.27	3.27
Medium soil	CY	0.018		3.45	3.45
Heavy/wet soil	CY	0.019		3.65	3.65
Loose rock	CY	0.020		3.88	3.88
Blasted rock	CY	0.021		4.14	4.14

2 c.y. capacity

	Unit	Man-Hrs	Material	Labor	Total
Light soil	CY	0.016		3.10	3.10
Medium soil	CY	0.017		3.27	3.27
Heavy/wet soil	CY	0.018		3.45	3.45
Loose rock	CY	0.019		3.65	3.65
Blasted rock	CY	0.020		3.88	3.88

2-1/2 c.y. capacity

	Unit	Man-Hrs	Material	Labor	Total
Light soil	CY	0.015		2.82	2.82
Medium soil	CY	0.015		2.96	2.96
Heavy/wet soil	CY	0.016		3.10	3.10
Loose rock	CY	0.017		3.27	3.27
Blasted rock	CY	0.018		3.45	3.45

Trencher, chain, 1' wide to 4' deep

	Unit	Man-Hrs	Material	Labor	Total
Light soil	CY	0.020		2.76	2.76
Medium soil	CY	0.023		3.16	3.16
Heavy soil	CY	0.027		3.68	3.68

Hand excavation

Bulk, wheeled 100'

	Unit	Man-Hrs	Material	Labor	Total
Normal soil	CY	0.889		57.00	57.00
Sand or gravel	CY	0.800		51.00	51.00
Medium clay	CY	1.143		73.00	73.00
Heavy clay	CY	1.600		100.00	100.00
Loose rock	CY	2.000		130.00	130.00

Trenches, up to 2' deep

	Unit	Man-Hrs	Material	Labor	Total
Normal soil	CY	1.000		64.00	64.00
Sand or gravel	CY	0.889		57.00	57.00
Medium clay	CY	1.333		85.00	85.00
Heavy clay	CY	2.000		130.00	130.00
Loose rock	CY	2.667		170.00	170.00

Trenches, to 6' deep

	Unit	Man-Hrs	Material	Labor	Total
Normal soil	CY	1.143		73.00	73.00
Sand or gravel	CY	1.000		64.00	64.00
Medium clay	CY	1.600		100.00	100.00
Heavy clay	CY	2.667		170.00	170.00
Loose rock	CY	4.000		260.00	260.00

© 2020 BNi Publications, Inc.

	Unit	Man-Hrs	Material	Labor	Total
31233.36 TRENCHING (Cont.)					
Trenching and continuous footing excavation					
Backfill trenches					
With compaction					
By hand	CY	0.667		42.50	42.50
By 60 hp tracked dozer	CY	0.020		2.76	2.76
By 200 hp tracked dozer	CY	0.009		1.72	1.72
By small front-end loader	CY	0.023		3.16	3.16
Spread dumped fill or gravel, no compaction					
6" layers	SY	0.013		1.84	1.84
12" layers	SY	0.016		2.21	2.21
Compaction in 6" layers					
By hand with air tamper	SY	0.016		1.36	1.36
Backfill trenches, sand bedding, no compaction					
By hand	CY	0.667	23.00	42.50	65.50
By small front-end loader	CY	0.023	23.00	4.44	27.44
31311.60 SOIL TREATMENT					
SOIL TREATMENT					
Soil treatment, termite control pretreatment					
Under slabs	SF	0.004	0.38	0.28	0.66
By walls	SF	0.005	0.38	0.34	0.72
31320.03 GEOTEXTILE					
GEOTEXTILE					
Filter cloth, light reinforcement					
Woven					
12'-6" wide x 50' long	SF	0.001	0.34	0.07	0.41
Various lengths	SF	0.001	0.51	0.07	0.58
Non-woven					
14'-8" wide x 430' long	SF	0.001	0.18	0.07	0.25
Various lengths	SF	0.001	0.26	0.07	0.33
31320.05 SOIL STABILIZATION					
SOIL STABILIZATION					
Straw bale secured with rebar	LF	0.027	7.54	1.70	9.24
Filter barrier, 18" high filter fabric	LF	0.080	1.82	5.10	6.92
Sediment fence, 36" fabric with 6" mesh	LF	0.100	4.32	6.38	10.70
Soil stabilization with tar paper, burlap, straw and stakes	SF	0.001	0.36	0.07	0.43
31360.01 SLOPE PROTECTION					
SLOPE PROTECTION					
Gabions, stone filled					
6" deep	SY	0.200	30.25	27.75	58.00
9" deep	SY	0.229	37.00	31.50	68.50
12" deep	SY	0.267	49.00	37.00	86.00
18" deep	SY	0.320	63.00	44.25	107.25
36" deep	SY	0.533	110.00	74.00	184.00
31370.01 RIPRAP					
RIPRAP					
Riprap					
Crushed stone blanket, max size 2-1/2"	TON	0.533	35.25	82.00	117.25
Stone, quarry run, 300 lb. stones	TON	0.492	44.25	76.00	120.25
400 lb. stones	TON	0.457	46.00	71.00	117.00
500 lb. stones	TON	0.427	48.00	66.00	114.00
750 lb. stones	TON	0.400	49.75	62.00	111.75
Dry concrete riprap in bags 3" thick, 80 lb. per bag	BAG	0.027	5.96	4.11	10.07
31411.60 STEEL SHEET PILING					
STEEL SHEET PILING					
Steel sheet piling,12" wide					
20' long	SF	0.096	21.00	17.00	38.00
35' long	SF	0.069	21.00	12.25	33.25
50' long	SF	0.048	21.00	8.51	29.51
Over 50' long	SF	0.044	21.00	7.74	28.74

	Unit	Man-Hrs	Material	Labor	Total
31413.30 TRENCH SHEETING					
TRENCH SHEETING					
Closed timber, including pull and salvage, excavation					
8' deep	SF	0.064	2.87	9.88	12.75
10' deep	SF	0.067	2.93	10.50	13.43
12' deep	SF	0.071	3.01	11.00	14.01
14' deep	SF	0.075	3.14	11.75	14.89
16' deep	SF	0.080	3.16	12.25	15.41
18' deep	SF	0.091	3.26	14.00	17.26
20' deep	SF	0.098	4.12	15.25	19.37
31500.01 TRENCH BOX					
TRENCH BOX					
10' x 10' Steel, 4" Wall, Rental Rate					
4 Hour	EA				160.00
Day	EA				160.00
Week	EA				400.00
Month	EA				1,210.00
10 x 24 Steel 6" Wall, Rental Rate					
4 Hour	EA				310.00
Day	EA				310.00
Week	EA				780.00
Month	EA				2,340.00
31520.01 COFFERDAMS					
COFFERDAMS					
Cofferdam, steel, driven from shore					
15' deep	SF	0.137	20.25	24.25	44.50
20' deep	SF	0.128	20.25	22.75	43.00
25' deep	SF	0.120	20.25	21.25	41.50
30' deep	SF	0.113	20.25	20.00	40.25
40' deep	SF	0.107	20.25	19.00	39.25
Driven from barge					
20' deep	SF	0.148	20.25	26.25	46.50
30' deep	SF	0.137	20.25	24.25	44.50
40' deep	SF	0.128	20.25	22.75	43.00
50' deep	SF	0.120	20.25	21.25	41.50
31620.01 PILE TESTING					
PILE TESTING					
Pile test					
50 ton to 100 ton	EA				20,670.00
To 200 ton	EA				29,160.00
To 300 ton	EA				33,730.00
To 400 ton	EA				39,500.00
To 600 ton	EA				49,380.00
31621.65 STEEL PILES					
STEEL PILES					
H-section piles					
8x8					
36 lb/ft					
30' long	LF	0.080	21.75	14.25	36.00
40' long	LF	0.064	21.75	11.25	33.00
50' long	LF	0.053	21.75	9.46	31.21
10x10					
42 lb/ft					
30' long	LF	0.080	25.50	14.25	39.75
40' long	LF	0.064	25.50	11.25	36.75
50' long	LF	0.053	25.50	9.46	34.96
57 lb/ft					
30' long	LF	0.080	34.50	14.25	48.75
40' long	LF	0.064	34.50	11.25	45.75
50' long	LF	0.053	34.50	9.46	43.96
12x12					
53 lb/ft					
30' long	LF	0.087	32.00	15.50	47.50
40' long	LF	0.069	32.00	12.25	44.25

© 2020 BNi Publications, Inc.

	Unit	Man-Hrs	Material	Labor	Total
31621.65 STEEL PILES (Cont.)					
53 lb/ft					
50' long	LF	0.053	32.00	9.46	41.46
74 lb/ft					
30' long	LF	0.087	44.75	15.50	60.25
40' long	LF	0.069	44.75	12.25	57.00
50' long	LF	0.053	44.75	9.46	54.21
14x14					
73 lb/ft					
40' long	LF	0.087	44.25	15.50	59.75
50' long	LF	0.069	44.25	12.25	56.50
60' long	LF	0.053	44.25	9.46	53.71
89 lb/ft					
40' long	LF	0.087	54.00	15.50	69.50
50' long	LF	0.069	54.00	12.25	66.25
60' long	LF	0.053	54.00	9.46	63.46
102 lb/ft					
40' long	LF	0.087	62.00	15.50	77.50
50' long	LF	0.069	62.00	12.25	74.25
60' long	LF	0.053	62.00	9.46	71.46
117 lb/ft					
40' long	LF	0.091	71.00	16.25	87.25
50' long	LF	0.071	71.00	12.50	83.50
60' long	LF	0.055	71.00	9.73	80.73
Splice					
8"	EA	1.333	110.00	85.00	195.00
10"	EA	1.600	120.00	100.00	220.00
12"	EA	1.600	160.00	100.00	260.00
14"	EA	2.000	200.00	130.00	330.00
Driving cap					
8"	EA	0.800	51.00	51.00	102.00
10"	EA	1.000	51.00	64.00	115.00
12"	EA	1.000	51.00	64.00	115.00
14"	EA	1.143	51.00	73.00	124.00
Standard point					
8"	EA	0.800	80.00	51.00	131.00
10"	EA	1.000	94.00	64.00	158.00
12"	EA	1.143	110.00	73.00	183.00
14"	EA	1.333	130.00	85.00	215.00
Heavy duty point					
8"	EA	0.889	67.00	57.00	124.00
10"	EA	1.143	79.00	73.00	152.00
12"	EA	1.333	100.00	85.00	185.00
14"	EA	1.600	130.00	100.00	230.00
Tapered friction piles, fluted casing, up to 50'					
With 4000 psi concrete no reinforcing					
12" dia.	LF	0.048	21.50	8.51	30.01
14" dia.	LF	0.049	24.75	8.73	33.48
16" dia.	LF	0.051	29.75	8.96	38.71
18" dia.	LF	0.056	33.50	10.00	43.50
31621.66 STEEL PIPE PILES					
STEEL PIPE PILES					
Concrete filled, 3000# concrete, up to 40'					
8" dia.	LF	0.069	24.00	12.25	36.25
10" dia.	LF	0.071	31.00	12.50	43.50
12" dia.	LF	0.074	36.00	13.00	49.00
14" dia.	LF	0.077	39.50	13.50	53.00
16" dia.	LF	0.080	45.00	14.25	59.25
18" dia.	LF	0.083	62.00	14.75	76.75
Pipe piles, non-filled					
8" dia.	LF	0.053	21.75	9.46	31.21
10" dia.	LF	0.055	27.25	9.73	36.98
12" dia.	LF	0.056	33.25	10.00	43.25
14" dia.	LF	0.060	35.00	10.75	45.75
16" dia.	LF	0.062	40.00	11.00	51.00

	Unit	Man-Hrs	Material	Labor	Total
31621.66 STEEL PIPE PILES (Cont.)					
Pipe piles, non-filled					
18" dia.	LF	0.064	52.00	11.25	63.25
Splice					
8" dia.	EA	1.600	97.00	100.00	197.00
10" dia.	EA	1.600	110.00	100.00	210.00
12" dia.	EA	2.000	120.00	130.00	250.00
14" dia.	EA	2.000	130.00	130.00	260.00
16" dia.	EA	2.667	160.00	170.00	330.00
18" dia.	EA	2.667	210.00	170.00	380.00
Standard point					
8" dia.	EA	1.600	130.00	100.00	230.00
10" dia.	EA	1.600	170.00	100.00	270.00
12" dia.	EA	2.000	180.00	130.00	310.00
14" dia.	EA	2.000	200.00	130.00	330.00
16" dia.	EA	2.667	250.00	170.00	420.00
18" dia.	EA	2.667	360.00	170.00	530.00
Heavy duty point					
8" dia.	EA	2.000	230.00	130.00	360.00
10" dia.	EA	2.000	320.00	130.00	450.00
12" dia.	EA	2.667	340.00	170.00	510.00
14" dia.	EA	2.667	470.00	170.00	640.00
16" dia.	EA	3.200	470.00	200.00	670.00
18" dia.	EA	3.200	520.00	200.00	720.00
31621.90 WOOD AND TIMBER PILES					
WOOD AND TIMBER PILES					
Treated wood piles, 12" butt, 8" tip					
25' long	LF	0.096	18.00	17.00	35.00
30' long	LF	0.080	19.25	14.25	33.50
35' long	LF	0.069	19.25	12.25	31.50
40' long	LF	0.060	19.25	10.75	30.00
12" butt, 7" tip					
40' long	LF	0.060	21.75	10.75	32.50
45' long	LF	0.053	21.75	9.46	31.21
50' long	LF	0.048	24.75	8.51	33.26
55' long	LF	0.044	24.75	7.74	32.49
60' long	LF	0.040	24.75	7.09	31.84
31631.35 PRESTRESSED PILING					
PRESTRESSED PILING					
Prestressed concrete piling, less than 60' long					
10" sq.	LF	0.040	20.75	7.09	27.84
12" sq.	LF	0.042	29.00	7.40	36.40
14" sq.	LF	0.043	30.25	7.56	37.81
16" sq.	LF	0.044	37.25	7.74	44.99
18" sq.	LF	0.047	51.00	8.30	59.30
20" sq.	LF	0.048	70.00	8.51	78.51
24" sq.	LF	0.049	89.00	8.73	97.73
More than 60' long					
12" sq.	LF	0.034	29.75	6.08	35.83
14" sq.	LF	0.035	32.75	6.19	38.94
16" sq.	LF	0.036	39.25	6.30	45.55
18" sq.	LF	0.036	52.00	6.42	58.42
20" sq.	LF	0.037	70.00	6.54	76.54
24" sq.	LF	0.038	83.00	6.67	89.67
Straight cylinder, less than 60' long					
12" dia.	LF	0.044	27.00	7.74	34.74
14" dia.	LF	0.045	36.50	7.92	44.42
16" dia.	LF	0.046	44.50	8.10	52.60
18" dia.	LF	0.047	56.00	8.30	64.30
20" dia.	LF	0.048	67.00	8.51	75.51
24" dia.	LF	0.049	83.00	8.73	91.73
More than 60' long					
12" dia.	LF	0.035	27.00	6.19	33.19
14" dia.	LF	0.036	36.50	6.30	42.80
16" dia.	LF	0.036	44.50	6.42	50.92

© 2020 BNi Publications, Inc.

	Unit	Man-Hrs	Material	Labor	Total

31631.35 PRESTRESSED PILING (Cont.)

More than 60' long

	Unit	Man-Hrs	Material	Labor	Total
18" dia.	LF	0.037	56.00	6.54	62.54
20" dia.	LF	0.038	67.00	6.67	73.67
24" dia.	LF	0.038	84.00	6.81	90.81

Concrete sheet piling

	Unit	Man-Hrs	Material	Labor	Total
12" thick x 20' long	SF	0.096	31.00	17.00	48.00
25' long	SF	0.087	31.00	15.50	46.50
30' long	SF	0.080	31.00	14.25	45.25
35' long	SF	0.074	31.00	13.00	44.00
40' long	SF	0.069	31.00	12.25	43.25
16" thick x 40' long	SF	0.053	42.25	9.46	51.71
45' long	SF	0.051	42.25	8.96	51.21
50' long	SF	0.048	42.25	8.51	50.76
55' long	SF	0.046	42.25	8.10	50.35
60' long	SF	0.044	42.25	7.74	49.99

31640.01 CAISSONS, INCLUDES CASING

CAISSONS, INCLUDES CASING

Caisson, 3000# conc., 60# reinf./CY, stable ground

	Unit	Man-Hrs	Material	Labor	Total
18" dia., 0.065 CY/ LF	LF	0.192	17.75	34.00	51.75
24" dia., 0.116 CY/ LF	LF	0.200	28.50	35.50	64.00
30" dia., 0.182 CY/ LF	LF	0.240	43.50	42.50	86.00
36" dia., 0.262 CY/ LF	LF	0.274	61.00	48.75	109.75
48" dia., 0.465 CY/ LF	LF	0.320	110.00	57.00	167.00
60" dia., 0.727 CY/ LF	LF	0.436	180.00	77.00	257.00
72" dia., 1.05 CY/ LF	LF	0.533	270.00	95.00	365.00
84" dia., 1.43 CY/ LF	LF	0.686	320.00	120.00	440.00

Wet ground, casing required but pulled

	Unit	Man-Hrs	Material	Labor	Total
18" dia.	LF	0.240	19.50	42.50	62.00
24" dia.	LF	0.267	31.00	47.25	78.25
30" dia.	LF	0.300	47.50	53.00	100.50
36" dia.	LF	0.320	66.00	57.00	123.00
48" dia.	LF	0.400	120.00	71.00	191.00
60" dia.	LF	0.533	200.00	95.00	295.00
72" dia.	LF	0.800	290.00	140.00	430.00
84" dia.	LF	1.200	350.00	210.00	560.00

Soft rock

	Unit	Man-Hrs	Material	Labor	Total
18" dia.	LF	0.686	19.50	120.00	139.50
24" dia.	LF	1.200	31.00	210.00	241.00
30" dia.	LF	1.600	47.50	280.00	327.50
36" dia.	LF	2.400	66.00	430.00	496.00
48" dia.	LF	3.200	120.00	570.00	690.00
60" dia.	LF	4.800	200.00	850.00	1,050.00
72" dia.	LF	5.333	290.00	950.00	1,240.00
84" dia.	LF	6.000	350.00	1,060.00	1,410.00

	Unit	Man-Hrs	Material	Labor	Total

32111.71 ASPHALT REPAIR

ASPHALT REPAIR

	Unit	Man-Hrs	Material	Labor	Total
Coal tar seal coat, rubber add., fuel resist.	SY	0.011	2.68	0.72	3.40
Bituminous surface treatment, single	SY	0.008	2.46	0.51	2.97
Double	SY	0.001	3.27	0.05	3.32
Bituminous prime coat	SY	0.001	1.65	0.06	1.71
Tack coat	SY	0.001	0.80	0.05	0.85
Crack sealing, concrete paving	LF	0.005	1.37	0.34	1.71
Bituminous paving for pipe trench, 4" thick	SY	0.160	15.75	19.00	34.75
Polypropylene, nonwoven paving fabric	SY	0.004	2.02	0.25	2.27
Rubberized asphalt	SY	0.073	3.27	4.64	7.91
Asphalt slurry seal	SY	0.047	8.08	3.00	11.08

32121.60 ASPHALT SURFACES

ASPHALT SURFACES

	Unit	Man-Hrs	Material	Labor	Total
Asphalt wearing surface, flexible pavement					
1" thick	SY	0.016	4.52	2.83	7.35
1-1/2" thick	SY	0.019	6.82	3.40	10.22
2" thick	SY	0.024	9.09	4.25	13.34
3" thick	SY	0.032	13.75	5.67	19.42
Binder course					
1-1/2" thick	SY	0.018	6.45	3.15	9.60
2" thick	SY	0.022	8.58	3.87	12.45
3" thick	SY	0.029	12.75	5.16	17.91
4" thick	SY	0.032	17.00	5.67	22.67
5" thick	SY	0.036	21.25	6.30	27.55
6" thick	SY	0.040	25.75	7.09	32.84
Bituminous sidewalk, no base					
2" thick	SY	0.028	9.84	3.35	13.19
3" thick	SY	0.030	14.75	3.56	18.31

32131.30 CONCRETE PAVING

CONCRETE PAVING

	Unit	Man-Hrs	Material	Labor	Total
Concrete paving, reinforced, 5000 psi concrete					
6" thick	SY	0.150	28.75	26.50	55.25
7" thick	SY	0.160	33.50	28.50	62.00
8" thick	SY	0.171	38.25	30.50	68.75
9" thick	SY	0.185	43.00	32.75	75.75
10" thick	SY	0.200	47.75	35.50	83.25
11" thick	SY	0.218	53.00	38.75	91.75
12" thick	SY	0.240	57.00	42.50	99.50
15" thick	SY	0.300	72.00	53.00	125.00
Concrete paving, for pipe trench, reinforced					
7" thick	SY	0.240	57.00	28.50	85.50
8" thick	SY	0.267	62.00	31.75	93.75
9" thick	SY	0.300	66.00	35.75	101.75
10" thick	SY	0.343	71.00	40.75	111.75
Fibrous concrete					
5" thick	SY	0.185	29.50	32.75	62.25
8" thick	SY	0.200	37.50	35.50	73.00
Roller compacted concrete (RCC)					
8" thick	SY	0.240	36.25	42.50	78.75
12" thick	SY	0.300	55.00	53.00	108.00
Steel edge forms up to					
12" deep	LF	0.027	1.08	1.70	2.78
15" deep	LF	0.032	1.39	2.04	3.43
Paving finishes					
Belt dragged	SY	0.040		2.55	2.55
Curing	SY	0.008	0.41	0.51	0.92

32131.31 SIDEWALKS

SIDEWALKS

	Unit	Man-Hrs	Material	Labor	Total
Walks, with wire mesh, base not incl.					
4" thick	SF	0.027	1.99	1.70	3.69
5" thick	SF	0.032	2.70	2.04	4.74
6" thick	SF	0.040	3.32	2.55	5.87

© 2020 BNi Publications, Inc.

DIVISION 32 EXTERIOR IMPROVEMENTS

	Unit	Man-Hrs	Material	Labor	Total
32141.60 PAVERS, MASONRY					
PAVERS, MASONRY					
Brick walk laid on sand, sand joints					
Laid flat (4.5 per sf)	SF	0.089	4.16	6.91	11.07
Laid on edge (7.2 per sf)	SF	0.133	6.66	10.25	16.91
Precast concrete patio blocks					
2" thick					
Natural	SF	0.027	3.58	2.07	5.65
Colors	SF	0.027	4.53	2.07	6.60
Exposed aggregates, local aggregate					
Natural	SF	0.027	10.00	2.07	12.07
Colors	SF	0.027	10.00	2.07	12.07
Granite or limestone aggregate	SF	0.027	10.00	2.07	12.07
White tumblestone aggregate	SF	0.027	10.75	2.07	12.82
Stone pavers, set in mortar					
Bluestone					
1" thick					
Irregular	SF	0.200	10.00	15.50	25.50
Snapped rectangular	SF	0.160	14.75	12.50	27.25
1-1/2" thick, random rectangular	SF	0.200	18.00	15.50	33.50
2" thick, random rectangular	SF	0.229	20.50	17.75	38.25
Slate					
Natural cleft					
Irregular, 3/4" thick	SF	0.229	10.75	17.75	28.50
Random rectangular					
1-1/4" thick	SF	0.200	23.25	15.50	38.75
1-1/2" thick	SF	0.222	26.25	17.25	43.50
Granite blocks					
3" thick, 3" to 6" wide					
4" to 12" long	SF	0.267	13.25	20.75	34.00
6" to 15" long	SF	0.229	8.67	17.75	26.42
32170.03 GUARDRAILS					
GUARDRAILS					
Pipe bollard, steel pipe, concrete filled, painted					
6" dia.	EA	0.667	280.00	42.50	322.50
8" dia.	EA	1.000	370.00	64.00	434.00
12" dia.	EA	2.667	580.00	170.00	750.00
Corrugated steel, guardrail, galvanized	LF	0.040	35.00	4.75	39.75
End section, wrap around or flared	EA	0.800	94.00	51.00	145.00
Timber guardrail, 4" x 8"	LF	0.030	40.75	3.56	44.31
Guardrail, 3 cables, 3/4" dia.					
Steel posts	LF	0.120	20.00	14.25	34.25
Wood posts	LF	0.096	20.00	11.50	31.50
Steel box beam					
6" x 6"	LF	0.133	82.00	15.75	97.75
6" x 8"	LF	0.150	87.00	17.75	104.75
Concrete posts	EA	0.400	54.00	25.50	79.50
Barrel type impact barrier	EA	0.800	680.00	51.00	731.00
Light shield, 6' high	LF	0.160	44.75	10.25	55.00
32170.04 PARKING BARRIERS					
PARKING BARRIERS					
Timber, treated, 4' long					
4" x 4"	EA	0.667	12.50	42.50	55.00
6" x 6"	EA	0.800	23.50	51.00	74.50
Precast concrete, 6' long, with dowels					
12" x 6"	EA	0.400	65.00	25.50	90.50
12" x 8"	EA	0.444	77.00	28.25	105.25
32172.30 PAVEMENT MARKINGS					
PAVEMENT MARKINGS					
Pavement line marking, paint					
4" wide	LF	0.002	0.29	0.12	0.41
6" wide	LF	0.004	0.29	0.28	0.57
8" wide	LF	0.007	0.44	0.42	0.86

	Unit	Man-Hrs	Material	Labor	Total
32172.30 PAVEMENT MARKINGS (Cont.)					
Pavement line marking, paint					
Reflective paint, 4" wide	LF	0.007	0.60	0.42	1.02
Airfield markings, retro-reflective					
White	LF	0.007	0.99	0.42	1.41
Yellow	LF	0.007	1.06	0.42	1.48
Preformed tape, 4" wide					
Inlaid reflective	LF	0.001	2.67	0.07	2.74
Reflective paint	LF	0.002	1.82	0.12	1.94
Thermoplastic					
White	LF	0.004	1.12	0.25	1.37
Yellow	LF	0.004	1.12	0.25	1.37
12" wide, thermoplastic, white	LF	0.011	3.18	0.72	3.90
Directional arrows, reflective preformed tape	EA	0.800	160.00	51.00	211.00
Messages, reflective preformed tape (per letter)	EA	0.400	80.00	25.50	105.50
Handicap symbol, preformed tape	EA	0.800	33.00	51.00	84.00
Parking stall painting	EA	0.160	7.62	10.25	17.87
32311.30 CHAIN LINK FENCE					
CHAIN LINK FENCE					
Chain link fence, 9 ga., galvanized, with posts 10' o.c.					
4' high	LF	0.057	7.38	3.64	11.02
5' high	LF	0.073	9.87	4.64	14.51
6' high	LF	0.100	11.25	6.38	17.63
7' high	LF	0.123	12.75	7.85	20.60
8' high	LF	0.160	14.75	10.25	25.00
For barbed wire with hangers, add					
3 strand	LF	0.040	2.69	2.55	5.24
6 strand	LF	0.067	4.56	4.25	8.81
Corner or gate post, 3" post					
4' high	EA	0.267	86.00	17.00	103.00
5' high	EA	0.296	95.00	19.00	114.00
6' high	EA	0.348	110.00	22.25	132.25
7' high	EA	0.400	130.00	25.50	155.50
8' high	EA	0.444	130.00	28.25	158.25
4" post					
4' high	EA	0.296	150.00	19.00	169.00
5' high	EA	0.348	170.00	22.25	192.25
6' high	EA	0.400	190.00	25.50	215.50
7' high	EA	0.444	210.00	28.25	238.25
8' high	EA	0.500	230.00	32.00	262.00
Gate with gate posts, galvanized, 3' wide					
4' high	EA	2.000	95.00	130.00	225.00
5' high	EA	2.667	120.00	170.00	290.00
6' high	EA	2.667	150.00	170.00	320.00
7' high	EA	4.000	180.00	260.00	440.00
8' high	EA	4.000	190.00	260.00	450.00
Fabric, galvanized chain link, 2" mesh, 9 ga.					
4' high	LF	0.027	4.01	1.70	5.71
5' high	LF	0.032	4.91	2.04	6.95
6' high	LF	0.040	6.87	2.55	9.42
8' high	LF	0.053	11.50	3.40	14.90
Line post, no rail fitting, galvanized, 2-1/2" dia.					
4' high	EA	0.229	28.00	14.50	42.50
5' high	EA	0.250	30.50	16.00	46.50
6' high	EA	0.267	33.25	17.00	50.25
7' high	EA	0.320	37.75	20.50	58.25
8' high	EA	0.400	42.25	25.50	67.75
1-7/8" H beam					
4' high	EA	0.229	34.75	14.50	49.25
5' high	EA	0.250	39.00	16.00	55.00
6' high	EA	0.267	46.50	17.00	63.50
7' high	EA	0.320	53.00	20.50	73.50
8' high	EA	0.400	57.00	25.50	82.50

© 2020 BNi Publications, Inc.

32311.30 CHAIN LINK FENCE (Cont.)

	Unit	Man-Hrs	Material	Labor	Total
Line post, no rail fitting, galvanized, 2-1/2" dia.					
2-1/4" H beam					
4' high	EA	0.229	25.50	14.50	40.00
5' high	EA	0.250	31.75	16.00	47.75
6' high	EA	0.267	36.25	17.00	53.25
7' high	EA	0.320	42.25	20.50	62.75
8' high	EA	0.400	49.00	25.50	74.50
Vinyl coated, 9 ga., with posts 10' o.c.					
4' high	LF	0.057	7.98	3.64	11.62
5' high	LF	0.073	9.50	4.64	14.14
6' high	LF	0.100	11.25	6.38	17.63
7' high	LF	0.123	12.50	7.85	20.35
8' high	LF	0.160	14.25	10.25	24.50
For barbed wire w/hangers, add					
3 strand	LF	0.040	2.90	2.55	5.45
6 Strand	LF	0.067	4.68	4.25	8.93
Corner, or gate post, 4' high					
3" dia.	EA	0.267	99.00	17.00	116.00
4" dia.	EA	0.267	150.00	17.00	167.00
6" dia.	EA	0.320	180.00	20.50	200.50
Gate, with posts, 3' wide					
4' high	EA	2.000	110.00	130.00	240.00
5' high	EA	2.667	130.00	170.00	300.00
6' high	EA	2.667	150.00	170.00	320.00
7' high	EA	4.000	170.00	260.00	430.00
8' high	EA	4.000	190.00	260.00	450.00
Line post, no rail fitting, 2-1/2" dia.					
4' high	EA	0.229	26.25	14.50	40.75
5' high	EA	0.250	28.50	16.00	44.50
6' high	EA	0.267	31.25	17.00	48.25
7' high	EA	0.320	35.50	20.50	56.00
8' high	EA	0.400	39.50	25.50	65.00
Corner post, no top rail fitting, 4" dia.					
4' high	EA	0.267	140.00	17.00	157.00
5' high	EA	0.296	160.00	19.00	179.00
6' high	EA	0.348	180.00	22.25	202.25
7' high	EA	0.400	200.00	25.50	225.50
8' high	EA	0.444	210.00	28.25	238.25
Fabric, vinyl, chain link, 2" mesh, 9 ga.					
4' high	LF	0.027	3.76	1.70	5.46
5' high	LF	0.032	4.59	2.04	6.63
6' high	LF	0.040	6.43	2.55	8.98
8' high	LF	0.053	10.75	3.40	14.15
Swing gates, galvanized, 4' high					
Single gate					
3' wide	EA	2.000	200.00	130.00	330.00
4' wide	EA	2.000	220.00	130.00	350.00
Double gate					
10' wide	EA	3.200	530.00	200.00	730.00
12' wide	EA	3.200	570.00	200.00	770.00
14' wide	EA	3.200	590.00	200.00	790.00
16' wide	EA	3.200	660.00	200.00	860.00
18' wide	EA	4.571	710.00	290.00	1,000.00
20' wide	EA	4.571	750.00	290.00	1,040.00
22' wide	EA	4.571	830.00	290.00	1,120.00
24' wide	EA	5.333	850.00	340.00	1,190.00
26' wide	EA	5.333	890.00	340.00	1,230.00
28' wide	EA	6.400	950.00	410.00	1,360.00
30' wide	EA	6.400	1,010.00	410.00	1,420.00
5' high					
Single gate					
3' wide	EA	2.667	210.00	170.00	380.00
4' wide	EA	2.667	250.00	170.00	420.00

32311.30 CHAIN LINK FENCE (Cont.)

	Unit	Man-Hrs	Material	Labor	Total
5' high					
Double gate					
10' wide	EA	4.000	570.00	260.00	830.00
12' wide	EA	4.000	610.00	260.00	870.00
14' wide	EA	4.000	1,050.00	260.00	1,310.00
16' wide	EA	4.000	690.00	260.00	950.00
18' wide	EA	4.571	710.00	290.00	1,000.00
20' wide	EA	4.571	800.00	290.00	1,090.00
22' wide	EA	4.571	840.00	290.00	1,130.00
24' wide	EA	5.333	880.00	340.00	1,220.00
26' wide	EA	5.333	920.00	340.00	1,260.00
28' wide	EA	6.400	1,020.00	410.00	1,430.00
30' wide	EA	6.400	1,060.00	410.00	1,470.00
6' high					
Single gate					
3' wide	EA	2.667	270.00	170.00	440.00
4' wide	EA	2.667	290.00	170.00	460.00
Double gate					
10' wide	EA	4.000	650.00	260.00	910.00
12' wide	EA	4.000	740.00	260.00	1,000.00
14' wide	EA	4.000	780.00	260.00	1,040.00
16' wide	EA	4.000	840.00	260.00	1,100.00
18' wide	EA	4.571	900.00	290.00	1,190.00
20' wide	EA	4.571	930.00	290.00	1,220.00
22' wide	EA	4.571	1,000.00	290.00	1,290.00
24' wide	EA	5.333	1,070.00	340.00	1,410.00
26' wide	EA	5.333	1,110.00	340.00	1,450.00
28' wide	EA	6.400	1,200.00	410.00	1,610.00
30' wide	EA	6.400	1,260.00	410.00	1,670.00
7' high					
Single gate					
3' wide	EA	4.000	330.00	260.00	590.00
4' wide	EA	4.000	370.00	260.00	630.00
Double gate					
10' wide	EA	5.333	850.00	340.00	1,190.00
12' wide	EA	5.333	930.00	340.00	1,270.00
14' wide	EA	5.333	1,000.00	340.00	1,340.00
16' wide	EA	5.333	1,070.00	340.00	1,410.00
18' wide	EA	6.400	1,140.00	410.00	1,550.00
20' wide	EA	6.400	1,210.00	410.00	1,620.00
22' wide	EA	6.400	1,270.00	410.00	1,680.00
24' wide	EA	8.000	1,370.00	510.00	1,880.00
26' wide	EA	8.000	1,460.00	510.00	1,970.00
28' wide	EA	10.000	1,540.00	640.00	2,180.00
30' wide	EA	10.000	1,760.00	640.00	2,400.00
8' high					
Single gate					
3' wide	EA	4.000	370.00	260.00	630.00
4' wide	EA	4.000	400.00	260.00	660.00
Double gate					
10' wide	EA	5.333	970.00	340.00	1,310.00
12' wide	EA	5.333	1,030.00	340.00	1,370.00
14' wide	EA	5.333	1,100.00	340.00	1,440.00
16' wide	EA	5.333	1,210.00	340.00	1,550.00
18' wide	EA	6.400	1,260.00	410.00	1,670.00
20' wide	EA	6.400	1,300.00	410.00	1,710.00
22' wide	EA	6.400	1,380.00	410.00	1,790.00
24' wide	EA	8.000	1,530.00	510.00	2,040.00
26' wide	EA	8.000	1,580.00	510.00	2,090.00
28' wide	EA	10.000	1,680.00	640.00	2,320.00
30' wide	EA	10.000	1,850.00	640.00	2,490.00
Vinyl coated swing gates, 4' high					
Single gate					
3' wide	EA	2.000	310.00	130.00	440.00
4' wide	EA	2.000	340.00	130.00	470.00

© 2020 BNi Publications, Inc.

32311.30 CHAIN LINK FENCE (Cont.)

	Unit	Man-Hrs	Material	Labor	Total
Vinyl coated swing gates, 4' high					
Double gate					
10' wide	EA	3.200	800.00	200.00	1,000.00
12' wide	EA	3.200	860.00	200.00	1,060.00
14' wide	EA	3.200	880.00	200.00	1,080.00
16' wide	EA	3.200	990.00	200.00	1,190.00
18' wide	EA	4.571	1,060.00	290.00	1,350.00
20' wide	EA	4.571	1,120.00	290.00	1,410.00
22' wide	EA	4.571	1,250.00	290.00	1,540.00
24' wide	EA	5.333	1,280.00	340.00	1,620.00
26' wide	EA	5.333	1,340.00	340.00	1,680.00
28' wide	EA	6.400	1,420.00	410.00	1,830.00
30' wide	EA	6.400	1,510.00	410.00	1,920.00
5' high					
Single gate					
3' wide	EA	2.667	320.00	170.00	490.00
4' wide	EA	2.667	370.00	170.00	540.00
Double gate					
10' wide	EA	4.000	860.00	260.00	1,120.00
12' wide	EA	4.000	920.00	260.00	1,180.00
14' wide	EA	4.000	990.00	260.00	1,250.00
16' wide	EA	4.000	1,030.00	260.00	1,290.00
18' wide	EA	4.571	1,060.00	290.00	1,350.00
20' wide	EA	4.571	1,200.00	290.00	1,490.00
22' wide	EA	4.571	1,260.00	290.00	1,550.00
24' wide	EA	5.333	1,320.00	340.00	1,660.00
26' wide	EA	5.333	1,380.00	340.00	1,720.00
28' wide	EA	6.400	1,540.00	410.00	1,950.00
30' wide	EA	6.400	1,590.00	410.00	2,000.00
6' high					
Single gate					
3' wide	EA	2.667	400.00	170.00	570.00
4' wide	EA	2.667	440.00	170.00	610.00
Double gate					
10' wide	EA	4.000	980.00	260.00	1,240.00
12' wide	EA	4.000	1,100.00	260.00	1,360.00
14' wide	EA	4.000	1,170.00	260.00	1,430.00
16' wide	EA	4.000	1,260.00	260.00	1,520.00
18' wide	EA	4.571	1,350.00	290.00	1,640.00
20' wide	EA	4.571	1,400.00	290.00	1,690.00
22' wide	EA	4.571	1,500.00	290.00	1,790.00
24' wide	EA	5.333	1,610.00	340.00	1,950.00
26' wide	EA	5.333	1,660.00	340.00	2,000.00
28' wide	EA	6.400	1,800.00	410.00	2,210.00
30' wide	EA	6.400	1,900.00	410.00	2,310.00
7' high					
Single gate					
3' wide	EA	4.000	490.00	260.00	750.00
4' wide	EA	4.000	550.00	260.00	810.00
Double gate					
10' wide	EA	5.333	1,270.00	340.00	1,610.00
12' wide	EA	5.333	1,400.00	340.00	1,740.00
14' wide	EA	5.333	1,500.00	340.00	1,840.00
16' wide	EA	5.333	1,600.00	340.00	1,940.00
18' wide	EA	6.400	1,700.00	410.00	2,110.00
20' wide	EA	6.400	1,810.00	410.00	2,220.00
22' wide	EA	6.400	1,910.00	410.00	2,320.00
24' wide	EA	8.000	2,050.00	510.00	2,560.00
26' wide	EA	8.000	2,190.00	510.00	2,700.00
28' wide	EA	10.000	2,300.00	640.00	2,940.00
30' wide	EA	10.000	2,640.00	640.00	3,280.00
8' high					
Single gate					
3' wide	EA	4.000	550.00	260.00	810.00
4' wide	EA	4.000	590.00	260.00	850.00

	Unit	Man-Hrs	Material	Labor	Total
32311.30 CHAIN LINK FENCE (Cont.)					
8' high					
Double gate					
10' wide	EA	5.333	1,450.00	340.00	1,790.00
12' wide	EA	5.333	1,540.00	340.00	1,880.00
14' wide	EA	5.333	1,660.00	340.00	2,000.00
16' wide	EA	5.333	1,810.00	340.00	2,150.00
18' wide	EA	6.400	1,890.00	410.00	2,300.00
20' wide	EA	6.400	1,960.00	410.00	2,370.00
22' wide	EA	6.400	2,060.00	410.00	2,470.00
24' wide	EA	8.000	2,290.00	510.00	2,800.00
28' wide	EA	8.000	2,370.00	510.00	2,880.00
30' wide	EA	10.000	2,520.00	640.00	3,160.00
Motor operator for gates, no wiring	EA				5,830.00
Drilling fence post holes					
In soil					
By hand	EA	0.400		25.50	25.50
By machine auger	EA	0.200		17.00	17.00
In rock					
By jackhammer	EA	2.667		230.00	230.00
By rock drill	EA	0.800		68.00	68.00
Aluminum privacy slats, installed vertically	SF	0.020	0.99	1.27	2.26
Post hole, dig by hand	EA	0.533		34.00	34.00
Set fence post in concrete	EA	0.400	9.68	25.50	35.18
32319.01 SHRUB & TREE MAINTENANCE					
SHRUB & TREE MAINTENANCE					
Moving shrubs on site					
12" ball	EA	1.000		64.00	64.00
24" ball	EA	1.333		85.00	85.00
3' high	EA	0.800		51.00	51.00
4' high	EA	0.889		57.00	57.00
5' high	EA	1.000		64.00	64.00
18" spread	EA	1.143		73.00	73.00
30" spread	EA	1.333		85.00	85.00
Moving trees on site					
24" ball	EA	1.200		140.00	140.00
48" ball	EA	1.600		190.00	190.00
Trees					
3' high	EA	0.480		57.00	57.00
6' high	EA	0.533		63.00	63.00
8' high	EA	0.600		71.00	71.00
10' high	EA	0.800		95.00	95.00
Palm trees					
7' high	EA	0.600		71.00	71.00
10' high	EA	0.800		95.00	95.00
20' high	EA	2.400		290.00	290.00
40' high	EA	4.800		570.00	570.00
Guying trees					
4" dia.	EA	0.400	13.00	25.50	38.50
8" dia.	EA	0.500	13.00	32.00	45.00
32319.02 FERTILIZING					
FERTILIZING					
Fertilizing (23#/1000 sf)					
By square yard	SY	0.002	0.03	0.17	0.20
By acre	ACRE	10.000	190.00	850.00	1,040.00
Liming (70#/1000 sf)					
By square yard	SY	0.003	0.03	0.22	0.25
By acre	ACRE	13.333	190.00	1,130.00	1,320.00
32319.03 WEED CONTROL					
WEED CONTROL					
Weed control, bromicil, 15 lb./acre, wettable powder	ACRE	4.000	330.00	260.00	590.00
Vegetation control, by application of plant killer	SY	0.003	0.02	0.20	0.22
Weed killer, lawns and fields	SY	0.002	0.27	0.10	0.37

© 2020 BNi Publications, Inc.

DIVISION 32 EXTERIOR IMPROVEMENTS

32840.04 LAWN IRRIGATION

	Unit	Man-Hrs	Material	Labor	Total
LAWN IRRIGATION					
Residential system, complete					
Minimum	ACRE				19,250.00
Maximum	ACRE				36,630.00
Commercial system, complete					
Minimum	ACRE				29,220.00
Maximum	ACRE				46,190.00
Components					
Pipe					
Schedule 40, PVC					
1/2"	LF	0.042	0.43	2.68	3.11
3/4"	LF	0.044	0.61	2.83	3.44
1"	LF	0.046	0.93	2.91	3.84
1-1/4"	LF	0.046	1.23	2.91	4.14
1-1/2"	LF	0.047	1.46	3.00	4.46
2"	LF	0.050	2.16	3.19	5.35
2-1/2"	LF	0.053	3.27	3.40	6.67
3"	LF	0.057	4.47	3.64	8.11
4"	LF	0.067	6.32	4.25	10.57
6"	LF	0.080	11.00	5.10	16.10
Fittings					
Tee					
1/2"	EA	0.133	0.84	8.51	9.35
3/4"	EA	0.133	0.97	8.51	9.48
1"	EA	0.133	1.75	8.51	10.26
1-1/4"	EA	0.145	3.17	9.28	12.45
1-1/2"	EA	0.160	3.61	10.25	13.86
2"	EA	0.178	5.11	11.25	16.36
2-1/2"	EA	0.200	19.25	12.75	32.00
3"	EA	0.229	24.75	14.50	39.25
4"	EA	0.267	37.50	17.00	54.50
6"	EA	0.320	160.00	20.50	180.50
Ell					
1/2"	EA	0.123	0.72	7.85	8.57
3/4"	EA	0.133	0.80	8.51	9.31
1"	EA	0.133	1.41	8.51	9.92
1-1/4"	EA	0.133	2.47	8.51	10.98
1-1/2"	EA	0.133	2.82	8.51	11.33
2"	EA	0.145	4.23	9.28	13.51
2-1/2"	EA	0.160	14.00	10.25	24.25
3"	EA	0.178	17.50	11.25	28.75
4"	EA	0.200	24.75	12.75	37.50
6"	EA	0.267	110.00	17.00	127.00
Coupling					
1/2"	EA	0.123	0.53	7.85	8.38
3/4"	EA	0.133	0.72	8.51	9.23
1"	EA	0.133	1.25	8.51	9.76
1-1/4"	EA	0.133	1.58	8.51	10.09
1-1/2"	EA	0.133	1.66	8.51	10.17
2"	EA	0.145	2.64	9.28	11.92
2-1/2"	EA	0.160	5.99	10.25	16.24
3"	EA	0.178	10.50	11.25	21.75
4"	EA	0.200	11.25	12.75	24.00
6"	EA	0.267	47.75	17.00	64.75
45 Ell					
1/2"	EA	0.123	1.06	7.85	8.91
3/4"	EA	0.133	1.75	8.51	10.26
1"	EA	0.133	2.47	8.51	10.98
1-1/4"	EA	0.133	3.35	8.51	11.86
1-1/2"	EA	0.133	4.04	8.51	12.55
2"	EA	0.145	5.27	9.28	14.55
2-1/2"	EA	0.160	15.75	10.25	26.00
3"	EA	0.178	22.75	11.25	34.00
4"	EA	0.200	36.00	12.75	48.75

32840.04 LAWN IRRIGATION (Cont.)

	Unit	Man-Hrs	Material	Labor	Total
45 Ell					
6"	EA	0.267	120.00	17.00	137.00
Riser, 1/2" diameter					
2" (close)	EA	0.200	0.60	12.75	13.35
3"	EA	0.200	0.72	12.75	13.47
4"	EA	0.229	0.88	14.50	15.38
5"	EA	0.229	0.97	14.50	15.47
6"	EA	0.229	1.25	14.50	15.75
3/4" diameter					
2" (close)	EA	0.200	0.60	12.75	13.35
3"	EA	0.200	0.72	12.75	13.47
4"	EA	0.229	0.80	14.50	15.30
5"	EA	0.229	1.06	14.50	15.56
6"	EA	0.229	1.13	14.50	15.63
1" diameter					
2" (close)	EA	0.200	0.88	12.75	13.63
3"	EA	0.200	1.13	12.75	13.88
4"	EA	0.229	1.32	14.50	15.82
5"	EA	0.229	1.66	14.50	16.16
6"	EA	0.229	1.73	14.50	16.23
Valve Box					
Concrete, Square					
12" x 22"	EA	1.000	86.00	64.00	150.00
18" x 20"	EA	1.143	110.00	73.00	183.00
24" x 13"	EA	1.333	96.00	85.00	181.00
Round					
12"	EA	0.800	38.00	51.00	89.00
Plastic					
Square					
12"	EA	1.000	40.00	64.00	104.00
18"	EA				150.00
Round					
6"	EA	1.000	9.99	64.00	73.99
10"	EA	1.000	22.00	64.00	86.00
12"	EA	1.143	32.00	73.00	105.00
Sprinkler, Pop-Up					
Spray					
2" high	EA	1.333	5.93	85.00	90.93
3" high	EA	1.333	6.50	85.00	91.50
4" high	EA	1.600	7.06	100.00	107.06
6" high	EA	1.600	14.75	100.00	114.75
12" high	EA	1.600	19.00	100.00	119.00
Rotor					
4" high	EA	1.333	27.75	85.00	112.75
6" high	EA	1.600	37.00	100.00	137.00
Impact					
Brass	EA	1.333	37.00	85.00	122.00
Plastic	EA	1.600	18.50	100.00	118.50
Shrub Head					
Spray	EA	1.333	11.25	85.00	96.25
Rotor	EA	1.600	27.75	100.00	127.75
Time Clocks					
Minimum	EA	2.000	180.00	130.00	310.00
Average	EA	2.667	350.00	170.00	520.00
Maximum	EA	4.000	3,180.00	260.00	3,440.00
Valves					
Anti-siphon					
Brass					
3/4"	EA	1.333	76.00	85.00	161.00
1"	EA	1.333	94.00	85.00	179.00
Plastic					
3/4"	EA	1.333	55.00	85.00	140.00
1"	EA	1.333	66.00	85.00	151.00

© 2020 BNi Publications, Inc.

DIVISION 32 EXTERIOR IMPROVEMENTS

	Unit	Man-Hrs	Material	Labor	Total
32840.04 LAWN IRRIGATION (Cont.)					
Valves					
Ball Valve					
Plastic					
1/2"	EA	1.333	7.23	85.00	92.23
3/4"	EA	1.333	7.89	85.00	92.89
1"	EA	1.333	10.50	85.00	95.50
1-1/2"	EA	1.600	21.00	100.00	121.00
2"	EA	1.600	27.50	100.00	127.50
Brass					
1/2"	EA	1.333	13.50	85.00	98.50
3/4"	EA	1.333	21.50	85.00	106.50
1"	EA	1.333	33.50	85.00	118.50
1-1/2"	EA	1.600	64.00	100.00	164.00
2"	EA	1.600	97.00	100.00	197.00
Gate valves, Brass					
1/2"	EA	1.333	15.75	85.00	100.75
3/4"	EA	1.333	26.25	85.00	111.25
1"	EA	1.333	36.75	85.00	121.75
1-1/2"	EA	1.600	63.00	100.00	163.00
2"	EA	1.600	79.00	100.00	179.00
Vacuum Breakers					
Brass					
3/4"	EA	2.667	54.00	170.00	224.00
1"	EA	2.667	74.00	170.00	244.00
1-1/2"	EA	2.667	150.00	170.00	320.00
2"	EA	2.667	210.00	170.00	380.00
Plastic					
3/4"	EA	2.667	66.00	170.00	236.00
1"	EA	2.667	77.00	170.00	247.00
1-1/2"	EA	2.667	120.00	170.00	290.00
2"	EA	2.667	140.00	170.00	310.00
Backflow Preventors, Brass					
3/4"	EA	26.667	320.00	1,700.00	2,020.00
1"	EA	26.667	360.00	1,700.00	2,060.00
1-1/2"	EA	26.667	780.00	1,700.00	2,480.00
2"	EA	32.000	970.00	2,040.00	3,010.00
Pressure Regulators, Brass					
3/4"	EA	0.800	140.00	51.00	191.00
1"	EA	0.800	190.00	51.00	241.00
1-1/2"	EA	0.889	570.00	57.00	627.00
2"	EA	1.000	680.00	64.00	744.00
Quick Coupler Valve					
3/4"	EA	1.333	100.00	85.00	185.00
1"	EA	1.333	150.00	85.00	235.00
32911.91 TOPSOIL					
TOPSOIL					
Spread topsoil, with equipment					
Minimum	CY	0.080		15.50	15.50
Maximum	CY	0.100		19.50	19.50
By hand					
Minimum	CY	0.800		51.00	51.00
Maximum	CY	1.000		64.00	64.00
Area prep. seeding (grade, rake and clean)					
Square yard	SY	0.006		0.40	0.40
By acre	ACRE	32.000		2,040.00	2,040.00
Remove topsoil and stockpile on site					
4" deep	CY	0.067		13.00	13.00
6" deep	CY	0.062		12.00	12.00
Spreading topsoil from stock pile					
By loader	CY	0.073		14.25	14.25
By hand	CY	0.800		160.00	160.00
Top dress by hand	SY	0.008		1.55	1.55

	Unit	Man-Hrs	Material	Labor	Total
32911.91 TOPSOIL (Cont.)					
Spread topsoil, with equipment					
Place imported top soil					
By loader					
4" deep	SY	0.008		1.55	1.55
6" deep	SY	0.009		1.72	1.72
By hand					
4" deep	SY	0.089		5.67	5.67
6" deep	SY	0.100		6.38	6.38
Plant bed preparation, 18" deep					
With backhoe/loader	SY	0.020		3.88	3.88
By hand	SY	0.133		8.51	8.51
32921.90 SEEDING					
SEEDING					
Mechanical seeding, 175 lb/acre					
By square yard	SY	0.002	0.23	0.13	0.36
By acre	ACRE	8.000	930.00	680.00	1,610.00
450 lb/acre					
By square yard	SY	0.002	0.59	0.17	0.76
By acre	ACRE	10.000	2,310.00	850.00	3,160.00
Seeding by hand, 10 lb per 100 SY					
By square yard	SY	0.003	0.66	0.17	0.83
By acre	ACRE	13.333	2,580.00	850.00	3,430.00
Reseed disturbed areas	SF	0.004	0.06	0.25	0.31
32932.30 PLANTS					
PLANTS					
Euonymus coloratus, 18" (Purple Wintercreeper)	EA	0.133	3.01	8.51	11.52
Hedera Helix, 2-1/4" pot (English ivy)	EA	0.133	1.25	8.51	9.76
Liriope muscari, 2" clumps	EA	0.080	5.26	5.10	10.36
Santolina, 12"	EA	0.080	6.02	5.10	11.12
Vinca major or minor, 3" pot	EA	0.080	0.98	5.10	6.08
Cortaderia argentia, 2 gallon (Pampas Grass)	EA	0.080	19.00	5.10	24.10
Ophiopogan japonicus, 1 quart (4" pot)	EA	0.080	5.26	5.10	10.36
Ajuga reptans, 2-3/4" pot (carpet bugle)	EA	0.080	0.98	5.10	6.08
Pachysandra terminalis, 2-3/4" pot (Japanese Spurge)	EA	0.080	1.33	5.10	6.43
32933.30 SHRUBS					
SHRUBS					
Juniperus conferia litoralis, 18"-24" (Shore Juniper)	EA	0.320	44.00	20.50	64.50
Horizontalis plumosa, 18"-24" (Andorra Juniper)	EA	0.320	46.75	20.50	67.25
Sabina tamar-iscfolia-tamarix juniper, 18"-24"	EA	0.320	46.75	20.50	67.25
Chin San Jose, 18"-24" (San Jose Juniper)	EA	0.320	46.75	20.50	67.25
Sargenti, 18"-24" (Sargent's Juniper)	EA	0.320	44.00	20.50	64.50
Nandina domestica, 18"-24" (Heavenly Bamboo)	EA	0.320	29.50	20.50	50.00
Raphiolepis Indica Springtime, 18"-24"	EA	0.320	31.75	20.50	52.25
Osmanthus Heterophyllus Gulftide, 18"-24"	EA	0.320	34.00	20.50	54.50
Ilex Cornuta Burfordi Nana, 18"-24"	EA	0.320	38.75	20.50	59.25
Glabra, 18"-24" (Inkberry Holly)	EA	0.320	36.50	20.50	57.00
Azalea, Indica types, 18"-24"	EA	0.320	41.25	20.50	61.75
Kurume types, 18"-24"	EA	0.320	46.00	20.50	66.50
Berberis Julianae, 18"-24" (Wintergreen Barberry)	EA	0.320	27.00	20.50	47.50
Pieris Japonica Japanese, 18"-24"	EA	0.320	27.00	20.50	47.50
Ilex Cornuta Rotunda, 18"-24"	EA	0.320	32.00	20.50	52.50
Juniperus Horiz. Plumosa, 24"-30"	EA	0.400	29.50	25.50	55.00
Rhodopendrow Hybrids, 24"-30"	EA	0.400	79.00	25.50	104.50
Aucuba Japonica Varigata, 24"-30"	EA	0.400	26.75	25.50	52.25
Ilex Crenata Willow Leaf, 24"-30"	EA	0.400	29.50	25.50	55.00
Cleyera Japonica, 30"-36"	EA	0.500	34.50	32.00	66.50
Pittosporum Tobira, 30"-36"	EA	0.500	40.25	32.00	72.25
Prumus Laurocerasus, 30"-36"	EA	0.500	74.00	32.00	106.00
Ilex Cornuta Burfordi, 30"-36" (Burford Holly)	EA	0.500	39.25	32.00	71.25
Abelia Grandiflora, 24"-36" (Yew Podocarpus)	EA	0.400	27.00	25.50	52.50
Podocarpos Macrophylla, 24"-36"	EA	0.400	44.00	25.50	69.50
Pyracantha Coccinea Lalandi, 3'-4' (Firethorn)	EA	0.500	25.25	32.00	57.25
Photinia Frazieri, 3'-4' (Red Photinia)	EA	0.500	40.00	32.00	72.00

© 2020 BNi Publications, Inc.

DIVISION 32 EXTERIOR IMPROVEMENTS

	Unit	Man-Hrs	Material	Labor	Total
32933.30 SHRUBS (Cont.)					
Forsythia Suspensa, 3'-4' (Weeping Forsythia)	EA	0.500	25.25	32.00	57.25
Camellia Japonica, 3'-4' (Common Camellia)	EA	0.500	44.50	32.00	76.50
Juniperus Chin Torulosa, 3'-4' (Hollywood Juniper)	EA	0.500	47.25	32.00	79.25
Cupressocyparis Leylandii, 3'-4'	EA	0.500	39.75	32.00	71.75
Ilex Opaca Fosteri, 5'-6' (Foster's Holly)	EA	0.667	160.00	42.50	202.50
Opaca, 5'-6' (American Holly)	EA	0.667	230.00	42.50	272.50
Nyrica Cerifera, 4'-5' (Southern Wax Myrtles)	EA	0.571	50.00	36.50	86.50
Ligustrum Japonicum, 4'-5' (Japanese Privet)	EA	0.571	39.25	36.50	75.75
32934.30 TREES					
TREES					
Cornus Florida, 5'-6' (White flowering Dogwood)	EA	0.667	120.00	42.50	162.50
Prunus Serrulata Kwanzan, 6'-8' (Kwanzan Cherry)	EA	0.800	130.00	51.00	181.00
Caroliniana, 6'-8' (Carolina Cherry Laurel)	EA	0.800	150.00	51.00	201.00
Cercis Canadensis, 6'-8' (Eastern Redbud)	EA	0.800	100.00	51.00	151.00
Koelreuteria Paniculata, 8'-10' (Goldenrain Tree)	EA	1.000	180.00	64.00	244.00
Acer Platanoides, 1-3/4"-2" (11'-13')	EA	1.333	240.00	85.00	325.00
Rubrum, 1-3/4"-2" (11'-13') (Red Maple)	EA	1.333	180.00	85.00	265.00
Saccharum, 1-3/4"-2" (Sugar Maple)	EA	1.333	320.00	85.00	405.00
Fraxinus Pennsylvanica, 1-3/4"-2"	EA	1.333	150.00	85.00	235.00
Celtis Occidentalis, 1-3/4"-2"	EA	1.333	230.00	85.00	315.00
Glenditsia Triacantos Inermis, 2"	EA	1.333	210.00	85.00	295.00
Prunus Cerasifera "Thundercloud", 6'-8'	EA	0.800	120.00	51.00	171.00
Yeodensis, 6'-8' (Yoshino Cherry)	EA	0.800	130.00	51.00	181.00
Lagerstroemia Indica, 8'-10' (Crapemyrtle)	EA	1.000	210.00	64.00	274.00
Crataegus Phaenopyrum, 8'-10'	EA	1.000	320.00	64.00	384.00
Quercus Borealis, 1-3/4"-2" (Northern Red Oak)	EA	1.333	190.00	85.00	275.00
Quercus Acutissima, 1-3/4"-2" (8'-10')	EA	1.333	180.00	85.00	265.00
Saliz Babylonica, 1-3/4"-2" (Weeping Willow)	EA	1.333	90.00	85.00	175.00
Tilia Cordata Greenspire, 1-3/4"-2" (10'-12')	EA	1.333	400.00	85.00	485.00
Malus, 2"-2-1/2" (8'-10') (Flowering Crabapple)	EA	1.333	190.00	85.00	275.00
Platanus Occidentalis, (12'-14')	EA	1.600	300.00	100.00	400.00
Pyrus Calleryana Bradford, 2"-2-1/2"	EA	1.333	230.00	85.00	315.00
Quercus Palustris, 2"-2-1/2" (12'-14') (Pin Oak)	EA	1.333	260.00	85.00	345.00
Phellos, 2-1/2"-3" (Willow Oak)	EA	1.600	280.00	100.00	380.00
Nigra, 2"-2-1/2" (Water Oak)	EA	1.333	240.00	85.00	325.00
Magnolia Soulangeana, 4'-5' (Saucer Magnolia)	EA	0.667	140.00	42.50	182.50
Grandiflora, 6'-8' (Southern Magnolia)	EA	0.800	190.00	51.00	241.00
Cedrus Deodara, 10'-12' (Deodare Cedar)	EA	1.333	320.00	85.00	405.00
Gingko Biloba, 10'-12' (2"-2-1/2")	EA	1.333	300.00	85.00	385.00
Pinus Thunbergi, 5'-6' (Japanese Black Pine)	EA	0.667	120.00	42.50	162.50
Strobus, 6'-8' (White Pine)	EA	0.800	130.00	51.00	181.00
Taeda, 6'-8' (Loblolly Pine)	EA	0.800	110.00	51.00	161.00
Quercus Virginiana, 2"-2-1/2" (Live Oak)	EA	1.600	280.00	100.00	380.00
32940.02 LANDSCAPE ACCESSORIES					
LANDSCAPE ACCESSORIES					
Steel edging, 3/16" x 4"	LF	0.010	1.29	0.63	1.92
Landscaping stepping stones, 15"x15", white	EA	0.040	5.83	2.55	8.38
Wood chip mulch	CY	0.533	40.75	34.00	74.75
2" thick	SY	0.016	2.49	1.02	3.51
4" thick	SY	0.023	4.70	1.45	6.15
6" thick	SY	0.029	7.04	1.85	8.89
Gravel mulch, 3/4" stone	CY	0.800	32.25	51.00	83.25
White marble chips, 1" deep	SF	0.008	0.63	0.51	1.14
Peat moss					
2" thick	SY	0.018	3.46	1.13	4.59
4" thick	SY	0.027	6.66	1.70	8.36
6" thick	SY	0.033	10.25	2.12	12.37
Landscaping timbers, treated lumber					
4" x 4"	LF	0.027	3.58	1.70	5.28
6" x 6"	LF	0.029	8.32	1.82	10.14
8" x 8"	LF	0.033	10.00	2.12	12.12

32943.30 PREFABRICATED PLANTERS

	Unit	Man-Hrs	Material	Labor	Total
PREFABRICATED PLANTERS					
Concrete precast, circular					
24" dia., 18" high	EA	0.800	420.00	51.00	471.00
42" dia., 30" high	EA	1.000	560.00	64.00	624.00
Fiberglass, circular					
36" dia., 27" high	EA	0.400	710.00	25.50	735.50
60" dia., 39" high	EA	0.444	1,640.00	28.25	1,668.25
Tapered, circular					
24" dia., 36" high	EA	0.364	560.00	23.25	583.25
40" dia., 36" high	EA	0.400	930.00	25.50	955.50
Square					
2' by 2', 17" high	EA	0.364	480.00	23.25	503.25
4' by 4', 39" high	EA	0.444	1,640.00	28.25	1,668.25
Rectangular					
4' by 1', 18" high	EA	0.400	530.00	25.50	555.50

© 2020 BNi Publications, Inc.

	Unit	Man-Hrs	Material	Labor	Total

33011.01 PIPELINE RESTORATION

PIPELINE RESTORATION
Relining existing water main

	Unit	Man-Hrs	Material	Labor	Total
6" dia.	LF	0.240	8.62	42.50	51.12
8" dia.	LF	0.253	9.71	44.75	54.46
10" dia.	LF	0.267	10.75	47.25	58.00
12" dia.	LF	0.282	11.75	50.00	61.75
14" dia.	LF	0.300	12.75	53.00	65.75
16" dia.	LF	0.320	13.75	57.00	70.75
18" dia.	LF	0.343	15.00	61.00	76.00
20" dia.	LF	0.369	16.50	65.00	81.50
24" dia.	LF	0.400	17.50	71.00	88.50
36" dia.	LF	0.480	19.00	85.00	104.00
48" dia.	LF	0.533	21.25	95.00	116.25
72" dia.	LF	0.600	27.00	110.00	137.00

Replacing in-line gate valves

	Unit	Man-Hrs	Material	Labor	Total
6" valve	EA	3.200	970.00	570.00	1,540.00
8" valve	EA	4.000	1,520.00	710.00	2,230.00
10" valve	EA	4.800	2,290.00	850.00	3,140.00
12" valve	EA	6.000	3,970.00	1,060.00	5,030.00
16" valve	EA	6.857	9,010.00	1,220.00	10,230.00
18" valve	EA	8.000	13,630.00	1,420.00	15,050.00
20" valve	EA	9.600	18,740.00	1,700.00	20,440.00
24" valve	EA	12.000	26,780.00	2,130.00	28,910.00
36" valve	EA	16.000	73,340.00	2,840.00	76,180.00

33052.31 PIPE JACKING

PIPE JACKING
Pipe casing, horizontal jacking

	Unit	Man-Hrs	Material	Labor	Total
18" dia.	LF	0.711	110.00	110.00	220.00
21" dia.	LF	0.762	130.00	120.00	250.00
24" dia.	LF	0.800	140.00	120.00	260.00
27" dia.	LF	0.800	150.00	120.00	270.00
30" dia.	LF	0.842	170.00	130.00	300.00
36" dia.	LF	0.914	190.00	140.00	330.00
42" dia.	LF	1.000	220.00	150.00	370.00
48" dia.	LF	1.067	270.00	160.00	430.00

33110.03 CHILLED WATER SYSTEMS

CHILLED WATER SYSTEMS
Chilled water pipe, 2" thick insulation, w/casing
Align and tack weld on sleepers

	Unit	Man-Hrs	Material	Labor	Total
1-1/2" dia.	LF	0.022	26.75	2.59	29.34
3" dia.	LF	0.034	43.00	4.07	47.07
4" dia.	LF	0.048	49.50	5.70	55.20
6" dia.	LF	0.060	56.00	7.12	63.12
8" dia.	LF	0.069	79.00	8.14	87.14
10" dia.	LF	0.080	100.00	9.50	109.50
12" dia.	LF	0.096	120.00	11.50	131.50
14" dia.	LF	0.104	160.00	12.50	172.50
16" dia.	LF	0.120	210.00	14.25	224.25

Align and tack weld on trench bottom

	Unit	Man-Hrs	Material	Labor	Total
18" dia.	LF	0.133	210.00	15.75	225.75
20" dia.	LF	0.150	280.00	17.75	297.75

Preinsulated fittings
Align and tack weld on sleepers
Elbows

	Unit	Man-Hrs	Material	Labor	Total
1-1/2"	EA	0.500	640.00	44.75	684.75
3"	EA	0.800	810.00	72.00	882.00
4"	EA	1.000	1,050.00	89.00	1,139.00
6"	EA	1.333	1,450.00	120.00	1,570.00
8"	EA	1.600	2,060.00	140.00	2,200.00

Tees

	Unit	Man-Hrs	Material	Labor	Total
1-1/2"	EA	0.533	980.00	47.75	1,027.75
3"	EA	0.889	1,380.00	79.00	1,459.00
4"	EA	1.143	1,050.00	100.00	1,150.00
6"	EA	1.600	2,260.00	140.00	2,400.00

DIVISION 33 UTILITIES

	Unit	Man-Hrs	Material	Labor	Total

33110.03 CHILLED WATER SYSTEMS (Cont.)

Tees
8"	EA	2.000	3,010.00	180.00	3,190.00

Reducers
3"	EA	0.667	780.00	60.00	840.00
4"	EA	0.800	1,230.00	72.00	1,302.00
6"	EA	1.000	1,660.00	89.00	1,749.00
8"	EA	1.333	1,800.00	120.00	1,920.00

Anchors, not including concrete
4"	EA	1.000	410.00	89.00	499.00
6"	EA	1.000	600.00	89.00	689.00

Align and tack weld on trench bottom
Elbows
10"	EA	1.500	2,360.00	180.00	2,540.00
12"	EA	1.714	2,820.00	200.00	3,020.00
14"	EA	1.846	3,550.00	220.00	3,770.00
16"	EA	2.000	3,820.00	240.00	4,060.00
18"	EA	2.182	4,260.00	260.00	4,520.00
20"	EA	2.400	5,140.00	290.00	5,430.00

Tees
10"	EA	1.500	3,820.00	180.00	4,000.00
12"	EA	1.714	4,850.00	200.00	5,050.00
14"	EA	1.846	5,140.00	220.00	5,360.00
16"	EA	2.000	5,440.00	240.00	5,680.00
18"	EA	2.182	6,170.00	260.00	6,430.00
20"	EA	2.400	7,060.00	290.00	7,350.00

Reducers
10"	EA	1.000	2,910.00	120.00	3,030.00
12"	EA	1.091	3,530.00	130.00	3,660.00
14"	EA	1.200	3,820.00	140.00	3,960.00
16"	EA	1.333	4,700.00	160.00	4,860.00
18"	EA	1.500	5,140.00	180.00	5,320.00
20"	EA	1.714	5,440.00	200.00	5,640.00

Anchors, not including concrete
10"	EA	1.000	780.00	120.00	900.00
12"	EA	1.091	860.00	130.00	990.00
14"	EA	1.200	990.00	140.00	1,130.00
16"	EA	1.333	1,390.00	160.00	1,550.00
18"	EA	1.500	1,930.00	180.00	2,110.00
20"	EA	1.714	2,610.00	200.00	2,810.00

33110.04 DUCTILE IRON PIPE

DUCTILE IRON PIPE
Ductile iron pipe, cement lined, slip-on joints
4"	LF	0.067	19.25	7.91	27.16
6"	LF	0.071	22.25	8.38	30.63
8"	LF	0.075	29.00	8.90	37.90
10"	LF	0.080	40.00	9.50	49.50
12"	LF	0.096	49.25	11.50	60.75
14"	LF	0.120	62.00	14.25	76.25
16"	LF	0.133	76.00	15.75	91.75
18"	LF	0.150	86.00	17.75	103.75
20"	LF	0.171	98.00	20.25	118.25

Mechanical joint pipe
4"	LF	0.092	20.75	11.00	31.75
6"	LF	0.100	24.75	11.75	36.50
8"	LF	0.109	32.50	13.00	45.50
10"	LF	0.120	42.75	14.25	57.00
12"	LF	0.160	54.00	19.00	73.00
14"	LF	0.185	68.00	22.00	90.00
16"	LF	0.218	75.00	26.00	101.00
18"	LF	0.240	84.00	28.50	112.50
20"	LF	0.267	97.00	31.75	128.75

© 2020 BNi Publications, Inc.

33110.04 DUCTILE IRON PIPE (Cont.)

Ductile iron pipe, cement lined, slip-on joints
Fittings, mechanical joint
90 degree elbow

	Unit	Man-Hrs	Material	Labor	Total
4"	EA	0.533	240.00	34.00	274.00
6"	EA	0.615	320.00	39.25	359.25
8"	EA	0.800	450.00	51.00	501.00
10"	EA	1.143	660.00	73.00	733.00
12"	EA	1.600	880.00	100.00	980.00
14"	EA	2.000	1,370.00	130.00	1,500.00
16"	EA	2.667	1,710.00	170.00	1,880.00
18"	EA	3.200	2,570.00	200.00	2,770.00
20"	EA	4.000	2,860.00	260.00	3,120.00

45 degree elbow

	Unit	Man-Hrs	Material	Labor	Total
4"	EA	0.533	210.00	34.00	244.00
6"	EA	0.615	280.00	39.25	319.25
8"	EA	0.800	400.00	51.00	451.00
10"	EA	1.143	570.00	73.00	643.00
12"	EA	1.600	690.00	100.00	790.00
14"	EA	2.000	1,140.00	130.00	1,270.00
16"	EA	2.667	1,370.00	170.00	1,540.00
18"	EA	4.000	2,000.00	260.00	2,260.00
20"	EA	4.000	2,370.00	260.00	2,630.00

Tee

	Unit	Man-Hrs	Material	Labor	Total
4"x3"	EA	1.000	340.00	64.00	404.00
4"x4"	EA	1.000	370.00	64.00	434.00
6"x3"	EA	1.143	430.00	73.00	503.00
6"x4"	EA	1.143	440.00	73.00	513.00
6"x6"	EA	1.143	480.00	73.00	553.00
8"x4"	EA	1.333	600.00	85.00	685.00
8"x6"	EA	1.333	680.00	85.00	765.00
8"x8"	EA	1.333	640.00	85.00	725.00
10"x4"	EA	1.600	800.00	100.00	900.00
10"x6"	EA	1.600	880.00	100.00	980.00
10"x8"	EA	1.600	910.00	100.00	1,010.00
10"x10"	EA	1.600	1,020.00	100.00	1,120.00
12"x4"	EA	2.000	900.00	130.00	1,030.00
12"x6"	EA	2.000	970.00	130.00	1,100.00
12"x8"	EA	2.000	1,050.00	130.00	1,180.00
12"x10"	EA	2.000	1,200.00	130.00	1,330.00
12"x12"	EA	2.133	1,280.00	140.00	1,420.00
14"x4"	EA	2.286	1,570.00	150.00	1,720.00
14"x6"	EA	2.286	1,670.00	150.00	1,820.00
14"x8"	EA	2.286	1,700.00	150.00	1,850.00
14"x10"	EA	2.286	1,750.00	150.00	1,900.00
14"x12"	EA	2.462	1,800.00	160.00	1,960.00
14"x14"	EA	2.462	1,780.00	160.00	1,940.00
16"x4"	EA	2.667	2,030.00	170.00	2,200.00
16"x6"	EA	2.667	2,070.00	170.00	2,240.00
16"x8"	EA	2.667	1,840.00	170.00	2,010.00
16"x10"	EA	2.667	1,870.00	170.00	2,040.00
16"x12"	EA	2.667	1,830.00	170.00	2,000.00
16"x14"	EA	2.667	1,930.00	170.00	2,100.00
16"x16"	EA	2.667	1,970.00	170.00	2,140.00
18"x6"	EA	2.909	2,360.00	190.00	2,550.00
18"x8"	EA	2.909	2,400.00	190.00	2,590.00
18"x10"	EA	2.909	2,440.00	190.00	2,630.00
18"x12"	EA	2.909	2,480.00	190.00	2,670.00
18"x14"	EA	2.909	2,770.00	190.00	2,960.00
18"x16"	EA	2.909	2,740.00	190.00	2,930.00
18"x18"	EA	2.909	3,110.00	190.00	3,300.00
20"x6"	EA	3.200	3,000.00	200.00	3,200.00
20"x8"	EA	3.200	3,030.00	200.00	3,230.00
20"x10"	EA	3.200	3,090.00	200.00	3,290.00
20"x12"	EA	3.200	3,140.00	200.00	3,340.00

	Unit	Man-Hrs	Material	Labor	Total

33110.04 DUCTILE IRON PIPE (Cont.)

Tee

	Unit	Man-Hrs	Material	Labor	Total
20"x14"	EA	3.200	3,230.00	200.00	3,430.00
20"x16"	EA	3.200	3,770.00	200.00	3,970.00
20"x18"	EA	3.200	3,940.00	200.00	4,140.00
20"x20"	EA	3.200	4,030.00	200.00	4,230.00

Cross

	Unit	Man-Hrs	Material	Labor	Total
4"x3"	EA	1.333	360.00	85.00	445.00
4"x4"	EA	1.333	390.00	85.00	475.00
6"x3"	EA	1.600	400.00	100.00	500.00
6"x4"	EA	1.600	430.00	100.00	530.00
6"x6"	EA	1.600	470.00	100.00	570.00
8"x4"	EA	1.778	660.00	110.00	770.00
8"x6"	EA	1.778	710.00	110.00	820.00
8"x8"	EA	1.778	780.00	110.00	890.00
10"x4"	EA	2.000	910.00	130.00	1,040.00
10"x6"	EA	2.000	970.00	130.00	1,100.00
10"x8"	EA	2.000	1,050.00	130.00	1,180.00
10"x10"	EA	2.000	1,250.00	130.00	1,380.00
12"x4"	EA	2.286	1,170.00	150.00	1,320.00
12"x6"	EA	2.286	1,310.00	150.00	1,460.00
12"x8"	EA	2.286	1,280.00	150.00	1,430.00
12"x10"	EA	2.462	1,480.00	160.00	1,640.00
12"x12"	EA	2.462	1,600.00	160.00	1,760.00
14"x4"	EA	2.667	1,510.00	170.00	1,680.00
14"x6"	EA	2.667	1,710.00	170.00	1,880.00
14"x8"	EA	2.667	1,780.00	170.00	1,950.00
14"x10"	EA	2.667	1,910.00	170.00	2,080.00
14"x12"	EA	2.909	2,060.00	190.00	2,250.00
14"x14"	EA	2.909	2,260.00	190.00	2,450.00
16"x4"	EA	3.200	1,970.00	200.00	2,170.00
16"x6"	EA	3.200	2,030.00	200.00	2,230.00
16"x8"	EA	3.200	2,140.00	200.00	2,340.00
16"x10"	EA	3.200	2,280.00	200.00	2,480.00
16"x12"	EA	3.200	2,390.00	200.00	2,590.00
16"x14"	EA	3.200	2,590.00	200.00	2,790.00
16"x16"	EA	3.200	2,740.00	200.00	2,940.00
18"x6"	EA	3.556	2,540.00	230.00	2,770.00
18"x8"	EA	3.556	2,630.00	230.00	2,860.00
18"x10"	EA	3.556	2,740.00	230.00	2,970.00
18"x12"	EA	3.556	2,880.00	230.00	3,110.00
18"x14"	EA	3.556	3,430.00	230.00	3,660.00
18"x16"	EA	3.556	3,660.00	230.00	3,890.00
18"x18"	EA	3.556	3,860.00	230.00	4,090.00
20"x6"	EA	3.810	3,060.00	240.00	3,300.00
20"x8"	EA	3.810	3,140.00	240.00	3,380.00
20"x10"	EA	3.810	3,280.00	240.00	3,520.00
20"x12"	EA	3.810	3,430.00	240.00	3,670.00
20"x14"	EA	3.810	3,600.00	240.00	3,840.00
20"x16"	EA	3.810	4,170.00	240.00	4,410.00
20"x18"	EA	4.000	4,460.00	260.00	4,720.00
20"x20"	EA	4.000	4,720.00	260.00	4,980.00

33110.06 PLASTIC PIPE

PLASTIC PIPE

PVC, class 150 pipe

	Unit	Man-Hrs	Material	Labor	Total
4" dia.	LF	0.060	5.31	7.12	12.43
6" dia.	LF	0.065	10.00	7.70	17.70
8" dia.	LF	0.069	16.00	8.14	24.14
10" dia.	LF	0.075	22.75	8.90	31.65
12" dia.	LF	0.080	33.50	9.50	43.00

Schedule 40 pipe

	Unit	Man-Hrs	Material	Labor	Total
1-1/2" dia.	LF	0.047	1.34	3.00	4.34
2" dia.	LF	0.050	1.99	3.19	5.18
2-1/2" dia.	LF	0.053	3.01	3.40	6.41
3" dia.	LF	0.057	4.09	3.64	7.73

© 2020 BNi Publications, Inc.

33110.06 PLASTIC PIPE (Cont.)

	Unit	Man-Hrs	Material	Labor	Total
Schedule 40 pipe					
4" dia.	LF	0.067	5.78	4.25	10.03
6" dia.	LF	0.080	11.00	5.10	16.10
90 degree elbows					
1"	EA	0.133	1.12	8.51	9.63
1-1/2"	EA	0.133	2.14	8.51	10.65
2"	EA	0.145	3.35	9.28	12.63
2-1/2"	EA	0.160	10.25	10.25	20.50
3"	EA	0.178	12.25	11.25	23.50
4"	EA	0.200	19.75	12.75	32.50
6"	EA	0.267	62.00	17.00	79.00
45 degree elbows					
1"	EA	0.133	1.72	8.51	10.23
1-1/2"	EA	0.133	3.01	8.51	11.52
2"	EA	0.145	3.91	9.28	13.19
2-1/2"	EA	0.160	10.25	10.25	20.50
3"	EA	0.178	15.75	11.25	27.00
4"	EA	0.200	25.50	12.75	38.25
6"	EA	0.267	63.00	17.00	80.00
Tees					
1"	EA	0.160	1.48	10.25	11.73
1-1/2"	EA	0.160	2.86	10.25	13.11
2"	EA	0.178	4.12	11.25	15.37
2-1/2"	EA	0.200	13.50	12.75	26.25
3"	EA	0.229	18.00	14.50	32.50
4"	EA	0.267	29.25	17.00	46.25
6"	EA	0.320	98.00	20.50	118.50
Couplings					
1"	EA	0.133	0.91	8.51	9.42
1-1/2"	EA	0.133	1.30	8.51	9.81
2"	EA	0.145	2.01	9.28	11.29
2-1/2"	EA	0.160	4.42	10.25	14.67
3"	EA	0.178	6.91	11.25	18.16
4"	EA	0.200	9.02	12.75	21.77
6"	EA	0.267	28.50	17.00	45.50
Drainage pipe					
PVC schedule 80					
1" dia.	LF	0.047	2.03	3.00	5.03
1-1/2" dia.	LF	0.047	2.46	3.00	5.46
ABS, 2" dia.	LF	0.050	3.14	3.19	6.33
2-1/2" dia.	LF	0.053	4.47	3.40	7.87
3" dia.	LF	0.057	5.26	3.64	8.90
4" dia.	LF	0.067	7.17	4.25	11.42
6" dia.	LF	0.080	12.00	5.10	17.10
8" dia.	LF	0.063	16.00	7.50	23.50
10" dia.	LF	0.075	21.25	8.90	30.15
12" dia.	LF	0.080	34.75	9.50	44.25
90 degree elbows					
1"	EA	0.133	3.38	8.51	11.89
1-1/2"	EA	0.133	4.22	8.51	12.73
2"	EA	0.145	5.09	9.28	14.37
2-1/2"	EA	0.160	12.25	10.25	22.50
3"	EA	0.178	12.50	11.25	23.75
4"	EA	0.200	22.25	12.75	35.00
6"	EA	0.267	48.75	17.00	65.75
45 degree elbows					
1"	EA	0.133	5.50	8.51	14.01
1-1/2"	EA	0.133	6.99	8.51	15.50
2"	EA	0.145	8.66	9.28	17.94
2-1/2"	EA	0.160	16.25	10.25	26.50
3"	EA	0.178	17.25	11.25	28.50
4"	EA	0.200	32.75	12.75	45.50
6"	EA	0.267	76.00	17.00	93.00

	Unit	Man-Hrs	Material	Labor	Total

33110.06 PLASTIC PIPE (Cont.)

ABS, 2" dia.

Tees

	Unit	Man-Hrs	Material	Labor	Total
1"	EA	0.160	3.57	10.25	13.82
1-1/2"	EA	0.160	11.50	10.25	21.75
2"	EA	0.178	14.00	11.25	25.25
2-1/2"	EA	0.200	16.25	12.75	29.00
3"	EA	0.229	17.75	14.50	32.25
4"	EA	0.267	33.75	17.00	50.75
6"	EA	0.320	67.00	20.50	87.50

Couplings

	Unit	Man-Hrs	Material	Labor	Total
1"	EA	0.133	2.98	8.51	11.49
1-1/2"	EA	0.133	5.09	8.51	13.60
2"	EA	0.145	7.50	9.28	16.78
2-1/2"	EA	0.160	15.75	10.25	26.00
3"	EA	0.178	16.25	11.25	27.50
4"	EA	0.200	17.00	12.75	29.75
6"	EA	0.267	28.50	17.00	45.50

Pressure pipe

PVC, class 200 pipe

	Unit	Man-Hrs	Material	Labor	Total
3/4"	LF	0.040	0.26	2.55	2.81
1"	LF	0.042	0.38	2.68	3.06
1-1/4"	LF	0.044	0.64	2.83	3.47
1-1/2"	LF	0.047	0.77	3.00	3.77
2"	LF	0.050	1.26	3.19	4.45
2-1/2"	LF	0.053	1.91	3.40	5.31
3"	LF	0.057	2.92	3.64	6.56
4"	LF	0.067	5.09	4.25	9.34
6"	LF	0.080	10.25	5.10	15.35
8"	LF	0.069	19.75	8.14	27.89

90 degree elbows

	Unit	Man-Hrs	Material	Labor	Total
3/4"	EA	0.133	0.84	8.51	9.35
1"	EA	0.133	0.93	8.51	9.44
1-1/4"	EA	0.133	1.39	8.51	9.90
1-1/2"	EA	0.133	1.77	8.51	10.28
2"	EA	0.145	2.77	9.28	12.05
2-1/2"	EA	0.160	8.44	10.25	18.69
3"	EA	0.178	13.00	11.25	24.25
4"	EA	0.200	23.50	12.75	36.25
6"	EA	0.267	49.50	17.00	66.50
8"	EA	0.400	83.00	25.50	108.50

45 degree elbows

	Unit	Man-Hrs	Material	Labor	Total
3/4"	EA	0.133	0.95	8.51	9.46
1"	EA	0.133	1.22	8.51	9.73
1-1/4"	EA	0.133	1.76	8.51	10.27
1-1/2"	EA	0.133	2.13	8.51	10.64
2"	EA	0.145	3.00	9.28	12.28
2-1/2"	EA	0.160	4.92	10.25	15.17
3"	EA	0.178	11.25	11.25	22.50
4"	EA	0.200	21.25	12.75	34.00
6"	EA	0.267	44.25	17.00	61.25
8"	EA	0.400	90.00	25.50	115.50

Tees

	Unit	Man-Hrs	Material	Labor	Total
3/4"	EA	0.160	0.80	10.25	11.05
1"	EA	0.160	1.05	10.25	11.30
1-1/4"	EA	0.160	1.51	10.25	11.76
1-1/2"	EA	0.160	2.10	10.25	12.35
2"	EA	0.178	3.09	11.25	14.34
2-1/2"	EA	0.200	4.86	12.75	17.61
3"	EA	0.229	15.00	14.50	29.50
4"	EA	0.267	21.25	17.00	38.25
6"	EA	0.320	63.00	20.50	83.50
8"	EA	0.444	130.00	28.25	158.25

Couplings

	Unit	Man-Hrs	Material	Labor	Total
3/4"	EA	0.133	0.49	8.51	9.00
1"	EA	0.133	0.73	8.51	9.24

© 2020 BNi Publications, Inc.

	Unit	Man-Hrs	Material	Labor	Total

33110.06 PLASTIC PIPE (Cont.)

Couplings

	Unit	Man-Hrs	Material	Labor	Total
1-1/4"	EA	0.133	0.95	8.51	9.46
1-1/2"	EA	0.133	1.04	8.51	9.55
2"	EA	0.145	1.46	9.28	10.74
2-1/2"	EA	0.160	3.09	10.25	13.34
3"	EA	0.178	4.86	11.25	16.11
4"	EA	0.178	6.83	11.25	18.08
6"	EA	0.200	18.00	12.75	30.75
8"	EA	0.267	32.50	17.00	49.50

33121.31 CORPORATION STOPS

CORPORATION STOPS

Stop for flared copper service pipe

	Unit	Man-Hrs	Material	Labor	Total
3/4"	EA	0.400	51.00	35.75	86.75
1"	EA	0.444	69.00	39.75	108.75
1-1/4"	EA	0.533	190.00	47.75	237.75
1-1/2"	EA	0.667	220.00	60.00	280.00
2"	EA	0.800	310.00	72.00	382.00

33121.32 THRUST BLOCKS

THRUST BLOCKS

Thrust block, 3000# concrete

	Unit	Man-Hrs	Material	Labor	Total
1/4 c.y.	EA	1.333	120.00	110.00	230.00
1/2 c.y.	EA	1.600	180.00	130.00	310.00
3/4 c.y.	EA	2.667	220.00	220.00	440.00
1 c.y.	EA	5.333	310.00	430.00	740.00

33121.33 TAPPING SADDLES & SLEEVES

TAPPING SADDLES & SLEEVES

Tapping saddle, tap size to 2"

	Unit	Man-Hrs	Material	Labor	Total
4" saddle	EA	0.400	71.00	25.50	96.50
6" saddle	EA	0.500	83.00	32.00	115.00
8" saddle	EA	0.667	96.00	42.50	138.50
10" saddle	EA	0.800	110.00	51.00	161.00
12" saddle	EA	1.143	130.00	73.00	203.00
14" saddle	EA	1.600	150.00	100.00	250.00

Tapping sleeve

	Unit	Man-Hrs	Material	Labor	Total
4x4	EA	0.533	860.00	34.00	894.00
6x4	EA	0.615	1,110.00	39.25	1,149.25
6x6	EA	0.615	1,130.00	39.25	1,169.25
8x4	EA	0.800	1,160.00	51.00	1,211.00
8x6	EA	0.800	1,180.00	51.00	1,231.00
10x4	EA	0.960	1,880.00	110.00	1,990.00
10x6	EA	0.960	2,720.00	110.00	2,830.00
10x8	EA	0.960	2,840.00	110.00	2,950.00
10x10	EA	1.000	2,900.00	120.00	3,020.00
12x4	EA	1.000	2,930.00	120.00	3,050.00
12x6	EA	1.091	2,950.00	130.00	3,080.00
12x8	EA	1.200	3,020.00	140.00	3,160.00
12x10	EA	1.333	3,180.00	160.00	3,340.00
12x12	EA	1.500	3,290.00	180.00	3,470.00

Tapping valve, mechanical joint

	Unit	Man-Hrs	Material	Labor	Total
4" valve	EA	3.000	850.00	360.00	1,210.00
6" valve	EA	4.000	1,020.00	480.00	1,500.00
8" valve	EA	6.000	1,520.00	710.00	2,230.00
10" valve	EA	8.000	2,420.00	950.00	3,370.00
12" valve	EA	12.000	4,280.00	1,430.00	5,710.00

Tap hole in pipe

	Unit	Man-Hrs	Material	Labor	Total
4" hole	EA	1.000		64.00	64.00
6" hole	EA	1.600		100.00	100.00
8" hole	EA	2.667		170.00	170.00
10" hole	EA	3.200		200.00	200.00
12" hole	EA	4.000		260.00	260.00

	Unit	Man-Hrs	Material	Labor	Total

33121.35 VALVE BOXES

VALVE BOXES
Valve box, adjustable, for valves up to 20"

	Unit	Man-Hrs	Material	Labor	Total
3' deep	EA	0.267	300.00	17.00	317.00
4' deep	EA	0.320	360.00	20.50	380.50
5' deep	EA	0.400	420.00	25.50	445.50

33121.61 GATE VALVES

GATE VALVES
Gate valve (AWWA) mechanical joint, with adjustable box

	Unit	Man-Hrs	Material	Labor	Total
4" valve	EA	0.800	1,340.00	95.00	1,435.00
6" valve	EA	0.960	1,520.00	110.00	1,630.00
8" valve	EA	1.200	2,020.00	140.00	2,160.00
10" valve	EA	1.412	3,030.00	170.00	3,200.00
12" valve	EA	1.714	4,040.00	200.00	4,240.00
14" valve	EA	2.000	10,120.00	240.00	10,360.00
16" valve	EA	2.182	13,490.00	260.00	13,750.00
18" valve	EA	2.400	16,860.00	290.00	17,150.00

Flanged, with box, post indicator (AWWA)

	Unit	Man-Hrs	Material	Labor	Total
4" valve	EA	0.960	1,210.00	110.00	1,320.00
6" valve	EA	1.091	1,420.00	130.00	1,550.00
8" valve	EA	1.333	2,020.00	160.00	2,180.00
10" valve	EA	1.600	3,030.00	190.00	3,220.00
12" valve	EA	2.000	4,400.00	240.00	4,640.00
14" valve	EA	2.400	10,110.00	290.00	10,400.00
16" valve	EA	3.000	13,490.00	360.00	13,850.00

33121.93 FIRE HYDRANTS

FIRE HYDRANTS
Standard, 3 way post, 6" mechanical joint

	Unit	Man-Hrs	Material	Labor	Total
2' deep	EA	8.000	2,150.00	950.00	3,100.00
4' deep	EA	9.600	2,310.00	1,140.00	3,450.00
6' deep	EA	12.000	2,570.00	1,430.00	4,000.00
8' deep	EA	13.714	2,890.00	1,630.00	4,520.00

33123.31 WATER METERS

WATER METERS
Water meter, displacement type

	Unit	Man-Hrs	Material	Labor	Total
1"	EA	0.800	220.00	72.00	292.00
1-1/2"	EA	0.889	750.00	79.00	829.00
2"	EA	1.000	1,130.00	89.00	1,219.00

33211.30 WELLS

WELLS
Domestic water, drilled and cased

	Unit	Man-Hrs	Material	Labor	Total
4" dia.	LF	0.480	30.50	85.00	115.50
6" dia.	LF	0.533	33.50	95.00	128.50
8" dia.	LF	0.600	39.50	110.00	149.50

33310.01 CAST IRON FLANGED PIPE

CAST IRON FLANGED PIPE
Cast iron flanged sections
4" pipe, with one bolt set

	Unit	Man-Hrs	Material	Labor	Total
3' section	EA	0.218	60.00	26.00	86.00
4' section	EA	0.240	83.00	28.50	111.50
5' section	EA	0.267	110.00	31.75	141.75
6' section	EA	0.300	130.00	35.75	165.75
8' section	EA	0.343	160.00	40.75	200.75
10' section	EA	0.480	230.00	57.00	287.00
12' section	EA	0.800	240.00	95.00	335.00
15' section	EA	1.200	300.00	140.00	440.00
18' section	EA	1.600	370.00	190.00	560.00

6" pipe, with one bolt set

	Unit	Man-Hrs	Material	Labor	Total
3' section	EA	0.240	100.00	28.50	128.50
4' section	EA	0.282	150.00	33.50	183.50
5' section	EA	0.320	190.00	38.00	228.00
6' section	EA	0.369	220.00	43.75	263.75
8' section	EA	0.533	270.00	63.00	333.00

© 2020 BNi Publications, Inc.

	Unit	Man-Hrs	Material	Labor	Total

33310.01 CAST IRON FLANGED PIPE (Cont.)

6" pipe, with one bolt set

	Unit	Man-Hrs	Material	Labor	Total
10' section	EA	0.600	380.00	71.00	451.00
12' section	EA	0.800	420.00	95.00	515.00
15' section	EA	1.200	520.00	140.00	660.00
18' section	EA	1.714	620.00	200.00	820.00

8" pipe, with one bolt set

	Unit	Man-Hrs	Material	Labor	Total
3' section	EA	0.300	160.00	35.75	195.75
4' section	EA	0.343	230.00	40.75	270.75
5' section	EA	0.400	280.00	47.50	327.50
6' section	EA	0.480	340.00	57.00	397.00
8' section	EA	0.686	430.00	81.00	511.00
10' section	EA	0.800	600.00	95.00	695.00
12' section	EA	1.200	650.00	140.00	790.00
15' section	EA	1.600	810.00	190.00	1,000.00
18' section	EA	2.000	970.00	240.00	1,210.00

10" pipe, with one bolt set

	Unit	Man-Hrs	Material	Labor	Total
3' section	EA	0.308	300.00	36.50	336.50
4' section	EA	0.353	490.00	42.00	532.00
5' section	EA	0.414	570.00	49.25	619.25
6' section	EA	0.500	690.00	59.00	749.00
8' section	EA	0.727	910.00	86.00	996.00
10' section	EA	0.857	990.00	100.00	1,090.00
12' section	EA	1.333	1,080.00	160.00	1,240.00
15' section	EA	1.714	1,350.00	200.00	1,550.00
18' section	EA	2.400	1,620.00	290.00	1,910.00

12" pipe, with one bolt set

	Unit	Man-Hrs	Material	Labor	Total
3' section	EA	0.333	370.00	39.50	409.50
4' section	EA	0.387	550.00	46.00	596.00
5' section	EA	0.462	680.00	55.00	735.00
6' section	EA	0.545	820.00	65.00	885.00
8' section	EA	0.800	1,090.00	95.00	1,185.00
10' section	EA	0.923	1,260.00	110.00	1,370.00
12' section	EA	1.500	1,600.00	180.00	1,780.00
15' section	EA	2.000	1,810.00	240.00	2,050.00
18' section	EA	2.667	2,080.00	320.00	2,400.00

33310.02 CAST IRON FITTINGS

CAST IRON FITTINGS

Mechanical joint, with 2 bolt kits

90 deg bend

	Unit	Man-Hrs	Material	Labor	Total
4"	EA	0.533	88.00	34.00	122.00
6"	EA	0.615	150.00	39.25	189.25
8"	EA	0.800	330.00	51.00	381.00
10"	EA	1.143	500.00	73.00	573.00
12"	EA	1.600	760.00	100.00	860.00
14"	EA	2.000	1,040.00	130.00	1,170.00
16"	EA	2.667	1,200.00	170.00	1,370.00

45 deg bend

	Unit	Man-Hrs	Material	Labor	Total
4"	EA	0.533	73.00	34.00	107.00
6"	EA	0.615	120.00	39.25	159.25
8"	EA	0.800	260.00	51.00	311.00
10"	EA	1.143	390.00	73.00	463.00
12"	EA	1.600	660.00	100.00	760.00
14"	EA	2.000	810.00	130.00	940.00
16"	EA	2.667	1,060.00	170.00	1,230.00

Tee, with 3 bolt kits

	Unit	Man-Hrs	Material	Labor	Total
4" x 4"	EA	0.800	150.00	51.00	201.00
6" x 6"	EA	1.000	260.00	64.00	324.00
8" x 8"	EA	1.333	730.00	85.00	815.00
10" x 10"	EA	2.000	910.00	130.00	1,040.00
12" x 12"	EA	2.667	1,620.00	170.00	1,790.00

Wye, with 3 bolt kits

	Unit	Man-Hrs	Material	Labor	Total
6" x 6"	EA	1.000	320.00	64.00	384.00
8" x 8"	EA	1.333	670.00	85.00	755.00
10" x 10"	EA	2.000	960.00	130.00	1,090.00

DIVISION 33 UTILITIES

	Unit	Man-Hrs	Material	Labor	Total
33310.02 CAST IRON FITTINGS (Cont.)					
Wye, with 3 bolt kits					
12" x 12"	EA	2.667	1,880.00	170.00	2,050.00
Reducer, with 2 bolt kits					
6" x 4"	EA	1.000	140.00	64.00	204.00
8" x 6"	EA	1.333	230.00	85.00	315.00
10" x 8"	EA	2.000	640.00	130.00	770.00
12" x 10"	EA	2.667	770.00	170.00	940.00
Flanged, 90 deg bend, 125 lb.					
4"	EA	0.667	180.00	42.50	222.50
6"	EA	0.800	220.00	51.00	271.00
8"	EA	1.000	310.00	64.00	374.00
10"	EA	1.333	550.00	85.00	635.00
12"	EA	2.000	770.00	130.00	900.00
14"	EA	2.667	1,520.00	170.00	1,690.00
16"	EA	2.667	2,270.00	170.00	2,440.00
Tee					
4"	EA	1.000	280.00	64.00	344.00
6"	EA	1.143	390.00	73.00	463.00
8"	EA	1.333	600.00	85.00	685.00
10"	EA	1.600	1,100.00	100.00	1,200.00
12"	EA	2.000	1,480.00	130.00	1,610.00
14"	EA	2.667	3,300.00	170.00	3,470.00
16"	EA	4.000	4,960.00	260.00	5,220.00
33310.03 VITRIFIED CLAY PIPE					
VITRIFIED CLAY PIPE					
Vitrified clay pipe, extra strength					
6" dia.	LF	0.109	5.73	13.00	18.73
8" dia.	LF	0.114	6.87	13.50	20.37
10" dia.	LF	0.120	10.50	14.25	24.75
12" dia.	LF	0.160	15.00	19.00	34.00
15" dia.	LF	0.240	27.50	28.50	56.00
18" dia.	LF	0.267	41.25	31.75	73.00
24" dia.	LF	0.343	75.00	40.75	115.75
30" dia.	LF	0.480	130.00	57.00	187.00
36" dia.	LF	0.686	180.00	81.00	261.00
33310.04 SANITARY SEWERS					
SANITARY SEWERS					
Clay					
6" pipe	LF	0.080	9.41	9.50	18.91
8" pipe	LF	0.086	12.50	10.25	22.75
10" pipe	LF	0.092	15.75	11.00	26.75
12" pipe	LF	0.100	25.00	11.75	36.75
PVC					
4" pipe	LF	0.060	4.05	7.12	11.17
6" pipe	LF	0.063	8.11	7.50	15.61
8" pipe	LF	0.067	12.25	7.91	20.16
10" pipe	LF	0.071	16.25	8.38	24.63
12" pipe	LF	0.075	24.25	8.90	33.15
Cleanout					
4" pipe	EA	1.000	18.00	64.00	82.00
6" pipe	EA	1.000	39.75	64.00	103.75
8" pipe	EA	1.000	120.00	64.00	184.00
Connect new sewer line					
To existing manhole	EA	2.667	100.00	170.00	270.00
To new manhole	EA	1.600	75.00	100.00	175.00
33360.01 DRAINAGE FIELDS					
DRAINAGE FIELDS					
Perforated PVC pipe, for drain field					
4" pipe	LF	0.053	2.71	6.33	9.04
6" pipe	LF	0.057	5.08	6.78	11.86

© 2020 BNi Publications, Inc.

	Unit	Man-Hrs	Material	Labor	Total

33360.05 SEPTIC TANKS

SEPTIC TANKS

Septic tank, precast concrete

	Unit	Man-Hrs	Material	Labor	Total
1000 gals	EA	4.000	1,020.00	480.00	1,500.00
2000 gals	EA	6.000	2,740.00	710.00	3,450.00
5000 gals	EA	12.000	9,350.00	1,430.00	10,780.00
25,000 gals	EA	48.000	53,590.00	5,700.00	59,290.00
40,000 gals	EA	80.000	63,560.00	9,500.00	73,060.00

Leaching pit, precast concrete, 72" diameter

	Unit	Man-Hrs	Material	Labor	Total
3' deep	EA	3.000	780.00	360.00	1,140.00
6' deep	EA	3.429	1,370.00	410.00	1,780.00
8' deep	EA	4.000	1,740.00	480.00	2,220.00

33391.33 MANHOLES

MANHOLES

Precast sections, 48" dia.

	Unit	Man-Hrs	Material	Labor	Total
Base section	EA	2.000	360.00	240.00	600.00
1'0" riser	EA	1.600	100.00	190.00	290.00
1'4" riser	EA	1.714	120.00	200.00	320.00
2'8" riser	EA	1.846	180.00	220.00	400.00
4'0" riser	EA	2.000	340.00	240.00	580.00
2'8" cone top	EA	2.400	220.00	290.00	510.00

Precast manholes, 48" dia.

	Unit	Man-Hrs	Material	Labor	Total
4' deep	EA	4.800	700.00	570.00	1,270.00
6' deep	EA	6.000	1,070.00	710.00	1,780.00
7' deep	EA	6.857	1,220.00	810.00	2,030.00
8' deep	EA	8.000	1,380.00	950.00	2,330.00
10' deep	EA	9.600	1,540.00	1,140.00	2,680.00

Cast-in-place, 48" dia., with frame and cover

	Unit	Man-Hrs	Material	Labor	Total
5' deep	EA	12.000	630.00	1,430.00	2,060.00
6' deep	EA	13.714	830.00	1,630.00	2,460.00
8' deep	EA	16.000	1,210.00	1,900.00	3,110.00
10' deep	EA	19.200	1,410.00	2,280.00	3,690.00

Brick manholes, 48" dia. with cover, 8" thick

	Unit	Man-Hrs	Material	Labor	Total
4' deep	EA	8.000	670.00	620.00	1,290.00
6' deep	EA	8.889	840.00	690.00	1,530.00
8' deep	EA	10.000	1,080.00	780.00	1,860.00
10' deep	EA	11.429	1,340.00	890.00	2,230.00
12' deep	EA	13.333	1,680.00	1,040.00	2,720.00
14' deep	EA	16.000	2,040.00	1,240.00	3,280.00

Inverts for manholes

	Unit	Man-Hrs	Material	Labor	Total
Single channel	EA	3.200	110.00	250.00	360.00
Triple channel	EA	4.000	130.00	310.00	440.00

Frames and covers, 24" diameter

	Unit	Man-Hrs	Material	Labor	Total
300 lb	EA	0.800	410.00	51.00	461.00
400 lb	EA	0.889	430.00	57.00	487.00
500 lb	EA	1.143	500.00	73.00	573.00
Watertight, 350 lb	EA	2.667	520.00	170.00	690.00
For heavy equipment, 1200 lb	EA	4.000	1,130.00	260.00	1,390.00

Steps for manholes

	Unit	Man-Hrs	Material	Labor	Total
7" x 9"	EA	0.160	18.25	10.25	28.50
8" x 9"	EA	0.178	23.00	11.25	34.25

Curb inlet, 4' throat, cast-in-place

	Unit	Man-Hrs	Material	Labor	Total
12"-30" pipe	EA	12.000	380.00	1,430.00	1,810.00
36"-48" pipe	EA	13.714	420.00	1,630.00	2,050.00
Raise existing frame and cover, when repaving	EA	4.800		570.00	570.00

33410.04 PIPE

PIPE

Concrete pipe

Plain, bell and spigot joint, Class II

	Unit	Man-Hrs	Material	Labor	Total
6" pipe	LF	0.109	7.56	13.00	20.56
8" pipe	LF	0.120	7.89	14.25	22.14
10" pipe	LF	0.126	8.03	15.00	23.03
12" pipe	LF	0.133	10.75	15.75	26.50
15" pipe	LF	0.141	14.50	16.75	31.25
18" pipe	LF	0.150	18.00	17.75	35.75

	Unit	Man-Hrs	Material	Labor	Total

33410.04 PIPE (Cont.)

Plain, bell and spigot joint, Class II

	Unit	Man-Hrs	Material	Labor	Total
21" pipe	LF	0.160	21.75	19.00	40.75
24" pipe	LF	0.171	27.50	20.25	47.75

Reinforced, class III, tongue and groove joint

	Unit	Man-Hrs	Material	Labor	Total
12" pipe	LF	0.133	15.50	15.75	31.25
15" pipe	LF	0.141	17.50	16.75	34.25
18" pipe	LF	0.150	19.25	17.75	37.00
21" pipe	LF	0.160	25.00	19.00	44.00
24" pipe	LF	0.171	32.75	20.25	53.00
27" pipe	LF	0.185	38.75	22.00	60.75
30" pipe	LF	0.200	42.50	23.75	66.25
36" pipe	LF	0.218	64.00	26.00	90.00
42" pipe	LF	0.240	87.00	28.50	115.50
48" pipe	LF	0.267	120.00	31.75	151.75
54" pipe	LF	0.300	130.00	35.75	165.75
60" pipe	LF	0.343	170.00	40.75	210.75
66" pipe	LF	0.400	220.00	47.50	267.50
72" pipe	LF	0.480	240.00	57.00	297.00

Flared end-section, concrete

	Unit	Man-Hrs	Material	Labor	Total
12" pipe	LF	0.133	70.00	15.75	85.75
15" pipe	LF	0.141	83.00	16.75	99.75
18" pipe	LF	0.150	98.00	17.75	115.75
24" pipe	LF	0.171	110.00	20.25	130.25
30" pipe	LF	0.200	140.00	23.75	163.75
36" pipe	LF	0.218	190.00	26.00	216.00
42" pipe	LF	0.240	210.00	28.50	238.50
48" pipe	LF	0.267	230.00	31.75	261.75
54" pipe	LF	0.300	250.00	35.75	285.75

Corrugated metal pipe, coated, paved invert

16 ga.

	Unit	Man-Hrs	Material	Labor	Total
8" pipe	LF	0.080	11.00	9.50	20.50
10" pipe	LF	0.083	14.75	9.82	24.57
12" pipe	LF	0.086	16.50	10.25	26.75
15" pipe	LF	0.092	20.25	11.00	31.25
18" pipe	LF	0.100	24.00	11.75	35.75
21" pipe	LF	0.109	29.50	13.00	42.50
24" pipe	LF	0.120	35.00	14.25	49.25
30" pipe	LF	0.133	46.00	15.75	61.75
36" pipe	LF	0.150	63.00	17.75	80.75
12 ga., 48" pipe	LF	0.171	110.00	20.25	130.25

10 ga.

	Unit	Man-Hrs	Material	Labor	Total
60" pipe	LF	0.200	140.00	23.75	163.75
72" pipe	LF	0.240	180.00	28.50	208.50

Galvanized or aluminum, plain

16 ga.

	Unit	Man-Hrs	Material	Labor	Total
8" pipe	LF	0.080	9.24	9.50	18.74
10" pipe	LF	0.083	13.00	9.82	22.82
12" pipe	LF	0.086	14.75	10.25	25.00
15" pipe	LF	0.092	18.50	11.00	29.50
18" pipe	LF	0.100	22.00	11.75	33.75
24" pipe	LF	0.120	33.25	14.25	47.50
30" pipe	LF	0.133	44.25	15.75	60.00
36" pipe	LF	0.150	55.00	17.75	72.75
12 ga., 48" pipe	LF	0.171	100.00	20.25	120.25
10 ga., 60" pipe	LF	0.200	140.00	23.75	163.75

Galvanized or aluminum, coated oval arch

16 ga.

	Unit	Man-Hrs	Material	Labor	Total
17" x 13"	LF	0.109	34.00	13.00	47.00
21" x 15"	LF	0.120	45.75	14.25	60.00

14 ga.

	Unit	Man-Hrs	Material	Labor	Total
28" x 20"	LF	0.133	64.00	15.75	79.75
35" x 24"	LF	0.171	96.00	20.25	116.25

12 ga.

	Unit	Man-Hrs	Material	Labor	Total
42" x 29"	LF	0.200	110.00	23.75	133.75
57" x 38"	LF	0.240	170.00	28.50	198.50

© 2020 BNi Publications, Inc.

	Unit	Man-Hrs	Material	Labor	Total
33410.04 PIPE (Cont.)					
12 ga.					
64" x 43"	LF	0.253	200.00	30.00	230.00
Oval arch culverts, plain					
16 ga.					
17" x 13"	LF	0.109	16.00	13.00	29.00
21" x 15"	LF	0.120	23.00	14.25	37.25
14 ga.					
28" x 20"	LF	0.133	42.75	15.75	58.50
35" x 24"	LF	0.171	54.00	20.25	74.25
12 ga.					
57" x 38"	LF	0.200	87.00	23.75	110.75
64" x 43"	LF	0.240	110.00	28.50	138.50
71" x 47"	LF	0.253	150.00	30.00	180.00
Nestable corrugated metal pipe					
16 ga.					
10" pipe	LF	0.083	12.75	9.82	22.57
12" pipe	LF	0.086	16.00	10.25	26.25
15" pipe	LF	0.092	20.75	11.00	31.75
18" pipe	LF	0.100	24.00	11.75	35.75
24" pipe	LF	0.120	33.75	14.25	48.00
30" pipe	LF	0.133	41.75	15.75	57.50
14 ga., 36" pipe	LF	0.150	48.00	17.75	65.75
Headwalls, cast-in-place, 30 deg wingwall					
12" pipe	EA	2.000	420.00	160.00	580.00
15" pipe	EA	2.000	510.00	160.00	670.00
18" pipe	EA	2.286	620.00	190.00	810.00
24" pipe	EA	2.286	920.00	190.00	1,110.00
30" pipe	EA	2.667	1,110.00	220.00	1,330.00
36" pipe	EA	4.000	1,200.00	330.00	1,530.00
42" pipe	EA	4.000	1,500.00	330.00	1,830.00
48" pipe	EA	5.333	1,590.00	430.00	2,020.00
54" pipe	EA	6.667	1,800.00	540.00	2,340.00
60" pipe	EA	8.000	2,160.00	650.00	2,810.00
4" cleanout for storm drain					
4" pipe	EA	1.000	670.00	64.00	734.00
6" pipe	EA	1.000	810.00	64.00	874.00
8" pipe	EA	1.000	1,120.00	64.00	1,184.00
Connect new drain line					
To existing manhole	EA	2.667	140.00	170.00	310.00
To new manhole	EA	1.600	120.00	100.00	220.00
33441.31 CATCH BASINS					
CATCH BASINS					
Standard concrete catch basin					
Cast-in-place, 3'8" x 3'8", 6" thick wall					
2' deep	EA	6.000	540.00	710.00	1,250.00
3' deep	EA	6.000	730.00	710.00	1,440.00
4' deep	EA	8.000	950.00	950.00	1,900.00
5' deep	EA	8.000	1,120.00	950.00	2,070.00
6' deep	EA	9.600	1,250.00	1,140.00	2,390.00
4'x4', 8" thick wall, cast-in-place					
2' deep	EA	6.000	580.00	710.00	1,290.00
3' deep	EA	6.000	810.00	710.00	1,520.00
4' deep	EA	8.000	1,070.00	950.00	2,020.00
5' deep	EA	8.000	1,240.00	950.00	2,190.00
6' deep	EA	9.600	1,370.00	1,140.00	2,510.00
Frames and covers, cast iron					
Round					
24" dia.	EA	2.000	430.00	130.00	560.00
26" dia.	EA	2.000	480.00	130.00	610.00
28" dia.	EA	2.000	570.00	130.00	700.00
Rectangular					
23"x23"	EA	2.000	380.00	130.00	510.00
27"x20"	EA	2.000	460.00	130.00	590.00
24"x24"	EA	2.000	450.00	130.00	580.00

	Unit	Man-Hrs	Material	Labor	Total
33441.31 CATCH BASINS (Cont.)					
Rectangular					
26"x26"	EA	2.000	490.00	130.00	620.00
Curb inlet frames and covers					
27"x27"	EA	2.000	770.00	130.00	900.00
24"x36"	EA	2.000	560.00	130.00	690.00
24"x25"	EA	2.000	520.00	130.00	650.00
24"x22"	EA	2.000	450.00	130.00	580.00
20"x22"	EA	2.000	590.00	130.00	720.00
Airfield catch basin frame and grating, galvanized					
2'x4'	EA	2.000	790.00	130.00	920.00
2'x2'	EA	2.000	550.00	130.00	680.00
33461.90 UNDERDRAIN					
UNDERDRAIN					
Drain tile, clay					
6" pipe	LF	0.053	4.52	6.33	10.85
8" pipe	LF	0.056	7.21	6.62	13.83
12" pipe	LF	0.060	14.50	7.12	21.62
Porous concrete, standard strength					
6" pipe	LF	0.053	5.14	6.33	11.47
8" pipe	LF	0.056	5.56	6.62	12.18
12" pipe	LF	0.060	7.35	7.12	14.47
15" pipe	LF	0.067	13.25	7.91	21.16
18" pipe	LF	0.080	17.75	9.50	27.25
Corrugated metal pipe, perforated type					
6" pipe	LF	0.060	7.49	7.12	14.61
8" pipe	LF	0.063	8.85	7.50	16.35
10" pipe	LF	0.067	10.75	7.91	18.66
12" pipe	LF	0.071	15.25	8.38	23.63
18" pipe	LF	0.075	18.75	8.90	27.65
Perforated clay pipe					
6" pipe	LF	0.069	5.98	8.14	14.12
8" pipe	LF	0.071	8.02	8.38	16.40
12" pipe	LF	0.073	14.00	8.63	22.63
Drain tile, concrete					
6" pipe	LF	0.053	4.08	6.33	10.41
8" pipe	LF	0.056	6.35	6.62	12.97
12" pipe	LF	0.060	12.75	7.12	19.87
Perforated rigid PVC underdrain pipe					
4" pipe	LF	0.040	2.10	4.75	6.85
6" pipe	LF	0.048	4.04	5.70	9.74
8" pipe	LF	0.053	6.17	6.33	12.50
10" pipe	LF	0.060	9.43	7.12	16.55
12" pipe	LF	0.069	14.50	8.14	22.64
Underslab drainage, crushed stone					
3" thick	SF	0.008	0.33	0.95	1.28
4" thick	SF	0.009	0.45	1.09	1.54
6" thick	SF	0.010	0.68	1.18	1.86
8" thick	SF	0.010	0.90	1.23	2.13
Plastic filter fabric for drain lines	SF	0.008	0.50	0.51	1.01
Gravel fill in trench, crushed or bank run, 1/2" to 3/4"	CY	0.600	36.25	71.00	107.25
33510.01 GAS DISTRIBUTION					
GAS DISTRIBUTION					
Gas distribution lines					
Polyethylene, 60 psi coils					
1-1/4" dia.	LF	0.053	1.92	4.76	6.68
1-1/2" dia.	LF	0.057	2.61	5.10	7.71
2" dia.	LF	0.067	3.30	5.96	9.26
3" dia.	LF	0.080	6.99	7.15	14.14
30' pipe lengths					
3" dia.	LF	0.089	5.73	7.94	13.67
4" dia.	LF	0.100	8.95	8.94	17.89
6" dia.	LF	0.133	14.25	12.00	26.25
8" dia.	LF	0.160	26.25	14.25	40.50

© 2020 BNi Publications, Inc.

	Unit	Man-Hrs	Material	Labor	Total

33510.01 GAS DISTRIBUTION (Cont.)

Gas distribution lines
Steel, schedule 40, plain end

	Unit	Man-Hrs	Material	Labor	Total
1" dia.	LF	0.067	5.42	5.96	11.38
2" dia.	LF	0.073	9.02	6.50	15.52
3" dia.	LF	0.080	13.00	7.15	20.15
4" dia.	LF	0.160	15.75	19.00	34.75
5" dia.	LF	0.171	29.75	20.25	50.00
6" dia.	LF	0.200	39.75	23.75	63.50
8" dia.	LF	0.218	49.75	26.00	75.75

Natural gas meters, direct digital reading, threaded

	Unit	Man-Hrs	Material	Labor	Total
250 cfh 5 lbs	EA	1.600	130.00	140.00	270.00
425 cfh 10 lbs	EA	1.600	320.00	140.00	460.00
800 cfh 20 lbs	EA	2.000	450.00	180.00	630.00
1,000 cfh 25 lbs	EA	2.000	1,330.00	180.00	1,510.00
1,400 cfh 100 lbs	EA	2.667	3,090.00	240.00	3,330.00
2,300 cfh 100 lbs	EA	4.000	4,300.00	360.00	4,660.00
5,000 cfh 100 lbs	EA	8.000	6,310.00	720.00	7,030.00

Gas pressure regulators
Threaded

	Unit	Man-Hrs	Material	Labor	Total
3/4"	EA	1.000	61.00	89.00	150.00
1"	EA	1.333	64.00	120.00	184.00
1-1/4"	EA	1.333	67.00	120.00	187.00
1-1/2"	EA	1.333	440.00	120.00	560.00
2"	EA	1.600	450.00	140.00	590.00

Flanged

	Unit	Man-Hrs	Material	Labor	Total
3"	EA	2.000	1,590.00	180.00	1,770.00
4"	EA	2.667	2,370.00	240.00	2,610.00

33560.01 STORAGE TANKS

STORAGE TANKS
Oil storage tank, underground, single wall, no excv.
Steel

	Unit	Man-Hrs	Material	Labor	Total
500 gals	EA	3.000	4,040.00	360.00	4,400.00
1,000 gals	EA	4.000	5,470.00	480.00	5,950.00
4,000 gals	EA	8.000	8,380.00	950.00	9,330.00
5,000 gals	EA	12.000	9,830.00	1,430.00	11,260.00
10,000 gals	EA	24.000	17,500.00	2,850.00	20,350.00

Fiberglass, double wall

	Unit	Man-Hrs	Material	Labor	Total
550 gals	EA	4.000	11,370.00	480.00	11,850.00
1,000 gals	EA	4.000	14,620.00	480.00	15,100.00
2,000 gals	EA	6.000	15,880.00	710.00	16,590.00
4,000 gals	EA	12.000	18,440.00	1,430.00	19,870.00
6,000 gals	EA	16.000	20,120.00	1,900.00	22,020.00
8,000 gals	EA	24.000	22,580.00	2,850.00	25,430.00
10,000 gals	EA	30.000	23,150.00	3,560.00	26,710.00
12,000 gals	EA	40.000	25,100.00	4,750.00	29,850.00
15,000 gals	EA	53.333	26,920.00	6,330.00	33,250.00
20,000 gals	EA	60.000	32,980.00	7,130.00	40,110.00

Above ground
Steel, single wall

	Unit	Man-Hrs	Material	Labor	Total
275 gals	EA	2.400	2,290.00	290.00	2,580.00
500 gals	EA	4.000	5,720.00	480.00	6,200.00
1,000 gals	EA	4.800	7,810.00	570.00	8,380.00
1,500 gals	EA	6.000	9,960.00	710.00	10,670.00
2,000 gals	EA	8.000	12,320.00	950.00	13,270.00
5,000 gals	EA	12.000	14,470.00	1,430.00	15,900.00
Fill cap	EA	0.800	140.00	72.00	212.00
Vent cap	EA	0.800	140.00	72.00	212.00
Level indicator	EA	0.800	220.00	72.00	292.00

33633.30 STEAM METERS

STEAM METERS
In-line turbine, direct reading, 300 lb, flanged

	Unit	Man-Hrs	Material	Labor	Total
2"	EA	1.000	3,880.00	89.00	3,969.00
3"	EA	1.333	4,160.00	120.00	4,280.00
4"	EA	1.600	4,570.00	140.00	4,710.00

	Unit	Man-Hrs	Material	Labor	Total

33633.30 STEAM METERS (Cont.)

In-line turbine, direct reading, 300 lb
Threaded, 2"

	Unit	Man-Hrs	Material	Labor	Total
5" line	EA	8.000	7,350.00	720.00	8,070.00
6" line	EA	8.000	7,490.00	720.00	8,210.00
8" line	EA	8.000	7,620.00	720.00	8,340.00
10" line	EA	8.000	8,040.00	720.00	8,760.00
12" line	EA	8.000	8,180.00	720.00	8,900.00
14" line	EA	8.000	8,460.00	720.00	9,180.00
16" line	EA	8.000	9,010.00	720.00	9,730.00

33711.60 UTILITY POLES & FITTINGS

UTILITY POLES & FITTINGS
Wood pole, creosoted

	Unit	Man-Hrs	Material	Labor	Total
25'	EA	2.353	450.00	200.00	650.00
40'	EA	3.791	860.00	310.00	1,170.00
55'	EA	7.547	1,340.00	630.00	1,970.00
Treated, wood preservative, 6"x6"					
8'	EA	0.500	100.00	41.50	141.50
16'	EA	1.600	250.00	130.00	380.00
20'	EA	2.000	360.00	170.00	530.00
Aluminum, brushed, no base					
8'	EA	2.000	650.00	170.00	820.00
20'	EA	3.200	1,020.00	270.00	1,290.00
40'	EA	6.250	3,060.00	520.00	3,580.00
Steel, no base					
10'	EA	2.500	760.00	210.00	970.00
20'	EA	3.810	1,110.00	320.00	1,430.00
35'	EA	6.250	1,880.00	520.00	2,400.00
Concrete, no base					
13'	EA	5.517	980.00	460.00	1,440.00
30'	EA	12.121	2,670.00	1,010.00	3,680.00
50'	EA	18.182	5,920.00	1,510.00	7,430.00
60'	EA	20.000	7,550.00	1,660.00	9,210.00

33711.90 ELECTRIC MANHOLES

ELECTRIC MANHOLES
Precast, handhole, 4' deep

	Unit	Man-Hrs	Material	Labor	Total
2'x2'	EA	3.478	480.00	290.00	770.00
3'x3'	EA	5.556	640.00	460.00	1,100.00
4'x4'	EA	10.256	1,380.00	850.00	2,230.00
Power manhole, complete, precast, 8' deep					
4'x4'	EA	14.035	1,980.00	1,160.00	3,140.00
6'x6'	EA	20.000	2,640.00	1,660.00	4,300.00
8'x8'	EA	21.053	3,130.00	1,750.00	4,880.00
6' deep, 9' x 12'	EA	25.000	3,460.00	2,080.00	5,540.00
Cast-in-place, power manhole, 8' deep					
4'x4'	EA	14.035	2,350.00	1,160.00	3,510.00
6'x6'	EA	20.000	3,030.00	1,660.00	4,690.00
8'x8'	EA	21.053	3,360.00	1,750.00	5,110.00

© 2020 BNi Publications, Inc.

34111.30 RAILROAD BALLAST, RAIL, APPURTENANCES

	Unit	Man-Hrs	Material	Labor	Total
RAILROAD BALLAST, RAIL, APPURTENANCES					
Rail					
90 lb	LF	0.010	29.00	1.14	30.14
100 lb	LF	0.010	33.25	1.14	34.39
115 lb	LF	0.010	37.25	1.14	38.39
132 lb	LF	0.010	41.50	1.14	42.64
Rail relay					
90 lb	LF	0.010	13.50	1.14	14.64
100 lb	LF	0.010	14.75	1.14	15.89
115 lb	LF	0.010	18.00	1.14	19.14
132 lb	LF	0.010	21.75	1.14	22.89
New angle bars, per pair					
90 lb	EA	0.012	110.00	1.42	111.42
100 lb	EA	0.012	120.00	1.42	121.42
115 lb	EA	0.012	150.00	1.42	151.42
132 lb	EA	0.012	170.00	1.42	171.42
Angle bar relay					
90 lb	EA	0.012	44.50	1.42	45.92
100 lb	EA	0.012	45.50	1.42	46.92
115 lb	EA	0.012	47.75	1.42	49.17
132 lb	EA	0.012	51.00	1.42	52.42
New tie plates					
90 lb	EA	0.009	14.50	1.01	15.51
100 lb	EA	0.009	15.25	1.01	16.26
115 lb	EA	0.009	16.50	1.01	17.51
132 lb	EA	0.009	17.50	1.01	18.51
Tie plate relay					
90 lb	EA	0.009	4.56	1.01	5.57
100 lb	EA	0.009	6.41	1.01	7.42
115 lb	EA	0.009	6.41	1.01	7.42
132 lb	EA	0.009	7.90	1.01	8.91
Track accessories					
Wooden cross ties, 8'	EA	0.060	56.00	7.12	63.12
Concrete cross ties, 8'	EA	0.120	140.00	14.25	154.25
Tie plugs, 5"	EA	0.006	6.85	0.71	7.56
Track bolts and nuts, 1"	EA	0.006	5.59	0.71	6.30
Lockwashers, 1"	EA	0.004	1.46	0.47	1.93
Track spikes, 6"	EA	0.024	1.38	2.85	4.23
Wooden switch ties	BF	0.006	2.37	0.71	3.08
Rail anchors	EA	0.022	5.68	2.59	8.27
Ballast	TON	0.120	17.75	14.25	32.00
Gauge rods	EA	0.096	42.75	11.50	54.25
Compromise splice bars	EA	0.160	540.00	19.00	559.00
Turnout					
90 lb	EA	24.000	16,940.00	2,850.00	19,790.00
100 lb	EA	24.000	17,850.00	2,850.00	20,700.00
110 lb	EA	24.000	19,200.00	2,850.00	22,050.00
115 lb	EA	24.000	19,650.00	2,850.00	22,500.00
132 lb	EA	24.000	21,460.00	2,850.00	24,310.00
Turnout relay					
90 lb	EA	24.000	10,840.00	2,850.00	13,690.00
100 lb	EA	24.000	11,970.00	2,850.00	14,820.00
110 lb	EA	24.000	12,430.00	2,850.00	15,280.00
115 lb	EA	24.000	13,100.00	2,850.00	15,950.00
132 lb	EA	24.000	14,230.00	2,850.00	17,080.00
Railroad track in place, complete					
New rail					
90 lb	LF	0.240	190.00	28.50	218.50
100 lb	LF	0.240	190.00	28.50	218.50
110 lb	LF	0.240	200.00	28.50	228.50
115 lb	LF	0.240	200.00	28.50	228.50
132 lb	LF	0.240	210.00	28.50	238.50
Rail relay					
90 lb	LF	0.240	110.00	28.50	138.50
100 lb	LF	0.240	120.00	28.50	148.50

	Unit	Man-Hrs	Material	Labor	Total

34111.30 RAILROAD BALLAST, RAIL, APPURTENANCES

Rail relay

	Unit	Man-Hrs	Material	Labor	Total
110 lb	LF	0.240	120.00	28.50	148.50
115 lb	LF	0.240	130.00	28.50	158.50
132 lb	LF	0.240	130.00	28.50	158.50

No. 8 turnout

	Unit	Man-Hrs	Material	Labor	Total
90 lb	EA	32.000	38,610.00	3,800.00	42,410.00
100 lb	EA	32.000	42,930.00	3,800.00	46,730.00
110 lb	EA	32.000	47,030.00	3,800.00	50,830.00
115 lb	EA	32.000	48,060.00	3,800.00	51,860.00
132 lb	EA	32.000	49,090.00	3,800.00	52,890.00

No. 8 turnout relay

	Unit	Man-Hrs	Material	Labor	Total
90 lb	EA	32.000	28,080.00	3,800.00	31,880.00
100 lb	EA	32.000	29,520.00	3,800.00	33,320.00
110 lb	EA	32.000	31,020.00	3,800.00	34,820.00
115 lb	EA	32.000	34,520.00	3,800.00	38,320.00
132 lb	EA	32.000	36,710.00	3,800.00	40,510.00

Railroad crossings, asphalt, based on 8" thick x 20'

Including track and approach

	Unit	Man-Hrs	Material	Labor	Total
12' roadway	EA	6.000	910.00	710.00	1,620.00
15' roadway	EA	6.857	1,070.00	810.00	1,880.00
18' roadway	EA	8.000	1,250.00	950.00	2,200.00
21' roadway	EA	9.600	1,400.00	1,140.00	2,540.00
24' roadway	EA	12.000	1,580.00	1,430.00	3,010.00

Precast concrete inserts

	Unit	Man-Hrs	Material	Labor	Total
12' roadway	EA	2.400	1,450.00	290.00	1,740.00
15' roadway	EA	3.000	1,740.00	360.00	2,100.00
18' roadway	EA	4.000	2,080.00	480.00	2,560.00
21' roadway	EA	4.800	2,680.00	570.00	3,250.00
24' roadway	EA	5.333	3,240.00	630.00	3,870.00

Molded rubber, with headers

	Unit	Man-Hrs	Material	Labor	Total
12' roadway	EA	2.400	8,340.00	290.00	8,630.00
15' roadway	EA	3.000	10,440.00	360.00	10,800.00
18' roadway	EA	4.000	12,360.00	480.00	12,840.00
21' roadway	EA	4.800	13,630.00	570.00	14,200.00
24' roadway	EA	5.333	16,610.00	630.00	17,240.00

© 2020 BNi Publications, Inc.

41221.33 INDUSTRIAL HOISTS

	Unit	Man-Hrs	Material	Labor	Total
INDUSTRIAL HOISTS					
Industrial hoists, electric, light to medium duty					
500 lb	EA	4.000	9,870.00	330.00	10,200.00
1000 lb	EA	4.211	10,400.00	350.00	10,750.00
2000 lb	EA	4.444	10,860.00	370.00	11,230.00
3000 lb	EA	4.706	11,240.00	390.00	11,630.00
4000 lb	EA	5.000	11,850.00	420.00	12,270.00
5000 lb	EA	5.333	14,200.00	440.00	14,640.00
6000 lb	EA	5.517	16,100.00	460.00	16,560.00
7500 lb	EA	5.714	18,230.00	470.00	18,700.00
10,000 lb	EA	5.926	45,950.00	490.00	46,440.00
15,000 lb	EA	6.154	57,640.00	510.00	58,150.00
20,000 lb	EA	6.667	68,200.00	550.00	68,750.00
25,000 lb	EA	7.273	71,160.00	600.00	71,760.00
30,000 lb	EA	8.000	74,270.00	660.00	74,930.00
Heavy duty					
500 lb	EA	4.000	16,010.00	330.00	16,340.00
1000 lb	EA	4.211	22,400.00	350.00	22,750.00
2000 lb	EA	4.444	24,760.00	370.00	25,130.00
3000 lb	EA	4.706	25,670.00	390.00	26,060.00
4000 lb	EA	5.000	26,810.00	420.00	27,230.00
5000 lb	EA	5.333	27,340.00	440.00	27,780.00
6000 lb	EA	5.517	29,620.00	460.00	30,080.00
7500 lb	EA	5.714	34,020.00	470.00	34,490.00
10,000 lb	EA	5.926	36,300.00	490.00	36,790.00
15,000 lb	EA	6.154	44,050.00	510.00	44,560.00
20,000 lb	EA	6.667	53,460.00	550.00	54,010.00
25,000 lb	EA	7.273	60,000.00	600.00	60,600.00
30,000 lb	EA	8.000	66,680.00	660.00	67,340.00
Air powered hoists					
500 lb	EA	4.000	9,270.00	330.00	9,600.00
1000 lb	EA	4.000	9,720.00	330.00	10,050.00
2000 lb	EA	4.211	9,870.00	350.00	10,220.00
4000 lb	EA	4.706	10,780.00	390.00	11,170.00
6000 lb	EA	6.154	11,620.00	510.00	12,130.00
Overhead traveling bridge crane					
Single girder, 20' span					
3 ton	EA	12.000	25,300.00	1,430.00	26,730.00
5 ton	EA	12.000	29,050.00	1,430.00	30,480.00
7.5 ton	EA	12.000	36,490.00	1,430.00	37,920.00
10 ton	EA	15.000	36,790.00	1,780.00	38,570.00
15 ton	EA	15.000	45,380.00	1,780.00	47,160.00
30' span					
3 ton	EA	12.000	31,280.00	1,430.00	32,710.00
5 ton	EA	12.000	37,870.00	1,430.00	39,300.00
10 ton	EA	15.000	52,740.00	1,780.00	54,520.00
15 ton	EA	15.000	59,640.00	1,780.00	61,420.00
Double girder, 40' span					
3 ton	EA	26.667	49,230.00	3,170.00	52,400.00
5 ton	EA	26.667	51,820.00	3,170.00	54,990.00
7.5 ton	EA	26.667	51,280.00	3,170.00	54,450.00
10 ton	EA	34.286	64,310.00	4,070.00	68,380.00
15 ton	EA	34.286	70,680.00	4,070.00	74,750.00
25 ton	EA	34.286	122,420.00	4,070.00	126,490.00
50' span					
3 ton	EA	26.667	58,560.00	3,170.00	61,730.00
5 ton	EA	26.667	59,790.00	3,170.00	62,960.00
7.5 ton	EA	26.667	61,480.00	3,170.00	64,650.00
10 ton	EA	34.286	67,300.00	4,070.00	71,370.00
15 ton	EA	34.286	82,790.00	4,070.00	86,860.00
25 ton	EA	34.286	109,230.00	4,070.00	113,300.00

	Unit	Man-Hrs	Material	Labor	Total

41221.35 JIB CRANES

JIB CRANES

Self supporting, swinging 8' boom, 200 deg rotation

	Unit	Man-Hrs	Material	Labor	Total
1000 lb	EA	6.667	4,710.00	600.00	5,310.00
2000 lb	EA	6.667	5,160.00	600.00	5,760.00
3000 lb	EA	13.333	5,540.00	1,200.00	6,740.00
4000 lb	EA	13.333	6,070.00	1,200.00	7,270.00
6000 lb	EA	13.333	7,360.00	1,200.00	8,560.00
10,000 lb	EA	13.333	10,400.00	1,200.00	11,600.00

Wall mounted, 180 deg rotation

	Unit	Man-Hrs	Material	Labor	Total
2000 lb	EA	6.667	2,510.00	600.00	3,110.00
3000 lb	EA	6.667	3,040.00	600.00	3,640.00
4000 lb	EA	13.333	1,900.00	1,200.00	3,100.00
6000 lb	EA	13.333	3,800.00	1,200.00	5,000.00
10,000 lb	EA	13.333	7,210.00	1,200.00	8,410.00

© 2020 BNi Publications, Inc.

Assemblies

The following Assemblies Tables list dozens of commonly specified types of construction systems, each with all of the details that make up its costs. These assemblies are developed by using the unit price data from the front of this manual, provide a bridge between unit prices and square foot costs, and can be used in conjunction with either. The data has been updated to reflect current construction costs.

All prices are updated to January 1, 2021 and are national averages.
For more in-depth information contact Design, Cost and Data at 800-533-5680, or go to www.DCD.com

449

All prices are updated to January 1, 2021 and are national averages.
For more in-depth information contact Design, Cost and Data at 800-533-5680, or go to www.DCD.com

A SUBSTRUCTURE

A1010 FOUNDATIONS

A1010.15 FOOTINGS

		Quan.	Unit	Material	Labor	Equip.	Total
A1010.15.10	**Strip Footing, 1' thick 2' wide**					**Unit:**	**LF**
031124201220	Keyway forms (5 uses),2x4	1	LF	$0.31	$3.26	$0.00	$3.57
032100605000	Reinforcing,straight dowels,24" long,1" dia	1	EA	$5.83	$1.66	$0.00	$7.49
032100701020	Reinforcing,foundations,#5-#6	0.005	TON	$8.25	$4.76	$0.00	$13.01
033100502000	Place concrete,footing,3500# or 4000#,by chute	0.07	CY	$9.83	$1.19	$0.00	$11.02
033500101040	Concrete finish,broom,darby	2	SF	$0.00	$1.28	$0.00	$1.28
312316502220	Hand compaction of backfill,with air tamper	0.2	CY	$0.00	$7.30	$0.00	$7.30
312333601140	Trenching,hydraulic excavator,1/2 cy,medium soil	0.75	CY	$0.00	$1.84	$2.40	$4.24
031113602090	Job built,wall footing forms,continuous,5 uses	2	SF	$1.91	$10.87	$0.00	$12.78
				$26.13	**$32.16**	**$2.40**	**$60.69**

		Quan.	Unit	Material	Labor	Equip.	Total
A1010.15.15	**Strip Footing, 18" thick 3' wide**					**Unit:**	**LF**
031113602090	Job built,wall footing forms,continuous,5 uses	3	SF	$2.87	$16.31	$0.00	$19.18
312333601140	Trenching,hydraulic excavator,1/2 cy,medium soil	1.125	CY	$0.00	$2.76	$3.60	$6.36
312316502220	Hand compaction of backfill,with air tamper	0.4	CY	$0.00	$14.59	$0.00	$14.59
033500101040	Concrete finish,broom,darby	3	SF	$0.00	$1.92	$0.00	$1.92
033100502000	Place concrete,footing,3500# or 4000#,by chute	0.15	CY	$21.07	$2.55	$0.00	$23.62
032100701020	Reinforcing,foundations,#5-#6	0.01	TON	$16.50	$9.51	$0.00	$26.01
031124201220	Keyway forms (5 uses),2x4	1	LF	$0.31	$3.26	$0.00	$3.57
032100605000	Reinforcing,straight dowels,24" long,1" dia	1	EA	$5.83	$1.66	$0.00	$7.49
				$46.58	**$52.56**	**$3.60**	**$102.74**

A1010.20 FOUNDATION WALLS

		Quan.	Unit	Material	Labor	Equip.	Total
A1010.20.10	**Foundation Wall 6' high, 1' thick**					**Unit:**	**SF**
032101101040	Reinforcing,wall,#7-#8	0.003	TON	$4.71	$2.22	$0.00	$6.93
071113101020	Dampproofing,asphalt,troweled,1 coat	2	SF	$1.36	$3.41	$0.00	$4.77
033500104160	Break ties and patch holes	2	SF	$0.00	$2.04	$0.00	$2.04
033500104020	Wall finishes,burlap rub,w/cement paste	2	SF	$0.26	$1.70	$0.00	$1.96
031114103190	Job built,ext wall forms,8' high,5 uses	2	SF	$2.66	$10.87	$0.00	$13.53
031003004030	Snap ties,long-end with washers, 12" long	1	EA	$2.26	$0.00	$0.00	$2.26
033100901040	Place wall conc,2500# or 3000#,to 8',by pump	0.037	CY	$5.17	$1.89	$1.30	$8.36
				$16.42	**$22.13**	**$1.30**	**$39.85**

		Quan.	Unit	Material	Labor	Equip.	Total
A1010.20.15	**Foundation Wall 10' high, 18" thick**					**Unit:**	**SF**
033500104020	Wall finishes,burlap rub,w/cement paste	2	SF	$0.26	$1.70	$0.00	$1.96
033500104160	Break ties and patch holes	2	SF	$0.00	$2.04	$0.00	$2.04
033100901040	Place wall conc,2500# or 3000#,to 8',by pump	0.055	CY	$7.69	$2.81	$1.92	$12.42
032101101040	Reinforcing,wall,#7-#8	0.005	TON	$7.86	$3.70	$0.00	$11.56
031114103290	Wall forms,ext,job built,over 8' high wall,5 uses	2	SF	$3.25	$13.05	$0.00	$16.30
031003004030	Snap ties,long-end with washers, 12" long	1	EA	$2.26	$0.00	$0.00	$2.26
071113101020	Dampproofing,asphalt,troweled,1 coat	2	SF	$1.36	$3.41	$0.00	$4.77
				$22.68	**$26.71**	**$1.92**	**$51.31**

All prices are updated to January 1, 2021 and are national averages.
For more in-depth information contact Design, Cost and Data at 800-533-5680, or go to www.DCD.com

451

A SUBSTRUCTURE

A1010 FOUNDATIONS

A1010.25 SPREAD FOOTINGS

		Quan.	Unit	Material	Labor	Equip.	Total
A1010.25.10	**Spread Footing 6' by 6' by 2' thick**...						**EA**
031113903100	Job built,mat foundation forms,5 uses	48	SF	$46.56	$313.15	$0.00	$359.71
032100605000	Reinforcing,straight dowels,24" long,1" dia	4	EA	$23.32	$6.66	$0.00	$29.98
032100901040	Reinforcing,slab,bars,#7-#8	0.147	TON	$230.99	$122.38	$0.00	$353.37
033100805060	Foundation mat,2500#-3000# conc,over 20 cy,pump	2.677	CY	$375.97	$51.28	$35.14	$462.39
033500101040	Concrete finish,broom,darby	36	SF	$0.00	$22.99	$0.00	$22.99
				$676.84	**$516.46**	**$35.14**	**$1,228.44**

		Quan.	Unit	Material	Labor	Equip.	Total
A1010.25.20	**Spread Footing 12' x 12' by 3' thick**...						**EA**
031113903100	Job built,mat foundation forms,5 uses	72	SF	$69.84	$469.73	$0.00	$539.57
033500101040	Concrete finish,broom,darby	36	SF	$0.00	$22.99	$0.00	$22.99
033100805060	Foundation mat,2500#-3000# conc,over 20 cy,pump	4	CY	$561.77	$76.62	$52.50	$690.89
032100901040	Reinforcing,slab,bars,#7-#8	0.221	TON	$347.26	$183.98	$0.00	$531.24
032100605000	Reinforcing,straight dowels,24" long,1" dia	4	EA	$23.32	$6.66	$0.00	$29.98
				$1,002.19	**$759.98**	**$52.50**	**$1,814.67**

A1010.30 PILE CAPS

		Quan.	Unit	Material	Labor	Equip.	Total
A1010.30.20	**Pile Cap 4' by 4' by 2' thick**...						**EA**
031113801600	Pile cap forms,job built,square/rect,5 uses	32	SF	$41.24	$208.77	$0.00	$250.01
032100605000	Reinforcing,straight dowels,24" long,1" dia	4	EA	$23.32	$6.66	$0.00	$29.98
032101601060	Reinforcing,pile caps,#9-#10	0.09	TON	$141.42	$108.98	$0.00	$250.40
033100702020	Pile cap concrete,3500# or 4000#,by pump	1.18	CY	$175.03	$51.66	$35.40	$262.09
033500101040	Concrete finish,broom,darby	16	SF	$0.00	$10.22	$0.00	$10.22
				$381.01	**$386.29**	**$35.40**	**$802.70**

		Quan.	Unit	Material	Labor	Equip.	Total
A1010.30.25	**Pile Cap 4' by 8' by 18" thick**...						**EA**
031113801600	Pile cap forms,job built,square/rect,5 uses	36	SF	$46.39	$234.86	$0.00	$281.25
033500101040	Concrete finish,broom,darby	32	SF	$0.00	$20.43	$0.00	$20.43
033100702020	Pile cap concrete,3500# or 4000#,by pump	1.77	CY	$262.54	$77.50	$53.10	$393.14
032100605000	Reinforcing,straight dowels,24" long,1" dia	4	EA	$23.32	$6.66	$0.00	$29.98
032101601060	Reinforcing,pile caps,#9-#10	0.09	TON	$141.42	$108.98	$0.00	$250.40
				$473.67	**$448.43**	**$53.10**	**$975.20**

All prices are updated to January 1, 2021 and are national averages.
For more in-depth information contact Design, Cost and Data at 800-533-5680, or go to www.DCD.com

452

A SUBSTRUCTURE

A1020 SPECIAL FOUNDATIONS

A1020.10 PILES, CONCRETE

		Quan.	Unit	Material	Labor	Equip.	Total
A1020.10.10	**Prestressed concrete piling, less than 60', 12" sq** ....**Unit: LF**						
316313501002	Prestressed concrete piling,less than 60',12" sq	1	LF	$29.08	$3.40	$4.00	$36.48
A1020.10.15	**Prestressed concrete piling, less than 60', 18" sq** ....**Unit: LF**						
316313501008	Prestressed concrete piling,less than 60',18" sq	1	LF	$51.49	$3.82	$4.49	$59.80
A1020.10.20	**Prestressed concrete piling, less than 60', 24" sq** ....**Unit: LF**						
316313501012	Prestressed concrete piling,less than 60',24" sq	1	LF	$89.08	$4.01	$4.72	$97.81
A1020.10.25	**Prestressed conc piling, more than 60' long, 12" sq** ....**Unit: LF**						
316313501120	Prestressed conc piling,more than 60' long,12" sq	1	LF	$29.67	$2.80	$3.29	$35.76
A1020.10.30	**Prestressed conc piling, more than 60' long, 18" sq** ....**Unit: LF**						
316313501180	Prestressed conc piling,more than 60' long,18" sq	1	LF	$51.69	$2.95	$3.47	$58.11
A1020.10.35	**Prestressed conc piling, more than 60' long, 24" sq** ....**Unit: LF**						
316313501220	Prestressed conc piling,more than 60' long,24" sq	1	LF	$83.29	$3.07	$3.61	$89.97
A1020.10.40	**Prestressed, strt cyl, less than 60', 12" dia** ....**Unit: LF**						
316313501500	Prestressed,strt cyl,less than 60',12" dia	1	LF	$27.05	$3.56	$4.18	$34.79
A1020.10.45	**Prestressed, strt cyl, less than 60', 18" dia** ....**Unit: LF**						
316313501580	Prestressed,strt cyl,less than 60',18" dia	1	LF	$56.42	$3.82	$4.49	$64.73
A1020.10.50	**Prestressed, strt cyl, less than 60', 24" dia** ....**Unit: LF**						
316313501620	Prestressed,strt cyl,less than 60',24" dia	1	LF	$82.70	$4.01	$4.72	$91.43
A1020.10.55	**Prestressed strt cyl, more than 60' long, 12" dia** ....**Unit: LF**						
316313501700	Prestressed strt cyl,more than 60' long,12" dia	1	LF	$27.05	$2.85	$3.35	$33.25
A1020.10.60	**Prestressed strt cyl, more than 60' long, 18" dia** ....**Unit: LF**						
316313501760	Prestressed strt cyl,more than 60' long,18" dia	1	LF	$56.42	$3.01	$3.54	$62.97
A1020.10.65	**Prestressed strt cyl, more than 60' long, 24" dia** ....**Unit: LF**						
316313501800	Prestressed strt cyl,more than 60' long,24" dia	1	LF	$84.35	$3.13	$3.68	$91.16
A1020.12.10	**Mobilization, equip, pile driving rig, minimum** .... **EA**						
015400801360	Mobilization, equip, pile driving rig, minimum	1.000	EA	$11,102.78	$0.00	$0.00	$11,102.78
A1020.12.15	**Mobilization, equip, pile driving rig, average** .... **EA**						
015400801380	Mobilization, equip, pile driving rig, average	1.000	EA	$22,207.65	$0.00	$0.00	$22,207.65
A1020.12.20	**Mobilization, equip, pile driving rig, maximum** .... **EA**						
015400801400	Mobilization, equip, pile driving rig, maximum	1.000	EA	$39,973.66	$0.00	$0.00	$39,973.66
A1020.14.10	**Pile test, 50 ton to 100 ton** .... **EA**						
316200101020	Pile test, 50 ton to 100 ton	1.000	EA	$20,674.50	$0.00	$0.00	$20,674.50
A1020.14.15	**Pile test, 50 ton to 300 ton** .... **EA**						
316200101060	Pile test, 50 ton to 300 ton	1.000	EA	$33,726.00	$0.00	$0.00	$33,726.00
A1020.14.20	**Pile test, 50 ton to 600 ton** .... **EA**						
316200101100	Pile test, 50 ton to 600 ton	1.000	EA	$49,376.25	$0.00	$0.00	$49,376.25

All prices are updated to January 1, 2021 and are national averages.
For more in-depth information contact Design, Cost and Data at 800-533-5680, or go to www.DCD.com

453

A SUBSTRUCTURE

A1020 SPECIAL FOUNDATIONS

A1020.15 PILES, STEEL

		Quan.	Unit	Material	Labor	Equip.	Total
A1020.15.10	**Friction piles, stl casing, w/4000 psi conc, 12" dia** ....**Unit: LF**						
316216505040	Friction piles,stl casing,w/4000 psi conc,12" dia	1	LF	$21.53	$3.91	$4.60	$30.04
A1020.15.15	**Friction piles, stl casing, w/4000 psi conc, 18" dia** ....**Unit: LF**						
316216505100	Friction piles,stl casing,w/4000 psi conc,18" dia	1	LF	$33.45	$4.61	$5.41	$43.47
A1020.15.20	**Concrete filled, 3000#, up to 40', 12" dia** ....**Unit: LF**						
316216601140	Concrete filled,3000#,up to 40',12" dia	1	LF	$35.90	$6.02	$7.08	$49.00
A1020.15.25	**Concrete filled, 3000#, up to 40', 18" dia** ....**Unit: LF**						
316216601200	Concrete filled,3000#,up to 40',18" dia	1	LF	$62.16	$6.81	$8.00	$76.97
A1020.15.30	**Pipe piles, non-filled, 12" dia** ....**Unit: LF**						
316216602060	Pipe piles,non-filled,12" dia	1	LF	$33.34	$4.61	$5.41	$43.36
A1020.15.35	**Pipe piles, non-filled, 18" dia** ....**Unit: LF**						
316216602120	Pipe piles,non-filled,18" dia	1	LF	$52.30	$5.22	$6.13	$63.65
A1020.15.40	**Pipe piles, standard point, 12" dia** ....**Unit: EA**						
316216602760	Pipe piles,standard point,12" dia	1	EA	$183.92	$127.70	$0.00	$311.62
A1020.15.45	**Pipe piles, standard point, 18" dia** ....**Unit: EA**						
316216602820	Pipe piles,standard point,18" dia	1	EA	$356.34	$170.27	$0.00	$526.61
A1020.15.50	**Pipe piles, heavy duty point, 12" dia** ....**Unit: EA**						
316216602940	Pipe piles,heavy duty point,12" dia	1	EA	$344.85	$170.27	$0.00	$515.12
A1020.15.55	**Pipe piles, heavy duty point, 18" dia** ....**Unit: EA**						
316216603000	Pipe piles,heavy duty point,18" dia	1	EA	$517.28	$204.32	$0.00	$721.60
A1020.16.10	**Mobilization, equip, pile driving rig, minimum** .... **EA**						
015400801360	Mobilization, equip, pile driving rig, minimum	1.000	EA	$11,102.78	$0.00	$0.00	$11,102.78
A1020.16.15	**Mobilization, equip, pile driving rig, average** .... **EA**						
015400801380	Mobilization, equip, pile driving rig, average	1.000	EA	$22,207.65	$0.00	$0.00	$22,207.65
A1020.16.20	**Mobilization, equip, pile driving rig, maximum** .... **EA**						
015400801400	Mobilization, equip, pile driving rig, maximum	1.000	EA	$39,973.66	$0.00	$0.00	$39,973.66
A1020.17.10	**Pile test, 50 ton to 100 ton** .... **EA**						
316200101020	Pile test, 50 ton to 100 ton	1.000	EA	$20,674.50	$0.00	$0.00	$20,674.50
A1020.17.15	**Pile test, 50 ton to 300 ton** .... **EA**						
316200101060	Pile test, 50 ton to 300 ton	1.000	EA	$33,726.00	$0.00	$0.00	$33,726.00
A1020.17.20	**Pile test, 50 ton to 600 ton** .... **EA**						
316200101100	Pile test, 50 ton to 600 ton	1.000	EA	$49,376.25	$0.00	$0.00	$49,376.25
A1020.20.10	**Treated wood piles, 12" butt, 8" tip, 25' long** .... **LF**						
316219000100	Treated wood piles, 12" butt, 8" tip, 25' long	1.000	LF	$18.10	$7.56	$8.72	$34.38

All prices are updated to January 1, 2021 and are national averages.
For more in-depth information contact Design, Cost and Data at 800-533-5680, or go to www.DCD.com

454

A SUBSTRUCTURE

A1020 SPECIAL FOUNDATIONS

A1020.20 PILES, WOOD

		Quan.	Unit	Material	Labor	Equip.	Total
A1020.20.15	**Treated wood piles, 12" butt, 8" tip, 40' long**						**Unit: LF**
316219000125	Treated wood piles,12" butt,8" tip,40' long	1	LF	$19.28	$4.89	$5.75	$29.92
A1020.20.20	**Treated wood piles, 12" butt, 7" tip, 40' long**						**Unit: LF**
316219000130	Treated wood piles,12" butt,7" tip,40' long	1	LF	$21.74	$4.89	$5.75	$32.38
A1020.20.25	**Treated wood piles, 12" butt, 7" tip, 60' long**						**Unit: LF**
316219000160	Treated wood piles,12" butt,7" tip,60' long	1	LF	$24.79	$3.26	$3.83	$31.88
A1020.21.10	**Mobilization, equip, pile driving rig, minimum**						**EA**
015400801360	Mobilization, equip, pile driving rig, minimum	1.000	EA	$11,102.78	$0.00	$0.00	$11,102.78
A1020.21.15	**Mobilization, equip, pile driving rig, average**						**EA**
015400801380	Mobilization, equip, pile driving rig, average	1.000	EA	$22,207.65	$0.00	$0.00	$22,207.65
A1020.21.20	**Mobilization, equip, pile driving rig, maximum**						**EA**
015400801400	Mobilization, equip, pile driving rig, maximum	1.000	EA	$39,973.66	$0.00	$0.00	$39,973.66
A1020.22.10	**Pile test, 50 ton to 100 ton**						**EA**
316200101020	Pile test, 50 ton to 100 ton	1.000	EA	$20,674.50	$0.00	$0.00	$20,674.50
A1020.22.15	**Pile test, 50 ton to 300 ton**						**EA**
316200101060	Pile test, 50 ton to 300 ton	1.000	EA	$33,726.00	$0.00	$0.00	$33,726.00
A1020.22.20	**Pile test, 50 ton to 600 ton**						**EA**
316200101100	Pile test, 50 ton to 600 ton	1.000	EA	$49,376.25	$0.00	$0.00	$49,376.25

A1020.25 CAISSONS

		Quan.	Unit	Material	Labor	Equip.	Total
A1020.25.10	**Caisson, incl 3000# conc, in stable ground, 18" dia**						**Unit: LF**
316400101020	Caisson,incl 3000# conc,in stable ground,18" dia	1	LF	$17.77	$15.66	$18.40	$51.83
A1020.25.15	**Caisson, incl 3000# conc, in stable ground, 24" dia**						**Unit: LF**
316400101040	Caisson,incl 3000# conc,in stable ground,24" dia	1	LF	$28.42	$16.31	$19.17	$63.90
A1020.25.20	**Caisson, incl 3000# conc, in stable ground, 36" dia**						**Unit: LF**
316400101080	Caisson,incl 3000# conc,in stable ground,36" dia	1	LF	$60.57	$22.37	$26.29	$109.23
A1020.25.25	**Caisson, incl 3000# conc, in stable ground, 48" dia**						**Unit: LF**
316400101100	Caisson,incl 3000# conc,in stable ground,48" dia	1	LF	$108.20	$26.10	$30.67	$164.97
A1020.27.15	**Test, 50 ton to 300 ton**						**EA**
316200101060	Pile test, 50 ton to 300 ton	1.000	EA	$33,726.00	$0.00	$0.00	$33,726.00
A1020.27.20	**Test, 50 ton to 600 ton**						**EA**
316200101100	Pile test, 50 ton to 600 ton	1.000	EA	$49,376.25	$0.00	$0.00	$49,376.25
A1020.21.15	**Mobilization, equip, rig, average**						**EA**
015400801380	Mobilization, equip, pile driving rig, average	1.000	EA	$22,207.65	$0.00	$0.00	$22,207.65
A1020.21.20	**Mobilization, equip, rig, maximum**						**EA**
015400801400	Mobilization, equip, pile driving rig, maximum	1.000	EA	$39,973.66	$0.00	$0.00	$39,973.66

All prices are updated to January 1, 2021 and are national averages.
For more in-depth information contact Design, Cost and Data at 800-533-5680, or go to www.DCD.com

455

A   SUBSTRUCTURE

A1020   SPECIAL FOUNDATIONS

A1020.30   GRADE BEAM

		Quan.	Unit	Material	Labor	Equip.	Total
A1020.30.10	**GRADE BEAM, 1' Wide x 2' High**						**LF**
032100801040	Reinforcing,grade beams,#7-#8	0.05	TON	$78.57	$39.18	$0.00	$117.75
312333603820	Spread dumped fill or gravel,by hand w/air tamp	6	SY	$0.00	$6.13	$2.04	$8.17
312333603740	Spread dumped fill or gravel,no comp,6" layers	2	SY	$0,00	$1.69	$2.00	$3.69
312333601140	Trenching,hydraulic excavator,1/2 cy,medium soil	0.75	CY	$0.00	$1.84	$2.40	$4.24
033500104160	Break ties and patch holes	2	SF	$0.00	$2.04	$0.00	$2.04
033100601120	Place conc,grade beam,3000# or 4000#,by pump	0.07	CY	$10.38	$2.68	$1.84	$14.90
031113701100	Job built,grade beam forms,5 uses	4	SF	$4.10	$21.75	$0.00	$25.85
031003004030	Snap ties,long-end with washers, 12" long	1	EA	$2.26	$0.00	$0.00	$2.26
033500104020	Wall finishes,burlap rub,w/cement paste	4	SF	$0.53	$3.41	$0.00	$3.94
				$95.84	**$78.72**	**$8.28**	**$182.84**

		Quan.	Unit	Material	Labor	Equip.	Total
A1020.30.25	**GRADE BEAM, 18" Wide x 3' High** ....**Unit: LF**						
033500104160	Break ties and patch holes	2	SF	$0.00	$2.04	$0.00	$2.04
031113701100	Job built,grade beam forms,5 uses	6	SF	$6.15	$32.62	$0.00	$38.77
312333603820	Spread dumped fill or gravel,by hand w/air tamp	6	SY	$0.00	$6.13	$2.04	$8.17
312333603740	Spread dumped fill or gravel,no comp,6" layers	2	SY	$0.00	$1.69	$2.00	$3.69
312333601140	Trenching,hydraulic excavator,1/2 cy,medium soil	1.8	CY	$0.00	$4.42	$5.76	$10.18
032100801040	Reinforcing,grade beams,#7-#8	0.12	TON	$188.56	$94.02	$0.00	$282.58
031003004030	Snap ties,long-end with washers, 12" long	1	EA	$2.26	$0.00	$0.00	$2.26
033100601120	Place conc,grade beam,3000# or 4000#,by pump	0.18	CY	$26.70	$6.90	$4.72	$38.32
033500104020	Wall finishes,burlap rub,w/cement paste	6	SF	$0.79	$5.11	$0.00	$5.90
				$224.46	**$152.93**	**$14.52**	**$391.91**

All prices are updated to January 1, 2021 and are national averages.
For more in-depth information contact Design, Cost and Data at 800-533-5680, or go to www.DCD.com

456

A SUBSTRUCTURE

A1030   SLAB ON GRADE

A1030.10 SLAB ON GRADE

		Quan.	Unit	Material	Labor	Equip.	Total
A1030.10.05	**SLAB ON GRADE, 4" thick, 20' by 20'** ....**Unit: SF**						
033500101020	Concrete finish,broom,screed	1	SF	$0.00	$0.64	$0.00	$0.64
312313104030	Prepare and roll subbase,average	0.111	SY	$0.00	$0.05	$0.06	$0.11
312313103020	Base course,bank run gravel,4" deep	0.111	SY	$0.35	$0.04	$0.05	$0.44
033500101060	Concrete finish,float	1	SF	$0.00	$0.85	$0.00	$0.85
033100802040	Place conc,slab/mat,3500# or 4000#,by pump	0.013	CY	$1.93	$0.28	$0.19	$2.40
032100901000	Reinforcing,slab,bars,#3-#4	0.001	TON	$1.88	$1.11	$0.00	$2.99
031124205040	Metal formwork,straight edge,4" high	0.1	LF	$2.35	$0.41	$0.00	$2.76
072600101010	Vapor barrier,polyethylene,6 mil	1	SF	$0.08	$0.26	$0.00	$0.34
				$6.59	**$3.64**	**$0.30**	**$10.53**
A1030.10.10	**SLAB ON GRADE, 6" thick, 20' by 20'** ....**Unit: SF**						
032100901020	Reinforcing,slab,bars,#5-#6	0.002	TON	$3.31	$1.90	$0.00	$5.21
312313103020	Base course,bank run gravel,4" deep	0.111	SY	$0.35	$0.04	$0.05	$0.44
312313104030	Prepare and roll subbase,average	0.111	SY	$0.00	$0.05	$0.06	$0.11
072600101010	Vapor barrier,polyethylene,6 mil	1	SF	$0.08	$0.26	$0.00	$0.34
033100802040	Place conc,slab/mat,3500# or 4000#,by pump	0.019	CY	$2.82	$0.42	$0.28	$3.52
031113904004	Mat foundation form,job built,edge,6" high,5 use	0.1	LF	$0.10	$0.50	$0.00	$0.60
033500101060	Concrete finish,float	1	SF	$0.00	$0.85	$0.00	$0.85
033500101020	Concrete finish,broom,screed	1	SF	$0.00	$0.64	$0.00	$0.64
				$6.66	**$4.66**	**$0.39**	**$11.71**
A1030.10.20	**SLAB ON GRADE, 8" thick, 20' by 20'** ....**Unit: SF**						
033500101060	Concrete finish,float	1	SF	$0.00	$0.85	$0.00	$0.85
312313104030	Prepare and roll subbase,average	0.111	SY	$0.00	$0.05	$0.06	$0.11
072600101010	Vapor barrier,polyethylene,6 mil	1	SF	$0.08	$0.26	$0.00	$0.34
033500101020	Concrete finish,broom,screed	1	SF	$0.00	$0.64	$0.00	$0.64
033100802040	Place conc,slab/mat,3500# or 4000#,by pump	0.025	CY	$3.71	$0.55	$0.38	$4.64
032100901020	Reinforcing,slab,bars,#5-#6	0.003	TON	$4.97	$2.85	$0.00	$7.82
031113904014	Mat foundation form,job built,edge,12" high,5 use	0.1	LF	$0.09	$0.54	$0.00	$0.63
312313103020	Base course,bank run gravel,4" deep	0.111	SY	$0.35	$0.04	$0.05	$0.44
				$9.20	**$5.78**	**$0.49**	**$15.47**

All prices are updated to January 1, 2021 and are national averages.
For more in-depth information contact Design, Cost and Data at 800-533-5680, or go to www.DCD.com

457

B SHELL

All prices are updated to January 1, 2021 and are national averages.
For more in-depth information contact Design, Cost and Data at 800-533-5680, or go to www.DCD.com

458

B SHELL

B1010 FLOOR CONSTRUCTION

B1010.10 COLUMNS, CONCRETE

		Quan.	Unit	Material	Labor	Equip.	Total
B1010.10.10	**C.I.P. COLUMNS, SQUARE, 12" by 12", 10' high** .... **EA**						
033500104020	Wall finishes,burlap rub,w/cement paste	40	SF	$5.27	$34.05	$0.00	$39.32
031113201290	Job built,column forms,12"x 12",5 uses	40	SF	$52.89	$414.22	$0.00	$467.11
031124202070	Chamfer strips,wood,1" wide	40	LF	$20.21	$57.99	$0.00	$78.20
032100301020	Reinforcing,columns,#9-#10	0.086	TON	$134.61	$104.14	$0.00	$238.75
033100202020	Place concrete,columns,2500#-3500#,by pump	0.37	CY	$54.89	$18.90	$12.95	$86.74
				$267.87	**$629.30**	**$12.95**	**$910.12**

		Quan.	Unit	Material	Labor	Equip.	Total
B1010.10.15	**C.I.P. COLUMNS, ROUND, 1' dia., 10' high** .... **EA**						
033500104020	Wall finishes,burlap rub,w/cement paste	31.4	SF	$4.14	$26.73	$0.00	$30.87
033100202020	Place concrete,columns,2500#-3500#,by pump	0.291	CY	$43.17	$14.86	$10.18	$68.21
031113202060	Column,round fiber form,1 use,12" dia	10	LF	$71.32	$133.14	$0.00	$204.46
032100301020	Reinforcing,columns,#9-#10	0.086	TON	$134.61	$104.14	$0.00	$238.75
				$253.24	**$278.87**	**$10.18**	**$542.29**

B1010.20 COLUMNS, STEEL

		Quan.	Unit	Material	Labor	Equip.	Total
B1010.20.10	**COLUMNS, W Series (Wide Flange), 8" by 8", 10' high** .... **EA**						
051200100140	Beams and girders,A-36,bolted	0.15	TON	$461.18	$53.38	$62.73	$577.29
051200101040	Column base plates,over 150 lb each	150	LB	$212.85	$90.00	$0.00	$302.85
078100101040	Fireproofing,sprayed on,1" thick,on columns	3.33	SF	$3.04	$3.40	$0.00	$6.44
				$677.07	**$146.78**	**$62.73**	**$886.58**

		Quan.	Unit	Material	Labor	Equip.	Total
B1010.20.15	**COLUMNS, W Series (Wide Flange), 12" by 12", 10' high** .... **EA**						
078100101040	Fireproofing,sprayed on,1" thick,on columns	5	SF	$4.57	$5.11	$0.00	$9.68
051200100140	Beams and girders,A-36,bolted	0.225	TON	$691.76	$80.07	$94.09	$865.92
051200101040	Column base plates,over 150 lb each	150	LB	$212.85	$90.00	$0.00	$302.85
				$909.18	**$175.18**	**$94.09**	**$1,178.45**

All prices are updated to January 1, 2021 and are national averages.
For more in-depth information contact Design, Cost and Data at 800-533-5680, or go to www.DCD.com

459

B SHELL

B1010 FLOOR CONSTRUCTION

B1010.25 COLUMNS, WOOD

		Quan.	Unit	Material	Labor	Equip.	Total
B1010.25.10	**COLUMNS, Wood 8" by 8", 10' high**...						**EA**
061300101440	Mill framing,column,douglas fir,8 x 8	10	LF	$102.08	$76.62	$52.50	$231.20
051200101020	Column base plates,up to 150 lb each	50	LB	$86.90	$24.00	$0.00	$110.90
060523101100	Anchor bolts,threaded,incl nuts,3/4" D,15" L	2	EA	$20.81	$8.15	$0.00	$28.96
				$209.79	**$108.77**	**$52.50**	**$371.06**
B1010.25.15	**COLUMNS, Wood 12" by 12", 10' high**..						**EA**
051200101020	Column base plates,up to 150 lb each	50	LB	$86.90	$24.00	$0.00	$110.90
060523101100	Anchor bolts,threaded,incl nuts,3/4" D,15" L	2	EA	$20.81	$8.15	$0.00	$28.96
061300101480	Mill framing,column,douglas fir,12 x 12	10	LF	$221.01	$85.13	$58.33	$364.47
				$328.72	**$117.28**	**$58.33**	**$504.33**

B1010.30 COLUMNS, PRECAST

		Quan.	Unit	Material	Labor	Equip.	Total
B1010.30.10	**COLUMNS Precast, 10" by 10", 10' high**..						**EA**
051200101020	Column base plates,up to 150 lb each	50	LB	$86.90	$24.00	$0.00	$110.90
034100200100	Prestressed concrete columns,10"x 10',10' long	1	EA	$331.23	$78.29	$92.00	$501.52
				$418.13	**$102.29**	**$92.00**	**$612.42**
B1010.30.15	**COLUMNS Precast, 12" by 12", 20' high**..						**EA**
051200101020	Column base plates,up to 150 lb each	50	LB	$86.90	$24.00	$0.00	$110.90
034100200240	Prestressed concrete columns,12"x 12",20' long	1	EA	$915.78	$97.86	$115.00	$1,128.64
				$1,002.68	**$121.86**	**$115.00**	**$1,239.54**

All prices are updated to January 1, 2021 and are national averages.
For more in-depth information contact Design, Cost and Data at 800-533-5680, or go to www.DCD.com

460

B SHELL

B1010   FLOOR CONSTRUCTION

B1010.50 FLOOR, CONCRETE

		Quan.	Unit	Material	Labor	Equip.	Total
B1010.50.10	**FLOOR SYSTEM, C.I.P. Beams & Slab 20' by 20' Bay Size**						**SF**
033100302020	Place elev slab conc,3500# or 4000#,by pump	0.031	CY	$4.60	$0.73	$0.50	$5.83
033500101020	Concrete finish,broom,screed	1	SF	$0.00	$0.64	$0.00	$0.64
032100401060	Reinforcing,elevated slab,#9-#10	0.007	TON	$10.96	$4.24	$0.00	$15.20
032100101012	Reinforcing,beams-girders,#9-#10	0.003	TON	$4.70	$2.85	$0.00	$7.55
031500106220	Reinf access,chairs,3" high,plain	2	EA	$3.41	$3.33	$0.00	$6.74
031113401100	Job built,slab forms,drop panel,5 uses	0.81	SF	$1.38	$3.64	$0.00	$5.02
031113002100	Job built,beam side forms,5 uses	0.6	SF	$0.96	$3.56	$0.00	$4.52
031113001120	Job built,beam bottom forms,5 uses	0.2	SF	$0.36	$1.86	$0.00	$2.22
015400101180	Staging/scaffolding,measured by SF surface,ave	1	SF	$1.11	$0.00	$0.00	$1.11
033500101060	Concrete finish,float	1	SF	$0.00	$0.85	$0.00	$0.85
				$27.48	**$21.70**	**$0.50**	**$49.68**

B1010.60 FLOOR, PRECAST

		Quan.	Unit	Material	Labor	Equip.	Total
B1010.60.10	**FLOOR SYSTEM, Precast Beam & Slab with Topping 20' by 20' Bay Size**						**SF**
033500101060	Concrete finish,float	1	SF	$0.00	$0.85	$0.00	$0.85
031113301080	Job built curb forms,6" high,5 uses	0.2	LF	$0.19	$1.09	$0.00	$1.28
034100300110	Prestr flat slab,6" thk,4' w,20' span,110 psf	1	SF	$20.17	$1.63	$1.92	$23.72
034100103340	Precast beams,girder,joists,5000 lb/lf LL,20' span	0.2	LF	$32.13	$1.57	$1.84	$35.54
033100302020	Place elev slab conc,3500# or 4000#,by pump	0.012	CY	$1.78	$0.28	$0.19	$2.25
032100905080	Reinforcing,slab,galv mesh,4x4,w4.0xw4.0	1.1	SF	$1.38	$0.61	$0.00	$1.99
031500106220	Reinf access,chairs,3" high,plain	1	EA	$1.71	$1.66	$0.00	$3.37
033500101040	Concrete finish,broom,darby	1	SF	$0.00	$0.64	$0.00	$0.64
				$57.36	**$8.33**	**$3.95**	**$69.64**

B1010.70 FLOOR, CONCRETE & STEEL ON WALL

		Quan.	Unit	Material	Labor	Equip.	Total
B1010.70.10	**FLOOR SYSTEM, Concrete Deck on Open Web Joists on Wall System 30' Span**						**SF**
031500106220	Reinf access,chairs,3" high,plain	1	EA	$1.71	$1.66	$0.00	$3.37
032100905080	Reinforcing,slab,galv mesh,4x4,w4.0xw4.0	1.05	SF	$1.32	$0.58	$0.00	$1.90
033100302020	Place elev slab conc,3500# or 4000#,by pump	0.012	CY	$1.78	$0.28	$0.19	$2.25
033500101040	Concrete finish,broom,darby	1	SF	$0.00	$0.64	$0.00	$0.64
033500101060	Concrete finish,float	1	SF	$0.00	$0.85	$0.00	$0.85
053100101020	Open type decking,galv,1-1/2" d,18 ga	1.05	SF	$3.88	$0.69	$0.80	$5.37
				$8.69	**$4.70**	**$0.99**	**$14.38**

All prices are updated to January 1, 2021 and are national averages.
For more in-depth information contact Design, Cost and Data at 800-533-5680, or go to www.DCD.com

461

B SHELL

B1010 FLOOR CONSTRUCTION

B1010.75 FLOOR, CONCRETE & W SERIES STEEL

		Quan.	Unit	Material	Labor	Equip.	Total
B1010.75.10	**FLOOR SYSTEM, Concrete on W (Wide Flange) System 20' by 20' Bay Size**						**SF**
031113301080	Job built curb forms,6" high,5 uses	0.2	LF	$0.19	$1.09	$0.00	$1.28
078100101120	Fireproofing,1-1/2" thick,on beams	1.93	SF	$3.10	$2.82	$0.00	$5.92
053100101020	Open type decking,galv,1-1/2" d,18 ga	1	SF	$3.69	$0.65	$0.77	$5.11
051200100140	Beams and girders,A-36,bolted	0.015	TON	$46.12	$5.34	$6.27	$57.73
033500101060	Concrete finish,float	1	SF	$0.00	$0.85	$0.00	$0.85
033500101040	Concrete finish,broom,darby	1	SF	$0.00	$0.64	$0.00	$0.64
033100302020	Place elev slab conc,3500# or 4000#,by pump	0.012	CY	$1.78	$0.28	$0.19	$2.25
031500106220	Reinf access,chairs,3" high,plain	1	EA	$1.71	$1.66	$0.00	$3.37
032100401020	Reinforcing,elevated slab,#5-#6	0.002	TON	$3.30	$1.48	$0.00	$4.78
				$59.89	**$14.81**	**$7.23**	**$81.93**

B1010.80 FLOOR, LAMINATED WOOD

		Quan.	Unit	Material	Labor	Equip.	Total
B1010.80.10	**FLOOR SYSTEM, Laminated Wood System 20' by 20' Bay Size**						**SF**
060523101284	Joist and beam hangers,18 ga,2 x 10	0.2	EA	$0.45	$1.45	$0.00	$1.90
061813103550	Laminated beams, gluelam beam, 9-1/2" wide x 30"	0.1	LF	$9.57	$0.47	$0.32	$10.36
061813103280	Laminated beams, gluelam beam, 7-1/2" wide x 18"	0.15	LF	$10.17	$0.61	$0.42	$11.20
061100301220	Floor joists,16" oc,2x10	1	SF	$1.62	$1.12	$0.00	$2.74
061600102080	Sub-flooring,plywood,CDX,3/4" thick	1	SF	$1.60	$1.09	$0.00	$2.69
				$23.41	**$4.74**	**$0.74**	**$28.89**

B1010.85 FLOOR, WOOD

		Quan.	Unit	Material	Labor	Equip.	Total
B1010.85.10	**FLOOR SYSTEM, Wooden Beams & Joists 16' by 16' Bay Size**						**SF**
060523101284	Joist and beam hangers,18 ga,2 x 10	0.25	EA	$0.57	$1.81	$0.00	$2.38
061100301220	Floor joists,16" oc,2x10	1	SF	$1.62	$1.12	$0.00	$2.74
061300101044	Mill framing,beam,douglas fir,6 x 12	0.188	LF	$2.20	$1.07	$0.73	$4.00
061300101090	Mill framing,beam,douglas fir,8 x 16	0.125	LF	$2.51	$0.77	$0.52	$3.80
061600102080	Sub-flooring,plywood,CDX,3/4" thick	1	SF	$1.60	$1.09	$0.00	$2.69
				$8.50	**$5.86**	**$1.25**	**$15.61**

All prices are updated to January 1, 2021 and are national averages.
For more in-depth information contact Design, Cost and Data at 800-533-5680, or go to www.DCD.com

462

B SHELL

B1020 ROOF CONSTRUCTION

B1020.15 ROOF, CONCRETE

		Quan.	Unit	Material	Labor	Equip.	Total
B1020.15.10	**ROOF SYSTEM, W Series Structural System, Concrete Deck, 20' by 20' Bay Size ...... SF**						
031500106220	Reinf access,chairs,3" high,plain	1	EA	$1.71	$1.66	$0.00	$3.37
078100101120	Fireproofing,1-1/2" thick,on beams	1.7	SF	$2.73	$2.48	$0.00	$5.21
053100101020	Open type decking,galv,1-1/2" d,18 ga	1	SF	$3.69	$0.65	$0.77	$5.11
051200100140	Beams and girders,A-36,bolted	0.012	TON	$36.89	$4.27	$5.02	$46.18
033500101040	Concrete finish,broom,darby	1	SF	$0.00	$0.64	$0.00	$0.64
032100905080	Reinforcing,slab,galv mesh,4x4,w4.0xw4.0	1	SF	$1.26	$0.56	$0.00	$1.82
031113301080	Job built curb forms,6" high,5 uses	1	LF	$0.97	$5.44	$0.00	$6.41
033100302020	Place elev slab conc,3500# or 4000#,by pump	0.01	CY	$1.48	$0.24	$0.16	$1.88
				$48.73	**$15.94**	**$5.95**	**$70.62**

B1020.20 ROOF, CONCRETE & STEEL JOISTS ON WALLS

		Quan.	Unit	Material	Labor	Equip.	Total
B1020.20.10	**ROOF SYSTEM, Concrete Deck on Open Web Joists on Wall System 30' Span .... SF**						
032100905080	Reinforcing,slab,galv mesh,4x4,w4.0xw4.0	1.05	SF	$1.32	$0.58	$0.00	$1.90
053100101020	Open type decking,galv,1-1/2" d,18 ga	1.05	SF	$3.88	$0.69	$0.80	$5.37
052100100120	Joist,K series	0.003	TON	$6.10	$0.78	$0.92	$7.80
033500101040	Concrete finish,broom,darby	1	SF	$0.00	$0.64	$0.00	$0.64
031500106220	Reinf access,chairs,3" high,plain	1	EA	$1.71	$1.66	$0.00	$3.37
033100302020	Place elev slab conc,3500# or 4000#,by pump	0.012	CY	$1.78	$0.28	$0.19	$2.25
				$14.79	**$4.63**	**$1.91**	**$21.33**

B1020.25 ROOF, CONCRETE & STEEL JOISTS & GIRDERS

		Quan.	Unit	Material	Labor	Equip.	Total
B1020.25.10	**ROOF SYSTEM, Concrete Deck & Open Web Joists and Girders 20' by 20' Bay Size .. SF**						
052100100120	Joist,K series	0.004	TON	$8.13	$1.04	$1.23	$10.40
053100101020	Open type decking,galv,1-1/2" d,18 ga	1.05	SF	$3.88	$0.69	$0.80	$5.37
033500101040	Concrete finish,broom,darby	1	SF	$0.00	$0.64	$0.00	$0.64
033100302020	Place elev slab conc,3500# or 4000#,by pump	0.012	CY	$1.78	$0.28	$0.19	$2.25
032100905080	Reinforcing,slab,galv mesh,4x4,w4.0xw4.0	1.05	SF	$1.32	$0.58	$0.00	$1.90
031500106220	Reinf access,chairs,3" high,plain	1	EA	$1.71	$1.66	$0.00	$3.37
				$16.82	**$4.89**	**$2.22**	**$23.93**

All prices are updated to January 1, 2021 and are national averages.
For more in-depth information contact Design, Cost and Data at 800-533-5680, or go to www.DCD.com

463

B SHELL

B2010 EXTERIOR WALLS

B2010.10 WALL

		Quan.	Unit	Material	Labor	Equip.	Total
B2010.10.10	**WALL SYSTEM, Brick Veneer on Concrete Backup Block, 10 ' high**						**SF**
042200100160	CMU,lightweight block,hollow,load bearing,8"	1	SF	$2.74	$5.18	$0.00	$7.92
040523101120	Horizontal joint reinf,truss type,6" wide,8" wall	1	LF	$0.21	$0.26	$0.00	$0.47
040523103440	Brick anchor,corrugated,3-1/2" long,16 ga	1	EA	$0.57	$1.04	$0.00	$1.61
040523501020	Masonry flashing,0.030" elastomeric	0.1	SF	$0.13	$0.41	$0.00	$0.54
042113101020	Standard brick,red (6.4/sf),veneer	1	SF	$5.67	$10.37	$0.00	$16.04
				$9.32	**$17.26**	**$0.00**	**$26.58**
B2010.10.15	**WALL SYSTEM, Brick Veneer on Metal Stud Wall, 10 ' high**						**SF**
071100101140	Silicone dampprofing,spray on,brick,2 coats	1	SF	$1.07	$0.51	$0.00	$1.58
092116100144	Metal stud,20 ga,3-5/8",24" oc	1	SF	$0.47	$1.09	$0.00	$1.56
072116102120	Insul,wall,foil back,3",R11	1	SF	$0.72	$0.57	$0.00	$1.29
061600307000	Wall sheathing,gypsum,1/2" thick	1	SF	$0.59	$1.00	$0.00	$1.59
042113101020	Standard brick,red (6.4/sf),veneer	1	SF	$5.67	$10.37	$0.00	$16.04
040523103440	Brick anchor,corrugated,3-1/2" long,16 ga	1	EA	$0.57	$1.04	$0.00	$1.61
040523501020	Masonry flashing,0.030" elastomeric	0.1	SF	$0.13	$0.41	$0.00	$0.54
				$9.22	**$14.99**	**$0.00**	**$24.21**
B2010.10.20	**WALL SYSTEM, Stucco on Metal Stud Wall, 10 ' high**						**SF**
040523501020	Masonry flashing,0.030" elastomeric	0.1	SF	$0.13	$0.41	$0.00	$0.54
061600307000	Wall sheathing,gypsum,1/2" thick	1	SF	$0.59	$1.00	$0.00	$1.59
071113100120	Building paper,15# felt	1	SF	$0.20	$2.04	$0.00	$2.24
072116102120	Insul,wall,foil back,3",R11	1	SF	$0.72	$0.57	$0.00	$1.29
092116100144	Metal stud,20 ga,3-5/8",24" oc	1	SF	$0.47	$1.09	$0.00	$1.56
092236202400	Stucco lath,paper backed,max	1	SY	$6.22	$9.32	$0.00	$15.54
092400103000	Stucco,portland,3 coats,1" thick,sand finish	1	SY	$8.44	$26.42	$0.00	$34.86
				$16.77	**$40.85**	**$0.00**	**$57.62**
B2010.10.25	**WALL SYSTEM, C.I.P. Concrete, 10 ' high**						**SF**
033100901040	Place wall conc,2500# or 3000#,to 8',by pump	0.037	CY	$5.17	$1.89	$1.30	$8.36
033500104020	Wall finishes,burlap rub,w/cement paste	2	SF	$0.26	$1.70	$0.00	$1.96
033500104160	Break ties and patch holes	2	SF	$0.00	$2.04	$0.00	$2.04
031114103290	Wall forms,ext,job built,over 8' high wall,5 uses	2	SF	$3.25	$13.05	$0.00	$16.30
031003004030	Snap ties,long-end with washers, 12" long	1	EA	$2.26	$0.00	$0.00	$2.26
032101101040	Reinforcing,wall,#7-#8	0.005	TON	$7.86	$3.70	$0.00	$11.56
				$18.80	**$22.38**	**$1.30**	**$42.48**

All prices are updated to January 1, 2021 and are national averages.
For more in-depth information contact Design, Cost and Data at 800-533-5680, or go to www.DCD.com

464

B SHELL

B2010   EXTERIOR WALLS

B2010.10 WALL (Cont)

	Quan.	Unit	Material	Labor	Equip.	Total
B2010.10.30 **WALL SYSTEM, Precast wall, 8'x 20', gray cem, liner fin, 8" wall**						**SF**
034500100160 Precast wall,8'x 20',gray cem,liner fin,8" wall	1	SF	$19.31	$1.22	$1.44	$21.97
B2010.10.35 **WALL SYSTEM, Tilt-up Concrete, 20' wide by 20' high, 12" thick**						**SF**
033500101040 Concrete finish,broom,darby	1	SF	$0.00	$0.64	$0.00	$0.64
033500101060 Concrete finish,float	1	SF	$0.00	$0.85	$0.00	$0.85
033100802060 Place conc,slab/mat,3500# or 4000#,by hand buggy	0.025	CY	$3.71	$0.85	$0.00	$4.56
032100901040 Reinforcing,slab,bars,#7-#8	0.002	TON	$3.14	$1.66	$0.00	$4.80
031113905100 Formwork for openings,5 uses	0.16	SF	$0.23	$1.49	$0.00	$1.72
031113904014 Mat foundation form,job built,edge,12" high,5 use	0.2	LF	$0.18	$1.09	$0.00	$1.27
			$7.26	**$6.58**	**$0.00**	**$13.84**
B2010.10.40 **WALL SYSTEM, Concrete Block, 10 ' high**						**SF**
040523101020 Standard steel bar reinforcing,horizontal,#3 - #4	2	LB	$1.28	$4.98	$0.00	$6.26
040523501020 Masonry flashing,0.030" elastomeric	0.1	SF	$0.13	$0.41	$0.00	$0.54
042200104100 CMU,hollow,split ground face,12"	1	SF	$5.28	$6.22	$0.00	$11.50
040516103060 Grouting concrete block,12"	1	SF	$2.71	$1.60	$1.40	$5.71
			$9.40	**$13.21**	**$1.40**	**$24.01**

All prices are updated to January 1, 2021 and are national averages.
For more in-depth information contact Design, Cost and Data at 800-533-5680, or go to www.DCD.com

465

B SHELL

B2020 EXTERIOR WINDOWS

B2020.10 STEEL WINDOWS

		Quan.	Unit	Material	Labor	Equip.	Total
B2020.10.10	**Steel windows, primed, casements, operable, minimum**						**Unit: SF**
085123101020	Steel windows,primed,casements,operable,minimum	1	SF	$54.23	$4.24	$0.00	$58.47
B2020.10.15	**Steel windows, primed, casements, operable, maximum**						**Unit: SF**
085123101040	Steel windows,primed,casements,operable,maximum	1	SF	$81.27	$4.80	$0.00	$86.07
B2020.10.20	**Steel windows, primed, casements, fixed sash**						**Unit: SF**
085123101060	Steel windows,primed,casements,fixed sash	1	SF	$43.34	$3.60	$0.00	$46.94
B2020.10.25	**Steel windows, primed, double hung**						**Unit: SF**
085123101080	Steel windows,primed,double hung	1	SF	$81.27	$4.00	$0.00	$85.27
B2020.10.30	**Industrial windows, horizontally pivoted sash**						**Unit: SF**
085123101120	Industrial windows,horizontally pivoted sash	1	SF	$68.97	$4.80	$0.00	$73.77
B2020.10.35	**Industrial windows, fixed sash**						**Unit: SF**
085123101130	Industrial windows,fixed sash	1	SF	$54.22	$4.00	$0.00	$58.22
B2020.10.40	**Industrial windows, security sash, operable**						**Unit: SF**
085123101140	Industrial windows,security sash,operable	1	SF	$86.14	$4.80	$0.00	$90.94
B2020.10.45	**Industrial windows, security sash, fixed**						**Unit: SF**
085123101150	Industrial windows,security sash,fixed	1	SF	$76.39	$4.00	$0.00	$80.39
B2020.10.50	**Picture window**						**Unit: SF**
085123101155	Picture window	1	SF	$36.98	$4.00	$0.00	$40.98
B2020.10.55	**Projecting sash window, minimum**						**Unit: SF**
085123101170	Projecting sash window,minimum	1	SF	$64.05	$4.50	$0.00	$68.55
B2020.10.60	**Projecting sash window, maximum**						**Unit: SF**
085123101180	Projecting sash window,maximum	1	SF	$78.80	$4.50	$0.00	$83.30
B2020.10.65	**Mullions**						**Unit: SF**
085123101930	Mullions	1	LF	$16.88	$3.60	$0.00	$20.48

B2020.15 ALUMINUM WINDOWS

		Quan.	Unit	Material	Labor	Equip.	Total
B2020.15.10	**Aluminum window, fixed, 6 Sf to 8 Sf**						**Unit: SF**
085113100240	Aluminum window,fixed,6 Sf to 8 Sf	1	SF	$19.21	$10.29	$0.00	$29.50
B2020.15.15	**Aluminum window, fixed 12 Sf to 16 Sf**						**Unit: SF**
085113100250	Aluminum window,fixed 12 Sf to 16 Sf	1	SF	$17.07	$8.00	$0.00	$25.07
B2020.15.20	**Aluminum window, projecting, 6 Sf to 8 Sf**						**Unit: SF**
085113100260	Aluminum window,projecting,6 Sf to 8 Sf	1	SF	$42.56	$18.00	$0.00	$60.56
B2020.15.25	**Aluminum window, projecting, 12 Sf to 16 Sf**						**Unit: SF**
085113100270	Aluminum window,projecting,12 Sf to 16 Sf	1	SF	$38.36	$12.00	$0.00	$50.36
B2020.15.30	**Aluminum window, horiz sliding, 6 Sf to 8 Sf**						**Unit: SF**
085113100280	Aluminum window,horiz sliding,6 Sf to 8 Sf	1	SF	$27.68	$9.00	$0.00	$36.68
B2020.15.35	**Aluminum window, horiz sliding, 12 Sf to 16 Sf**						**Unit: SF**
085113100290	Aluminum window,horiz sliding,12 Sf to 16 Sf	1	SF	$25.54	$7.20	$0.00	$32.74
B2020.15.40	**Aluminum window, double hung, 6 Sf to 8 Sf**						**Unit: SF**
085113101160	Aluminum window,double hung,6 Sf to 8 Sf	1	SF	$38.36	$14.40	$0.00	$52.76
B2020.15.45	**Aluminum window, double hung, 10 Sf to 12 Sf**						**Unit: SF**
085113101180	Aluminum window,double hung,10 Sf to 12 Sf	1	SF	$34.09	$12.00	$0.00	$46.09

All prices are updated to January 1, 2021 and are national averages.
For more in-depth information contact Design, Cost and Data at 800-533-5680, or go to www.DCD.com

466

B SHELL

B2020 EXTERIOR WINDOWS

B2020.30 STOREFRONT

		Quan.	Unit	Material	Labor	Equip.	Total
B2020.30.10	**Storefront, aluminum & glass, minimum**						**Unit: SF**
084100100140	Storefront,aluminum & glass,minimum	1	SF	$29.34	$9.00	$0.00	$38.34
B2020.30.15	**Storefront, aluminum & glass, average**						**Unit: SF**
084100100150	Storefront,aluminum & glass,average	1	SF	$43.66	$10.29	$0.00	$53.95
B2020.30.20	**Storefront, aluminum & glass, maximum**						**Unit: SF**
084100100160	Storefront,aluminum & glass,maximum	1	SF	$87.30	$12.00	$0.00	$99.30

B2020.35 WINDOW WALL

		Quan.	Unit	Material	Labor	Equip.	Total
B2020.35.10	**Window wall system, complete, minimum**						**Unit: SF**
084400103010	Window wall system,complete,minimum	1	SF	$42.64	$7.20	$0.00	$49.84
B2020.35.15	**Window wall system, complete, average**						**Unit: SF**
084400103030	Window wall system,complete,average	1	SF	$68.20	$8.00	$0.00	$76.20
B2020.35.20	**Window wall system, complete, maximum**						**Unit: SF**
084400103050	Window wall system,complete,maximum	1	SF	$157.76	$10.29	$0.00	$168.05

For bronze, add 20% to material
For stainless steel, add 50% to material

B2030 EXTERIOR DOORS

B2030.15 DOORS, WOOD

		Quan.	Unit	Material	Labor	Equip.	Total
B2030.15.10	**Wood Doors**						**Unit: EA**
087100101260	Hinges,4 x 4 butts,steel,standard	1.5	PAIR	$45.87	$0.00	$0.00	$45.87
099123304060	Int painting, trim, brush, second coat, avg	40	LF	$8.45	$8.38	$0.00	$16.83
099123303980	Int painting, trim, brush, first coat, avg	40	LF	$8.45	$9.90	$0.00	$18.35
099123302680	Int painting, doors, wood, brush, second coat, avg	42	SF	$6.65	$28.58	$0.00	$35.23
087100201300	Latchset,heavy duty,cylindrical	1	EA	$191.40	$40.78	$0.00	$232.18
081400900260	Door frame,pine,interior,3-0 x 7-0	1	EA	$140.66	$93.20	$0.00	$233.86
081400101970	Door,flush,solid core,1-3/4",birch,3-0 x 7-0	1	EA	$269.98	$81.55	$0.00	$351.53
062023101070	Molding,casing,wood,11/16 x 3-1/2	40	LF	$109.39	$124.27	$0.00	$233.66
099123302600	Int painting, doors, wood, brush, first coat, avg	42	SF	$8.87	$41.57	$0.00	$50.44
				$789.72	$428.23	$0.00	$1,217.95

All prices are updated to January 1, 2021 and are national averages.
For more in-depth information contact Design, Cost and Data at 800-533-5680, or go to www.DCD.com

467

B SHELL

B2030 EXTERIOR DOORS

B2030.20 DOORS, STEEL

		Quan.	Unit	Material	Labor	Equip.	Total
B2030.20.10	**Steel Doors**						**EA**
099113101840	Ext painting, doors, metal, roller, first coat, avg	42	SF	$7.21	$19.05	$0.00	$26.26
087100201300	Latchset, heavy duty, cylindrical	1	EA	$191.40	$40.78	$0.00	$232.18
099113102300	Ext painting, door frames, metal, brush, second coat, avg	20	LF	$4.22	$9.07	$0.00	$13.29
099113102220	Ext painting, door frames, metal, brush, first coat, avg	20	LF	$4.22	$17.01	$0.00	$21.23
087100101260	Hinges, 4 x 4 butts, steel, standard	1.5	PAIR	$45.87	$0.00	$0.00	$45.87
081113401550	Door frames, mtl, stk, 16 ga, 6-3/4"x 1-3/4", 3-0 x 7-0	1	EA	$198.96	$90.00	$0.00	$288.96
081113101240	Door, metal, flush hollow, 20 ga, 1-3/4", 3-0 x 7-0	1	EA	$498.04	$72.49	$0.00	$570.53
099113101920	Ext painting, doors, metal, roller, second coat, avg	42	SF	$7.21	$12.70	$0.00	$19.91
				$957.13	**$261.10**	**$0.00**	**$1,218.23**

B2030.25 DOORS, ALUMINUM

		Quan.	Unit	Material	Labor	Equip.	Total
B2030.25.10	**Alum door, narrow stile, single, 2-6 x 7-0**						**Unit: EA**
081116101520	Alum door, narrow stile, single, 2-6 x 7-0	1	EA	$939.63	$360.00	$0.00	$1,299.63
B2030.25.15	**Alum door, narrow stile, single, 3-0 x 7-0**						**Unit: EA**
081116101540	Alum door, narrow stile, single, 3-0 x 7-0	1	EA	$988.28	$360.00	$0.00	$1,348.28
B2030.25.20	**Alum door, narrow stile, single, 3-6 x 7-0**						**Unit: EA**
081116101560	Alum door, narrow stile, single, 3-6 x 7-0	1	EA	$1,012.61	$360.00	$0.00	$1,372.61
B2030.25.25	**Alum door, narrow stile, double, 5-0 x 7-0**						**Unit: EA**
081116101580	Alum door, narrow stile, double, 5-0 x 7-0	1	EA	$1,567.56	$720.00	$0.00	$2,287.56
B2030.25.30	**Alum door, narrow stile, double, 6-0 x 7-0**						**Unit: EA**
081116101600	Alum door, narrow stile, double, 6-0 x 7-0	1	EA	$1,591.88	$720.00	$0.00	$2,311.88
B2030.25.35	**Alum door, narrow stile, double, 7-0 x 7-0**						**Unit: EA**
081116101620	Alum door, narrow stile, double, 7-0 x 7-0	1	EA	$1,662.63	$720.00	$0.00	$2,382.63
B2030.25.40	**Alum door, wide stile, single, 2-6 x 7-0**						**Unit: EA**
081116101720	Alum door, wide stile, single, 2-6 x 7-0	1	EA	$1,316.52	$360.00	$0.00	$1,676.52
B2030.25.45	**Alum door, wide stile, single, 3-0 x 7-0**						**Unit: EA**
081116101740	Alum door, wide stile, single, 3-0 x 7-0	1	EA	$1,360.73	$360.00	$0.00	$1,720.73
B2030.25.50	**Alum door, wide stile, single, 3-6 x 7-0**						**Unit: EA**
081116101760	Alum door, wide stile, single, 3-6 x 7-0	1	EA	$1,402.95	$360.00	$0.00	$1,762.95
B2030.25.55	**Alum door, wide stile, double, 5-0 x 7-0**						**Unit: EA**
081116101780	Alum door, wide stile, double, 5-0 x 7-0	1	EA	$2,413.95	$720.00	$0.00	$3,133.95
B2030.25.60	**Alum door, wide stile, double, 6-0 x 7-0**						**Unit: EA**
081116101800	Alum door, wide stile, double, 6-0 x 7-0	1	EA	$2,524.50	$720.00	$0.00	$3,244.50
B2030.25.70	**Alum door, wide stile, double, 7-0 x 7-0**						**Unit: EA**
081116101820	Alum door, wide stile, double, 7-0 x 7-0	1	EA	$2,568.72	$720.00	$0.00	$3,288.72

All prices are updated to January 1, 2021 and are national averages.
For more in-depth information contact Design, Cost and Data at 800-533-5680, or go to www.DCD.com

468

B SHELL

B3010 ROOF COVERINGS

B3010.10 BUILT-UP

		Quan.	Unit	Material	Labor	Equip.	Total
B3010.10.10	**Built-Up Roofing, 20' by 20' Bay size**						**SF**
075113102110	Roofing,walkway,built-up,3'x 3'x 3/4" thick	1	SF	$3.82	$2.08	$0.00	$5.90
075113102280	Cant strip,4"x 4",mineral fiber	0.15	LF	$0.07	$0.23	$0.00	$0.30
072113101080	Insul,rigid,glass board,roof,1.63" thick,R6.67	1	SF	$1.40	$0.54	$0.00	$1.94
076200108640	Gravel stop,aluminum,0.032",8"	0.15	LF	$0.61	$0.36	$0.00	$0.97
075113101500	Roofing,built-up,felt incl gravel,3-ply	0.11	SQ	$13.26	$22.84	$0.00	$36.10
				$19.16	**$26.05**	**$0.00**	**$45.21**

B3010.15 MEMBRANE

		Quan.	Unit	Material	Labor	Equip.	Total
B3010.15.10	**Membrane Roofing, 20' by 20' Bay size**						**SF**
075300108100	Walkway for membrane roofs,1/2" thick	1	SF	$2.70	$2.08	$0.00	$4.78
076200108640	Gravel stop,aluminum,0.032",8"	0.15	LF	$0.61	$0.36	$0.00	$0.97
075300108000	Ballast, 3/4" through 1-1/2" dia. river gravel,	1	SF	$0.52	$0.62	$0.00	$1.14
075300102110	Elastic sheet roofing,epdm rubber,60 mil	1	SF	$2.44	$0.78	$0.00	$3.22
075113102280	Cant strip,4"x 4",mineral fiber	0.15	LF	$0.07	$0.23	$0.00	$0.30
072113101080	Insul,rigid,glass board,roof,1.63" thick,R6.67	1	SF	$1.40	$0.54	$0.00	$1.94
				$7.74	**$4.61**	**$0.00**	**$12.35**

All prices are updated to January 1, 2021 and are national averages.
For more in-depth information contact Design, Cost and Data at 800-533-5680, or go to www.DCD.com

469

All prices are updated to January 1, 2021 and are national averages.
For more in-depth information contact Design, Cost and Data at 800-533-5680, or go to www.DCD.com

470

C INTERIORS

C1010 INTERIOR PARTITIONS

C1010.10 MASONRY

		Quan.	Unit	Material	Labor	Equip.	Total
C1010.10.10	**Concrete Block Partitions**						**SF**
042200100160	CMU,lightweight block,hollow,load bearing,8"	1	SF	$2.74	$5.18	$0.00	$7.92
092300101020	Gypsum plaster,trowel finish,2 coats,walls	0.11	SY	$0.47	$1.97	$0.00	$2.44
096516101020	Vinyl cove molding,6" high	0.2	LF	$0.50	$0.26	$0.00	$0.76
099123304180	Int painting, walls, roller, first coat, avg	1	SF	$0.17	$0.20	$0.00	$0.37
099123304260	Int painting, walls, roller, second coat, avg	1	SF	$0.17	$0.18	$0.00	$0.35
040523101120	Horizontal joint reinf,truss type,6" wide,8" wall	1	LF	$0.21	$0.26	$0.00	$0.47
				$4.26	**$8.05**	**$0.00**	**$12.31**

C1010.15 DRYWALL

		Quan.	Unit	Material	Labor	Equip.	Total
C1010.15.10	**Drywall Partitions/Metal Stud Framing**						**SF**
096516101020	Vinyl cove molding,6" high	0.2	LF	$0.50	$0.26	$0.00	$0.76
099123304180	Int painting, walls, roller, first coat, avg	1	SF	$0.17	$0.20	$0.00	$0.37
092900100400	Drywall,1/2" thick,nailed,walls	1	SF	$0.39	$0.59	$0.00	$0.98
092116100142	Metal stud,20 ga,3-5/8",16" oc	1	SF	$0.63	$1.30	$0.00	$1.93
092900101224	Drywall,taping & finishing joints,average	1	SF	$0.07	$0.54	$0.00	$0.61
099123304260	Int painting, walls, roller, second coat, avg	1	SF	$0.17	$0.18	$0.00	$0.35
				$1.93	**$3.07**	**$0.00**	**$5.00**

C1010.20 PLASTER

		Quan.	Unit	Material	Labor	Equip.	Total
C1010.20.10	**Plaster Partitions/Metal Stud Framing**						**SF**
099123304260	Int painting, walls, roller, second coat, avg	1	SF	$0.17	$0.18	$0.00	$0.35
092116100142	Metal stud,20 ga,3-5/8",16" oc	1	SF	$0.63	$1.30	$0.00	$1.93
092236101090	Gypsum lath,plain,1/2" thick,clipped	0.11	SY	$0.54	$0.40	$0.00	$0.94
092300101020	Gypsum plaster,trowel finish,2 coats,walls	0.11	SY	$0.47	$1.97	$0.00	$2.44
096516101020	Vinyl cove molding,6" high	0.2	LF	$0.50	$0.26	$0.00	$0.76
099123304180	Int painting, walls, roller, first coat, avg	1	SF	$0.17	$0.20	$0.00	$0.37
				$2.48	**$4.31**	**$0.00**	**$6.79**

All prices are updated to January 1, 2021 and are national averages.
For more in-depth information contact Design, Cost and Data at 800-533-5680, or go to www.DCD.com

471

C INTERIORS

C1020 INTERIOR DOORS

C1020.10 METAL DOOR

		Quan.	Unit	Material	Labor	Equip.	Total
C1020.10.10	**Metal Door/Metal Frame**						**SF**
099123302300	Int painting, doors, metal, roller, second coat, avg	42	SF	$8.87	$12.03	$0.00	$20.90
099123302220	Int painting, doors, metal, roller, first coat, avg	42	SF	$8.87	$17.59	$0.00	$26.46
087100201300	Latchset,heavy duty,cylindrical	1	EA	$191.40	$40.78	$0.00	$232.18
087100101260	Hinges,4 x 4 butts,steel,standard	1.5	PAIR	$45.87	$0.00	$0.00	$45.87
081113101240	Door,metal,flush hollow,20 ga,1-3/4",3-0 x 7-0	1	EA	$498.04	$72.49	$0.00	$570.53
081113401550	Door frames,mtl,stk,16 ga,6-3/4"x 1-3/4",3-0 x 7-0	1	EA	$198.96	$90.00	$0.00	$288.96
				$952.01	**$232.89**	**$0.00**	**$1,184.90**

C1020.20 WOOD DOOR

		Quan.	Unit	Material	Labor	Equip.	Total
C1020.20.10	**Wood Door/Wood Frame**						**SF**
099123302680	Int painting, doors, wood, brush, second coat, avg	42	SF	$6.65	$28.58	$0.00	$35.23
062023101070	Molding,casing,wood,11/16 x 3-1/2	40	LF	$109.39	$124.27	$0.00	$233.66
081400101970	Door,flush,solid core,1-3/4",birch,3-0 x 7-0	1	EA	$269.98	$81.55	$0.00	$351.53
081400900260	Door frame,pine,interior,3-0 x 7-0	1	EA	$140.66	$93.20	$0.00	$233.86
087100101260	Hinges,4 x 4 butts,steel,standard	1.5	PAIR	$45.87	$0.00	$0.00	$45.87
087100201300	Latchset,heavy duty,cylindrical	1	EA	$191.40	$40.78	$0.00	$232.18
099123303980	Int painting, trim, brush, first coat, avg	40	LF	$8.45	$9.90	$0.00	$18.35
099123304060	Int painting, trim, brush, second coat, avg	40	LF	$8.45	$8.38	$0.00	$16.83
099123302600	Int painting, doors, wood, brush, first coat, avg	42	SF	$8.87	$41.57	$0.00	$50.44
				$789.72	**$428.23**	**$0.00**	**$1,217.95**

C1020.25 WOOD DOOR, METAL FRAME

		Quan.	Unit	Material	Labor	Equip.	Total
C1020.25.10	**Wood Door/Metal Frame**						**SF**
099123302600	Int painting, doors, wood, brush, first coat, avg	42	SF	$8.87	$41.57	$0.00	$50.44
099123302680	Int painting, doors, wood, brush, second coat, avg	42	SF	$6.65	$28.58	$0.00	$35.23
087100201300	Latchset,heavy duty,cylindrical	1	EA	$191.40	$40.78	$0.00	$232.18
087100101260	Hinges,4 x 4 butts,steel,standard	1.5	PAIR	$45.87	$0.00	$0.00	$45.87
081400101970	Door,flush,solid core,1-3/4",birch,3-0 x 7-0	1	EA	$269.98	$81.55	$0.00	$351.53
081113401550	Door frames,mtl,stk,16 ga,6-3/4"x 1-3/4",3-0 x 7-0	1	EA	$198.96	$90.00	$0.00	$288.96
				$721.73	**$282.48**	**$0.00**	**$1,004.21**

All prices are updated to January 1, 2021 and are national averages.
For more in-depth information contact Design, Cost and Data at 800-533-5680, or go to www.DCD.com

472

C INTERIORS

C1030 FITTINGS

C1030.10 WASHROOM ACCESSORIES

		Quan.	Unit	Material	Labor	Equip.	Total
C1030.10.10	**Toilet partition, plastic lam, ceiling mount**						**Unit: EA**
102113000120	Toilet partition,plastic lam,ceiling mount	1	EA	$1,204.16	$217.47	$0.00	$1,421.63
C1030.10.12	**Toilet partition, plastic lam, floor mount**						**Unit: EA**
102113000140	Toilet partition,plastic lam,floor mount	1	EA	$793.95	$163.10	$0.00	$957.05
C1030.10.14	**Toilet partition, metal, ceiling mount**						**Unit: EA**
102113000160	Toilet partition,metal,ceiling mount	1	EA	$821.98	$217.47	$0.00	$1,039.45
C1030.10.16	**Toilet partition, metal, floor mount**						**Unit: EA**
102113000180	Toilet partition,metal,floor mount	1	EA	$783.45	$163.10	$0.00	$946.55
C1030.10.20	**Wheelchair partition, plastic lam, ceiling mount**						**Unit: EA**
102113000200	Wheelchair partition,plastic lam,ceiling mount	1	EA	$1,798.07	$217.47	$0.00	$2,015.54
C1030.10.22	**Wheelchair partition, plastic lam, floor mount**						**Unit: EA**
102113000210	Wheelchair partition,plastic lam,floor mount	1	EA	$1,577.17	$163.10	$0.00	$1,740.27
C1030.10.25	**Wheelchair partition, painted metal, ceiling mount**						**Unit: EA**
102113000240	Wheelchair partition,painted metal,ceiling mount	1	EA	$1,284.34	$217.47	$0.00	$1,501.81
C1030.10.27	**Wheelchair partition, painted metal, floor mount**						**Unit: EA**
102113000260	Wheelchair partition,painted metal,floor mount	1	EA	$1,166.18	$163.10	$0.00	$1,329.28
C1030.10.30	**Urinal screen, plastic lam, wall hung**						**Unit: EA**
102113002000	Urinal screen,plastic lam,wall hung	1	EA	$554.84	$81.55	$0.00	$636.39
C1030.10.32	**Urinal screen, plastic lam, floor mount**						**Unit: EA**
102113002100	Urinal screen,plastic lam,floor mount	1	EA	$500.89	$81.55	$0.00	$582.44
C1030.10.34	**Urinal screen, porcelain enamel steel, floor mount**						**Unit: EA**
102113002120	Urinal screen,porcelain enamel st,floor mount	1	EA	$642.17	$81.55	$0.00	$723.72
C1030.10.36	**Urinal screen, painted metal, floor mount**						**Unit: EA**
102113002140	Urinal screen,painted metal,floor mount	1	EA	$423.84	$81.55	$0.00	$505.39
C1030.10.38	**Urinal screen, stainless steel, floor mount**						**Unit: EA**
102113002160	Urinal screen,stainless steel,floor mount	1	EA	$809.14	$81.55	$0.00	$890.69
C1030.10.40	**Toilet partn, front door/side divider, porcelain enamel steel**						**Unit: EA**
102113005040	Toilet partn,front door/side divider,porc enl stl	1	EA	$1,322.87	$163.10	$0.00	$1,485.97
C1030.10.42	**Toilet partn, front door/side divider, painted steel**						**Unit: EA**
102113005060	Toilet partn,front door/side divider,painted steel	1	EA	$777.02	$163.10	$0.00	$940.12
C1030.10.44	**Toilet partn, front door/side divider, stnls stl**						**Unit: EA**
102113005080	Toilet partn,front door/side divider,stnls stl	1	EA	$1,926.51	$163.10	$0.00	$2,089.61
C1030.15.10	**Bath accessory, ash receiver, wall mounted, alum**						**Unit: EA**
102816001040	Bath accessory,ash receiver,wall mounted,alum	1	EA	$167.99	$32.62	$0.00	$200.61
C1030.15.12	**Commercial hand dryer, surface mounted, 110 volt**						**Unit: EA**
102816001300	Commercial hand dryer,surface mounted,110 volt	1	EA	$810.15	$81.55	$0.00	$891.70

All prices are updated to January 1, 2021 and are national averages.
For more in-depth information contact Design, Cost and Data at 800-533-5680, or go to www.DCD.com

473

C INTERIORS

C1030 FITTINGS

C1030.15 WASHROOM ACCESSORIES (Cont.)

		Quan.	Unit	Material	Labor	Equip.	Total
C1030.15.14	**Mirror, 1/4" plate glass, up to 10 Sf**						**Unit: SF**
102816001420	Mirror,1/4" plate glass,up to 10 Sf	1	SF	$12.40	$6.52	$0.00	$18.92
C1030.15.16	**Mirror, SS frame, 18"x 24"**						**Unit: EA**
102816001440	Mirror,SS frame,18"x 24"	1	EA	$94.83	$21.75	$0.00	$116.58
C1030.15.18	**Mirror, SS frame, 24"x36"**						**Unit: EA**
102816001510	Mirror,SS frame,24"x36"	1	EA	$122.61	$36.24	$0.00	$158.85
C1030.15.20	**Mirror, SS frame, 30"x30"**						**Unit: EA**
102816001560	Mirror,SS frame,30"x30"	1	EA	$376.62	$65.24	$0.00	$441.86
C1030.15.22	**Mirror, SS frame, 48"x72"**						**Unit: EA**
102816001600	Mirror,SS frame,48"x72"	1	EA	$738.35	$108.73	$0.00	$847.08
C1030.15.24	**Mirror, SS frame, 18"x 24", w/shelf**						**Unit: EA**
102816001640	Mirror,SS frame,18"x 24",w/shelf	1	EA	$291.95	$26.10	$0.00	$318.05
C1030.15.26	**Sanitary napkin dispenser, SS, wall mounted**						**Unit: EA**
102816001820	Sanitary napkin dispenser,SS,wall mounted	1	EA	$704.48	$43.49	$0.00	$747.97
C1030.15.28	**Toilet tissue disp, SS, wall mounted, single**						**Unit: EA**
102816001920	Toilet tissue disp,SS,wall mounted,single	1	EA	$79.31	$16.31	$0.00	$95.62
C1030.15.30	**Toilet tissue disp, SS, wall mounted, double**						**Unit: EA**
102816001940	Toilet tissue disp,SS,wall mounted,double	1	EA	$152.21	$18.64	$0.00	$170.85
C1030.15.32	**Towel dispenser, SS, flush mounted**						**Unit: EA**
102816001950	Towel dispenser,SS,flush mounted	1	EA	$304.42	$36.24	$0.00	$340.66
C1030.15.34	**Towel dispenser, SS, surface**						**Unit: EA**
102816001960	Towel dispenser,SS,surface	1	EA	$433.86	$32.62	$0.00	$466.48
C1030.15.36	**Combination towel dispenser & waste receptacle**						**Unit: EA**
102816001970	Combination towel dispenser & waste receptacle	1	EA	$660.04	$43.49	$0.00	$703.53
C1030.15.38	**Waste receptacle, SS, wall mounted**						**Unit: EA**
102816002100	Waste receptacle,SS,wall mounted	1	EA	$498.77	$54.37	$0.00	$553.14

C2010 STAIR CONSTRUCTION

C2010.10 STAIRS, CONCRETE

		Quan.	Unit	Material	Labor	Equip.	Total
C2010.10.10	**Stair, Reinforced Concrete, 4' wide by 12' high**						**EA**
033101102160	Place concrete,stairs,3500# or 4000#,by pump	3	CY	$442.87	$131.35	$90.00	$664.22
055213100140	Railing,pipe,1-1/4" D,welded,3 rail,primed	20	LF	$812.90	$360.00	$0.00	$1,172.90
032101004210	Stair nosing, galv steel, 4' long	20	EA	$495.00	$88.80	$0.00	$583.80
032101001040	Reinforcing,stairs,#7-#8	0.25	TON	$392.83	$237.86	$0.00	$630.69
031114001060	Job built,stairway forms,5 uses	80	SF	$141.50	$745.60	$0.00	$887.10
055213100180	Railing,1-1/4" D,wall mounted,welded,primed	20	LF	$424.16	$221.54	$0.00	$645.70
				$2,709.26	**$1,785.15**	**$90.00**	**$4,584.41**

All prices are updated to January 1, 2021 and are national averages.
For more in-depth information contact Design, Cost and Data at 800-533-5680, or go to www.DCD.com

474

C INTERIORS

C3020   FLOOR FINISHES

C3020.20 FLOORING, TILE

		Quan.	Unit	Material	Labor	Equip.	Total
C3020.20.10	**Unglazed tile, cement bed, face mount, 2"x 2"** ....**Unit: SF**						
093013106150	Unglazed tile,cement bed,face mount,2"x 2"	1	SF	$9.38	$5.18	$0.00	$14.56
C3020.20.12	**Unglazed tile, cement bed, face mount, 6"x 6"** ....**Unit: SF**						
093013106164	Unglazed tile,cement bed,face mount,6"x 6"	1	SF	$3.12	$4.44	$0.00	$7.56
C3020.20.14	**Unglazed tile, cement bed, face mount, 12"x 12"** ....**Unit: SF**						
093013106166	Unglazed tile,cement bed,face mount,12"x 12"	1	SF	$2.75	$3.89	$0.00	$6.64
C3020.20.16	**Unglazed tile, adhesive, white grout, 2"x 2"** ....**Unit: SF**						
093013106230	Unglazed tile,adhesive,white grout,2"x 2"	1	SF	$7.81	$5.18	$0.00	$12.99
C3020.20.18	**Unglazed tile, adhesive, white grout, 6"x 6"** ....**Unit: SF**						
093013106262	Unglazed tile,adhesive,white grout,6"x 6"	1	SF	$2.61	$4.44	$0.00	$7.05
C3020.20.20	**Unglazed tile, adhesive, white grout, 12"x 12"** ....**Unit: SF**						
093013106264	Unglazed tile,adhesive,white grout,12"x 12"	1	SF	$2.29	$3.89	$0.00	$6.18

C3020.25 FLOORING, CARPET

		Quan.	Unit	Material	Labor	Equip.	Total
C3020.25.10	**Carpet, acrylic, 28 oz, medium** ....**Unit: SY**						
096800201000	Carpet,acrylic,28 oz,medium	0.11	SY	$1.94	$0.80	$0.00	$2.74
C3020.25.12	**Carpet, acrylic, 28 oz, heavy** ....**Unit: SY**						
096800201020	Carpet,acrylic,28 oz,heavy	0.11	SY	$2.33	$0.80	$0.00	$3.13
C3020.25.14	**Commercial carpet, nylon, 28 oz, medium** ....**Unit: SY**						
096800202120	Commercial carpet,nylon,28 oz, medium	0.11	SY	$3.37	$0.80	$0.00	$4.17
C3020.25.16	**Commercial carpet, nylon, 32 oz, heavy** ....**Unit: SY**						
096800202140	Commercial carpet,nylon,32 oz,heavy	0.11	SY	$4.10	$0.80	$0.00	$4.90
C3020.25.18	**Commercial carpet, wool, 30 oz, medium** ....**Unit: SY**						
096800202150	Commercial carpet,wool,30 oz,medium	0.11	SY	$5.56	$0.80	$0.00	$6.36
C3020.25.20	**Commercial carpet, wool, 36 oz, medium** ....**Unit: SY**						
096800202160	Commercial carpet,wool,36 oz,medium	0.11	SY	$5.86	$0.80	$0.00	$6.66
C3020.25.22	**Commercial carpet, wool, 42 oz, heavy** ....**Unit: SY**						
096800202180	Commercial carpet,wool,42 oz,heavy	0.11	SY	$7.76	$0.80	$0.00	$8.56

C3020.25 FLOORING,CARPET TILE

		Quan.	Unit	Material	Labor	Equip.	Total
C3020.25.24	**Carpet tile, foam back, needle punch, minimum** ....**Unit: SF**						
096800203022	Carpet tile,foam back,needle punch,minimum	1	SF	$4.08	$1.30	$0.00	$5.38
C3020.25.26	**Carpet tile, foam back, needle punch, average** ....**Unit: SF**						
096800203024	Carpet tile,foam back,needle punch,average	1	SF	$4.72	$1.45	$0.00	$6.17
C3020.25.28	**Carpet tile, foam back, needle punch, maximum** ....**Unit: SF**						
096800203026	Carpet tile,foam back,needle punch,maximum	1	SF	$7.48	$1.63	$0.00	$9.11

All prices are updated to January 1, 2021 and are national averages.
For more in-depth information contact Design, Cost and Data at 800-533-5680, or go to www.DCD.com

475

C INTERIORS

C3020 FLOOR FINISHES

C3020.30 FLOORING, CARPET PAD

		Quan.	Unit	Material	Labor	Equip.	Total
C3020.30.10	**Carpet pad, jute, minimum**						**Unit: SY**
096800101020	Carpet pad,jute,minimum	0.11	SY	$0.50	$0.33	$0.00	$0.83
C3020.30.12	**Carpet pad, jute, average**						**Unit: SY**
096800101022	Carpet pad,jute,average	0.11	SY	$0.66	$0.36	$0.00	$1.02
C3020.30.14	**Carpet pad, jute, maximum**						**Unit: SY**
096800101024	Carpet pad,jute,maximum	0.11	SY	$0.99	$0.40	$0.00	$1.39
C3020.30.20	**Carpet pad, sponge rubber, minimum**						**Unit: SY**
096800101040	Carpet pad,sponge rubber,minimum	0.11	SY	$0.60	$0.33	$0.00	$0.93
C3020.30.22	**Carpet pad, sponge rubber, average**						**Unit: SY**
096800101042	Carpet pad,sponge rubber,average	0.11	SY	$0.79	$0.36	$0.00	$1.15
C3020.30.24	**Carpet pad, sponge rubber, maximum**						**Unit: SY**
096800101044	Carpet pad,sponge rubber,maximum	0.11	SY	$1.13	$0.40	$0.00	$1.53
C3020.30.30	**Carpet pad, urethane, 3/8", minimum**						**Unit: SY**
096800101060	Carpet pad,urethane,3/8",minimum	0.11	SY	$0.60	$0.33	$0.00	$0.93
C3020.30.32	**Carpet pad, urethane, 3/8", average**						**Unit: SY**
096800101062	Carpet pad,urethane,3/8",average	0.11	SY	$0.70	$0.36	$0.00	$1.06
C3020.30.34	**Carpet pad, urethane, 3/8", maximum**						**Unit: SY**
096800101064	Carpet pad,urethane,3/8",maximum	0.11	SY	$0.91	$0.40	$0.00	$1.31

C3030 CEILING FINISHES

		Quan.	Unit	Material	Labor	Equip.	Total
C3030.10.10	**Plaster Ceilings**						**SF**
099123301920	Int painting, ceilings, roller, second coat, avg	1	SF	$0.17	$0.21	$0.00	$0.38
099123301840	Int painting, ceilings, roller, first coat, avg	1	SF	$0.17	$0.25	$0.00	$0.42
092236201050	Lath,metal,diamond expd,galv,2.5 lb,ceiling,nailed	0.11	SY	$0.46	$1.03	$0.00	$1.49
092116104540	Furring,on ceilings,1-1/2" channel,16" oc	1	SF	$0.47	$2.72	$0.00	$3.19
092300101000	Gypsum plaster,trowel finish,2 coats,ceilings	0.11	SY	$0.47	$2.09	$0.00	$2.56
				$1.74	**$6.30**	**$0.00**	**$8.04**
C3030.15.10	**Drywall Ceilings**						**SF**
092116104540	Furring,on ceilings,1-1/2" channel,16" oc	1	SF	$0.47	$2.72	$0.00	$3.19
092900100240	Drywall,1/2" thick,clipped,ceilings	1	SF	$0.42	$0.72	$0.00	$1.14
092900101226	Drywall,taping & finishing joints,maximum	1	SF	$0.11	$0.65	$0.00	$0.76
099123301840	Int painting, ceilings, roller, first coat, avg	1	SF	$0.17	$0.25	$0.00	$0.42
099123301920	Int painting, ceilings, roller, second coat, avg	1	SF	$0.17	$0.21	$0.00	$0.38
				$1.34	**$4.55**	**$0.00**	**$5.89**
C3030.25.10	**Acoustical Ceilings**						**SF**
095100105520	Ceiling suspension system,T-bar,2'x 2'	1	SF	$1.38	$0.72	$0.00	$2.10
095100103060	Acoustic tile,fiberglass,12"x 12",3/4" thick	1	SF	$2.32	$1.45	$0.00	$3.77
				$3.70	**$2.17**	**$0.00**	**$5.87**

All prices are updated to January 1, 2021 and are national averages.
For more in-depth information contact Design, Cost and Data at 800-533-5680, or go to www.DCD.com

476

D SERVICES

D1010 ELEVATORS

D1010.10 ELEVATORS, HYDRAULIC

		Quan.	Unit	Material	Labor	Equip.	Total
D1010.10.10	**Elevator, hydraulic, 3 stops, 3 op, 50 fpm, 2000 lb** .... **Unit: EA**						
142100101500	Elevator,hydraulic,3 stops,3 op,50 fpm,2000 lb	1	EA	$101,249	$1,267	$1,108	$103,624
D1010.10.15	**Elevator, hydraulic, 3 stops, 3 op, 50 fpm, 3000 lb** .... **Unit: EA**						
142100101520	Elevator,hydraulic,3 stops,3 op,50 fpm,3000 lb	1	EA	$114,261	$1,322	$1,156	$116,739
D1010.10.20	**Elevator, hydraulic, 3 stops, 3 op, 100 fpm, 2000 lb** .... **Unit: EA**						
142100101540	Elevator,hydraulic,3 stops,3 op,100 fpm,2000 lb	1	EA	$110,919	$1,267	$1,108	$113,294
D1010.10.25	**Elevator, hydraulic, 3 stops, 3 op, 100 fpm, 3000 lb** .... **Unit: EA**						
142100101560	Elevator,hydraulic,3 stops,3 op,100 fpm,3000 lb	1	EA	$125,139	$1,382	$1,209	$127,730
D1010.10.30	**Elevator, hydraulic, 3 stops, 3 op, 150 fpm, 2000 lb** .... **Unit: EA**						
142100101580	Elevator,hydraulic,3 stops,3 op,150 fpm,2000 lb	1	EA	$120,162	$1,267	$1,108	$122,537
D1010.10.32	**Elevator, hydraulic, 3 stops, 3 op, 150 fpm, 3000 lb** .... **Unit: EA**						
142100101600	Elevator,hydraulic,3 stops,3 op,150 fpm,3000 lb	1	EA	$140,782	$1,448	$1,266	$143,496

For each additional: 50 fpm add per stop, $3500
For each additional: 500 lb, add per stop, $3500
For each additional: Opening, add, $4200
For each additional: Stop, add per stop, $5300
For each additional: Bonderized steel door, add per opening, $400
For each additional: Colored aluminum door, add per opening, $1500
For each additional: Stainless steel door, add per opening, $650

D1010.15 ELEVATORS, ELECTRIC

		Quan.	Unit	Material	Labor	Equip.	Total
D1010.15.10	**Elevator, electric, 8 stop, 8 openings, 300 fpm, 3000 lb**...**EA**						
142100101020	Elevator, electric, 8 stop, 8 op, 300 fpm, 3000 lb	1.000	EA	$270,187	$2,937	$2,510	$275,635
D1010.15.15	**Elevator, electric, 8 stop, 8 openings, 300 fpm, 4000 lb**...**EA**						
142100101060	Elevator, electric, 8 stop, 8 op, 300 fpm, 4000 lb	1.000	EA	$287,963	$3,264	$2,788	$294,016
D1010.15.20	**Elevator, electric, 8 stop, 8 openings, 300 fpm, 5000 lb**...**EA**						
142100101070	Elevator, electric, 8 stop, 8 op, 300 fpm, 5000 lb	1.000	EA	$319,959	$3,497	$2,988	$326,444
D1010.15.25	**Elevator, electric, 8 stop, 8 openings, 400 fpm, 3000 lb**...**EA**						
142100101090	Elevator, electric, 8 stop, 8 op, 400 fpm, 3000 lb	1.000	EA	$283,057	$2,937	$2,510	$288,504
D1010.15.30	**Elevator, electric, 8 stop, 8 openings, 400 fpm, 4000 lb**...**EA**						
142100101120	Elevator, electric, 8 stop, 8 op, 400 fpm, 4000 lb	1.000	EA	$307,871	$3,264	$2,788	$313,924
D1010.15.35	**Elevator, electric, 8 stop, 8 openings, 400 fpm, 5000 lb**...**EA**						
142100101140	Elevator, electric, 8 stop, 8 op, 400 fpm, 5000 lb	1.000	EA	$350,533	$3,497	$2,988	$357,018

All prices are updated to January 1, 2021 and are national averages.
For more in-depth information contact Design, Cost and Data at 800-533-5680, or go to www.DCD.com

477

D SERVICES

D1010 ELEVATORS

D1010.15 ELEVATORS, ELECTRIC (Cont.)

		Quan.	Unit	Material	Labor	Equip.	Total
D1010.15.40	**Elevator, electric, 8 stop, 8 openings, 600 fpm, 3000 lb**............................**EA**						
142100101160	Elevator, electric, 8 stop, 8 op, 600 fpm, 3000 lb	1.000	EA	$398,669	$3,264	$2,788	$404,722
D1010.15.45	**Elevator, electric, 8 stop, 8 openings, 600 fpm, 4000 lb**............................**EA**						
142100101190	Elevator, electric, 8 stop, 8 op, 600 fpm, 4000 lb	1.000	EA	$412,391	$3,582	$3,060	$419,035
D1010.15.50	**Elevator, electric, 8 stop, 8 openings, 600 fpm, 5000 lb**............................**EA**						
142100101200	Elevator, electric, 8 stop, 8 op, 600 fpm, 5000 lb	1.000	EA	$423,768	$3,672	$3,137	$430,577
D1010.15.60	**Elevator, electric, 8 stop, 8 openings, 800 fpm, 3000 lb**............................**EA**						
142100101220	Elevator, electric, 8 stop, 8 op, 800 fpm, 3000 lb	1.000	EA	$472,828	$3,264	$2,788	$478,881
D1010.15.62	**Elevator, electric, 8 stop, 8 openings, 800 fpm, 4000 lb**............................**EA**						
142100101260	Elevator, electric, 8 stop, 8 op, 800 fpm, 4000 lb	1.000	EA	$483,494	$3,582	$3,060	$490,137
D1010.15.64	**Elevator, electric, 8 stop, 8 openings, 800 fpm, 5000 lb**............................**EA**						
142100101280	Elevator, electric, 8 stop, 8 op, 800 fpm, 5000 lb	1.000	EA	$486,693	$3,672	$3,137	$493,503

For each additional: 100 fpm add per stop, $13,000
For each additional: 500 lb, add per stop, $6500
For each additional: Opening add per stop, $12,000
For each additional: Stop add per stop, $4800
For each additional: Bypass floor, add per each, $2000
For each additional: Bonderized steel door, add per opening, $150
For each additional: Colored aluminum door, add per opening, $900
For each additional: Stainless steel door, add per opening, $600

D1010 ESCALATORS

D1020.30 ESCALATORS

		Quan.	Unit	Material	Labor	Equip.	Total
D1020.30.10	**Escalators, 32" wide, floor to floor, 12' high**............................**EA**						
143100101040	Escalators, 32" wide, floor to floor, 12' high	1.000	EA	$180,150	$2,448	$2,091	$184,689
D1020.30.15	**Escalators, 32" wide, floor to floor, 18' high**............................**EA**						
143100101060	Escalators, 32" wide, floor to floor, 18' high	1.000	EA	$211,986	$3,672	$3,137	$218,795
D1020.30.20	**Escalators, 32" wide, floor to floor, 25' high**............................**EA**						
143100101080	Escalators, 32" wide, floor to floor, 25' high	1.000	EA	$238,378	$5,875	$5,020	$249,273
D1020.30.25	**Escalators, 48" wide, floor to floor, 12' high**............................**EA**						
143100101090	Escalators, 48" wide, floor to floor, 12' high	1.000	EA	$200,705	$2,532	$2,163	$205,401
D1020.30.30	**Escalators, 48" wide, floor to floor, 18' high**............................**EA**						
143100101120	Escalators, 48" wide, floor to floor, 18' high	1.000	EA	$235,309	$3,865	$3,302	$242,477
D1020.30.35	**Escalators, 48" wide, floor to floor, 25' high**............................**EA**						
143100101140	Escalators, 48" wide, floor to floor, 25' high	1.000	EA	$281,264	$5,875	$5,020	$292,159

All prices are updated to January 1, 2021 and are national averages.
For more in-depth information contact Design, Cost and Data at 800-533-5680, or go to www.DCD.com

478

D   SERVICES

D2010   PLUMBING FIXTURES

D2010.10 WATER CLOSETS

		Quan.	Unit	Material	Labor	Equip.	Total
D2010.10.12	**Water closet, flush tank, floor mounted** .... **EA**						
224200901600	Toilets,floor support,average	1	EA	$181.50	$71.52	$0.00	$253.02
224213601010	Water closet,flush tank,floor mounted,average	1	EA	$785.29	$238.40	$0.00	$1,023.69
224213609040	Water closet,for trim and rough-in,maximum	1	EA	$399.30	$357.60	$0.00	$756.90
				$1,366.09	**$667.52**	**$0.00**	**$2,033.61**
D2010.10.18	**Water closet, flush tank, floor mount, handicap** .... **EA**						
224200901600	Toilets,floor support,average	1	EA	$181.50	$71.52	$0.00	$253.02
224213601050	Water closet,flush tank,floor mount,handicap,avrg	1	EA	$974.29	$357.60	$0.00	$1,331.89
224213609040	Water closet,for trim and rough-in,maximum	1	EA	$399.30	$357.60	$0.00	$756.90
				$1,555.09	**$786.72**	**$0.00**	**$2,341.81**
D2010.10.24	**Water closet, bowl, flush valve, floor mount** .... **EA**						
224213601220	Water closet,bowl,w/flush valve,floor mount,avrg	1	EA	$612.26	$238.40	$0.00	$850.66
224213609040	Water closet,for trim and rough-in,maximum	1	EA	$399.30	$357.60	$0.00	$756.90
224200901600	Toilets,floor support,average	1	EA	$181.50	$71.52	$0.00	$253.02
				$1,193.06	**$667.52**	**$0.00**	**$1,860.58**
D2010.10.30	**Water closet, bowl, flush valve, wall mounted** .... **EA**						
224213601280	Water closet,bowl,w/flush valve,wall mounted,avrg	1	EA	$652.19	$238.40	$0.00	$890.59
224213609040	Water closet,for trim and rough-in,maximum	1	EA	$399.30	$357.60	$0.00	$756.90
224200901540	Toilets,water closets,wall carrier,average	1	EA	$363.00	$89.40	$0.00	$452.40
				$1,414.49	**$685.40**	**$0.00**	**$2,099.89**

D2010.15 URINALS

		Quan.	Unit	Material	Labor	Equip.	Total
D2010.15.12	**Urinal, flush valve, floor mounted** .... **EA**						
224200901720	Urinals,floor support,average	1	EA	$193.60	$71.52	$0.00	$265.12
224213501010	Urinal,flush valve,floor mounted,average	1	EA	$705.43	$238.40	$0.00	$943.83
224213509040	Urinal,for trim and rough-in,maximum	1	EA	$432.58	$476.80	$0.00	$909.38
				$1,331.61	**$786.72**	**$0.00**	**$2,118.33**
D2010.15.18	**Urinal, flush valve, wall mounted** .... **EA**						
224213501080	Urinal,flush valve,wall mounted,average	1	EA	$678.81	$238.40	$0.00	$917.21
224213509040	Urinal,for trim and rough-in,maximum	1	EA	$432.58	$476.80	$0.00	$909.38
224200901660	Urinals,wall carrier,average	1	EA	$205.70	$89.40	$0.00	$295.10
				$1,317.09	**$804.60**	**$0.00**	**$2,121.69**

All prices are updated to January 1, 2021 and are national averages.
For more in-depth information contact Design, Cost and Data at 800-533-5680, or go to www.DCD.com

479

D SERVICES

D2010 PLUMBING FIXTURES

D2010.20 LAVATORIES

		Quan.	Unit	Material	Labor	Equip.	Total
D2010.20.12	**Lavatory, counter top, porcelain on CI**						**EA**
224216209040	Lavatory,for trim and rough-in,maximum	1	EA	$559.02	$357.60	$0.00	$916.62
224216202010	Lavatory,counter top,porcelain enamel on CI,avrg	1	EA	$352.72	$178.80	$0.00	$531.52
				$911.74	**$536.40**	**$0.00**	**$1,448.14**
D2010.20.17	**Lavatory, wall hung, china**						**EA**
224200901140	Lavatory,wall carrier,average	1	EA	$229.90	$89.40	$0.00	$319.30
224216202110	Lavatory,wall hung,china,average	1	EA	$372.68	$178.80	$0.00	$551.48
224216209040	Lavatory,for trim and rough-in,maximum	1	EA	$559.02	$357.60	$0.00	$916.62
				$1,161.60	**$625.80**	**$0.00**	**$1,787.40**
D2010.20.22	**Lavatory, wall hung, china, handicapped**						**EA**
224200901140	Lavatory,wall carrier,average	1	EA	$229.90	$89.40	$0.00	$319.30
224216202310	Lavatory,wall hung,china,handicapped,average	1	EA	$598.95	$238.40	$0.00	$837.35
224216209040	Lavatory,for trim and rough-in,maximum	1	EA	$559.02	$357.60	$0.00	$916.62
				$1,387.87	**$685.40**	**$0.00**	**$2,073.27**

D2010.25 BATHTUBS

		Quan.	Unit	Material	Labor	Equip.	Total
D2010.25.12	**Bathtub, 5' long**						**EA**
224219001020	Bathtub,5' long,average	1	EA	$1,397.55	$357.60	$0.00	$1,755.15
224219009020	Bathtub,for trim and rough-in,average	1	EA	$332.75	$357.60	$0.00	$690.35
				$1,730.30	**$715.20**	**$0.00**	**$2,445.50**
D2010.25.22	**Bathtub, 6' long**						**EA**
224219001080	Bathtub,6' long,average	1	EA	$1,464.10	$357.60	$0.00	$1,821.70
224219009020	Bathtub,for trim and rough-in,average	1	EA	$332.75	$357.60	$0.00	$690.35
				$1,796.85	**$715.20**	**$0.00**	**$2,512.05**
D2010.25.32	**Bathtub, square, whirlpool, 4'x 4'**						**EA**
224219001140	Bathtub,square,whirlpool,4'x 4',average	1	EA	$3,114.54	$715.20	$0.00	$3,829.74
224219009040	Bathtub,for trim and rough-in,maximum	1	EA	$945.01	$715.20	$0.00	$1,660.21
				$4,059.55	**$1,430.40**	**$0.00**	**$5,489.95**

All prices are updated to January 1, 2021 and are national averages.
For more in-depth information contact Design, Cost and Data at 800-533-5680, or go to www.DCD.com

480

D SERVICES

D2010 PLUMBING FIXTURES

D2010.30 SINKS

		Quan.	Unit	Material	Labor	Equip.	Total
D2010.30.22	**Kitchen sink, single, stainless, double bowl**..**EA**						
224216402100	Kitchen sink,single,stnls stl,double bowl,avrg	1	EA	$432.58	$238.40	$0.00	$670.98
224216409020	Sink,for trim and rough-in,average	1	EA	$532.40	$357.60	$0.00	$890.00
				$964.98	**$596.00**	**$0.00**	**$1,560.98**

		Quan.	Unit	Material	Labor	Equip.	Total
D2010.30.42	**Kitchen sink, porcelain on CI, double bowl**..**EA**						
224216402280	Kitchen sink,porcelain enamel,CI,double bowl,avrg	1	EA	$465.85	$238.40	$0.00	$704.25
224216409020	Sink,for trim and rough-in,average	1	EA	$532.40	$357.60	$0.00	$890.00
				$998.25	**$596.00**	**$0.00**	**$1,594.25**

		Quan.	Unit	Material	Labor	Equip.	Total
D2010.35.12	**Service sink, 24"x29"**..**EA**						
224200901420	Sink,industrial,wall carrier,average	1	EA	$242.00	$89.40	$0.00	$331.40
224216401020	Service sink,24"x29",average	1	EA	$958.32	$238.40	$0.00	$1,196.72
224216409040	Sink,for trim and rough-in,maximum	1	EA	$678.81	$476.80	$0.00	$1,155.61
				$1,879.13	**$804.60**	**$0.00**	**$2,683.73**

		Quan.	Unit	Material	Labor	Equip.	Total
D2010.35.22	**Mop sink, 24"x36"x10", average**..**EA**						
224200901420	Sink,industrial,wall carrier,average	1	EA	$242.00	$89.40	$0.00	$331.40
224216403020	Mop sink,24"x36"x10",average	1	EA	$705.43	$178.80	$0.00	$884.23
224216409040	Sink,for trim and rough-in,maximum	1	EA	$678.81	$476.80	$0.00	$1,155.61
				$1,626.24	**$745.00**	**$0.00**	**$2,371.24**

D2010.40 WATER COOLERS

		Quan.	Unit	Material	Labor	Equip.	Total
D2010.40.10	**Water Cooler**..**EA**						
224700101020	Electric water cooler,wall mounted	1	EA	$1,040.60	$238.40	$0.00	$1,279.00
224200901040	Water fountain,wall carrier,maximum	1	EA	$116.16	$119.20	$0.00	$235.36
224216409020	Sink,for trim and rough-in,average	1	EA	$532.40	$357.60	$0.00	$890.00
				$1,689.16	**$715.20**	**$0.00**	**$2,404.36**

All prices are updated to January 1, 2021 and are national averages.
For more in-depth information contact Design, Cost and Data at 800-533-5680, or go to www.DCD.com

D SERVICES

D2020 DOMESTIC WATER DISTRIBUTION

D2020.05 COPPER

		Quan.	Unit	Material	Labor	Equip.	Total
D2020.05.05	**3/4" L Copper, Including Hangers and Fittings, 100' Runs**						**LF**
221116202374	Copper,90 ells,3/4"	0.02	EA	$0.05	$0.75	$0.00	$0.80
221116200880	Copper fittings,reducing slip coupling,3/4"	0.08	EA	$0.22	$2.86	$0.00	$3.08
220629100150	A band,copper, 3/4"	0.1	EA	$0.19	$0.53	$0.00	$0.72
221116106190	Copper piping,L tube,3/4"	1	LF	$4.33	$2.38	$0.00	$6.71
				$4.79	**$6.52**	**$0.00**	**$11.31**
D2020.05.07	**1" L Copper, Including Hangers and Fittings, 100' Runs**						**LF**
220629100160	A band,copper,1"	0.1	EA	$0.19	$0.53	$0.00	$0.72
221116106240	Copper piping,L tube,1"	1	LF	$6.51	$2.55	$0.00	$9.06
221116200890	Copper fittings,reducing slip coupling,1"	0.08	EA	$0.47	$3.18	$0.00	$3.65
221116202376	Copper,90 ells,1"	0.02	EA	$0.12	$0.79	$0.00	$0.91
				$7.29	**$7.05**	**$0.00**	**$14.34**
D2020.05.09	**1-1/2" L Copper, Including Hangers and Fittings, 100' Runs**						**LF**
221116202379	Copper,90 ells,1-1/2"	0.08	EA	$1.12	$3.58	$0.00	$4.70
220629100180	A band,copper,1-1/2"	0.1	EA	$0.22	$0.60	$0.00	$0.82
221116106360	Copper piping,L tube,1-1/2"	1	LF	$12.00	$2.98	$0.00	$14.98
221116201000	Copper fittings,reducing slip coupling,1-1/2"	0.02	EA	$0.24	$0.95	$0.00	$1.19
				$13.58	**$8.11**	**$0.00**	**$21.69**
D2020.05.15	**2" L Copper, Including Hangers and Fittings, 100' Runs**						**LF**
221116202381	Copper,90 ells,2"	0.08	EA	$2.02	$3.81	$0.00	$5.83
221116201020	Copper fittings,reducing slip coupling,2"	0.02	EA	$0.40	$1.19	$0.00	$1.59
220629100190	A band,copper,2"	0.1	EA	$0.24	$0.65	$0.00	$0.89
221116106400	Copper piping,L tube,2"	1	LF	$18.73	$3.25	$0.00	$21.98
				$21.39	**$8.90**	**$0.00**	**$30.29**
D2020.05.17	**4" L Copper, Including Hangers and Fittings, 100' Runs**						**LF**
221116202390	Copper,90 ells,4"	0.08	EA	$13.89	$5.72	$0.00	$19.61
220629100220	A band,copper,4"	0.1	EA	$0.55	$0.89	$0.00	$1.44
221116106520	Copper piping,L tube,4"	1	LF	$61.76	$3.97	$0.00	$65.73
221116201050	Copper fittings,reducing slip coupling,4"	0.02	EA	$1.86	$1.79	$0.00	$3.65
				$78.06	**$12.37**	**$0.00**	**$90.43**

All prices are updated to January 1, 2021 and are national averages.
For more in-depth information contact Design, Cost and Data at 800-533-5680, or go to www.DCD.com

482

D SERVICES

D2020 DOMESTIC WATER DISTRIBUTION

D2020.05 BLACK STEEL

		Quan.	Unit	Material	Labor	Equip.	Total
D2020.05.30	**3/4" Black Steel, Schedule 40, Including Hangers and Fittings, 100' Runs .... LF**						
221116904160	Malleable iron,threaded,3/4",coupling	0.08	EA	$0.36	$1.91	$0.00	$2.27
221116904090	Malleable iron,threaded,3/4",90 deg ell	0.02	EA	$0.08	$0.48	$0.00	$0.56
221116901100	Black steel,extra heavy pipe,threaded,3/4" pipe	1	LF	$3.64	$2.86	$0.00	$6.50
220529100300	Hanger,3/4" pipe,clevis pipe hanger,black steel	0.1	EA	$0.19	$2.38	$0.00	$2.57
				$4.27	**$7.63**	**$0.00**	**$11.90**
D2020.05.35	**1" Black Steel, Schedule 40, Including Hangers and Fittings, 100' Runs .... LF**						
220529100400	Hanger,1" pipe,clevis pipe hanger,black steel	0.1	EA	$0.20	$2.38	$0.00	$2.58
221116901200	Black steel,extra heavy,threaded,1" pipe	1	LF	$4.68	$3.58	$0.00	$8.26
221116904180	Malleable iron,threaded,1",90 deg ell	0.02	EA	$0.12	$0.57	$0.00	$0.69
221116904240	Malleable iron,threaded,1",coupling	0.08	EA	$0.53	$2.29	$0.00	$2.82
				$5.53	**$8.82**	**$0.00**	**$14.35**
D2020.05.40	**1-1/2" Black Steel, Schedule 40, Including Hangers and Fittings, 100' Runs .... LF**						
221116901400	Black steel,extra heavy,threaded,1-1/2" pipe	1	LF	$7.03	$3.97	$0.00	$11.00
221116904270	Malleable iron,threaded,1-1/2",90 deg ell	0.02	EA	$0.25	$0.72	$0.00	$0.97
220529100600	Hanger,1-1/2" pipe,clevis pipe hanger,black steel	0.1	EA	$0.22	$2.38	$0.00	$2.60
221116904340	Malleable iron,threaded,1-1/2",coupling	0.08	EA	$0.94	$2.86	$0.00	$3.80
				$8.44	**$9.93**	**$0.00**	**$18.37**
D2020.05.45	**2-1/2" Black Steel, Schedule 40, Including Hangers and Fittings, 100' Runs .... LF**						
221116904430	Malleable iron,threaded,2-1/2",coupling	0.08	EA	$3.84	$9.54	$0.00	$13.38
220529100800	Hanger,2-1/2" pipe,clevis pipe hanger,black steel	0.1	EA	$0.42	$2.38	$0.00	$2.80
221116901500	Black steel,extra heavy,threaded,2-1/2" pipe	1	LF	$14.06	$8.94	$0.00	$23.00
221116904370	Malleable iron,threaded,2-1/2",90 deg ell	0.02	EA	$0.96	$1.79	$0.00	$2.75
				$19.28	**$22.65**	**$0.00**	**$41.93**
D2020.05.50	**4" Black Steel, Schedule 40, Including Hangers and Fittings, 100' Runs .... LF**						
221116904590	Malleable iron,threaded,4",coupling	0.08	EA	$10.43	$5.72	$0.00	$16.15
221116904540	Malleable iron,threaded,4",90 deg ell	0.02	EA	$3.04	$2.86	$0.00	$5.90
220529101100	Hanger,4" pipe,clevis pipe hanger,black steel	0.1	EA	$0.64	$2.38	$0.00	$3.02
221116901700	Black steel,extra heavy,threaded,4" pipe	1	LF	$28.37	$14.30	$0.00	$42.67
				$42.48	**$25.26**	**$0.00**	**$67.74**

All prices are updated to January 1, 2021 and are national averages.
For more in-depth information contact Design, Cost and Data at 800-533-5680, or go to www.DCD.com

483

D SERVICES

D2020 DOMESTIC WATER DISTRIBUTION

D2020.10 WATER HEATERS

		Quan.	Unit	Material	Labor	Equip.	Total
D2020.10.10	**Electric Water Heaters** ....**EA**						
223300101120	Water heater,electric,120 gal	1	EA	$1,669.80	$238.40	$0.00	$1,908.20
223300108200	Water heater, rough-in, Maximum	1	EA	$859.10	$715.20	$0.00	$1,574.30
337116005810	Utility pole,perforated strap for conduit,1-1/2"	6	LF	$18.19	$72.44	$0.00	$90.63
				$2,547.09	$1,026.04	$0.00	$3,573.13

D2020.25 SOLAR WATER HEATERS

		Quan.	Unit	Material	Labor	Equip.	Total
D2020.25.11	**Solar Hot Water heater, hydronic, 100-120 Gallons, minimum** ....**EA**						
223300201010	Solar Water heater, hydronic, 100-120 Gal., min.	1.000	EA	$14,356.65	$0.00	$0.00	$14,356.65
D2020.25.12	**Solar Hot Water heater, hydronic, 100-120 Gallons, average**............................**EA**						
223300201020	Solar Water heater, hydronic, 100-120 Gallons, average	1.000	EA	$15,118.95	$0.00	$0.00	$15,118.95
D2020.25.14	**Solar Hot Water heater, hydronic, 100-120 Gallons, maximum** ....**EA**						
223300201030	Solar Water heater, hydronic, 100-120 Gallons, max.	1.000	EA	$15,881.25	$0.00	$0.00	$15,881.25
D2020.25.20	**Solar Hot Water heater, direct-solar, 100-120 Gallons, minimum**.....................**EA**						
223300201050	Solar Water heater, direct, 100-120 Gallons, minimum	1.000	EA	$9,528.75	$0.00	$0.00	$9,528.75
D2020.25.25	**Solar Hot Water heater, direct-solar, 100-120 Gallons, average** ....**EA**						
223300201060	Solar Water heater, direct, 100-120 Gallons, average	1.000	EA	$9,973.43	$0.00	$0.00	$9,973.43
D2020.25.28	**Solar Hot Water heater, direct-solar, 100-120 Gallons, maximum**....................**EA**						
223300201070	Solar heater, direct, 100-120 Gallons, maximum	1.000	EA	$10,418.10	$0.00	$0.00	$10,418.10

All prices are updated to January 1, 2021 and are national averages.
For more in-depth information contact Design, Cost and Data at 800-533-5680, or go to www.DCD.com

484

D SERVICES

D2030   PIPING, SANITARY WASTE

D2030.10 PLASTIC, DWV

		Quan.	Unit	Material	Labor	Equip.	Total
D2030.10.05	**1-1/2" Plastic, PVC, DWV, Schedule 40, Including Hangers and Fittings, 100' Runs..... LF**						
220629100180	A band,copper,1-1/2"	0.1	EA	$0.22	$0.60	$0.00	$0.82
221116801080	PVC pipe,sch 40,1-1/2" pipe	1	LF	$1.69	$4.47	$0.00	$6.16
221116802460	PVC pipe,sch 40,1-1/2",90 deg elbow	0.02	EA	$0.03	$0.41	$0.00	$0.44
221116802530	PVC pipe,sch 40,1-1/2",coupling	0.08	EA	$0.08	$1.91	$0.00	$1.99
				$2.02	**$7.39**	**$0.00**	**$9.41**
D2030.10.07	**2" Plastic, PVC, DWV, Schedule 40, Including Hangers and Fittings, 100' Runs........... LF**						
221116802640	PVC pipe,sch 40,2",coupling	0.08	EA	$0.12	$2.29	$0.00	$2.41
221116802570	PVC pipe,sch 40,2",90 deg elbow	0.02	EA	$0.05	$0.48	$0.00	$0.53
221116801100	PVC pipe,sch 40,2" pipe	1	LF	$2.14	$5.11	$0.00	$7.25
220629100190	A band,copper,2"	0.1	EA	$0.24	$0.65	$0.00	$0.89
				$2.55	**$8.53**	**$0.00**	**$11.08**
D2030.10.10	**3" Plastic, PVC, DWV, Schedule 40, Including Hangers and Fittings, 100' Runs........... LF**						
221116801120	PVC pipe,sch 40,3" pipe	1	LF	$4.41	$7.15	$0.00	$11.56
221116802780	PVC pipe,sch 40,3",90 deg elbow	0.02	EA	$0.16	$1.19	$0.00	$1.35
221116802830	PVC pipe,sch 40,3",coupling	0.08	EA	$0.37	$4.77	$0.00	$5.14
220629100220	A band,copper,4"	0.1	EA	$0.55	$0.89	$0.00	$1.44
				$5.49	**$14.00**	**$0.00**	**$19.49**
D2030.10.13	**4" Plastic, PVC, DWV, Schedule 40, Including Hangers and Fittings, 100' Runs........... LF**						
221116802930	PVC pipe,sch 40,4",coupling	0.08	EA	$0.54	$5.72	$0.00	$6.26
220629100220	A band,copper,4"	0.1	EA	$0.55	$0.89	$0.00	$1.44
221116801130	PVC pipe,sch 40,4" pipe	1	LF	$6.30	$8.94	$0.00	$15.24
221116802870	PVC pipe,sch 40,4",90 deg elbow	0.02	EA	$0.29	$1.43	$0.00	$1.72
				$7.68	**$16.98**	**$0.00**	**$24.66**

All prices are updated to January 1, 2021 and are national averages.
For more in-depth information contact Design, Cost and Data at 800-533-5680, or go to www.DCD.com

485

D SERVICES

D2030 PIPING, SANITARY WASTE

D2030.10 CAST IRON

		Quan.	Unit	Material	Labor	Equip.	Total
D2030.10.50	**1-1/2" Cast Iron, No-Hub, Including Hangers and Fittings, 100' Runs .... LF**						
221316005180	CI Pipe,Abv Gr,no hub,1-1/2",coupling	0.02	EA	$0.45	$0.00	$0.00	$0.45
221316005000	CI Pipe,Abv Gr,no hub,1-1/2",1/4 bend	0.08	EA	$0.91	$1.91	$0.00	$2.82
220529100600	Hanger,1-1/2" pipe,clevis pipe hanger,black steel	0.1	EA	$0.22	$2.38	$0.00	$2.60
221316001000	CI Pipe,Abv Gr,no hub,1-1/2" pipe	1	LF	$12.27	$5.11	$0.00	$17.38
				$13.85	**$9.40**	**$0.00**	**$23.25**
D2030.10.55	**4" Cast Iron, No-Hub, Including Hangers and Fittings, 100' Runs.................................. LF**						
221316007100	CI Pipe,Abv Gr,no hub,4",coupling	0.02	EA	$0.44	$0.00	$0.00	$0.44
220529101100	Hanger,4" pipe,clevis pipe hanger,black steel	0.1	EA	$0.64	$2.38	$0.00	$3.02
221316001200	CI Pipe,Abv Gr,no hub,4" pipe	1	LF	$19.57	$11.92	$0.00	$31.49
221316006820	CI Pipe,Abv Gr,no hub,4",1/4 bend	0.08	EA	$2.07	$2.86	$0.00	$4.93
				$22.72	**$17.16**	**$0.00**	**$39.88**
D2030.10.57	**6" Cast Iron, No-Hub, Including Hangers and Fittings, 100' Runs.................................. LF**						
221316007700	CI Pipe,Abv Gr,no hub,6",coupling	0.02	EA	$1.12	$0.00	$0.00	$1.12
221316007600	CI Pipe,Abv Gr,no hub,6",1/4 bend	0.08	EA	$5.24	$4.77	$0.00	$10.01
221316001300	CI Pipe,Abv Gr,no hub,6" pipe	1	LF	$34.50	$14.30	$0.00	$48.80
220529101320	Hanger,6" pipe,clevis pipe hanger,black steel	0.1	EA	$1.02	$2.86	$0.00	$3.88
				$41.88	**$21.93**	**$0.00**	**$63.81**
D2030.10.60	**8" Cast Iron, No-Hub, Including Hangers and Fittings, 100' Runs.................................. LF**						
220529101420	Hanger,8" pipe,clevis pipe hanger,black steel	0.1	EA	$1.68	$2.86	$0.00	$4.54
221316001400	CI Pipe,Abv Gr,no hub,8" pipe	1	LF	$55.45	$23.84	$0.00	$79.29
221316007990	CI Pipe,Abv Gr,no hub,8",1/4 bend	0.08	EA	$9.09	$4.77	$0.00	$13.86
221316008090	CI Pipe,Abv Gr,no hub,8",coupling	0.02	EA	$2.11	$0.00	$0.00	$2.11
				$68.33	**$31.47**	**$0.00**	**$99.80**
D2030.10.62	**10" Cast Iron, No-Hub, Including Hangers and Fittings, 100' Runs................................. LF**						
221316001500	CI Pipe,Abv Gr,no hub,10" pipe	1	LF	$87.00	$28.61	$0.00	$115.61
221316008360	CI Pipe,Abv Gr,no hub,10",1/4 bend	0.08	EA	$18.17	$4.77	$0.00	$22.94
220529101500	Hanger,10" clevis pipe hanger,black steel	0.1	EA	$3.03	$2.86	$0.00	$5.89
221316008420	CI Pipe,Abv Gr,no hub,10",coupling	0.02	EA	$2.78	$0.00	$0.00	$2.78
				$110.98	**$36.24**	**$0.00**	**$147.22**

All prices are updated to January 1, 2021 and are national averages.
For more in-depth information contact Design, Cost and Data at 800-533-5680, or go to www.DCD.com

486

ASSEMBLIES

D SERVICES

D3010   ENERGY SUPPLY

D3010.10 HVAC SQUARE FOOT COSTS

	Quan.	Unit	Material	Labor	Equip.	Total
D3010.10.10 HVAC, per building, minimum						**SF**
019980103030 HVAC, per building, minimum	1.000	SF	$19.44	$0.00	$0.00	$19.44
D3010.10.12 HVAC, per building, average						**SF**
019980103050 HVAC, per building, average	1.000	SF	$27.19	$0.00	$0.00	$27.19
D3010.10.14 HVAC, per building, maximum						**SF**
019980103070 HVAC, per building, maximum	1.000	SF	$29.19	$0.00	$0.00	$29.19
D3010.10.20 HVAC, controls, minimum						**SF**
019980103210 HVAC Controls, minimum	1.000	SF	$3.69	$0.00	$0.00	$3.69
D3010.10.21 HVAC, controls, average						**SF**
019980103230 HVAC Controls, average	1.000	SF	$4.05	$0.00	$0.00	$4.05
D3010.10.23 HVAC, controls, maximum						**SF**
019980103250 HVAC Controls, maximum	1.000	SF	$4.88	$0.00	$0.00	$4.88
D3010.10.30 HVAC, ductwork, minimum						**SF**
019980103410 HVAC Ductwork, minimum	1.000	SF	$2.09	$0.00	$0.00	$2.09
D3010.10.31 HVAC, ductwork, average						**SF**
019980103430 HVAC Ductwork, average	1.000	SF	$4.18	$0.00	$0.00	$4.18
D3010.10.32 HVAC, ductwork, maximum						**SF**
019980103450 HVAC Ductwork, maximum	1.000	SF	$4.26	$0.00	$0.00	$4.26

D4010   SPRINKLERS

D4010.10 SPRINKLER SQUARE FOOT COSTS

	Quan.	Unit	Material	Labor	Equip.	Total
D4010.10.10 Sprinkler, per building, minimum						**SF**
019980102030 Fire Suppress., per building, minimum	1.000	SF	$1.46	$0.00	$0.00	$1.46
D4010.10.12 Sprinkler, per building, average						**SF**
019980102050 Fire Suppress., per building, average	1.000	SF	$3.36	$0.00	$0.00	$3.36
D4010.10.14 Sprinkler, per building, maximum						**SF**
019980102070 Fire Suppress., per building, maximum	1.000	SF	$4.84	$0.00	$0.00	$4.84

D SERVICES

D5010 ELECTRICAL

D5010.10 ELECTRICAL SQUARE FOOT COSTS

		Quan.	Unit	Material	Labor	Equip.	Total
D5010.10.10	**Electrical, per building, minimum**						**SF**
019980104030	Electrical, per building, minimum	1.000	SF	$24.19	$0.00	$0.00	$24.19
D5010.10.12	**Electrical, per building, average**						**SF**
019980104050	Electrical, per building, average	1.000	SF	$33.43	$0.00	$0.00	$33.43
D5010.10.14	**Electrical, per building, maximum**						**SF**
019980104070	Electrical, per building, maximum	1.000	SF	$50.09	$0.00	$0.00	$50.09
D5010.10.30	**Electrical, rough-in, minimum**						**SF**
019980104210	Electrical Rough-in, minimum	1.000	SF	$2.39	$0.00	$0.00	$2.39
D5010.10.32	**Electrical, rough-in, average**						**SF**
019980104230	Electrical Rough-in, average	1.000	SF	$4.27	$0.00	$0.00	$4.27
D5010.10.34	**Electrical, rough-in, maximum**						**SF**
019980104250	Electrical Rough-in, maximum	1.000	SF	$8.29	$0.00	$0.00	$8.29
D5010.10.50	**Electrical, Lighting, minimum**						**SF**
019980104410	Electrical Lighting, minimum	1.000	SF	$3.21	$0.00	$0.00	$3.21
D5010.10.52	**Electrical, Lighting, average**						**SF**
019980104430	Electrical Lighting, average	1.000	SF	$7.67	$0.00	$0.00	$7.67
D5010.10.54	**Electrical, Lighting, maximum**						**SF**
019980104450	Electrical Lighting, maximum	1.000	SF	$8.86	$0.00	$0.00	$8.86
D5010.10.60	**Electrical, switchgear, minimum**						**SF**
019980104510	Electrical Switchgear, minimum	1.000	SF	$1.67	$0.00	$0.00	$1.67
D5010.10.62	**Electrical, switchgear, average**						**SF**
019980104530	Electrical Switchgear, average	1.000	SF	$2.52	$0.00	$0.00	$2.52
D5010.10.64	**Electrical, switchgear, maximum**						**SF**
019980104550	Electrical Switchgear, maximum	1.000	SF	$3.22	$0.00	$0.00	$3.22

All prices are updated to January 1, 2021 and are national averages.
For more in-depth information contact Design, Cost and Data at 800-533-5680, or go to www.DCD.com

488

Square Foot Tables

The following Square Foot Tables list hundreds of actual projects for ten building types, each with associated building size, total square foot building cost and percentage of project costs for total mechanical and electrical components. This data provides an overview of construction costs by building type. These costs are for actual projects. The variations within similar building types may be due, among other factors, to size, location, quality and specified components, materials and processes. Depending upon all such factors, specific building costs can vary significantly and may not necessarily fall within the range of costs as presented. The data has been updated to reflect current construction costs.

All prices are updated to January 1, 2021 and are national averages.
For a more in-depth report of any of these buildings or additional case studies, contact Design, Cost and Data at 800-533-5680, or go to www.DCD.com

489

All prices are updated to January 1, 2021 and are national averages.
For a more in-depth report of any of these buildings or additional case studies, contact
Design, Cost and Data at 800-533-5680, or go to www.DCD.com

SQUARE FOOT TABLES

PROJECT	DESCRIPTION	CITY	STATE	SIZE	$/SF	NOTES
Commercial						
Bank	School Credit Union Administration Building	Katy	TX	30,700	$216.78	New
	FineMark National Bank & Trust	Fort Myers	FL	20,039	$408.96	New
	Florida Shores Bank	Pompano Beach	FL	11,697	$520.52	New
	Mobiloil Credit Union	Vidor	TX	9,252	$365.04	New
	Beaumont Community Credit Union	Beaumont	TX	3,267	$413.83	New
Office	Allendale Town Center	Allendale	NJ	80,226	$38.20	Addition/Renovation
	Roanoke Electric Cooperative	Ahoskie	NC	52,752	$217.92	New
	Regional Aviation & Training Center	Currituck	NC	39,930	$276.44	New
	Transportation/Warehouse Facility	Monroe	GA	32,400	$191.90	New
	Collection System Operations Facility	Walnut Creek	CA	27,179	$379.11	New
	ULTA - (Shell Only)	Pensacola	FL	10,850	$98.09	Renovation
	Daycare Center	Clawson	MI	4,270	$155.32	Adaptive Reuse
	Campgrounds Office & Retail	Cincinnati	OH	2,300	$340.27	New
Parking	Palm Avenue Parking Garage	Sarasota	FL	287,040	$58.13	New
	Reynolds Street Parking Deck	Augusta	GA	214,000	$69.15	New
	Awty Int. School Parking Structure	Houston	TX	174,582	$61.22	New
Retail	SNG Center - Mixed-Use	Fargo	ND	143,860	$102.89	New
	Roof & Lifeway/Steinmart Renovation	Pensacola	FL	88,299	$36.14	Renovation
	No Frills Supermarket	Omaha	NE	61,000	$110.07	New
	West Oaks Mall Redevelopment	Houston	TX	49,800	$195.89	Renovation
	World of Decor	Deerfield Beach	FL	47,500	$149.51	New
	Sarasota Yacht Club	Sarasota	FL	41,332	$439.28	New
	Karschs Village Market	Barnhart	MO	35,384	$85.80	New
	Fresh Thyme Farmers Market	Fishers	IN	28,784	$188.13	New
	Nashville Hangar Inc.	Nashville	TN	28,702	$197.26	New
	Party Time Plus	Billings	MT	26,000	$100.08	New
	Marshalls - (Shell Only)	Pensacola	FL	25,990	$47.89	Renovation
	Ed Hicks Mercedes-Benz USA	Corpus Christi	TX	25,273	$261.77	New
	Montana Honda & Marine	Billings	MT	22,963	$113.75	Addition
	Fresh Market - (Shell Only)	Pensacola	FL	21,000	$82.32	Renovation
	Theatre Exchange Interior Fit Up	Manitoba	CA	19,344	$132.78	Renovation
	DSW Shoes Renovation	Pensacola	FL	18,000	$92.17	Renovation
	Dormans Lighting & Design	Lutherville	MD	15,220	$124.94	Addition
	The Groves Exterior Renovation	Farmington	MI	15,137	$70.63	Renovation
	Don Gibson Theatre	Shelby	NC	13,386	$372.40	Renovation
	Tri Ford Showroom Expansion	Highland	IL	12,881	$121.80	Addition/Renovation
	Fiat of LeHigh Valley	Easton	PA	11,905	$155.97	New
	Sicardi Art Gallery	Houston	TX	6,175	$245.35	New
	Childrens Mercy Hospital Gift Shop	Kansas City	MO	5,010	$309.23	Tenant Build-out
Restaurant	LaMar Cebicheria Peruana Restaurant	San Francisco	CA	11,000	$316.16	Tenant Build-out
	Ulele Restaurant	Tampa	FL	8,905	$766.28	Adaptive Reuse
	Youells Oyster House	Allentown	PA	6,107	$251.55	New
	Mellow Mushroom Highlands Shell	Louisville	KY	5,802	$101.96	New
	Mellow Mushroom Highlands TBO	Louisville	KY	5,802	$169.11	Tenant Build-out
	Mellow Mushroom Pizza	Wilder	KY	5,500	$241.87	New
	Liberty Microbrewery	Plymouth	MI	3,425	$174.02	Addition
	700 South Deli	Linthicum	MD	3,200	$214.42	Tenant Build-out
	New York Pizza Department (NYPD)	Tempe	AZ	2,338	$328.05	Tenant Build-out
	Airport Restaurant Build Out	Eglin Air Force Base	FL	2,320	$282.41	Tenant Build-out

All prices are updated to January 1, 2021 and are national averages.
For a more in-depth report of any of these buildings or additional case studies, contact
Design, Cost and Data at 800-533-5680, or go to www.DCD.com

SQUARE FOOT TABLES

PROJECT	DESCRIPTION	CITY	STATE	SIZE	$/SF	NOTES
	Civic/Government					
Civic Center	Lincoln Center	Fort Collins	CO	38,160	$216.29	Addition/Renovation
	Rockport City Services Building	Rockport	TX	20,062	$223.75	New
	Sinclair Park Community Centre	Manitoba	CA	17,007	$316.81	Addition/Renovation
	Mt. Olive City Hall Complex	Mount Olive	IL	14,360	$121.48	New
	Teaneck Municipal Complex	Teaneck	NJ	12,870	$232.81	Addition/Renovation
	Cobb Community Center Additions	Pensacola	FL	5,200	$324.01	Addition/Renovation
	Newtown Municipal Center	Newtown	OH	5,077	$168.59	Adaptive Reuse
	Nederland City Hall	Nederland	TX	4,983	$375.09	New
Correctional	County Sheriffs Office	Morgantown	WV	31,645	$297.28	New
	Nederland Public Safety Complex	Nederland	TX	21,189	$217.30	Adaptive Reuse
	Detention Center & Sheriffs Office	Spencer	IA	16,983	$421.41	New
	Ogle City Sheriff & Coroner Admin	Oregon	IL	15,377	$283.95	New
	Chautauqua City Jail & Sheriff	Sedan	KS	12,257	$299.47	New
Courthouse	Courthouse HVAC System Replacement	Gainesville	FL	101,000	$43.19	Renovation
	Courthouse Renovation & Restoration	Springfield	IL	47,720	$184.63	Renovation
Fire Department	College Station Fire Station #6	College Station	TX	25,133	$350.16	New
	Mt. Orab Fire Station	Village of Mt. Orab	OH	18,170	$180.68	New
	Richardson Fire Station No. 4	Richardson	TX	14,090	$411.12	New
	Willowfork Fire Station No. 2	Katy	TX	13,358	$302.19	New
	Joint Fire & Rescue Station	Newtown	OH	13,125	$194.79	Addition/Renovation
	Little Miami Fire & Rescue	Fairfax	OH	12,316	$231.30	New
	Fire Station No. 11	Fort Smith	AR	12,155	$350.36	New
	Pearisburg Fire Station	Pearisburg	VA	11,818	$225.50	New
	Ponderosa Fire Station No. 62	Spring	TX	11,163	$302.54	New
	El Dorado Hills Fire Station 84	El Dorado Hills	CA	10,869	$455.55	New
	Wayne Fire Department	Goshen	OH	10,000	$99.16	New
	Fire Station No. 40	Jacksonville	FL	9,703	$399.75	New
	Rosenberg Fire Station No. 3	Rosenberg	TX	8,479	$378.94	New
	Little Rock Fire Station No. 23	Little Rock	AR	8,291	$487.53	New
	Cleveland Volunteer Fire Station	Cleveland	MS	6,910	$340.81	New
Government	Council Center For Scouting	Fargo	ND	20,466	$204.40	New
	Camp Crook Ranger Station	Camp Crook	SD	4,880	$504.83	New
	Beaumont Municipal Tennis Center	Beaumont	TX	4,460	$369.39	Addition
	Florence Transit Hub	Florence	KY	3,115	$527.64	New
	Knox Area Rescue Ministries	Knoxville	TN	1,762	$694.90	New
	Entrance Station Lake Mead	Clark County	NV	480	$2,819.31	New
	Vehicle Charging Stations	Denton	TX	6 spaces	$7,233.53	New
Library	Dover Public Library	Dover	DE	46,424	$443.19	New
	Clinton-Macomb Public Library	Clinton Township	MI	24,723	$129.49	Adaptive Reuse
	Crozet Western Albemarle Library	Crozet	VA	23,199	$359.80	New
	Upper Tampa Bay Regional Library	Tampa	FL	13,630	$249.02	Addition/Renovation
	Palmetto Branch Library	Palmetto	GA	11,200	$496.97	New
	Regional Library Expansion	Valrico	FL	10,970	$305.27	Addition/Renovation
Miscellaneous	City of Pampa Animal Welfare	Pampa	TX	13,578	$289.19	New
	Royal Winnipeg Ballet Renovations	Manitoba	CA	13,237	$78.02	Renovation
	Senior Services - Kitchen Facility	Batavia	OH	6,000	$123.50	New
	Historical Site Locomotive Shelter	Bismarck	ND	2,100	$165.06	New
Office	Federal Building & Courthouse Modernization	Denver	CO	41,600	$357.90	Renovation
	Brazos County Tax Office	Bryan	TX	13,143	$307.93	New
	Illinois Water District Office	Lincoln	IL	8,974	$160.26	New
	Arkansas River Resource Center	Little Rock	AR	4,926	$588.40	New

All prices are updated to January 1, 2021 and are national averages.
For a more in-depth report of any of these buildings or additional case studies, contact
Design, Cost and Data at 800-533-5680, or go to www.DCD.com

492

SQUARE FOOT TABLES

PROJECT	DESCRIPTION	CITY	STATE	SIZE	$/SF	NOTES
		Educational				
Athletic Facility	Physical Activity/Sports Science	Morgantown	WV	117,344	$244.33	New
	Indoor Football Practice Facility	Clemson	SC	81,992	$188.54	New
	Jesuit College Locker Room Addition	Dallas	TX	41,673	$225.42	Addition
	Multi-Purpose Gymnasium	Jacksonville	FL	22,844	$299.13	New
College Classroom	New Mexico Tech Geology Building	Socorro	NM	86,813	$325.86	New
	CSU Concourse & Training Room	Fort Collins	CO	53,050	$152.21	Addition/Renovation
	Jack Williamson Liberal Arts Center	Portales	NM	52,480	$244.58	Renovation
	UNLV Literature & Law Building	Las Vegas	NV	44,830	$203.35	Renovation
	Southern State Community College	Mount Orab	OH	43,833	$195.65	New
	SERT Building Iowa Lakes College	Estherville	IA	42,940	$134.09	Adaptive Reuse
Elementary	Cibolo Valley Elementary School	Cibolo	TX	153,130	$264.86	New
	Hill Farm Elementary School	Bryant	AR	88,800	$316.82	New
	CREC International Magnet School	South Windsor	CT	63,923	$435.46	New
	Pineville Elementary School	Pineville	WV	51,650	$231.89	New
	Crownpoint Elementary School	Crownpoint	NM	48,592	$432.07	New
	Janney Elementary School Addition	Washington	DC	10,000	$638.61	Addition
High School	Hmong College Prep Academy	Saint Paul	MN	154,434	$90.68	Addition/Renovation
	HFC High School North Building	Flossmoor	IL	136,555	$221.96	Addition/Renovation
	Somerset High School	Von Ormy	TX	125,800	$192.78	New
	Takoma Education Campus	Washington	DC	119,000	$238.43	Renovation
	High School Addition & Renovation	Decatur	GA	83,816	$276.83	Addition/Renovation
	Palmer Catholic Academy	Ponte Vedra Beach	FL	34,209	$150.00	New
	Elmwood High School Addition	Elmwood Park	IL	31,630	$371.42	Addition/Renovation
	High School Fine Arts Building	Heber Springs	AR	30,505	$433.80	New
	Alamo Heights High School Fine Arts	San Antonio	TX	25,536	$348.60	Addition/Renovation
	St. Patrick Catholic School	Jacksonville	FL	23,227	$319.96	New
	Springdale School Alteration	Corbett	OR	13,680	$136.51	Renovation
	Goddard School Addition Renovation	Anderson Township	OH	12,489	$90.96	Addition/Renovation
	ISD Outdoor Education Center	Sabine Pass	TX	10,193	$345.68	New
	Indian Mountain School Student Center	Lakeville	CT	9,335	$331.86	Addition
	First Impressions Academy	Fayetteville	NC	7,752	$190.94	New
	High School South Campus Field	Cincinnati	OH	5,580	$256.08	New
Middle School	Timberline Middle School	Waukee	IA	187,375	$171.88	New
	Red Bank Middle School	Chattanooga	TN	158,637	$284.58	New
	Jaime Escalante Middle School	Pharr	TX	156,538	$213.09	New
	Conservatory Green ECE-8 School	Denver	CO	113,616	$190.04	New
	Midland School Addition	Floral	AR	30,150	$255.54	Addition
Laboratory/Research	Science & Technology Building	Fayetteville	NC	65,048	$539.12	New
	NSU/US Geological Survey	Davie	FL	24,000	$112.03	Tenant Build-out
	Northeast Technology Center	Pryor	OK	11,909	$336.06	New
	Environmental Education Center	Bushkill Township	PA	9,275	$582.64	New
	Research & Education Center	Homestead	FL	5,760	$735.26	New
Multi-Purpose	BGSU Student Rec Center	Bowling Green	OH	179,549	$70.62	Renovation
	Kennedy Center Theatre/Studio Arts	Clinton	NY	96,100	$356.65	New
	Classroom & Administration Building	Houston	TX	65,234	$230.55	New
	NM State U Pete Domenici Building	Las Cruces	NM	53,341	$290.60	Addition/Renovation
	Widener University Freedom Hall	Chester	PA	36,700	$343.98	New
	Alumni Hall, Lincoln Park	Midland	PA	29,027	$280.51	New
	GSU Piedmont North Dining Hall	Atlanta	GA	12,300	$393.83	Addition
	NAU Dining Hall Expansion Phase II	Flagstaff	AZ	10,096	$502.26	New
	Neighborhood Resource Center	Richmond	TX	6,935	$216.82	New
	Heber Springs Cafeteria Remodel	Heber Springs	AR	5,585	$244.33	Renovation

All prices are updated to January 1, 2021 and are national averages.
For a more in-depth report of any of these buildings or additional case studies, contact
Design, Cost and Data at 800-533-5680, or go to www.DCD.com

SQUARE FOOT TABLES

PROJECT	DESCRIPTION	CITY	STATE	SIZE	$/SF	NOTES
			Hotels			
Hotels	Omni Dallas Hotel	Dallas	TX	1,161,450	$443.81	New
	John Ascuagas Nugget Hotel/Casino	Sparks	NV	449,820	$151.41	Addition
	Le Centre On Fourth Embassy Suites	Louisville	KY	408,229	$119.82	Adaptive Reuse
	Minneapolis Marriott West	Minneapolis	MN	237,362	$172.95	New
	Sheraton Centre Park Hotel	Dallas	TX	231,031	$247.51	New
	AmeriSuites	Chicago	IL	191,600	$156.50	Addition/Renovation
	Hampton Inn & Suites Hotel	Chicago	IL	162,000	$170.91	New
	Sheraton Harbor Island Hotel Tower	San Diego	CA	144,126	$208.37	Addition
	Compri Hotel	Los Angeles	CA	110,150	$184.54	New
	Best Western Columbia Hotel	San Diego	CA	108,040	$142.76	New
	Spooky Nook Warehouse Hotel	Manheim	PA	92,726	$135.95	Adaptive Reuse
	The Atrium Motel	Norfolk	VA	75,889	$145.99	New
	Staybridge Hotel At Preston Ridge	Alpharetta	GA	74,607	$187.19	New
	Hampton Inn & Suites	Allentown	PA	71,686	$156.12	New
	Hampton Inn Hotel	Carol Stream	IL	71,000	$191.72	New
	The Inn On Lake Superior	Duluth	MN	65,345	$154.22	New
	The Lancaster Hotel	Houston	TX	64,310	$322.73	Renovation
	Fairfield Inn	Helena	MT	31,009	$150.71	New
	The Edison Hotel	Miami	FL	28,875	$124.94	Renovation
	Western Executive Inn	Billings	MT	21,984	$111.55	New
	Country Hearth Inn	Preston	MN	21,028	$130.97	New
	Lawrence Welk Resort Hotel	Escondido	CA	19,874	$149.39	Addition
	Hanalei Hotel Conference Center	San Diego	CA	8,587	$237.22	Addition
	Summit At Vail, Multi-Purpose Lodge	Vail	CO	6,000	$283.23	New

All prices are updated to January 1, 2021 and are national averages.
For a more in-depth report of any of these buildings or additional case studies, contact
Design, Cost and Data at 800-533-5680, or go to www.DCD.com

SQUARE FOOT TABLES

PROJECT	DESCRIPTION	CITY	STATE	SIZE	$/SF	NOTES
Industrial						
Manufacturing	Brentwood Industries Manufacturing	Reading	PA	205,000	$43.98	New
	Lee Steel Corporate Plant	Romulus	MI	200,625	$95.66	New
	Siemens Westinghouse Fuel Cell Facility	Munhall	PA	191,090	$104.16	New
	Manufacturing Plant & Headquarters	Lansing	MI	188,975	$100.99	Addition
	Concepts Direct	Longmont	CO	117,900	$123.18	New
	Nypro Inc.	Clinton	MA	102,475	$126.36	Addition
	SWF Industrial	Wrightsville	PA	76,218	$77.85	New
	Headquarters & Manufacturing Facility	Lower Nazareth Township	PA	62,980	$37.29	Renovation
	Aerzen USA (Office/Manufacturing)	Coatesville	PA	40,000	$190.27	New
	Lee Steel Corporate Expansion	Wyoming	MI	34,821	$80.83	New
	Prescott Aerospace	Prescott	AZ	31,400	$116.45	New
	Battery Innovation Center	Newberry	IN	30,080	$454.35	New
	American Steel	Billings	MT	25,957	$84.46	New
	Phillip S. Luttazi Town Garage	Dover	MA	21,913	$145.33	New
	ITT Flygt - Industrial Facility	Milford	OH	16,991	$137.81	New
	Broadmoor Golf Maintenance	Colorado Springs	CO	16,064	$249.82	New
	Cooper B-Line Expansion	Highland	IL	15,290	$176.51	Addition/Renovation
	Robberson Ford Collision Center	Bend	OR	15,089	$144.89	New
	Brown Industrial Building	Truckee	CA	13,345	$143.13	New
	CTC Vehicle Maintenance Shops	Killeen	TX	11,250	$135.34	New
	Storage & Shop Facility	Billings	MT	8,763	$93.40	New
	Central Plant with Equipment Bay	Mesa	AZ	8,500	$962.99	New
Office	Woodlands Business Center	Richmond	VA	48,000	$83.66	New
	Wiregrass Research Center	Headland	AL	9,740	$258.37	New
Office/Warehouse	American Superconductor	Devens	MA	354,000	$177.79	New
	Castcon Stone Inc.	Saxonburg	PA	47,000	$119.08	New
	Minnesota DNR Headquarters	Tower	MN	37,802	$176.35	New
	Office & Warehouse	Miami	FL	14,815	$144.48	New
	DOT Office & Maintenance Building	Hillsboro	OH	10,876	$254.87	New
Warehouse	Distribution Center	Windsor	CT	303,750	$36.25	New
	Zany Brainy Distribution Center	Bridgeport	NJ	250,000	$43.29	New
	Galderma - Warehouse	Fort Worth	TX	70,000	$93.26	New
	Manzana Products Warehouse	Sebastopol	CA	41,395	$69.46	New
	Tactical Equip Maintenance Facility	Fort Campbell	KY	35,290	$250.61	New
	Sonoma Wine Company Canopy	Graton	CA	26,000	$58.96	New
	Administration/Chemical Storage Building	Killeen	TX	23,837	$356.50	New
	DOT Truck Storage Building	Hillsboro	OH	18,400	$97.26	New
	F.I. Storage Facility	Kentwood	MI	13,125	$71.52	New
	50 Columbia Drive Warehouse	Pooler	GA	10,000	$89.76	New
	DOT Salt Storage Building	Hillsboro	OH	9,100	$98.06	New
	Organizational Storage Facility	Fort Campbell	KY	8,040	$148.79	New
	Dwan Maintenance Building	Bloomington	MN	7,240	$200.94	Addition/Renovation
	Maintenance/Storage Building	Batavia	OH	7,200	$86.43	New
	DOT Cold Storage Building	Hillsboro	OH	5,040	$104.56	New
	Job Corp Warehouse	Hartford	CT	3,800	$495.71	New
	DOT Materials Storage Building	Hillsboro	OH	1,920	$116.90	New
	Aerial Vehicle Storage	Fort Campbell	KY	1,800	$223.41	New
	Petro, Oil, Lubricant Storage	Fort Campbell	KY	640	$312.31	New
	Hazardous Waste Storage Building	Fort Campbell	KY	640	$333.76	New

All prices are updated to January 1, 2021 and are national averages.
For a more in-depth report of any of these buildings or additional case studies, contact
Design, Cost and Data at 800-533-5680, or go to www.DCD.com

SQUARE FOOT TABLES

PROJECT	DESCRIPTION	CITY	STATE	SIZE	$/SF	NOTES
	Medical					
Clinic	HealthCare Emergency/Trauma Center	Topeka	KS	115,000	$421.22	Addition
	Sadler Clinic (Shell Only)	Conroe	TX	61,599	$131.13	New
	Pinellas County Health Department	Largo	FL	54,965	$273.25	Retrofit
	Sanford Moorhead Clinic	Moorhead	MN	49,250	$267.79	New
	County Health Department	Port Charlotte	FL	47,564	$303.63	New
	Sadler Clinic	Conroe	TX	41,066	$124.23	Tenant Build-out
	PineMed Medical Plaza	The Woodlands	TX	30,398	$138.54	New
	Outpatient Specialty Clinic	Vancouver	WA	20,139	$344.70	New
	Ambulatory Surgery Center	Stroudsburg	PA	19,929	$369.95	Addition/Renovation
	Thundermist Health Center	West Warwick	RI	18,217	$213.31	Adaptive Reuse
	E Texas Community Health Services	Nacogdoches	TX	12,500	$101.02	Retrofit
	North Mobile Health Center	Mt. Vernon	AL	6,765	$301.35	New
Dental Office	Construct Dental Clinic Roseburg	Roseburg	OR	7,750	$524.39	New
	Kitchens Pediatric Dental Clinic	Little Rock	AR	6,068	$315.67	New
	Dental Office Shell & Parking	Olympia	WA	5,302	$179.11	New
	Evans Family Dental	Austin	TX	2,354	$219.51	Tenant Build-out
Hospital	Union Hospital Addition	Terre Haute	IN	492,348	$329.92	Addition
	Regional Medical Center	Lafayette	LA	410,273	$552.16	New
	Houston Medical Pavilion	Warner Robins	GA	180,000	$65.05	Adaptive Reuse
	Langley AFB Hospital Renovation	Langley Air Force Base	VA	160,000	$551.26	Renovation
	Cass Regional Medical Center	Harrisonville	MO	137,524	$387.62	New
	Texas Spine & Joint Hospital	Tyler	TX	115,789	$256.73	Addition/Renovation
	Oktibbeha County Hospital Expansion	Starkville	MS	87,116	$336.41	New
	Childrens Mercy Hospital	Independence	MO	54,682	$324.12	New
	Oktibbeha County Hospital Renovation	Starkville	MS	30,263	$167.91	Renovation
	El Rio Community Health Center	Tucson	AZ	26,998	$247.56	New
	Pondella Public Health Center	Fort Myers	FL	26,400	$308.35	Renovation
	Topeka Ear Nose & Throat	Topeka	KS	24,073	$319.70	New
	Rapha Primary Care	Fayetteville	NC	19,907	$137.25	Renovation
	UNM Hospitals North Valley Center	Albuquerque	NM	16,500	$323.25	New
	El Rio Community Health Center	Tucson	AZ	14,000	$281.06	New
	VA Medical Center Area G Renovation	Houston	TX	12,000	$341.99	Renovation
	Surgical Suite Expansion	Dobbs Ferry	NY	9,000	$390.34	Renovation
	Legacy Emergency Room	Allen	TX	8,432	$647.41	New
	Oral & Maxillofacial Surgery Center	Fayetteville	NC	2,214	$550.86	Renovation
Nursing Home/Rehab	Senior Living Community	Hoschton	GA	56,251	$143.56	New
	Retirement Community	Carlisle	PA	47,075	$161.66	Addition/Renovation
	Assisted Living & Memory Center	Dacula	GA	38,221	$166.98	New
	Homestead Village Nursing Care	Lancaster	PA	28,149	$109.33	Renovation
	Jewish Services For The Aging	Tucson	AZ	24,993	$203.54	New
	Short-Term Rehabilitation	Olathe	KS	13,800	$273.81	Addition
	St. Katharine Retirement Center	El Reno	OK	12,000	$323.60	New/Addition
Office	Orthopedic Hospital/Medical Office	Allentown	PA	79,807	$205.10	Renovation
	Tomball Medical Office Building	Tomball	TX	54,380	$139.46	New
	Olathe Health Education Center	Olathe	KS	50,258	$311.86	New
	Home & Hospice Care	Providence	RI	47,734	$196.72	Renovation
	NE Georgia Medical Plaza 400	Dawsonville	GA	26,997	$274.47	Adaptive Reuse
	VA Medical Center/Pharmacy	Waco	TX	19,171	$159.81	Renovation
	Cancer Specialists of North Florida	Jacksonville	FL	18,654	$291.51	New
	MJHS Hospice Residence	N.Y.C.	NY	12,500	$150.84	Renovation
	Medical Office Building	Pelham	NH	8,399	$271.46	New
	Podiatry Group	Marietta	GA	6,768	$55.20	Renovation
	Marietta Podiatry Group	Marietta	GA	4,400	$252.11	New

All prices are updated to January 1, 2021 and are national averages.
For a more in-depth report of any of these buildings or additional case studies, contact
Design, Cost and Data at 800-533-5680, or go to www.DCD.com

SQUARE FOOT TABLES

PROJECT	DESCRIPTION	CITY	STATE	SIZE	$/SF	NOTES
	Office					
Office	Restaurant Support Center	Lenexa	KS	186,465	$266.92	New
	5000 NASA Boulevard	Fairmont	WY	132,000	$284.61	New
	Rockford Construction Office	Grand Rapids	MI	71,144	$113.72	Adaptive Reuse
	Woodlawn Office Bldg. (Shell Only)	Louisville	KY	60,000	$143.86	New
	Rosecrance Ware Center	Rockford	IL	44,800	$141.98	Adaptive Reuse
	Professional Center (Shell)	White Marsh	MD	43,025	$180.98	New
	Swan Skyline Office Plaza (Shell)	Tucson	AZ	37,200	$122.07	New
	Infinite Energy Phase IV	Gainesville	FL	36,500	$319.97	New
	Freedom Plaza Building	Cookeville	TN	28,488	$250.17	New
	Landmark Professional Building	Clayton	NC	27,231	$237.21	New
	FC Gulf Freeway Building (Shell)	Houston	TX	24,084	$270.05	New
	White Street Building (Shell Only)	Marietta	GA	23,809	$220.38	New
	Columbia Shores Office Condo	Vancouver	WA	22,574	$182.90	New
	Office & Design Studio	Chicago	IL	20,244	$128.41	Tenant Build-out
	Pinnacle III Office Tenant Finish	Leawood	KS	18,409	$61.13	Tenant Build-out
	Commerce Park (Shell)	Suwanee	GA	17,097	$125.37	New
	PCWA Business Center Interior	Auburn	CA	12,085	$63.59	Renovation
	Tenth Avenue Holdings Offices	N.Y.C.	NY	11,000	$89.26	Tenant Build-out
	Office Park - Building A (Shell)	Fort Collins	CO	10,000	$274.11	New
	Longshoremens Welfare Fund Building	Savannah	GA	8,160	$402.45	New
	Garry Street Office Building	Manitoba	CA	7,506	$160.58	Renovation
	Reserve Advisors	Milwaukee	WI	5,300	$51.48	Tenant Build-out
	510 Armory Street Office	Boston	MA	5,100	$98.57	Renovation
	Offices of Bonsall Shafferman	Bethlehem	PA	4,950	$72.91	Tenant Build-out
	FCT Capital Partners	Houston	TX	4,100	$85.29	Tenant Build-out
	Martin Rogers Associates Office	Wilkes-Barre	PA	4,000	$136.48	Addition/Renovation
	Cowan & Kohne Financial	Suwanee	GA	3,713	$128.52	Tenant Build-out
	212 Archer Street Office	Bel Air	MD	3,600	$181.80	New
	Utilities Analyses Inc.	Suwanee	GA	3,513	$119.21	Tenant Build-out
	Visual Lizard Interior Fit-Up	Manitoba	CA	2,430	$95.65	Tenant Build-out
	Richardson State Farm	Houston	TX	2,200	$115.65	Tenant Build-out
Mixed-Use	Office/Retail/Parking Mixed-Use	Jackson	MS	228,407	$262.41	New
	Korte & Luitjohan Office & Shop	Highland	IL	26,000	$126.09	New
Medical Office	Evanston Medical Office Building	Evanston	WY	9,157	$289.02	New
	Advanced Medical Group	Suwanee	GA	4,433	$122.72	Tenant Build-out
	Bothell Dental Office Build Out	Bothell	WA	2,203	$203.79	Tenant Build-out
Headquarters	CONSUL Energy Corporation Headquarters	Southpointe, Canonsburg	PA	317,500	$243.40	New
	Fairmont Supply Corporate Headquarters	Southpointe, Canonsburg	PA	75,255	$160.85	New
	Practice Velocity Corporate Headquarters	Machesney Park	IL	64,318	$101.07	Adaptive Reuse
	Enterprise Integration Headquarters	Jacksonville	FL	57,723	$62.88	Renovation
	Linear Technology	Cary	NC	20,000	$326.65	New
	PIPS Technology Inc.	Knoxville	TN	19,884	$259.65	New
	Lee Steel Corporate Offices	Novi	MI	15,781	$172.57	Renovation
	Weaver Cooke Headquarters	Goldsboro	NC	15,464	$310.53	New
	In Capital Holdings	Boca Raton	FL	13,000	$174.52	Tenant Build-out
	ACCION Regional Headquarters	Albuquerque	NM	7,580	$334.09	New
Civic Office	Miss Department of Environmental Quality	Jackson	MS	121,170	$97.32	Renovation
	County Central Office Complex	Pensacola	FL	74,630	$294.96	New
	State of WV Office Building	Fairmont	WV	70,442	$262.81	New
	JAX Chamber of Commerce Renovation	Jacksonville	FL	20,110	$216.99	Renovation

All prices are updated to January 1, 2021 and are national averages.
For a more in-depth report of any of these buildings or additional case studies, contact
Design, Cost and Data at 800-533-5680, or go to www.DCD.com

497

SQUARE FOOT TABLES

PROJECT	DESCRIPTION	CITY	STATE	SIZE	$/SF	NOTES

Recreational

PROJECT	DESCRIPTION	CITY	STATE	SIZE	$/SF	NOTES
Educational	The Pavilion at Ole Miss	Oxford	MS	235,301	$461.96	New
	University Laker Turf Building	Allendale	MI	137,662	$153.17	New
	CSU Recreation Center	Chico	CA	110,245	$476.63	New
	Intramural Recreation Penn State	State College	PA	59,303	$422.80	Addition/Renovation
	Center For Women's Athletics	Fayetteville	AR	39,183	$376.49	New
	Pickens Recreation Center	Pickens	SC	20,400	$187.94	New
	High School Concessions & Press Box	Loganville	GA	1,506	$482.87	New
Health Club	Brooklyn Yard Fitness Club (Shell)	Portland	OR	63,987	$118.32	New
	Title Boxing Club	Cedar Hill	TX	4,330	$73.35	Tenant Build-out
Recreational	Community Recreation Center	Williston	ND	223,787	$459.86	New
	Spirit Lake Casino & Resort	St. Michael	ND	112,277	$62.37	Renovation
	Phipps Tropical Forest	Pittsburgh	PA	80,000	$335.63	New
	Family Recreation Center	Colonie	NY	70,256	$245.30	New
	Youth Activity Center	Joplin	MO	62,056	$103.88	New
	New Holland Recreational Center	New Holland	PA	51,256	$135.45	Renovation
	Community College Recreation Center	Cedar Rapids	IA	43,500	$170.93	New
	Anderson Recreation Center	Anderson	SC	34,282	$383.25	New
	East Park Community Center	Nashville	TN	33,000	$307.43	New
	Church Family Life Center	Clemson	SC	31,509	$331.75	New/Renovation
	C.K. Ray Recreation Center	Conroe	TX	30,380	$156.57	Addition/Renovation
	St. Raphael Athletic & Wellness Center	Pawtucket	RI	30,268	$271.07	New
	The Forge For Families	Houston	TX	29,860	$255.57	New
	Christian Life Center	Birmingham	MI	26,966	$349.81	Addition
	Children's Sports Center	Woodbury	MN	26,219	$125.10	New
	Trinity River Audubon Center	Dallas	TX	20,791	$964.61	New
	Baptist Church Activity Center	Indianapolis	IN	16,636	$154.67	New
	Boys & Girls Club Syracuse	Syracuse	NY	12,107	$189.04	Addition
	Job Corp Recreational Building	Hartford	CT	11,300	$212.11	New
	Presbyterian Family Life Center	Strawberry Plains	TN	11,236	$172.35	New
	McDaniel Yacht Basin	North East	MD	7,620	$194.11	New
	Bicentennial Park	Cincinnati	OH	4,050	$909.31	New
	Bahosky Softball Complex	Bronx	NY	3,800	$491.75	New
Swimming Center	Resort & Indoor Waterpark	Cortland	NY	175,060	$274.72	New
	The Aquatic Center	Tunica	MS	45,008	$327.33	New
	Spirit Lake Phase 4	St. Michael	ND	26,630	$374.25	Addition/Renovation
	Family Aquatic Center	Beachwood	OH	7,500	$1,216.24	New
	Community Aquatic Park & Center	Billings	MT	6,730	$764.93	New
Theater	Cinema & IMAX Theatre	Lansing	MI	13,750	$231.22	New
	Academy Theater	N.Y.C.	NY	4,593	$234.91	Renovation
YMCA	David D. Hunting YMCA	Grand Rapids	MI	162,966	$210.71	New
	YMCA Recreational Center	Ann Arbor	MI	83,377	$286.80	New
	Floyd Co. YMCA & Aquatic Center	New Albany	IN	82,324	$349.20	New
	Wade Walker Park Family YMCA	Stone Mountain	GA	59,134	$364.48	New
	Alexandria YMCA	Alexandria	MN	55,150	$176.35	New
	Greater Nashua YMCA	Nashua	NH	49,980	$217.06	New
	Lancaster YMCA Harrisburg Ave.	Lancaster	PA	42,502	$369.13	New
	Greater Kingsport Family YMCA	Kingsport	TN	40,007	$263.67	New
	Eastside YMCA	Knoxville	TN	39,984	$261.97	New
	Highland County Family YMCA	Hillsboro	OH	33,228	$156.09	New
	Houston Texans YMCA	Houston	TX	31,628	$370.40	New
	Cypress Creek YMCA	Houston	TX	25,699	$156.22	Addition/Renovation

All prices are updated to January 1, 2021 and are national averages.
For a more in-depth report of any of these buildings or additional case studies, contact
Design, Cost and Data at 800-533-5680, or go to www.DCD.com

498

SQUARE FOOT TABLES

PROJECT	DESCRIPTION	CITY	STATE	SIZE	$/SF	NOTES
Religious						
Church	First United Methodist Church	Orlando	FL	121,536	$291.57	New
	Beautiful Savior Lutheran Church	Plymouth	MN	69,700	$119.25	New
	Solid Rock Baptist Church	Berlin	NJ	58,359	$107.82	New
	North Side Baptist Church	Greenville	SC	48,087	$275.35	New
	St. Martha Catholic Church	Porter	TX	46,748	$544.05	New
	Gracepoint Gospel Fellowship Church	Ramapo	NY	46,595	$202.36	New
	Good Shepherd Methodist Church	Odessa	TX	41,003	$322.30	New
	Davisville Church Addition	Southampton	PA	36,090	$190.55	Addition
	Immaculate Catholic Church	Columbia	IL	34,000	$266.45	New
	Keystone Community Church	Ada	MI	29,775	$156.89	New
	Grace Church	Des Moines	IA	29,296	$212.86	New
	Good Shepherd Church	Naperville	IL	27,869	$210.85	Addition/Renovation
	River Hills Baptist Church	Corpus Christi	TX	27,404	$319.22	New
	Good Shepherd Catholic Church	Smithville	MO	24,810	$219.30	New
	Prince of Peace Catholic Church	Chesapeake	VA	24,740	$274.77	Addition/Renovation
	Sanctuary Addition Christian Church	Oklahoma City	OK	23,820	$164.70	Addition
	St. Sylvester Catholic Church	Gulf Breeze	FL	22,000	$431.86	New
	St. Peters Catholic Sanctuary	Fallbrook	CA	20,764	$475.86	New
	Notre Dame Catholic Church	Houston	TX	20,280	$438.99	New
	St Eugene Catholic Church	Oklahoma City	OK	20,000	$481.16	New
	Chapin Presbyterian Church	Chapin	SC	19,900	$350.82	New
	St. Michaels Catholic Church	Glen Allen	VA	19,770	$376.38	New
	Shrine of Holy Spirit	Branson	MO	19,200	$358.18	New
	Wildwood United Methodist Church	Magnolia	TX	19,000	$255.93	New
	Episcopal Church of the Nativity	Scottsdale	AZ	18,288	$128.00	Adaptive Reuse
	Hardin Church of Christ	Knoxville	TN	17,149	$128.68	New
	First United Methodist Church	Crossville	TN	15,816	$503.64	New
	Good Shepherd Episcopal Church	Silver Spring	MD	15,200	$300.51	Addition/Renovation
	Ascension Catholic Church	LaPlace	LA	15,057	$396.69	New
	St. Patrick Catholic Church	Jacksonville	FL	14,139	$283.55	New
	Our Lady of Guadalupe Catholic Church	Rosenberg	TX	12,910	$437.35	New
	St. Timothy's Episcopal Church	Creve Coeur	MO	12,682	$218.03	New/Renovation
	St. Paul Lutheran Church	Pomaria	SC	12,072	$356.98	New
	Covenant Baptist Church	Florida City	FL	10,725	$266.36	New
	First United Methodist Church	Katy	TX	10,503	$323.51	Addition/Renovation
	Lake Ann United Methodist Church	Lake Ann	MI	9,975	$223.55	New
	United Methodist Church	Odenton	MD	8,783	$349.29	New
	Kent R. Hance Chapel at Texas Tech	Lubbock	TX	6,530	$634.03	New
	Haven for Hope Chapel	San Antonio	TX	2,232	$476.23	New
Multi-Purpose	Baptist Church Multi-Purpose Bldg	Maryville	TN	41,656	$118.82	New
	Good Shepherd Parish Center	San Diego	CA	28,752	$163.89	New
	Christian Life Center	Kansas City	MO	26,320	$318.31	New
	Baptist Church Outreach Center	Fort Smith	AR	25,000	$279.49	New
	St Rafael Administration Building	San Diego	CA	24,276	$176.52	New
	Catholic Church Social Hall	Chula Vista	CA	23,596	$293.69	New
	United Methodist Church	West Chester	PA	11,935	$256.82	Addition/Renovation
	Student Ministry Center	Knoxville	TN	11,700	$318.18	New
	Catholic Pastoral Ministries Center	Spring	TX	10,135	$408.50	New
	Christian Renewal Center	Dickinson	TX	8,500	$224.58	New
	Holy Family St Lawrence Parish Center	Essex Junction	VT	7,900	$235.52	New
	Presbyterian Church Addition	Gap	PA	7,414	$270.36	Addition/Renovation
	New Hope Church Addition/Alteration	Saint Louis	MO	5,564	$207.01	Renovation

All prices are updated to January 1, 2021 and are national averages.
For a more in-depth report of any of these buildings or additional case studies, contact
Design, Cost and Data at 800-533-5680, or go to www.DCD.com

499

SQUARE FOOT TABLES

PROJECT	DESCRIPTION	CITY	STATE	SIZE	$/SF	NOTES
Residential						
Apartment	Solace Apartments	Virginia Beach	VA	331,681	$104.79	New
	1221 Broadway Lofts	San Antonio	TX	205,137	$148.00	Adaptive Reuse
	Sustainable Fellwood Phase I	Savannah	GA	124,037	$138.45	New
	Kelly Cullen Community	San Francisco	CA	98,385	$573.66	Adaptive Reuse
	Bachelors Enlisted Quarters	Camp Williams	UT	76,253	$260.84	New
	Mockingbird Terrace Homes	Louisville	KY	71,110	$165.78	New
	Homeless Men's Residential	San Antonio	TX	67,908	$274.80	New
	Homeless Women's/Family Residence	San Antonio	TX	60,182	$264.80	New
	Magnolia Place	Lancaster	PA	39,714	$166.99	New
	Elkins First Ward Apartments	Elkins	WV	27,000	$119.88	Adaptive Reuse
	Young Burlington Apartments	Los Angeles	CA	24,399	$214.84	New
	The Lofts at 300 Bowman	Dickson City	PA	23,900	$89.56	Adaptive Reuse
	Peaceful Paths Emergency Svc Campus	Gainesville	FL	22,535	$153.73	New
	Wylie House - Ronald McDonald House	Kansas City	MO	21,885	$194.99	New
	Dogwood Manor Apartments	Oak Ridge	TN	19,975	$176.85	New
	Anderson Village Multi-Family	Austin	TX	12,500	$295.24	New
	Salvation Army Sally's House	Houston	TX	7,812	$257.65	Addition
	Stones River Apartment Complex	Murfreesboro	TN	7,548	$238.26	Addition
	Sunshine Park Apartments Renovation	Gainesville	FL	2,252	$126.29	Renovation
Assisted Living	Kenmore Apartments Senior Housing	Chicago	IL	90,528	$220.91	Renovation
	Country Meadows Retirement	Allentown	PA	53,237	$169.03	New
	Creekside Village Assisted Living	Harrisburg	PA	16,150	$146.90	New
	Landis Homes Retirement Community	Lititz	PA	14,255	$69.43	Renovation
Dormitory	NSU Graduate Student Housing	Davie	FL	203,500	$226.96	Renovation
	Rider University Student Housing	Lawrenceville	NJ	50,500	$244.12	New
	JWU Biscayne Commons Dormitory	Miami	FL	40,048	$267.78	New
	College Residence Dorm	Bloomfield	NJ	25,980	$329.72	Renovation
Single-Family Home	Island Residence	Grosse Ile	MI	19,237	$711.73	New
	MG Residence Restoration	Williamston	MI	9,768	$64.01	Renovation
	Concepcion House	Coral Gables	FL	6,067	$367.06	New
	Leal House	Miami	FL	5,935	$253.59	New/Renovation
	Monserrate Street Residence	Coral Gables	FL	5,885	$458.63	New
	Private Residence	Newburgh	IN	5,566	$365.63	New
	Private Residence	Austin	MN	5,489	$150.64	New
	Private Residence	Lake Wallenpaupack	PA	4,845	$329.92	New
	Island in the Grove	Boca Raton	FL	4,701	$377.14	New
	Private Residence	Benson	AZ	3,660	$183.96	New
	Fairhope Green Home	Fairhope	AL	3,610	$209.44	New
	PATH Concept House	Omaha	NE	3,490	$80.23	New
	Private Residence	La Jolla	CA	3,420	$370.20	New
	Solar House - Private Residence	Fly Creek	NY	3,304	$185.27	New
	Elliott Residence	Fort Collins	CO	3,300	$279.38	New
	Renfrew House	Manitoba	CA	3,206	$199.94	New
	Rosado I Hansen Residence	Tucson	AZ	3,175	$139.47	New
	306 W. Waldburg Residence	Savannah	GA	2,588	$174.90	New
	Nutter Green Home	Milford	OH	2,289	$166.78	New
	Guest House Residence	Ahwatuckee	AZ	1,913	$407.10	New
	Kiwi House	Baton Rouge	LA	1,515	$162.58	New
	Private Residence Renovation	Shavertown	PA	810	$168.99	Renovation

All prices are updated to January 1, 2021 and are national averages.
For a more in-depth report of any of these buildings or additional case studies, contact
Design, Cost and Data at 800-533-5680, or go to www.DCD.com

Metro Area Multipliers

The costs as presented in this book attempt to represent national averages. Costs, however, vary among regions, states and even between adjacent localities.

In order to more closely approximate the probable costs for specific locations throughout the U.S., this table of Metro Area Multipliers is provided. These adjustment factors can be used to modify costs obtained from this book to help account for regional variations of construction costs and to provide a more accurate estimate for specific areas. The factors are formulated by comparing costs in a specific area to the costs presented in this Costbook. An example of how to use these factors is shown below. Whenever local current costs are known, whether material prices or labor rates, they should be used when more accuracy is required.

Cost from Costbook Pages   X   Metro Area Multiplier Divided by 100   =   Adjusted Cost

For example, a project estimated to cost $1,000,000 using the Costbook pages can be adjusted to more closely approximate the cost in Los Angeles:

$$\$1,000,000 \quad X \quad \frac{133}{100} \quad = \quad \$1,330,000$$

© 2020 By BNi Publications Inc. ALL RIGHTS RESERVED

METRO AREA MULTPLIERS

State	Metropolitan Area	Multiplier
AK	ANCHORAGE	130
AL	ANNISTON	77
	AUBURN	75
	BIRMINGHAM	78
	DECATUR	75
	DOTHAN	75
	FLORENCE	75
	GADSDEN	77
	HUNTSVILLE	76
	MOBILE	76
	MONTGOMERY	76
	OPELIKA	75
	TUSCALOOSA	79
AR	FAYETTEVILLE	73
	FORT SMITH	73
	JONESBORO	74
	LITTLE ROCK	77
	NORTH LITTLE ROCK	77
	PINE BLUFF	75
	ROGERS	79
	SPRINGDALE	74
	TEXARKANA	75
AZ	FLAGSTAFF	80
	MESA	80
	PHOENIX	82
	TUCSON	76
	YUMA	76
CA	BAKERSFIELD	130
	CHICO	136
	FAIRFIELD	136
	FRESNO	139
	LODI	139
	LONG BEACH	133
	LOS ANGELES	133
	MERCED	139
	MODESTO	139
	NAPA	136
	OAKLAND	139
	ORANGE COUNTY	133
	PARADISE	136
	PORTERVILLE	132
	REDDING	136
	RIVERSIDE	133
	SACRAMENTO	136
	SALINAS	139
	SAN BERNARDINO	133
	SAN DIEGO	130

© 2020 By BNi Publications Inc. ALL RIGHTS RESERVED

METRO AREA MULTPLIERS

State	Metropolitan Area	Multiplier
CA	SAN FRANCISCO	139
	SAN JOSE	139
	SAN LUIS OBISPO	133
	SANTA BARBARA	133
	SANTA CRUZ	139
	SANTA ROSA	136
	STOCKTON	139
	TULARE	132
	VALLEJO	136
	VENTURA	133
	VISALIA	132
	WATSONVILLE	139
	YOLO	136
	YUBA CITY	136
CO	BOULDER	90
	COLORADO SPRINGS	89
	DENVER	90
	FORT COLLINS	86
	GRAND JUNCTION	87
	GREELEY	88
	LONGMONT	88
	LOVELAND	90
	PUEBLO	87
CT	BRIDGEPORT	127
	DANBURY	127
	HARTFORD	122
	MERIDEN	125
	NEW HAVEN	125
	NEW LONDON	122
	NORWALK	127
	NORWICH	122
	STAMFORD	127
	WATERBURY	125
DC	WASHINGTON	102
DE	DOVER	123
	NEWARK	122
	WILMINGTON	114
FL	BOCA RATON	84
	BRADENTON	82
	CAPE CORAL	81
	CLEARWATER	83
	DAYTONA BEACH	81
	FORT LAUDERDALE	85
	FORT MYERS	79
	FORT PIERCE	81
	FORT WALTON BEACH	79
	GAINESVILLE	79

© 2020 By BNi Publications Inc. ALL RIGHTS RESERVED.

METRO AREA MULTPLIERS

State	Metropolitan Area	Multiplier
FL	JACKSONVILLE	79
	LAKELAND	79
	MELBOURNE	81
	MIAMI	85
	NAPLES	82
	OCALA	80
	ORLANDO	81
	PANAMA CITY	79
	PENSACOLA	78
	PORT ST. LUCIE	81
	PUNTA GORDA	81
	SARASOTA	81
	ST. PETERSBURG	85
	TALLAHASSEE	80
	TAMPA	84
	TITUSVILLE	94
	WEST PALM BEACH	85
	WINTER HAVEN	85
GA	ALBANY	80
	ATHENS	80
	ATLANTA	77
	AUGUSTA	79
	COLUMBUS	76
	MACON	78
	SAVANNAH	79
HI	HONOLULU	133
IA	CEDAR FALLS	100
	CEDAR RAPIDS	105
	DAVENPORT	111
	DES MOINES	111
	DUBUQUE	104
	IOWA CITY	107
	SIOUX CITY	100
	WATERLOO	100
ID	BOISE CITY	83
	POCATELLO	88
IL	BLOOMINGTON	126
	CHAMPAIGN	121
	CHICAGO	144
	DECATUR	119
	KANKAKEE	126
	NORMAL	126
	PEKIN	123
	PEORIA	123
	ROCKFORD	126
	SPRINGFIELD	119
	URBANA	121

© 2020 By BNi Publications Inc. ALL RIGHTS RESERVED

METRO AREA MULTPLIERS

State	Metropolitan Area	Multiplier
IN	BLOOMINGTON	105
	ELKHART	105
	EVANSVILLE	104
	FORT WAYNE	105
	GARY	119
	GOSHEN	105
	INDIANAPOLIS	105
	KOKOMO	105
	LAFAYETTE	105
	MUNCIE	105
	SOUTH BEND	119
	TERRE HAUTE	104
KS	KANSAS CITY	111
	LAWRENCE	109
	TOPEKA	108
	WICHITA	97
KY	LEXINGTON	100
	LOUISVILLE	100
	OWENSBORO	99
LA	ALEXANDRIA	80
	BATON ROUGE	82
	BOSSIER CITY	82
	HOUMA	81
	LAFAYETTE	81
	LAKE CHARLES	81
	MONROE	80
	NEW ORLEANS	81
	SHREVEPORT	82
MA	BARNSTABLE	139
	BOSTON	139
	BROCKTON	134
	FITCHBURG	133
	LAWRENCE	139
	LEOMINSTER	133
	LOWELL	139
	NEW BEDFORD	139
	PITTSFIELD	133
	SPRINGFIELD	125
	WORCESTER	133
	YARMOUTH	139
MD	BALTIMORE	89
	CUMBERLAND	91
	HAGERSTOWN	91
ME	AUBURN	84
	BANGOR	83
	LEWISTON	84
	PORTLAND	84

© 2020 By BNi Publications Inc. ALL RIGHTS RESERVED.

METRO AREA MULTPLIERS

State	Metropolitan Area	Multiplier
MI	ANN ARBOR	118
	BATTLE CREEK	103
	BAY CITY	105
	BENTON HARBOR	118
	DETROIT	118
	EAST LANSING	108
	FLINT	110
	GRAND RAPIDS	87
	HOLLAND	93
	JACKSON	110
	KALAMAZOO	103
	LANSING	108
	MIDLAND	101
	MUSKEGON	93
	SAGINAW	103
MN	DULUTH	122
	MINNEAPOLIS	122
	ROCHESTER	122
	ST. CLOUD	118
	ST. PAUL	123
MO	COLUMBIA	114
	JOPLIN	97
	KANSAS CITY	115
	SPRINGFIELD	98
	ST. JOSEPH	114
	ST. LOUIS	115
MS	BILOXI	69
	GULFPORT	69
	HATTIESBURG	69
	JACKSON	69
	PASCAGOULA	69
MT	BILLINGS	98
	GREAT FALLS	96
	MISSOULA	98
NC	ASHEVILLE	74
	CHAPEL HILL	71
	CHARLOTTE	72
	DURHAM	71
	FAYETTEVILLE	71
	GOLDSBORO	71
	GREENSBORO	71
	GREENVILLE	71
	HICKORY	72
	HIGH POINT	72
	JACKSONVILLE	74
	LENOIR	74
	MORGANTON	72

© 2020 By BNi Publications Inc. ALL RIGHTS RESERVED

METRO AREA MULTPLIERS

State	Metropolitan Area	Multiplier
NC	RALEIGH	70
	ROCKY MOUNT	72
	WILMINGTON	74
	WINSTON SALEM	71
ND	BISMARCK	91
	FARGO	94
	GRAND FORKS	92
NE	LINCOLN	92
	OMAHA	92
NH	MANCHESTER	89
	NASHUA	89
	PORTSMOUTH	90
NJ	ATLANTIC CITY	140
	BERGEN	143
	BRIDGETON	138
	CAPE MAY	138
	HUNTERDON	141
	JERSEY CITY	143
	MIDDLESEX	142
	MILLVILLE	138
	MONMOUTH	127
	NEWARK	143
	OCEAN	138
	PASSAIC	144
	SOMERSET	141
	TRENTON	128
	VINELAND	138
NM	ALBUQUERQUE	81
	LAS CRUCES	81
	SANTA FE	80
NV	LAS VEGAS	128
	RENO	125
NY	ALBANY	116
	BINGHAMTON	113
	BUFFALO	111
	DUTCHESS COUNTY	116
	ELMIRA	114
	GLENS FALLS	114
	JAMESTOWN	110
	NASSAU	116
	NEW YORK	164
	NEWBURGH	116
	NIAGARA FALLS	125
	ROCHESTER	114
	ROME	116
	SCHENECTADY	116
	SUFFOLK	154

© 2020 By BNi Publications Inc. ALL RIGHTS RESERVED.

METRO AREA MULTPLIERS

State	Metropolitan Area	Multiplier
NY	SYRACUSE	112
	TROY	116
	UTICA	112
OH	AKRON	107
	CANTON	102
	CINCINNATI	103
	CLEVELAND	111
	COLUMBUS	104
	DAYTON	102
	ELYRIA	107
	HAMILTON	103
	LIMA	104
	LORAIN	107
	MANSFIELD	104
	MASSILLON	102
	MIDDLETOWN	102
	SPRINGFIELD	103
	STEUBENVILLE	104
	TOLEDO	107
	WARREN	107
	YOUNGSTOWN	107
OK	ENID	80
	LAWTON	83
	OKLAHOMA CITY	80
	TULSA	82
OR	ASHLAND	103
	CORVALLIS	110
	EUGENE	108
	MEDFORD	103
	PORTLAND	113
	SALEM	110
	SPRINGFIELD	108
PA	ALLENTOWN	118
	ALTOONA	112
	BETHLEHEM	120
	CARLISLE	111
	EASTON	120
	ERIE	110
	HARRISBURG	111
	HAZLETON	115
	JOHNSTOWN	111
	LANCASTER	107
	LEBANON	107
	PHILADELPHIA	133
	PITTSBURGH	110
	READING	119
	SCRANTON	114

© 2020 By BNi Publications Inc. ALL RIGHTS RESERVED

METRO AREA MULTPLIERS

State	Metropolitan Area	Multiplier
PA	SHARON	110
	STATE COLLEGE	112
	WILKES BARRE	115
	WILLIAMSPORT	115
	YORK	109
PR	MAYAGUEZ	72
	PONCE	72
	SAN JUAN	72
RI	PROVIDENCE	125
SC	AIKEN	71
	ANDERSON	69
	CHARLESTON	71
	COLUMBIA	71
	FLORENCE	72
	GREENVILLE	70
	MYRTLE BEACH	69
	NORTH CHARLESTON	71
	SPARTANBURG	71
	SUMTER	71
SD	RAPID CITY	78
	SIOUX FALLS	84
TN	CHATTANOOGA	78
	CLARKSVILLE	77
	JACKSON	76
	JOHNSON CITY	78
	KNOXVILLE	75
	MEMPHIS	78
	NASHVILLE	77
TX	ABILENE	74
	AMARILLO	74
	ARLINGTON	73
	AUSTIN	76
	BEAUMONT	76
	BRAZORIA	76
	BROWNSVILLE	70
	BRYAN	75
	COLLEGE STATION	75
	CORPUS CHRISTI	74
	DALLAS	74
	DENISON	74
	EDINBURG	70
	EL PASO	73
	FORT WORTH	73
	GALVESTON	75
	HARLINGEN	70
	HOUSTON	71
	KILLEEN	73

© 2020 By BNi Publications Inc. ALL RIGHTS RESERVED.

METRO AREA MULTPLIERS

State	Metropolitan Area	Multiplier
TX	LAREDO	72
	LONGVIEW	73
	LUBBOCK	75
	MARSHALL	69
	MCALLEN	70
	MIDLAND	73
	MISSION	70
	ODESSA	73
	PORT ARTHUR	76
	SAN ANGELO	73
	SAN ANTONIO	77
	SAN BENITO	70
	SAN MARCOS	75
	SHERMAN	70
	TEMPLE	73
	TEXARKANA	73
	TEXAS CITY	70
	TYLER	72
	VICTORIA	74
	WACO	73
	WICHITA FALLS	75
UT	OGDEN	77
	OREM	76
	PROVO	76
	SALT LAKE CITY	77
VA	CHARLOTTESVILLE	80
	LYNCHBURG	81
	NEWPORT NEWS	82
	NORFOLK	82
	PETERSBURG	79
	RICHMOND	80
	ROANOKE	83
	VIRGINIA BEACH	82
VT	BURLINGTON	80
WA	BELLEVUE	116
	BELLINGHAM	109
	BREMERTON	111
	EVERETT	115
	KENNEWICK	112
	OLYMPIA	114
	PASCO	112
	RICHLAND	112
	SEATTLE	116
	SPOKANE	93
	TACOMA	116
	YAKIMA	102

© 2020 By BNi Publications Inc. ALL RIGHTS RESERVED

METRO AREA MULTPLIERS

State	Metropolitan Area	Multiplier
WI	APPLETON	112
	BELOIT	115
	EAU CLAIRE	112
	GREEN BAY	111
WI	JANESVILLE	115
	KENOSHA	116
	LA CROSSE	112
	MADISON	114
	MILWAUKEE	118
	NEENAH	112
	OSHKOSH	112
	RACINE	117
	SHEBOYGAN	111
	WAUKESHA	118
	WAUSAU	111
WV	CHARLESTON	114
	HUNTINGTON	117
	PARKERSBURG	112
	WHEELING	110
WY	CASPER	85
	CHEYENNE	86

© 2020 By BNi Publications Inc. ALL RIGHTS RESERVED.

© 2020 By BNi Publications Inc. ALL RIGHTS RESERVED

INDEX

INDEX

INDEX

THE SIMPLE WAY TO CREATE ACCURATE SQUARE FOOT ESTIMATES!

Register (FREE!) on dcd.com and get:

- A full month of unlimited **FREE** access to Simpl•Est Square Foot
- A FREE copy of the 2021 DCD Guide to Construction Costs *(print and digital!)* as our gift to you!

Just go to www.dcd.com/simpl_est

With Simpl•Est Square Foot, you get a complete estimating solution
Simpl•Est Square Foot is amazingly powerful and amazingly SIMPLE!

You get unlimited access to a cost database featuring nearly 2,000 actual projects!

You get detailed square-foot cost breakdowns for schools, hospitals, municipal buildings, offices, muti-family units, restaurants, retail stores and more!

Powerful search tools let you quickly drill down to find projects that closely match what you or your client is planning ...

You can drill down on projects that match foundation types, roof types, interior and exterior wall types ... you can also drill down on new projects, renovations, adaptive re-use projects and more!

You can run multiple "what if" scenarios and answer the question "How much will it cost to build?"

Check out the costs of different building types. Get a reality check on your estimate. Demonstrate the impact of a change order. Estimate with greater confidence than ever before!

Simpl•Est Unit Price ®

Create a detailed estimate just by clicking on the items from the *BNi General Construction Costbook!* Set the quantities, change the labor rates, and a complete estimate will be printed instantly!

Simpl•Est Davis-Bacon ®

Fine tune your estimate with the most up-to-date prevailing wage rates for all commercial construction trades in hundreds of regions throughout the country.